Orchids
of Britain and Ireland

A Field and Site Guide

For Rita

Orchids

of Britain and Ireland

A Field and Site Guide

Anne and Simon Harrap

A & C BLACK
LONDON

ACKNOWLEDGEMENTS

We would especially like to thank Dr Tony Leech for much wisdom as well as practical help and advice (he read and re-read most of the book), and Lenny Thomson for her equally good-humoured helping hand. Julie Dando very, very patiently performed her design alchemy and has worked wonders, and at A&C Black Nigel Redman can claim the credit for initiating the project and provided help and support throughout, while Jim Martin exercised his considerable editorial skills. For the provision of additional photographs we would like to thank Richard Bateman, Robin Chittenden www.harlequinpictures.co.uk, Sean Cole, Bob Gibbons/Natural Image, Richard Gulliver, Michael Frost, Nigel Redman, Craig Robson, Paul Sterry/Nature Photographers Ltd and Peter Wakely (English Nature). We also thank Richard Millington for his delightful illustration of Bee Orchid varieties.

We are very grateful to the Botanical Society of the British Isles and CEH Monks Wood for allowing us reproduce the maps contained in the recent *New Atlas of the British and Irish Flora* (Preston *et al.* 2002), and for facilitating their reproduction here; we would particularly like to thank Henry Arnold, the Database Manager, for his time and trouble. Mark Van Beirs assisted with French translations, Keith and Karen Ashby with German, and Gareth Burnell with Latin. For providing references we thank the Library of the Royal Botanic Gardens, Kew and also Jan Gebbie (Scottish Natural Heritage) and Joan Chapman (Glasgow Natural History Society). The staff at Holt Public Library in Norfolk assisted cheerfully with our many requests.

Regarding matters botanical we especially thank Richard Bateman for answering many queries regarding taxonomy and nomenclature and for providing advance copies of papers; similarly Pete Hollingsworth assisted with our research on helleborines. Mavis and Richard Gulliver gave advice and unpublished material on Irish Lady's-tresses and Richard Hedley provided much information on Sword-leaved Helleborine (and suggested a translation for *Cephalanthera*), as did David Ball (Hampshire County Council). Plantlife International kindly provided copies of their *Back from the Brink* dossier on Sword-leaved Helleborine and Reg Land advised on Fen Orchid. Sean Cole supplied much information on Ghost Orchid as well as other species. Jill Sutcliffe (English Nature) kindly read through all the proofs and made many useful suggestions.

We would also like to thank Richard Abbott, Steve Alton, Debbie Allan, Norman Baldock, Ian Bonner, Janet Canning, David Carrington, Clive Chatteris, Robin Chittenden, Peter Clarke, Sean Cole, Les Colley, Richard Collingridge, David Cottridge, Phil Davey, Charles David, Ian Denholm, Tim Dixon, Stuart Dunlop, Bob Ellis, Tom Ennis, Rachael Fickweiler, Michael Foley, Maggie Gamble, Paul Hackman, Frank Hunt, James R. Hunter, Kevan Joynes, Brian Laney, Mandy Leivers, Ian Livermore, Alan Lewis, Alex Lockton, Tim McGrath, Steve Madge, Stephen Martin, Nigel Milbourne, Dr E. Charles Nelson, Malcolm Ogilvie, John Oxenford, Gavin Peplow, Michael Parsons, E. G. Philip, Chris Pogson, Rachel Remnant, A. J. Richards, Craig Robson, Dr Francis Rose, Martin Sanford, Brendan Sayers, M.-A. Selosse, Alan Showler, Terry Smith, Ron Stanbridge, Jon and Lucinda Starling, Malcolm Storey, Giles Strother, Ian Taylor, Peter Thompson, Chris Sydes, Darrell Watts, Dave White, Steve Whitehouse, Martin Woodcock and Julian Woodman.

Of course, we take responsibility for any errors in the text and would be delighted to receive comments and corrections. We can be contacted via our website: www.norfolknature.co.uk, or via the publishers.

Published in 2005 by A&C Black Publishers Ltd.,

37 Soho Square, London W1D 3QZ

Copyright © 2005 Anne and Simon Harrap

Photographs © 2005 Simon Harrap except where indicated otherwise

ISBN 0-7136-6956-X

A CIP catalogue record for this book is available from the British Library

A & C Black uses paper produced with elemental chlorine-free pulp, harvested from managed sustainable forests.

Printed in Hong Kong by Compass Press Limited

Designed by Fluke Art, Cornwall

10 9 8 7 6 5 4 3 2 1

www.acblack.com

Contents

Introduction

Why this book?

Orchid! The very word conjures up an image of the exotic, beautiful and, above all, rare. It is associated with wealth, power and the eminently desirable. Few people realise that orchids are very much part of the natural heritage of Britain and Ireland, and that there are no fewer than 56 species of native wild orchid. They range from the tiny, green Bog Orchid to the flamboyant Marsh Helleborine and the gorgeous Green-winged Orchid. They also include Lady's-slipper and Ghost Orchid, probably the two rarest native wild flowers in the British Isles, and Common Spotted and Early Purple Orchids, species found throughout the land.

The aim of this book is both to introduce wild orchids to a wider audience and to show those who think they know about orchids that there is always more to learn. For orchids need friends. Despite the many schemes designed to alleviate its effects, modern 'industrial' agriculture, combined with urbanisation, insensitive forestry practices and a rain of nutrients from car exhausts, has resulted in an ever-increasing homogenisation of the countryside. The beautiful, delicately woven tapestry of fields, pastures, woods and marshes created unwittingly by the hand of man over many generations is being put into the equivalent of a food blender that is reducing everything to a monotonous and anonymous wildlife desert. In the face of this assault, the majority of wild plants are in retreat, including *all* orchids. Do not be fooled by cheeky television presenters and glossy wildlife magazines. Although there is now more money for conservation in general and nature reserves are at last receiving some desperately needed cash, orchids and much other wildlife besides have disappeared from most of the landscape. If we can help more people to enjoy, appreciate and value orchids and the places where they grow, our purpose will have been served.

What is an orchid?

Orchids (the family Orchidaceae) are among the most diverse groups of plants, with over 1000 genera and at least 25,000 species. Indeed, the Orchidaceae is the largest and most highly-evolved family of flowering plants.

The family derives its name from the Greek *orchis*, meaning 'testicle', a reference to the appearance of the underground tubers of some species. The term *orchis* was first used by Theophrastus (*c.* 370-285 BC) in his *Natural History of Plants*; he was a student of Aristotle and is considered to be the 'father' of botany.

Most people would recognise an orchid, even those without any particular interest in botany or gardening – at least the gaudy, hot-house hybrids and some of the more colourful wild orchids. Giving a precise definition of an orchid is more difficult, especially a non-technical definition, but European orchids all share the following features:

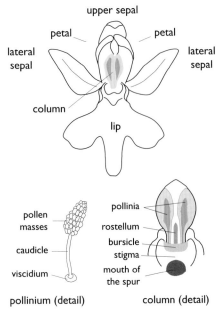

▲ A typical orchid flower.

- They are perennial herbs rather than trees or shrubs and lack any woody parts.
- The leaves are 'simple' and not divided into lobes or smaller leaflets.
- The leaves have no stalk and are arranged alternately along the stem.
- The flowers are carried in a single spike at the tip of the stem.

- The ovary is inferior, that is, placed below the sepals and petals.
- Male and female parts of the flower, the stamens and the stigma, are not separate but are fused together into a single structure, the column, that lies in the centre of the flower.
- The flower is made up of three sepals and three petals but one of the petals differs from the others, usually significantly so, and forms the lip (sometimes known as the labellum). This is often brightly coloured and patterned, and intricately shaped. The lip is actually the *uppermost* petal but usually lies at the bottom of the flower because either the ovary or its stalk is twisted (the flower is therefore resupinate).

Orchid Biology

ORCHIDS AND FUNGI

The relationship that orchids have with fungi impacts on all aspects of their biology and, more than anything else, defines them.

Their seeds require fungi in order to germinate and grow. The seedling spends months or years underground and during this period is completely dependent on the nutrients that it obtains from fungi and is mycotrophic (a term deriving from the Greek *mukes* meaning 'fungus' and *trephein* 'to feed'). Seed must, however, be produced in large quantities to ensure that some, at least, will find the correct conditions for successful germination and growth, including the presence of the correct fungi. In turn, the need to produce large quantities of seed has powered the evolution of elaborate flowers and complex pollination mechanisms.

Even when the orchid has appeared above ground as an adult or near-adult plant and is able to photosynthesise and manufacture its own carbohydrates, in many species it still maintains a relationship with fungi. In a few orchids the adult plant continues to be entirely dependent on fungi (the so-called saprophytic orchids). In others, it is probably largely independent of fungi and gains its nutrients almost entirely from photosynthesis (these are phototrophic). Most orchids, however, fall somewhere between these two extremes, with both sources of nutrition being utilised, perhaps in varying proportions depending on the season. The ability to utilise two sources of nutrition allows orchids to thrive in marginal habitats; some grow in heavy shade and many are found on poor soils. In the tropics, orchids have extensively colonised the soil-less trunks and branches of trees and are epiphytes. Finally, the ability to fall back on fungi as a source of nutrition explains why many orchids are able to become 'dormant' underground for a year or sometimes longer.

Mycorrhizas

It is thought that around 90% of the world's plants have a relationship with fungi. Such a relationship is known as a mycorrhiza and the fungi that form these attachments are known as mycorrhizal. Mycorrhizal fungi live in the soil and, unable to manufacture their own carbohydrates by photosynthesis or obtain sufficient for their needs by the decomposition of organic matter, they invade the root systems of green plants. But, rather than being parasitic, the fungus actually benefits the host plant by functioning as an extended root system. The mycelium of the fungus extends far into the soil and is able to provide the plant with minerals, especially phosphorus; it may also confer some degree of drought, pest or disease resistance. The plant in turn provides the fungus with carbohydrate that it has produced through the process of photosynthesis; most plants are able to divert up to 20% of their carbohydrate to fungi without coming to harm. The relationship between the plant and the fungus is therefore mutualistic (such mutually beneficial relationships were once termed symbiotic, but this term is now used for a wider range of interactions).

Fungi form several kinds of mycorrhiza:

- Ectomycorrhizal fungi form a sheath or mantle *over* the plant's roots (the Greek *ectos* means 'outside'). Ectomycorrhiza are the dominant type of mycorrhiza formed by forest trees and are critical to their growth. Most ectomycorrhizal fungi are macrofungi and many produce recognisable mushrooms.

- Endomycorrhizal fungi (also known as VAM fungi) *penetrate* the cells of the plant's roots (the Greek *endon* means 'within'). They are microfungi and do not produce distinctive fruiting bodies. Poorly-known, they cannot be seen without a microscope and have proved impossible to cultivate and study *in vitro*.
- Ericaceous mycorrhiza are formed with the roots of various ericaceous plants.
- Orchidaceous mycorrhiza are formed with orchids.

Orchid fungi

Orchid mycorrhizas differ fundamentally from other mycorrhizal systems in that the orchid does not provide the fungus with carbohydrates. There is no evidence for the transfer of nutrients from the orchid to the fungus, even in mature plants which are able to photosynthesise, and this is certainly true of orchid seedlings which develop entirely underground and have no green leaves. Rather, it is the fungus that provides the orchid with energy; there is good evidence that carbohydrate obtained by fungi from the decomposition of organic matter (or from trees, see below) is transferred to the orchid. In short, orchids are parasitic on fungi. To use the terminology of recent scientific papers, the orchid 'cheats' in its relationship with the fungus. Throughout the text we have placed 'infection' and 'partner' in inverted commas to emphasise the one-sided nature of the relationship between orchids and fungi.

The fungal hyphae pass through the outer layers of the orchid's root, rhizome or other underground organs and penetrate the cell walls to form loops and coils, called pelotons. At intervals, the orchid digests these pelotons and receives water, mineral salts, carbohydrate and other organic compounds from the fungus. So sophisticated is the orchid's use of fungi that it is able to control its spread and confine it to specialist cells; indeed, some orchids produce phytoalexins which act as a fungicide and prevent the fungi from reaching tubers and other storage organs. The main fungal associates of orchids are Basidiomycetes of the Rhizoctonia group (other members of the Rhizoctonia group are soil saprotrophs or pathogens).

The parasitic nature of the relationship between orchids and fungi is seldom explicitly acknowledged, perhaps because it tarnishes the orchids' glamour. Certainly in some older works the relationship was portrayed rather as a protracted battle in which the fungus 'infected' the seedling but was then beaten off and eventually a 'balance' established where the orchid had the upper hand at some times and the fungus at others.

'Saprophytic' orchids

Some species of orchid take the relationship with fungi to an extreme. Bird's-nest, Coralroot and Ghost Orchids have no green leaves (or have the green pigments very much reduced) and throughout their lives depend entirely on their fungal 'partner' for nutrition (they are fully mycotrophic). Furthermore, these species do not form associations with the usual orchid fungi of the Rhizoctonia group. It has been shown that both Bird's-nest and Coralroot Orchids form relationships instead with ectomycorrhizal fungi which are simultaneously in partnership with nearby trees. Via these fungi the orchids acquire carbohydrates from the trees and therefore they are, in effect, parasitic on the trees. It has been suggested that forming associations with such ectomycorrhizal fungi may provide the orchid with a stabler and more reliable source of nutrients, which is particularly important when it has no other source of nutrition.

Bird's-nest, Coralroot and Ghost Orchids are frequently but incorrectly described as saprophytic. Saprophytes (nowadays more properly known as saprotrophs) derive their nutrition from dead organic matter; these orchids acquire nutrients from a living fungus.

Woodland orchids

It has also been shown recently that some other orchids, such as Red, White and Broad-leaved Helleborines, also form relationships with ectomycorrhizal fungi and are therefore able to utilise nutrients provided unwittingly by nearby trees. This may explain their ability to thrive in low light levels and to become 'dormant' underground for long periods. Many are particularly associated with Beech trees.

Fungi and rare orchids

There is mounting evidence that some orchids are very specific about their fungal 'partners'. Various orchids in the genera *Liparis*, *Goodyera* and *Spiranthes* have been shown to associate with just one species of fungus and to use the same species, both as germinating seeds and as adult plants. Other orchids form a relationship with many different fungi as adult plants but are very specific as germinating seeds (and may associate as seeds with a different species of fungus to any of those used by adult plants). Yet other orchids seem to use a broad range of fungi for both germination and as adults.

Orchids that require a specific fungus in order to germinate and grow may be very limited in where they can live, compared to the more generalist orchids, and this has clear conservation implications. We would venture to guess that some of Britain and Ireland's orchids are rare and localised because their fungal partners are rare and localised. This may well explain why, for example, Burnt Orchid seldom colonises new sites. Any conservation programme, especially if it involves a reintroduction, may ultimately be unsuccessful if it fails to take this into account.

ORCHID SEEDS

Orchid seeds are rather small and, indeed, are often known as 'dust seeds'. They typically weigh 2-8 micrograms and, in British species, are 0.35-1.4mm in length. They are made up of a relatively simple embryo enclosed in a hardened carapace and surrounded by the much larger testa, a honeycomb of dead cell walls that traps air.

Small size confers several advantages. Large numbers of seeds can be produced at relatively little cost; in British orchids counts of between 376 and 25,000 seeds per capsule have been recorded (Lesser Twayblade and Greater Butterfly Orchid being the extremes). With many air spaces the seeds are ideally suited to wind dispersal and can travel long distances. They can also float on water, another effective means of

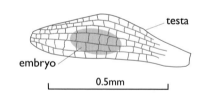

▲ *A typical orchid seed.*

dispersal. However, small size also imposes limitations. The seeds are so tiny that they contain very little in the way of food reserves (merely a few lipids and proteins) and they depend entirely upon fungi to provide their nutrients when they germinate.

GERMINATION AND UNDERGROUND GROWTH

The orchid seed germinates 2-10cm below the surface of the soil. The seedlings are very vulnerable to desiccation and require the presence of fungi, so it is important for the seed to avoid germinating on the soil's surface. To ensure this, almost all orchid seeds will only germinate in darkness, once rain has washed them down into the soil or they have been covered by fallen leaves. Unlike other plants, they do not require light following germination because they do not produce green leaves.

It is thought that most European orchids germinate in the spring (although there is only limited direct evidence for this) and therefore the seeds must have a mechanism to keep them dormant over the winter. Germination depends upon the uptake of water by the seed and the hard carapace forms a barrier against water, slowing or preventing germination for a while. In some orchids the carapace is incomplete and these seeds germinate much more easily and rapidly.

With its very limited reserves of nutrients, the orchid seed is dependent on fungi from the outset. In some species, such as Bird's-nest Orchid, seeds start to germinate *before* 'infection' by a fungus, although the breaking of the seed's dormancy almost certainly requires the fungus to be present in the immediate vicinity of the seed, which perhaps responds to a chemical signal from the fungus. In other species, such as Coralroot Orchid, the seeds will only start to germinate *after* it has been 'infected' by the specific fungal 'partner'. From the outset the seedling is able to control the extent of 'infection' by the fungus, confining it to certain areas.

Some species, including Bird's-nest and Coralroot Orchids, form relationships with a very restricted range of fungi, perhaps just one species. Their seeds will only germinate in the presence of the appropriate fungus. (The implication is that the seeds can remain dormant for relatively long periods, 'waiting' for the correct fungus to appear.) Other orchids form a relationship with a variety of common soil fungi that probably occur in all suitable habitats. Examples include the marsh orchids; their seeds will germinate and start to grow in the absence of the appropriate fungi, presumably because there is a very high probability that a suitable fungus will be encountered very soon.

Upon germination the seed forms a protocorm. This is a small, often parsnip- or top-shaped structure with a scatter of root-hairs on its surface; these are single-celled projections that facilitate fungal 'infection'. The protocorm usually goes on to develop roots and at this stage is often known as a mycorhizome. The primary function of these first roots is to host fungal activity rather then the supply of nutrients and water. In most orchids, as the seedling continues to develop, fungal activity is increasingly confined to the roots, and the mycorhizome, now free of fungal 'infection', is known as a rhizome. In some orchids the adult plant grows from a rhizome, but in many species the rhizome is largely replaced by tubers. In adult orchids, whether they grow from a rhizome or from a tuber, fungal activity is usually confined to the roots and, in some species, to the slender extremities of the tubers.

POLLINATION

Orchids are renowned for the beauty and complexity of their flowers. These flowers have not, however, evolved to amaze and delight us, but to fulfil the primary function of the plant, which is to reproduce itself.

Cross-pollination versus self-pollination

Most flowering plants reproduce sexually and the production of the next generation depends upon the successful unification of male and female gametes to produce seed; the male gamete is pollen and the female gametes are contained within the ovary. In most plants, including orchids, each flower produces both male and female gametes. It would seem a simple process therefore for pollen to be transferred *within* the same flower to the ovary. Indeed, why bother with the resources and energy needed to produce a flower at all when a small drab structure would be sufficient to bring pollen and ovary together? The answer lies in the advantages that cross-pollination brings to the species.

If pollen and ovary come from different individuals they will each carry a different set of genetic material and the resulting offspring will not, therefore, be genetically identical to its parents. This continual mixing of genetic material creates a large 'gene pool' which gives the species flexibility and adaptability. It also means that individual mutations are disseminated through the population rather than being passed, unchanged, to the offspring; cross-pollinated species therefore tend to be relatively uniform in appearance.

If a flower is pollinated with its own pollen (i.e. it is self-pollinated) its offspring will have limited genetic variation. In turn, their offspring will be similarly limited. In self-pollinated species the overall genetic variation is rather low and the 'gene pool' is limited, giving the species very little flexibility. Paradoxically, however, self-pollinated orchids can show more variation between colonies and are more likely to produce distinct varieties as mutations; these might produce, for example, differently coloured flowers and are passed down unchanged to the next generation. Bee Orchid is perhaps the best example of this.

There are circumstances where self-pollination is an advantage. If, for example, a single wind-blown seed produced a flowering Lizard Orchid many miles from other plants of the same species, it would have no chance of reproducing if it could only be cross-pollinated. If it is able to self-pollinate, it can produce seed and reproduce itself. Not surprisingly, self-pollination tends to be commoner in species that have scattered populations, or are at the edge of their range. Another factor may be a lack of pollinators, and species adapted to deep shade may well benefit from self-pollination; White Helleborine, a species which is routinely self-pollinated, is successful in Britain, whereas Red and Sword-leaved Helleborines, which are always cross-pollinated, have declined as increasing shade has made their woodland homes too dark for their pollinators. Self-pollination may therefore be a useful strategy in the short-term and it may only be over an evolutionary time scale, involving thousands of generations, that the advantages of cross-pollination come to the fore.

Most orchids are cross-pollinated but, rather cunningly, a large proportion have adaptations that prevent self-pollination but then allow the flowers to self-pollinate if, after a few days, a suitable pollinator has not come along. Conversely, the small number of routinely self-pollinated orchids are, at least occasionally, cross-pollinated by insects. In the world of orchids, nothing is straight-forward.

Insects as pollinators

Orchid flowers have evolved to use insects to carry pollen from one plant to another and employ a variety of mechanisms to attract suitable pollinators. Bright colours and scents advertise their presence and the lip of the flower acts as a convenient landing platform. Many offer their insect visitors a reward of nectar but a large proportion do not. Their bright colours and scents are instead a 'deceit' and they rely on the stupidity of insects, which are slow to learn that the flowers offer no reward. Fly, Early Spider and Late Spider Orchids (genus *Ophrys*), have evolved even more elaborate mechanisms that take advantage of the sexual behaviour of insects (see p.388).

Compared to most other flowering plants, orchids produce large quantities of seeds. Therefore large quantities of pollen have to be moved between the flowers because each pollen grain can only produce one seed. In most orchids the pollen grains are amalgamated together in large numbers to form pollinia. Due to their size and weight, these pollinia must be carried to other flowers by an insect and must be very securely attached if the process is to be completed successfully. The insect must be of the right size and shape, both to pick up the pollinium in the first place and to be positioned correctly in the next flower so that the pollinium makes contact with the stigma and effects fertilisation. European orchids are not usually pollinated with a whole pollinium, rather just fragments, and thus a single pollinium can, provided it remains on the insect, pollinate several flowers. But, if too small a quantity of pollen is deposited the capsule will mature without all the ovules being fertilised, and there will be many non-viable seeds.

Orchid Habitats

Britain and Ireland form a landscape that has been tamed, with virtually no truly wild places; even the moors and mountains of Wales and Scotland are not natural, having been stripped of their trees many generations ago. Orchids therefore have to find a niche in the habitats which mankind has moulded; some of these habitats are very rich in orchids whereas others are devoid of their grace and beauty.

It is possible to identify five factors which determine the suitability of any habitat.

Soil chemistry: Many orchids are fussy about the soil chemistry and, as any gardener knows, whether the soil is acid or alkaline determines to a great extent which plants will thrive. A high proportion of orchids favour soils that are rich in calcium; these are known as calcareous soils and they are alkaline with a high pH. Calcium is a major component of chalk and limestone and therefore soils derived from these are often excellent for orchids. A similar chemistry is produced by magnesium and some limestones are rich in this mineral; although they are not 'calcareous', the terms 'alkaline' or 'base-rich' can also be used to cover these soils. In practice, however, 'calcareous', 'alkaline' and 'base-rich' are used interchangeably. A small minority of orchids favour acid conditions, usually soils that are damp or wet, and these are usually to be found where peat is formed from bog mosses (*Sphagnum* spp.), or in pinewoods.

Soil fertility: Like most wild plants, orchids do best in a soil that is very low in nutrients. This is largely because a soil that is high in nutrients, either naturally or through the application of fertilisers, allows a limited range of larger and more aggressive species to thrive, and these will swamp any orchids. There is also evidence that some nutrients are actually toxic to some orchids (for example, high levels of phosphorus may be toxic to Green-winged Orchid).

Age: Orchids are great colonists and their dust-seeds enable them to spread long distances. Nevertheless, there are some unknown factors which limit the ability of many species to move into new habitats. Colonisation often takes place very slowly, probably over hundreds of years for some species. It follows that the older a habitat is, the more likely it is to support orchids and the greater the diversity of species.

Stability: Orchids are relatively long-lived plants and most have a period of immaturity lasting several years which they spend underground. Both as underground seedlings and as adult plants they cannot tolerate ground disturbance which would destroy their rhizomes or tubers. Therefore orchids can only occupy a habitat if it has a degree of permanence; ground that is regularly ploughed or otherwise disturbed cannot support orchids.

Disturbance: Despite the preference of many species for older, undisturbed habitats, our impression is that orchids are often found on areas that have been disturbed in the past, albeit a long time ago in some cases. Old quarries and sand and chalk pits are good examples of this. It is also increasingly obvious that the continuous, low-level ground disturbance produced by grazing animals is critical to the long-term survival of many species.

Deciduous woodland

Deciduous woodland can be rich in orchids but is, all too often, a disappointment. Woodland in Britain and Ireland falls into two broad categories; ancient woodland and secondary woodland.

Ancient woodland is found on sites which have probably had an uninterrupted cover of trees for thousands of years. Throughout Europe, only fragments of this primeval 'wildwood' remain and Britain and Ireland are no exception, with just 1-2% of the original cover left. Man has continuously been at work in these woodland fragments, which have been cut for timber, coppiced and grazed, but the continuity of tree cover has allowed a rich flora and fauna to survive and an ancient wood will undoubtedly have the greatest diversity of orchids. Such woods can usually be recognised on the ground by their substantial boundary banks and diverse flora, and on a map will often have a somewhat irregular outline; historical research, looking at old maps and documents, is often needed to confirm their provenance, but this is not necessary for the orchid hunter.

Secondary woodland grows where the continuity of tree cover has been broken. If a field that has been cultivated for decades or even centuries is planted with trees or allowed to 'tumble down' to woodland it may *look* like a wood but it will seldom, if ever, acquire the richness and diversity of ancient woodland (hence the planting of new 'community forests' and 'millennium woodlands' will do little for orchids). Many woodland plants and animals are very poor colonisers and are unable cross stretches of inhospitable territory. Importantly, a secondary wood may well lack the complex soil structure and diversity of soil fungi that is found in an ancient wood and thus lack suitable fungal 'partners' for some orchids. Overall, with the exception of a few species, secondary woodland will be poor in orchids (and will often have none).

Management is another factor that can determine how orchid-rich a wood is, whether ancient or secondary. Until the early 20th century most woodland was intensively managed. Many woods were coppiced – cut in small blocks on a rotation of around ten years to provide timber for hand-crafts, charcoal and firewood. Coppice stools grow again after each round of cutting, providing an endless supply of timber. In coppiced woodland periods of sunny, well-lit conditions are followed by increasing shade as the stools grow again, ideal for some orchids. Abundant labour also allowed rides to be cut and cleared for access and the limited technology of the day meant that felling and replanting for large timber was carried out at a relatively slow pace and in a piecemeal manner. All in all, the more extensive management of this period resulted in woods that were a patchwork of habitats and much sunnier due to the larger number of open rides and glades. Modern management techniques depend on the use of minimal labour supplemented by machinery. Coppicing has largely been abandoned (although now increasingly reinstated by conservation bodies), ride management is negligible and felling is undertaken in large blocks using heavy machinery. Under such regimes woods are darker than before and often suffer heavy ground disturbance.

A final factor to affect the suitability of woods is biological. There are ever increasing numbers of deer in Britain; indeed, it is said that there are more deer now than at any time since William the Conqueror. Deer eat orchids and some scarce species, for example Narrow-lipped Helleborine, can lose all their flowers to deer year after year. Another increasingly negative factor, at least in some parts of the country, is pheasant rearing. In a commercial pheasant-shoot large numbers of young birds are released into a wood and these can decimate the flora as they scratch and root *en masse*.

In spite of the many factors that can negatively effect a wood's suitability, there are still many wonderful woods in Britain and Ireland, and the best are often reserves. Characteristic species of ancient woodland include Common Twayblade, Common Spotted and Fly Orchids, and, especially in coppiced woodland, Early Purple and Greater Butterfly Orchids. In Kent, Lady Orchid is widespread and some favoured woods, from southern England to northern Scotland, hold the exquisite, sun-loving Sword-leaved Helleborine. Two of our rarest orchids, Red Helleborine and Ghost Orchid, are confined to deciduous woodland. The overall increase in the level of shade in modern woodland is not bad for all orchids: Bird's-nest Orchid and White, Violet and Narrow-lipped Helleborines can thrive in very shady woods.

Secondary woodland and plantations of deciduous trees are likely to be much poorer in species, although two of the more mobile species, Common Spotted Orchid and, in beech plantations, White Helleborine, can occur in large numbers. The strangely fickle Broad-leaved Helleborine and the enigmatic Green-flowered Helleborine seem to occur at random.

Coniferous woodland

The only coniferous trees that are native to Britain and Ireland are Juniper, Yew and Scots Pine and it is the last of these that forms a special habitat for orchids. Native Scots Pine is confined to Scotland, where the remnants of the so-called ancient 'Forest of Caledon' are concentrated on Speyside and Deeside in the east and around Beinn Eighe in Ross & Cromarty. These are home to Creeping Lady's-tresses and, more locally, Lesser Twayblade and Coralroot Orchid, with Heath Spotted Orchid in some of the more open areas.

Conifer plantations have been established all over Britain and Ireland but are usually planted with non-native species such as Sitka Spruce and Douglas Fir. They were often established on areas that had been open ground, such as heaths, moorland and sand dunes, but in the post-war period the Forestry Commission also had a policy of 'coniferisation' and converted large areas of ancient woodland into conifer plantations. Plants, including orchids, are great survivors and where an ancient woodland has been 'coniferised' there may sometimes be orchids in rides and along edges, with Common and Heath Spotted Orchids and Broad-leaved Helleborine the likeliest species. Otherwise, conifer plantations south of the Scottish border hold little interest with one notable exception: in parts of Norfolk and northern England, mature pine plantations hold some impressive colonies of Creeping Lady's-tresses. In Scotland, plantations of pines may acquire a great deal of interest as they mature, taking on some of the characteristics of native pine woods.

Carr woodland

Carr woodland is dominated by willows and Alder and develops in the wet, waterlogged conditions found on and around mires, bogs, rivers and lakes. These fast-growing trees are pioneer species and in a natural system carr woodland usually eventually dries out and other species of tree become dominant. Carr may hold orchids such as Common and Heath Spotted Orchids, 'inherited' from the open ground it colonised, but it also has two specialities. In Scotland, Coralroot Orchid is most abundant in carr and in southern England carr may be the 'natural' habitat of Green-flowered Helleborine.

Grassland

Grassland is a prime orchid habitat, with a large range of species possible, including Common and Heath Spotted Orchids, Greater and Lesser Butterfly Orchids, Common Fragrant, Green-winged, Early Purple, Pyramidal, Bee and Frog Orchids and Common Twayblade. Calcareous grassland, especially the chalk downs of southern England, is the richest; the specialities are Musk, Burnt, Man, Monkey, Early Spider and Late Spider Orchids and Autumn Lady's-tresses. Neutral grassland can also be productive and even acid grassland can hold species such as Heath Spotted and Heath Fragrant Orchids and, in northern Britain, Small White Orchid.

Grassland will always tend to develop into scrub and eventually woodland unless prevented by either grazing or mowing. It is possible to distinguish between a 'pasture', grassland which is grazed for some or all of the year but not cut, and a 'meadow', grassland from which stock are excluded so that it can be cut for hay (and often then grazed later in the year). The timing and intensity of grazing and mowing is very important in determining which orchids are able to thrive and even the animals concerned can be important; cattle are heavy beasts and can damage the turf but they are selective eaters and do not eat orchids (although may stand on them); sheep, lighter on their feet, eat everything. Some grazing regimes produce a very short turf beloved of Musk and Frog Orchids and Autumn Lady's-tresses, while longer grass can support Pyramidal, Man and even Lizard Orchids.

It is always worth investigating the various micro-habitats in any area of grassland, which may be favoured by different orchids. Steeper slopes are often particularly interesting, as are any ancient earthworks, which may have remained undisturbed for centuries.

Limestone pavements

This very specialised habitat is found widely in the north and west of Britain and in Ireland. The limestone bedrock was first scoured flat by the ice sheets and then weathered by the action of water and frost to produce blocks of rock (clints) with deep and sometimes treacherous crevices between them (grykes). Over time, soil may accumulate in the grykes and most pavements would, in a natural state, be wooded, but many were cleared of trees long ago and some are now rather bare. The range of orchids present on a limestone pavement depends in part on how much naked rock is exposed; many pavements have a substantial covering of turf and this holds all the species typical of calcareous grassland. Limestone pavements also have two specialities: the very local Dark-red Helleborine and, in the Burren in western Ireland, Dense-flowered Orchid, which grows on short turf.

Marshes and fens

'Marsh', 'swamp', 'fen' and 'bog' are all vague terms and are used interchangeably by the layman (and most botanists too) to describe any sort of waterlogged or seasonally flooded ground. In terms of their flora, however, there are many different varieties, only some of which are good for orchids. Wet ground can be categorised in terms of the source of its water, the water chemistry and the management that it receives. Broadly, the same factors which determine the orchids that can thrive in grassland operate in marshes too.

All the water may come from rainfall, in which case a 'bog' is formed, either a blanket bog of the sort which carpets the landscape in northern and western Britain and Ireland, or a raised bog, a much rarer habitat. Bogs are acidic and usually dominated by bog-mosses *Sphagnum* spp., the dead remains of which lead to an accumulation of peat. In general, bogs are poor for orchids, although Heath Spotted Orchid may be frequent on the higher and drier hummocks.

Alternatively, the bulk of the water may come from springs and seepages in the ground, in which case its chemistry is strongly influenced by the rocks it has passed through on the way to the surface. This flushing water may be acid or very alkaline or anything in between, but is usually low in nutrients. Such spring-fed marshes are often called 'mires' in the technical literature and can support some scarce and local orchids. In southern England valley mires are commonest, in which water seeps from the ground along the sides of a valley at the boundary of pervious and impervious rocks to form a long, narrow mire with a central stream. Valley mires are often found in heathland but formerly would have been widespread and almost every parish would have had its area of boggy ground; most were reclaimed for agriculture long ago. In the north and west spring-fed mires can be found *within* more extensive areas of acid bog and often form a focus for interesting plants.

Because there is a whole range of water chemistry each variety of mire grades into the next in a complex and often poorly understood manner. Similarly the mix of orchids changes subtly as the habitat becomes more or less favourable. And, even within a particular mire, there may be many micro-habitats; in an otherwise very alkaline mire hummocks of *Sphagnum* may produce locally acidic conditions.

Where mires are acidic they may hold the diminutive Bog Orchid, as well as the purple-flowered form of Early Marsh Orchid (subspecies *pulchella*) and Heath Spotted Orchid. Slightly more neutral conditions and drier ground favour Lesser Butterfly Orchid and the very local Heath Fragrant Orchid, as well as the ubiquitous Common Spotted Orchid. Alkaline mires support Marsh Helleborine, and Marsh Fragrant, Southern Marsh and Northern Marsh Orchids and, in some areas, the very local Pugsley's Marsh Orchid. Of the real rarities, Fen Orchid and the creamy-flowered subspecies of Early Marsh Orchid cling on in East Anglia.

As a third alternative, the water in a marsh may come from rivers and streams, either overflowing their banks from time to time or percolating through the soil. In this case the water may be acid or alkaline but is usually nutrient-rich, either naturally or frequently due to the run-off of fertilsers from agricultural land or the discharge of treated sewage. The nutrient-rich water leads to the growth of lush, tall vegetation, often dominated by Common Reed or by Nettles, Meadowsweet and Hemp Agrimony. This vegetation may be controlled, however, by mowing or grazing, in which case such waterside meadows can hold Southern, Northern and Irish Marsh Orchids, Early Marsh Orchid of the pink-flowered subspecies *incarnata* and Common Spotted Orchid.

Heaths and moors

Heathland is dominated by heather, one or more species of gorse and sometimes various grasses, and is generally found on sandy or gravely soils in the lowlands of southern England, whilst moorland is dominated by heather, grasses and a variety of dwarf shrubs and is generally found in the uplands of northern and western Britain and Ireland. Both heaths and moors are acidic and are likely to hold few orchids. Heathland itself is usually very dry but is frequently interspersed by valley mires, which can be rich in orchids (see above). Moorland tends to be wetter and may hold Heath Spotted Orchids where it grades into bog. In the north and west, damp moorland, especially on north-facing slopes, can hold Lesser Twayblade.

Pits, quarries and railway lines

When extraction has come to an end, quarries have large areas of bare rock or sparse soil and where the bedrock is chalk and limestone these can, over time, form superb orchid habitats. Any of the grassland orchids can occur and, if there is scrub, 'woodland' species such as Fly, Military and Lady Orchids are also possible. The timescale involved can be lengthy, with medieval workings now forming excellent sites. Railway lines go through cuttings which may also expose bare rock or produce thin, skeletal soils, while embankments may have been built up from calcareous spoil; disused railway lines are always worth investigating. Sandpits are unlikely to be calcareous but the bare ground can be favourable to some species, such as Bee Orchid, which can form substantial colonies so long as scrub does not take over.

Sadly, even these man-made habitats are under threat as any hole in the ground may be seen as a suitable site for landfill and many important orchid sites have been buried by rubbish.

Road verges, green lanes, churchyards and lawns

In the last few decades most hay meadows and permanent pastures have been lost, especially in England. These unimproved grasslands were ideal for orchids and species such as Green-winged Orchid, which were common and widespread not so long ago, are now highly localised. Road verges, green lanes and churchyards are now often the only areas where permanent, unimproved grassland can be found, although in many cases they are drenched with nutrients from farming operations and car exhausts, and too overgrown with rank vegetation to support orchids or, in the case of some churchyards, over-tidied and mown far too often. Nevertheless, Early Purple, Green-winged, Pyramidal and Bee Orchids and even rarities such as Man and Lizard Orchids can be found in these habitats. Some Wildlife Trusts have 'conservation churchyard' schemes that may help to identify the best sites and most counties operate a Roadside Nature Reserve policy to protect and correctly manage the best verges. Garden lawns are usually cut too frequently and managed with herbicides and fertilisers and are therefore unlikely to support orchids. On suitable soils, however, unimproved lawns, even relatively new ones, can be graced by Autumn Lady's-tresses. Increasingly, Common Spotted and Bee Orchids seem to be turning up on lawns and, once found, are often cherished by the householders.

Dunes and dune slacks

In coastal sand dunes the depressions are often damp and may be flooded in the winter. If the dune systems are made up from sand that is rich in shell fragments they will be neutral or calcium-rich, and such dune slacks and the surrounding slopes can then support a very rich variety of orchids. Specialities include Dune Helleborine, a British endemic found in the dune systems of Anglesey and northwest England; Lindisfarne Helleborine, endemic to the dunes of Holy Island in Northumberland, and Fen Orchid, found on the coast of South Wales, as well as the red-flowered subspecies of Early Marsh Orchid (subspecies *coccinea*) and, in northern England and Scotland, Coralroot Orchid. Other species may occur, sometimes in large numbers; Marsh Helleborine, and Common Spotted, Southern Marsh and Northern Marsh Orchids can be abundant and other species to look for include Broad-leaved and Green-flowered Helleborines, Common Twayblade, the pale pink subspecies of Early Marsh Orchid (subspecies *incarnata*), Frog, Pyramidal and Bee Orchids and even, in one or two areas, Man Orchid. In many places dune systems have been planted with conifers and although this is bad news for the specialised dune flora, Dune, Green-flowered and Broad-leaved Helleborines all take readily to the plantations.

Machair

Machair is species-rich grassland found on the wet and windy west-facing coasts of Scotland and Ireland but nowhere else in the world. Sand that contains many fragments of seashells, and hence rich in calcium, is blown onshore by Atlantic gales and settles on the low-lying coastal areas. Grassland develops on these low dunes and periods of extensive grazing have been interspersed with cultivation for crops. The uncultivated areas often support large numbers of orchids, including two specialities, the 'Hebridean Spotted Orchid' (the *hebridensis* subspecies of Common Spotted Orchid) and the very localised Hebridean Marsh Orchid, endemic to North Uist in the Outer Hebrides. Other orchids which can be found include the red-flowered subspecies of Early Marsh Orchid, Northern Marsh, Heath Fragrant, Lesser Butterfly and Frog Orchids, and Common Twayblade.

Orchid Conservation

Orchids face three major threats: habitat destruction, habitat change and human predation.

Habitat destruction has clearly taken the greatest toll. Farming, forestry and other developments have destroyed innumerable orchid sites, especially in the period since World War Two. Most of the destruction has been state-sponsored through the operations of the Common Agricultural Policy (CAP) and the Forestry Commission. Between 1945 and 1980 the Forestry Commission attempted to destroy and re-plant with conifers 200,000 hectares of ancient woodland, to say nothing of the tens of thousands of hectares of heathland, moorland and sand dunes that were destroyed. The CAP has been reformed in recent years and attitudes and policies at the Forestry Commission have changed (although there is still a great reluctance to undo much of the damage done in the name of near-worthless timber). But, despite much lip-service in recent years, few politicians have any commitment whatsoever to conservation and when push comes to shove development almost always takes precedence over wildlife. No wonder the government conservation agencies (English Nature, the Countryside Council for Wales and Scottish Natural Heritage) have often been accused of being lame ducks in the face of their political masters, despite the best efforts of their staff. In terms of habitat destruction, the prospects for orchids remain bleak.

Habitat change has only recently been acknowledged as a major issue. It has come to be recognised that orchids do not live in stable, 'climax' communities of plants, at least in the British Isles, rather in habitats that were created and maintained, albeit inadvertently, by people. Grassland, marshes, heathland and woodland are all the product of traditional land-use. Once these traditions died out, habitats started to change, slowly at first but then rapidly, and many have become unsuitable for orchids. Ironically, this applied especially to reserves, where a fence and a 'keep out' sign were often the limit of any management. Now, conservationists try to replicate the traditional land-uses, often at great expense, that created and maintained the habitats they manage. The reinstatement of grazing is often the single most important measure that can be taken to help orchids.

Human predation has often been seen as a major threat to orchids, be it innocent ramblers picking bunches of flowers or avaricious botanists determined to get another specimen for their collections or gardens. More recently, photographers and even visitors keen to merely *look* at plants have joined the list of 'threats'. The answer has traditionally been secrecy, and details of the locations of the greatest rarities were and still are jealously guarded; even the location of huge colonies of species such as Burnt and Early Spider Orchids was veiled in secrecy.

Human predation certainly poses a threat to those species that occur in such small numbers that a significant part of a population (or even the whole population) can be stolen. There are still cases where plants are dug up illegally, from Bog Orchid to Lizard Orchid. Perhaps the most notorious in recent years was the attack on the single Lady's-slipper growing in Silverdale in Lancashire. English Nature had made the bold decision to allow limited publicity and a large number of people had been able to admire this beautiful orchid. The fact that this particular plant was probably originally of garden origin does not in any way lessen the damage done.

Despite the odd incident, however, we are convinced that for most orchids human predation is, in the final analysis, irrelevant to their fortunes, especially in the face of habitat destruction and habitat change. Unnecessary secrecy has indeed probably led to the destruction or degradation of many sites, as those responsible for the land remain in ignorance of its importance. It has also deprived many people of the enjoyment of seeing the orchids and many potential friends for orchid conservation have surely been lost in this way.

There have been a few special conservation initiatives involving orchids. In 1983 the Sainsbury Orchid Conservation Project was established at the Royal Botanic Gardens, Kew. This has involved research into the propagation of orchids with a view to reintroducing some of the rarer species. A range of orchids has been involved, including Military and Fen Orchids, with a substantial effort going into the reintroduction of Lady's-slipper. Reintroductions are controversial, however, with some conservationists arguing that the time and effort could be better spent on conserving existing populations. A second initiative at the Royal Botanic Gardens was the establishment in 1997 of the Millennium Seed Bank. This is intended to store viable seeds for as many of the world's plants as possible, including, of course, British wild orchids. Techniques have been developed which should allow orchid seeds to be stored for long periods, although some species cannot yet be cultivated successfully.

What you can do

The first step in orchid conservation is accurate and up-to-date information on their distribution and abundance. Amateur botanists provide the vast majority of information on plant distribution in Britain and Ireland via the system of county recorders organised by the Botanical Society of the British Isles (BSBI); they are always pleased to receive records, with details of the species involved, numbers, date and location (for contact details see p.422). There is also always a need for volunteers to undertake practical habitat management on reserves and other sites; the local wildlife trusts are the first contact if you are keen to get involved.

The greatest contribution individuals can make to orchid conservation is, in our opinion, to become a 'local champion'. Getting to know an area intimately, finding and recording orchids and other wildlife, and then badgering local councils, wildlife trusts, government agencies or church-wardens to sit up and do what is necessary to safeguard the good areas. This may not make you popular in some quarters but may, in the end, get things done.

Orchids and the Law

All orchids and, indeed, almost all wild plants, are protected in Britain by the Wildlife and Countryside Act, 1981 and cannot be *uprooted* unless you are the owner or occupier of the land or have their permission to do so (although it is legal to pick them). In addition, some of the rarer orchids enjoy much greater protection under Schedule 8 of the Act and it is illegal for anyone, even the owner or occupier of the land, to uproot, destroy or pick these orchids. The term 'pick' is defined to include gathering or plucking any part of the plant, including collecting seeds. It is also illegal to posses any live or dead wild plant in Schedule 8, or any part of or anything derived from such a plant, or to trade in such items. Schedule 8 includes: Lady's-slipper, Red Helleborine and Ghost, Fen, Monkey, Military, Lizard, Late Spider and Early Spider Orchids (it also currently includes 'Young's Helleborine', now shown to be a poorly defined variant of Broad-leaved Helleborine, and 'Lapland Marsh Orchid', now a subspecies of Pugsley's Marsh Orchid). In Northern Ireland, Bird's-nest, Bog, Small White, Pugsley's Marsh, Green-winged and Bee Orchids, Marsh and Green-flowered Helleborines and Irish Lady's-tresses are specially protected under Schedule 8 of the Wildlife (NI) Order, 1985. In the Republic of Ireland, Sword-leaved Helleborine, Irish Lady's-tresses, Bog, Small White and Green-winged Orchids are specially protected under the Flora Protection Order, 1999.

▲ *Derbyshire, June. Grazing is critical to the survival of many orchid populations and is increasingly the linchpin of conservation management. Paradoxically, however, in the north and west, overgrazing has decimated species such as Small White Orchid.*

Field Guide

NOTES ON THE SPECIES ACCOUNTS

Introductions to the genera

Each genus has an introductory section giving some general information about the genus, including notes on identification for the more difficult species, such as the *Epipactis* helleborines and the marsh and spotted orchids. It also includes notes on various aspects of biology, such as growth, reproduction and pollination, that are common to all the members of the genus. For some genera that contain just one species worldwide, or where only one species is represented in Britain and Ireland, much briefer notes on distribution and the generic name are given.

Names

The scientific names used in the text and the order of the species accounts follow the list produced by Richard Bateman (Bateman 2005). Scientific names reflect the relationships between species and in recent years new evidence, especially from genetic studies, has greatly improved our understanding of these. This is reflected in new scientific names for some species.

Under the heading **Formerly** we give scientific names as used in publications that pre-date the Bateman list. We have tried to include most older scientific names if they have been in general use since the publication in 1968 of the second edition of Summerhayes' *Wild Orchids of Britain*. We have not, however, provided an exhaustive list of synonyms. In addition, some older English names are also mentioned. Under the heading **Other names** we give some alternative names in current use, especially in North America.

Habitat

The likely habitats for each species are outlined and more detail on many orchid habitats can be found above. The information applies to Britain and Ireland; in some cases orchids occupy a rather broader range of habitats elsewhere. Most maximum recorded heights above sea level come from the *New Atlas* (Preston *et al.* 2002).

Flowering period

A guide is given to the period in which the species is likely to be in flower (see also **chart of flowering periods** on p.420). Flowering times do vary, however, both predictably and unpredictably:

- Orchids growing further to the north and at higher altitudes tend to flower a little later (although there is often surprisingly little difference between southern England and Scotland).
- Orchids growing in wetter habitats will flower later than the same species growing in drier habitats.
- Orchids growing on or very near to the coast will tend to come into flower a little earlier than those inland.
- Orchids growing on sheltered south-facing slopes will flower earlier than those with an exposed, westerly aspect or those facing north.

There can also be marked and unpredictable variations between colonies, even those close to each other, and, in recent years, perhaps as a result of 'global warming', many orchids have been coming into flower earlier; it is worth bearing this in mind if you are hoping to see a species at its best.

Orchids are notorious for the wide variations from year to year in the number of plants in flower. It used to be thought that this was related to fluctuations in the size of the population and that some species, such as Bee Orchid, were monocarpic and therefore flowered just once before dying. It is now known that most orchids are relatively long-lived and the total population, including non-flowering plants and those 'dormant' underground, is often fairly stable. Fluctuations in the numbers flowering are related to growing conditions both in the current year and in the previous growing season (which may be either the previous summer or the previous winter, depending on the species). Growing conditions are, in turn, usually related to rainfall. Wet weather is conducive to growth but prolonged dry spells can be very bad for orchids and in some cases can severely restrict flowering.

Range

Details of the range is given for Britain and Ireland. A problem faced by all biologists (and many other people as well) is how to sort and classify records. County boundaries have changed several times over the years and it becomes very difficult to keep track; was a plant recorded in the 'Lincolnshire' of the 19th century in the same region as one recorded in 'Humberside' or 'North Lincolnshire' today? This problem is particularly acute in Wales and Scotland where there have been radical changes, and some of the modern administrative units are very large.

Wisely, most botanical recording uses the system of Watsonian vice-counties. This was devised in 1852 by Hewett Cottrell Watson, who divided Britain into 112 similarly-sized areas. He followed traditional county boundaries where he could and divided larger counties such as Yorkshire into smaller units. The value of the vice-county system is its stability, allowing past and present to be compared. In the majority of cases we have given records by vice-county, although we have amalgamated some (e.g. we often refer to Norfolk rather than West Norfolk and East Norfolk) and we have amended some vice-county names to become more recognisable (for example, West and East Ross becomes Ross & Cromarty; Westerness and Easterness becomes Inverness-shire). See p.418 for full details.

We have used two main sources for distributional information: The *New Atlas of the British and Irish Flora* (Preston *et al.* 2002) and the *Vice-county Census Catalogue* (Stace *et al.* 2003). We have also consulted a variety of county floras. These sources do not always agree, especially regarding the validity of older records and the origin of out-of-range species.

Orchid seeds have evolved for wind or water dispersal and can, in some circumstances, travel long distances. Nevertheless, a great deal of scepticism attaches to records of orchids away from their normal range. In some quarters, these are inevitably attributed to deliberate introductions, even where there is no evidence whatsoever for this (for example, the two tongue orchids). On the other hand, a non-natural origin has either been proven or is very strongly suggested for some controversial records (see **Other species** p. 416). It seems best to keep an open mind but our inclination is to give such records the 'benefit of the doubt'.

Under the subheading **World range**, details of the orchids' distribution outside Britain and Ireland is given. We have used several sources for this, including Brown (2003), Davies *et al.* (1983), Delforge (1995, 2001) and Hultén & Fries (1986). Again, these sources do not always agree and we have tried to present the best and most likely compromise.

Accompanying the text is a range map, where the distribution is given by 10km squares in three data classes: 1987-1999, 1970-1986 and pre 1970. These maps have been supplied by the Biological Records Centre.

Key to range maps:

Native Distribution
● 1987-99
● 1970-86
● pre 1970

Description

A detailed description of the orchid is given, taken in many cases from the living plant. We have depended on the literature for some details, especially measurements. It is worth remembering that many orchids can be taller than the range quoted; even in our limited experience we have found plants that are bigger than the books suggest.

Subspecies

Some orchids show definite patterns of variation which may be either geographical or ecological; plants in a particular region or a particular habitat may differ consistently in appearance from other areas. In these cases we have recognised different subspecies. There is much disagreement about which subspecies are worthy of recognition and we have not followed any one authority in this.

Variation and varieties

We give brief details of the normal range of variation which can be encountered. We also give details of some of the 'varieties'. Like all organisms, orchids are subject to random mutations of their DNA which may produce a variety of aberrant and deformed plants, and, like stamp collectors (and the butterfly collectors of old), orchidologists have traditionally been fascinated by these abnormalities. We do not share that obsession and consider that the odd plant that produces flowers that are deformed or unusually coloured in some way to be of little special interest. However, some deformities shed light on more primitive stages in the orchid's evolution. In addition, species such as Bee Orchid throw up the same mutation again and again in widely separated localities, and in such cases these 'varieties' (var. for short) are often given names. Unlike subspecies, varieties do not show definite geographical or ecological patterns and can pop up anywhere. In most cases we have followed Ettlinger (1997) in the use of varietal names.

Hybrids

Hybrids have, like varieties, long fascinated orchidologists and in some cases are either very attractive or throw light on the relationships between orchids. Hybrids between species in the same genus tend to occur much more frequently than hybrids between species in different genera and, for example, the frequency with which Frog Orchid hybridised with the spotted and marsh orchids was a long-standing clue to its true relationships. On the other hand, many hybrids are undistinguished and their true parentage, and even their status as a hybrid, may be the subject of guesswork, sometimes highly ambitious guesswork. All too often, plants are diagnosed as hybrids when they are merely aberrant individuals (or even within the range of normal variation). We have usually only included hybrids that are listed in Stace (2004) and have given the names used in that work.

Name and classification

The origin of the scientific name is discussed under this heading. In some cases the derivation is clear but in others there is disagreement (or the stated origin seems highly unlikely). We have used Delforge (1995), Gledhill (2002) and Société Française d'Orchidophilie (1998) as our main sources. Notes are also given on the classification of the species, including any recent changes, and on its relationships (see also the orchid family tree on p.417).

History and conservation

The date and, where known, the location of the first record for Britain and Ireland is given (largely from Clarke 1900). For the rarer species we have also given extensive details of their past and current distribution.

The conservation status of each species is mentioned. 'Nationally Scarce' denotes that the species is included in Scarce Plants in Britain (Stewart et al. 1994) which indicated that it has been recorded from 16 to 100 10km squares in Britain from 1970 onwards (the project did not include Ireland). Rarer species were treated in the British Red Data Book (Wiggington 1999), which includes all plants recorded from 15 or fewer 10km squares in the period from 1987 onwards. Each species is assigned to a threat category (Endangered, Vulnerable etc.).

We have extracted data from the New Atlas (Preston et al. 2002) to draw up a table for each species indicating the extent of its historic and current range and the amount by which it has declined. This information is put in context by a discussion of the possible reasons for decline (all orchids have declined), and current threats and conservation measures.

GENUS *CYPRIPEDIUM*
LADY'S-SLIPPERS

Lady's-slippers are the most primitive orchids in Europe, differing markedly in their floral structures from the other species, and have a cunning method of trapping insect pollinators.

Distribution

The genus *Cypripedium* contains 45 species distributed in Europe, temperate Asia and North and Central America. Around 30 species are found in China and 12 in North America but just three extend to Europe and only one occurs in Britain.

Classification

The lady's-slippers belong to the subfamily Cypripedioideae and are the only representatives of that subfamily in Britain and Europe.

Floral structures

Lady's-slippers are distinguished from all other British and European species by having two fertile stamens, one on either side of the column, plus a large, modified, third, sterile stamen known as the staminode. This is flattened, tongue-like, often boldly marked and projects into the large opening of the 'slipper'. The pollen is granular, sticky and glutinous. There are three receptive stigmas and the lip is shaped into a slipper or moccasin-like pouch. The two lateral sepals are joined for almost their entire length with just a notch at the tip to suggest their origin (the single structure is a synsepal). Members of the other orchid subfamilies have just one fertile stamen, pollen that is aggregated together into two pollinia and two stigmas (although these are often joined together).

Pollination

There is no nectar, and pollinating insects are tricked into entering the flower through the large opening on the top of the lip. They can only leave via the small rear openings, picking up pollen on the way.

Growth pattern

All lady's-slippers grow from a rhizome that has slender, fleshy roots. Each year the rhizome produces two buds at its tip: the larger will produce the next aerial shoot, the smaller may form a new branch of the rhizome but usually eventually dies. The aerial shoot will also die off at the end of each season, but the rhizome continues to grow from a bud that forms on its base (sympodial growth, as opposed to monopodial growth, in which the main stem continues to grow indefinitely behind the same growing point). In the lady's-slipper, the rhizome grows 5-10mm each year in a characteristic zig-zag pattern as the position of the larger bud alternates from left to right. The rhizome may die off slowly and rot at the rear while growing at the front, but up to 20 living segments may be present at any one time (and by counting the number of segments its age may be estimated). The rhizome also branches, roughly every five years, and each branch may eventually put up an aerial stem. Thus as a plant ages, the number of flowering shoots increases.

Fungal partners

Poorly known, and this lack of information is an obstacle to the conservation of the species.

Vegetative reproduction

The rhizome branches as it grows and eventually the basal portion dies, leaving the terminal branches as independent plants, clones of the 'mother plant'. In at least some species of *Cypripedium*, buds can also form on the tips of the roots as a means of propagation.

Name

The generic name *Cypripedium* derives from the Greek *Kypris*, a name for Aphrodite (goddess of love), and Latin *pes*, meaning 'foot' and thus 'Aphrodite's slipper'.

◀ *31 May, Khabarovsk, eastern Sibera. Lady's-slipper occurs right across Europe and Asia but is threatened almost everywhere.*

LADY'S-SLIPPER
Cypripedium calceolus

This spectacular species is Britain's rarest orchid with just one group of plants of native origin surviving at a closely guarded site in Yorkshire. Originally fairly widespread in the limestone districts of northern England, its large, showy flowers have been its downfall. Plants were pillaged from the wild for hundreds of years, either to be dried, pressed and stored away in dusty herbaria or to be transplanted to gardens.

Identification
Unmistakable.

Similar species
The leaves of non-flowering plants could be overlooked and resemble the leaves of Lily-of-the-valley.

Habitat
The surviving native plants are found in species-rich grassland on a fairly steep, well-drained,

▲ *30 May, Lancashire (Sean Cole). This plant, probably of garden origin, had been growing in this spot for perhaps a century but was vandalised a few weeks after this picture was taken in 2004.*

north-facing slope. They nestle in a sheltered limestone valley that has some trees and lies on the northern edge of a large block of woodland. In Europe, Lady's-slipper favours a variety of woodland, usually on calcareous soils, but in the northern parts of the range is also found in the open, in fens and marshy grassland. Overall, it appears to require relatively well-lit areas but likes to have its roots in cool, moist soil. In England suitable areas would have been found in open woodland on north or northwest facing slopes or where subsurface 'flushing' kept the ground damp but not waterlogged; the former English, sites were in ash, hazel and oak woods on steep, rocky slopes, always on limestone, at 150-260m above sea level. The correct balance of sun and shade seems to be critical. Too little light and the plant fails to flower and may even become 'dormant' underground, too much light and rank herbs and shrubs will swamp it, although in a more natural environment grazing animals may have suppressed much of the competing vegetation.

Flowering period
Late May to early or mid-June. Plants are in flower for two or three weeks and each flower lasts 11-17 days, withering on the sixth day after pollination.

Range
Confined to a single site in Yorkshire, although formerly more widespread. Artificially propagated plants have recently been planted out at several localities within its former range. **World range:** Europe and southern Siberia, extending eastwards to

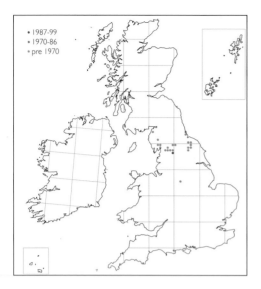

northern Mongolia, northeast China, Korea, the Russian Far East and Sakhalin. It is essentially a northern or boreal species, and in Europe the Lady's-slipper ranges north to northernmost Scandinavia. It is absent from the Mediterranean lowlands but is found in the mountains as far south as northern Spain, central Italy, northern Greece and Bulgaria. There are also outposts in the Crimea and Caucasus. It is also absent from the Atlantic fringes of Europe, for example central and western France, and the English populations were therefore always out on a limb.

How to find it

Potential visitors are asked to keep away from the native site in Yorkshire due to the fragility of the habitat. Visitors were welcome at a site at Silverdale in Lancashire where one can admire a plant, albeit probably of European origin, in a natural setting (it has hopefully survived the attack by vandals of 2004). Otherwise, we must hope that the reintroduction programme is a success and that self-sustaining populations of flowering plants will once more grace the dales of northern England. At present, just one of the reintroduction sites has public access – Ingleton Glen in North Yorkshire – but the young Lady's-slipper plants have not yet flowered there.

DESCRIPTION

Height: 15-70cm but usually around 30cm and rarely more than 60cm.

Stem: Glandular-hairy with three to four green or brown sheaths at the base. The species forms clumps of shoots, sometimes quite large, which may belong to one or more plants.

Leaves: Green and oval, elongated into a pointed tip; the three to four (sometimes five) leaves are arranged alternately up the stem. They are sparsely hairy (especially on the underside), ciliate along the margins, wavy edged and very prominently veined.

Spike: Each stem usually produces one or two flowers, very rarely three.

Bract: Leaf-like, longer than the flower and held erect behind it.

Ovary: Long, slender, six-ribbed, curved (but not twisted), with glandular hairs and a short stalk.

Flower: Large and conspicuous. The sepals are purplish-brown or claret with wavy edges, downy on their inner surface and hairy at the base. The upper sepal is lanceolate with a pointed tip and is held erect, whereas the two lateral sepals are fused and hang vertically below the lip (their tips forming two small teeth at the tip of the combined synsepal). The petals are purplish-brown, mottled with olive-yellow towards the base and with downy midribs and long hairs at the base. They are strap-shaped with pointed tips, variably twisted (through up to 360°) and hang at 'four' and 'eight o-clock' on either side of the lip. The lip is yellow and looks like a bag or clog (the 'slipper'). There is a large entrance on the upper side towards the rear and two small openings on either side of the column at the base. The edges of the large upper opening are rolled down and under, and the interior of the slipper is covered in sticky hairs with lines of reddish dots along its floor. The column projects forwards into the slipper and is divided into two parts: the staminode, which is yellowish-white variably marked with red spots and very conspicuous, and the large

▶ *Yorkshire (Peter Wakely, English Nature).*

fleshy stigma, which lies on the lower part of the column hidden inside the slipper. The two remaining stamens lie on either side of the base of the staminode, adjacent to the two small rear openings into the slipper. The flowers are delicately scented, and the scent is said to be sweet, recalling oranges.

Subspecies
None in Britain.

Variation and varieties
None in Britain.

BIOLOGY

Pollination and reproduction
It is thought that Lady's-slipper is pollinated by small bees, especially bees of the genus *Andrena*. The flowers do not produce nectar, however, and there is debate as to what it is that attracts the insects. A strong contender is the flower's scent, which comprises a complex mixture of chemicals that may mimic the bees' pheromones, chemical signals that are associated with feeding and mating behaviours. Other possible attractions, which could indeed combine with the scent lure, include the red spots on the staminode and floor of the slipper that may act as 'false' nectar guides. Alternatively, the bees may actually receive a reward for their visit, perhaps the oil secreted by the small hairs inside the slipper. Bees may also find shelter in the slipper in cold weather or overnight.

Whatever the attraction, bees land on the edge of the 'large opening' or try to land on the staminode and fall into the slipper. After a few minutes the bee tries to leave. However, the sides of the slipper are very smooth and slippery and the rim of the large opening curls over and inwards, making escape via this route impossible. The bee can only leave through the small openings on either side of the column where there are small stiff hairs to give it a foothold. The openings are only just big enough for the bee, which is forced to make contact with one of the stamens as it makes its escape,

picking up a load of pollen in the process. The bee goes on to visit another flower; when it eventually leaves this its back rubs against the stigma, which projects down into the slipper, and pollen from the first flower is deposited there; the surface of the stigma has minute, stiff, pointed papillae that act as a 'brush' to remove pollen from the bee's back. As it escapes, more pollen is carried away, ready to be deposited on the next flower and continue the process.

The mechanism is precise and in order to effect pollination the bee has to be a specific species that is the right size; bees that are too large or too small can escape without pollinating the flower. A wide variety of other insects also enters the slipper but these too are the wrong size and shape and either leave unharmed or may be trapped and die. Self-pollination is unlikely; the bee would have to reverse back into the flower just as it was on the point of escape. In addition, it seems that the flowers are, to a great extent, self-sterile.

The pollination strategy is not efficient and seed set is rather poor with few fertile capsules being produced. Bees are attracted to *large* groups of flowers, especially those in sunlight, but even in large populations in Europe an average of just 10% of flowers set seed. Nevertheless, each capsule contains 6,000-17,000 seeds which may be dispersed by rain as the seedpods seem to close up when dry and open when wet.

Lady's-slipper also reproduces vegetatively through division of the branching rhizome, and in many populations in Europe this is thought to be more important than seed in the recruitment of new plants to the population.

Development and growth
The Lady's-slipper grows from a slender, creeping, branched rhizome. Each branch of the rhizome may eventually put up an aerial stem, and so as a plant ages the number of flowering shoots increases. Alternatively, a clump of shoots may arise from several separate clones, each produced by vegetative reproduction, or by the development of

▲ 6 June, Lancashire. The 'large opening' of the flower, with the tongue-like staminode to the rear, is obvious.

seedlings at the base of the 'mother' plant.

The first green leaves are reported to appear in the fourth year after germination by some authors and in the first year by others. The immature plants have a slender stem with one or two small leaves and may remain in this state for several years. In England a seedling has been noted to flower nine years after it first appeared above ground, and in Europe the young plant takes six to ten years to produce flowers. Plants are long-lived and many are over 30 years old, with some over 100 years. Indeed, a lifespan of 192 years has been determined from the examination of the growth of a single rhizome in Estonia.

Hybrids

None in Britain.

Name and classification

The specific name *calceolus* means 'little shoe' or 'little slipper' and like the English name refers to the slipper-like appearance of the lip. An old name for the species was 'Calceolus Mariae' or 'Mary's Shoe'. Yellow Lady's-slipper *C. parviflorum* of North America is very closely related and is sometimes amalgamated with this species.

HISTORY AND CONSERVATION

A *Red Data Book* species that is classed as Critically Endangered and fully protected under Schedule 8 of the Wildlife and Countryside Act 1981. The species is also rare and threatened throughout much of its range in Europe and Asia.

The first British record dates from 1629 when John Parkinson, a London apothecary, recorded the species in his *Paradisi in Sole; Paradisus Terrestris* ('Paradises in the sun; Paradise on Earth'): 'In a wood called the Helkes in Lancashire neere the border of Yorke-shire.' This was the same wood that supplied the first British record of Sword-leaved Helleborine in 1666. Both species are now gone from there.

The Lady's-slipper was subsequently found widely but locally in the limestone districts

Past and present occurrence of Lady's-slipper in Britain and Ireland (based on presence or absence in 10km squares of the National Grid; data from the New Atlas).

	Britain	Ireland
total historical range, 1500-1999	22	0
current range	1 (0.04%*)	0
% lost, 1500-1969	95%	
% lost, 1970-1986	0%	
% lost, total	95%	

* current range as a % of the total number of 10km squares

of northern England. There was a single site in Derbyshire at the Heights of Abraham overlooking Matlock, and it was recorded in southern Cumbria around Whitbarrow and Scout Scar (northwest of Levens). The bulk of the records came, however, from three areas: first, West Yorkshire around Ingleborough (including Helkes Wood) and the Upper Wharfedale region around Litton, Kettlewell and Grassington; second, North Yorkshire on the southern flanks of the Cleveland Hills, especially the valley of the River Rye and its tributaries north and west of Helmsley; third, Castle Eden Dene in Co. Durham.

Such a large, conspicuous and attractive flower as the Lady's-slipper was an obvious subject for curiosity and avarice, and plants were picked or dug up from at least the 16th century onwards. In the late 18th and early 19th centuries, they were ruthlessly stripped from the wild, both for horticulture and as herbarium specimens. By the mid-19th century the species was rare and in 1917 the Lady's-slipper was declared extinct in Britain.

In 1930, Lady's-slipper was resurrected from the dead when a single plant was found in a remote Yorkshire dale (this is the plant that has survived to the present day). However, the last note of its rediscovery in print was in 1937, and the species quietly slipped from the botanical world's attention. As well as the site being a closely-guarded secret, the Lady's-slipper itself was being very coy. From 14 stems and just one flower in 1930 it dwindled to two to five stems by the late 1940s and 1950s and hardly ever bothered to flower; a single bloom was produced in 1934 and 1943 but not again until 1959.

Despite the secrecy, in the 1960s word started to get out and the Lady's-slipper again faced the old threat from collectors and a new threat from visiting botanists with big feet and heavy cameras. Indeed, the site was raided and half the plant was removed. Various individuals and groups attempted to protect the orchid and the ensuing conflict and confusion prompted the late Edgar Milne-Redhead, President of the Botanical Society of the British Isles, to set up the 'Cypripedium Committee' in 1970. The committee included representatives of various conservation and botanical interests with the aim of coordinating the orchid's conservation. The first priority was to safeguard the sole remaining wild plant, and this has been guarded every year since then. Visitors are asked to keep away, and even the committee has only rarely visited the site, whilst 'management visits' have also been curtailed for fear of damaging seedlings.

With careful protection and habitat management the Lady's-slipper has slowly increased in vigour at the wild site, with a steady increase in the number of shoots and flowers. In 1996, the peak year to date, there were 65 shoots and 23 flowers on the main clump (which may be just one plant, several clones or even include seedlings). Few or no flowers were being pollinated naturally and hand-pollination began in 1970. This has resulted in good seed set and the production of many capsules, some of which are left to mature on the plant while others are sent to Kew Gardens.

As part of the 'Species Recovery Programme', organised by English Nature, and with the goal of establishing self-sustaining populations of Lady's-slipper in the wild, ex-situ propagation began in 1983, when a donation from Sir Robert and Lady Sainsbury established the Sainsbury Orchid Conservation Project at the Royal Botanic Gardens, Kew. The fungus that

aids the Lady's-slipper seeds in germination and growth could not be identified, however, and this initially thwarted efforts to cultivate plants from seed. But, after much trial and error, a method of germinating seed in the absence of fungi was developed. This involves supplying the nutrients directly to the seedling in a sterile, asymbiotic medium. Although only about 10% of seeds germinate, large numbers of seedlings can now be produced from the hand-pollinated capsules of the wild plant.

The major problem has become the development of techniques to introduce these laboratory-grown seedlings into a natural environment. The first six seedlings were planted out at the native site in Yorkshire in autumn 1989, and by 2003 approximately 2,000 seedlings had been introduced into 23 locations (although some of the sites are very close to each other). Survival rates are not high, and slugs and snails are a particular problem. Up to 2004, just 105 plants survived at ten sites. Two have flowered, the first in the summer of 2000, 11 years after being planted out. Early reintroductions used two-year old seedlings (one year 'in flask' and another in compost), and survival rates were particularly poor as the tiny seedlings fell foul of slugs or bacterial and fungal infections. Fewer older seedlings are now used (three or even more years old). These are being planted in drier and more open micro-habitats and appear to have much better prospects for survival.

A single plant has been present at Silverdale in Lancashire for many years, although it is thought that it was planted there in the late 19th or early 20th century; its DNA suggests that it is from either Austria or possibly the Pyrenees. It did not flower for many years but slowly increased in vigour and by 2004 produced nine flowers. Sadly, later in the 2004 season this plant was vandalised and probably partially removed although fortunately it has survived this.

GENUS
CEPHALANTHERA
HELLEBORINES (I)

A genus of relatively primitive woodland orchids that are probably heavily dependent on fungi throughout their lives. Their flowers look very simple but are surprisingly similar to those of the apparently more complex and highly-evolved *Epipactis* helleborines.

Distribution

Around 15 species are found in Europe, North Africa and temperate Asia with a single representative in western North America. Eight species are found in Europe, with three in Britain.

Classification

Considered a relatively primitive genus due to the rather unspecialised reproductive structures. Closely related to the helleborines of the genus *Epipactis*, but the flowers are stemless (sessile), the ovary is often twisted and the column is simpler in structure.

Floral structures

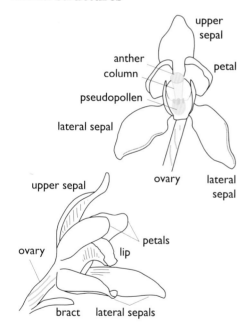

The column has a simple, sticky stigma and no rostellum or viscidium. The pollen is aggregated together into pollinia but as single grains that form a powdery mass; in more advanced orchids the pollen is grouped into tetrads that are held together by elastic threads, and it is these tetrads that are bound together in the

◀ *26 May, Cambridgeshire. White Helleborine*

pollinia. As in the *Epipactis* helleborines, the lip is divided by a narrow waist into the hypochile at the base and epichile at the tip.

Pollination

White Helleborine is largely self-pollinated but Red and Sword-leaved Helleborines are cross-pollinated. Their flowers do not produce nectar, however, and depend upon deceit, displaying bright yellow pseudopollen on the lip to entice potential pollinators to visit. The mechanism is rather simple: visiting insects brush against the stigma and pick up some of the sticky substance that it exudes, then, as the insects back out of the flower, the pollinia stick to this sticky mess and are carried away.

Growth pattern

The aerial stems grow from rhizomes that put out slender, fleshy roots.

Fungal partners

They are probably heavily dependent on fungi, and recent studies have shown that adult plants of both Red and White Helleborines do acquire nutrients via a fungal route and also have an association with ectomycorrhizal fungi; they may gain nutrients from the roots of nearby trees via these fungi. One member of the genus, the Phantom Orchid *C. austiniae* of western North America, produces no green leaves and is fully dependent on fungi.

Development from seed

Poorly known, and seedlings are rarely found.

Vegetative reproduction

White Helleborine may produce new shoots from buds on the roots, but Sword-leaved Helleborine is thought to lack any method of vegetative propagation.

Name

The name *Cephalanthera* means 'flowery-headed' and derives from the Greek *kephale* 'head' and *antheros* 'flowery' or 'blooming'.

RED HELLEBORINE

Cephalanthera rubra

With flowers that are closer to pink than red, this is one of the most striking and attractive of all British and Irish orchids. Sadly, it is also one of the rarest, with just a handful of plants known at three sites in southern England. Red Helleborine has always been rare in Britain but even in its traditional stronghold in the Cotswolds it has now declined to just a single site. On the edge of its range in Britain, it is capricious and seems to require exactly the right habitat with exactly the right mix of light and shade, but in Europe it is much less picky.

Identification

This species is so rare that identification is likely to be academic. If you are fortunate enough to be looking at a Red Helleborine you will have travelled specifically to see it. It is, however, possible that new sites may still be found in or around suitable woodland in southern England. Flowering plants are unmistakable, but non-flowering plants are very hard to find and difficult to distinguish with certainty from White Helleborine or even indeed from the *Epipactis* helleborines.

Habitat

Found in beechwoods growing either on chalk, as in the Chilterns and Hampshire, or on limestone, as in the Cotswolds, usually on free-draining slopes. At all three current sites it grows at the boundary of the chalk or limestone and the overlying acidic clay drift. All three sites are probably ancient woodland.

Although a woodland orchid, too much shade will prevent it from flowering regularly or successfully. It has long been known that the finest specimens were to be found in rather open spots within the woods, sometimes amongst tall grass, brambles and other undergrowth alongside paths or in scrubby places and on open banks. In such open situations, however, the growth of scrub can eventually overwhelm the helleborines. It may well be adapted to flower in the gaps caused by tree-falls, where a sudden increase in light allows it to flower for a year or two before the canopy closes again, light levels fall and the plant retreats to a 'dormant' state underground

▲ 24 June, Buckinghamshire. The plant appears spindly and fragile, almost top-heavy, and seemingly struggles to support such a large, elegant flower spike.

until conditions become favourable again. Alternatively, grazing animals in the primeval forests may have kept the development of rank vegetation and scrub at bay for long periods of time. In France and Germany, where Red Helleborine is locally common, it thrives best in situations where it receives a few hours of direct sunlight each day, in glades or along forest roads and tracks.

Flowering period
Mid-June to mid-July, sometimes late July, but usually at its best in the last week of June and first week of July.

Range
Currently known from single sites in north Hampshire, Buckinghamshire and east Gloucestershire. **World range:** Essentially a European species, ranging north to *c.* 60°N in southern Scandinavia, southernmost Finland and the Baltic States, east to the Urals and south to the Mediterranean, including Corsica, Sardinia, the Balearic Islands, Crete and Cyprus, and also to the Crimea and Caucasus. Found in North Africa in Morocco, Algeria and Tunisia and in Turkey, Israel, Syria and northern Iran. It appears to prefer a continental climate and is largely absent from the Low Countries, the milder western seaboard of France and, of course, Britain.

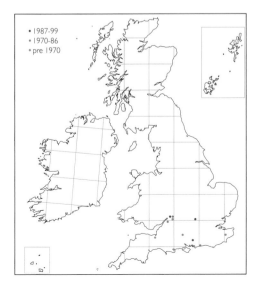

▲ *28 June, Buckinghamshire. Confined to beechwoods, Red Helleborine acquires nutrients from its fungal 'partner' throughout its life.*

How to find it
Red Helleborine is a shy flowerer, and even when it flowers, there may be many more non-flowering plants in the vicinity, and it can remain in a vegetative state for many years. It is nevertheless worth looking for, especially in beechwoods on chalk or limestone, where recent felling or tree-falls have let in more light. But realistically, the only chance to see this species is at one of the known sites. The populations are very small and vulnerable and although visitors are not encouraged, low-key open days are organised at the Hampshire site during the flowering season (contact the Hampshire Wildlife Trust for details).

DESCRIPTION
Height: 15-60cm.
Stem: Slender, often wavy and with abundant short glandular hairs on the upper portion. The stem is dusky green, variably washed brownish-purple towards the tip and sometimes with violet sheaths at the base.

Leaves: Dusky grey-green, held in two ranks alternately up the stem at about 45°. Most of the five to eight leaves are long, narrow and lanceolate, but the lower ones are shorter, blunter and duller green.

Spike: Rather open, with two to nine flowers (occasionally as many as 17). The ovaries are held more-or-less erect, and the flowers face upwards and outwards. The unopened buds are purplish-pink, becoming creamy at the base.

Bract: Dusky green, with numerous short glandular hairs, especially towards the base. The bracts are very narrow and pointed, the lower about one-and-a-half times the length of the ovary, the upper roughly equal in length.

Ovary: Dusky green, becoming brownish-purple at the base and with the ribs variably washed purplish. Slim, cylindrical, ribbed and twisted, the ovary has numerous glandular hairs.

Flower: A beautiful shade of pink, the flowers open widely. The sepals are elongated ovals, narrowing both towards the pointed tips and towards the base. They are lilac-pink, becoming whiter around the base, with numerous short glandular hairs on their outer surface. The petals are similar, although shorter, broader and less tapering at the base. When fully open the lateral sepals are held horizontally like outstretched arms, while the upper sepal and petals form a rather loose hood. The lip is divided into hypochile and epichile by a constriction around the mid-point. The basal portion (hypochile) is gutter-shaped and the sides curl up on either side of the purplish column and anther; it is white with fine yellow veins and pale-pink sides. The epichile is flatter (although still concave), arrow-shaped and tapers to a pointed tip that is bent downwards. It is whitish with variably pinker edges, a deep lilac-pink tip and seven to nine longitudinal yellow ridges. The column is violet-rose.

Subspecies
None.

Variation and varieties
None.

BIOLOGY

Pollination and reproduction
Red Helleborine is pollinated by small solitary bees, with members of the genus *Chelostoma* being important, at least in Europe. The flowers do not produce nectar, but studies in Sweden suggest that the bees are attracted to the helleborines because to the bees' eyes (which are not sensitive to the red end of the spectrum) they resemble certain blue bellflowers *Campanula* sp. that do produce nectar. And, not only do bees visit the bellflowers to collect nectar, but also male bees search for females around the flowers. The Red Helleborine may therefore be able to exploit the bee's sexual urges as well as its foraging behaviour. The pollination mechanism is, however, not efficient in England, perhaps due to an absence of bees of the right size and shape, and few flowers set seed. Many flowers remain unfertilised and fall off the plant complete with their ovaries.

Vegetative reproduction may be more important than reproduction by seed. If the central rhizome dies off, the short side roots, densely 'infected' with fungi, can remain alive and produce a bud at the tip that will grow into a new rhizome and eventually produce a new leafy shoot.

▲ 28 June, Buckinghamshire. The lip has a series of parallel raised ridges, probably related to the attraction of pollinating insects.

◀ 24 June, Buckinghamshire.

◄ *28 June, Buckingham-shire. The lateral sepals are spread wide.*

Development and growth

The aerial stems grow singly from a slender, horizontal rhizome. There is a heavy presence of fungi in the roots, especially the short side roots. Recent isotope studies have confirmed that mature plants acquire nitrogen and carbon via their fungal 'partner', gaining around 60% of their nitrogen and about 25% of their carbon in this way. Unexpectedly, the Red Helleborine has a particular association with ectomycorrhizal fungi and thus, like Coralroot and Bird's-nest Orchids, may gain nutrients via these fungi from the roots of nearby trees, especially Beech. But unlike the tree, it 'cheats' the fungus by giving nothing in return.

Red Helleborine may become 'dormant' underground, and gaps of up to four years between appearances have been recorded from Hampshire (although it is possible that shoots did emerge but were quickly grazed off). Indeed, it may be able to persist underground for much longer periods. After some trees were felled at the Hampshire site, a plant appeared in 2003 that had not been recorded in any of the previous 17 years. With 14 flowers, it was one of the most robust plants ever seen at this site, suggesting that it was not a newly emerged seedling. In addition, Red Helleborine may be relatively long-lived, and again at the

Hampshire site the plant first discovered in bloom in 1986 survived for at least another 18 years and flowered in all but four seasons.

There is no information on germination or early development. It has been stated that the first leaves are not produced until about six years after germination, and flowering does not occur until the plant is ten years of age. But, as with all such reports, the actual time-scale may be much shorter.

Hybrids

None.

Name and classification

The specific name *rubra* means 'red'.

HISTORY AND CONSERVATION

A *Red Data Book* species that is classed as Critically Endangered and fully protected under Schedule 8 of the Wildlife and Countryside Act 1981. The population is tiny, and in 2004 there were just over 30 shoots at three sites, producing ten flower spikes.

The first British record was published in 1797 in *English Botany*: 'Gathered last June on Hampton Common, Gloucestershire, by Mrs. Smith, of Barnham House in that neighbourhood.' The Cotswolds were for a long time the stronghold of the species with records from 'a great many of the Beech woods from Nailsworth to Birdlip, but it has seldom been seen in quantity and flowering is extremely erratic' (Lousley 1969). It was common enough at times, however: 'I once saw some fifty or sixty plants together, but only about ten bore spikes of flowers, and somebody cut those before the next morning' (Riddelsdell et al. 1948). There are also old records from south Somerset, west Gloucestershire, West Sussex and Kent, but no specimens have survived from the latter two counties to confirm the identifications and although this is a very distinctive plant the reliability of these reports is uncertain.

Following its discovery, the number of sites in the Cotswolds gradually dwindled and there is now just one (although it is quite possible that the plant is lurking unseen at others). At this beechwood reserve there were up to 40 shoots in the 1970s, but by the late 1990s, probably due to increased shade, it had declined to only three shoots with just one of these flowering. Happily, there has since been a partial recovery to around ten shoots with at least one flowering each year. This may have been encouraged by some limited felling to let in more light.

Red Helleborine was found in the Chilterns in Buckinghamshire in 1955 when three flowering spikes were discovered in a clearing in a beechwood. There were ten the following year, together with 64 non-flowering plants within about 25m. After this spectacular discovery, however, there was a sharp decline, and no flowers were recorded from 1960. Indeed, no plants were seen at all for several years in the 1970s. But from 1980 onwards odd non-flowering plants reappeared and flowering resumed in 1983. There was a distinct increase from 1989 (probably encouraged by the felling of a handful of trees in 1987), and since then about 10-14 plants have appeared each year, a little over half of them producing flowers.

Red Helleborine was recorded in Hampshire in 1926 and then refound in north Hampshire in 1986 when a single flower spike was located. It is thought that this plant may have been stimulated into flowering by the felling of a few trees some years before; the wood where it grows had been heavily shaded by Beech and Yew. Subsequently the whole area was thinned and then clear-felled, mown and hand-weeded. Wire cages have been used to protect the plants, but despite this the flower spikes have been damaged by careless photographers on three occasions. And, despite the careful management, there has been just a modest increase with one to eight plants appearing and producing one or two flower spikes almost every year.

Red Helleborine is clearly sensitive to light levels. Another factor that affects the plants is grazing: deer, rabbits and slugs undoubtedly damage the helleborines and prevent flowering. Slug pellets are used in the Cotswolds for this reason, although their effect on the fungal 'partner' is unknown. Conversely, grazing also keeps down the surrounding vegetation and reduces competition, and the scratching and scraping of rabbits may provide suitable conditions for the establishment of new plants. Thus in the Cotswolds the management regime now includes some limited raking and also fencing the area against deer over the summer and then removing the fences in an attempt to 'get the best of both worlds'.

British populations of Red Helleborine produce few young plants and seed production is low. An individual plant in Hampshire produced 96 flowers over 14 seasons but just nine capsules were recorded, despite some flowers being hand-pollinated in nine of those years. In the Chilterns natural pollination levels are also low, and seed is only occasionally set; hand-pollination was also undertaken for a while but analyses of the seeds showed that only around 20% were viable.

The capricious flowering and poor seed-set of Red Helleborine in England recalls Sword-leaved Helleborine, a species that is also pollinated by small solitary bees. Both helleborines will flower once a certain level of light is achieved, but much brighter, sunlit conditions with a variety of genuinely nectar-producing flowers in the vicinity are probably required if they are to be visited by the correct pollinators and set seed. The spectacle of large numbers of flowering plants may also boost pollination rates and the tiny British populations of Red Helleborine may be especially handicapped if this is true.

With so few plants, management of the three populations is necessarily tentative. The most effective techniques may be to mimic 'natural systems': limited felling to produce a mosaic of woodland and glades; winter grazing to suppress rank vegetation; and protection from deer and rabbits when flowering and fruiting.

Past and present occurrence of Red Helleborine in Britain and Ireland (based on presence or absence in 10km squares of the National Grid; data from the New Atlas).

	Britain	Ireland
total historical range, 1500-1999	10	0
current range	3 (0.1%*)	0
% lost, 1500-1969	50%	
% lost, 1970-1986	20%	
% lost, total	70%	

* current range as a % of the total number of 10km squares

◀ *28 June, Buckinghamshire. As in all helleborines, the lip is divided into two about half way along its length.*

SWORD-LEAVED HELLEBORINE
Cephalanthera longifolia

Other names: Narrow-leaved Helleborine

This is among the most striking and attractive orchids, but sadly also one of the most threatened. Sword-leaved Helleborine occurs very widely in Britain and Ireland but has suffered a dramatic decline over the last 200 years, and sites for the species are now few and far between. It has only been recorded recently from around a quarter of its historical range, and many populations are so small that they are in imminent danger of extinction. Fortunately, our understanding of the biology of this species has improved, and with appropriate management some sites have made a spectacular recovery.

Identification

A distinctive orchid, with graceful, gently arching foliage, long leaves alternating all the way up the stem and spires of pure white flowers that open just enough to display a large golden-yellow patch on the lip.

Similar species

White Helleborine is rather similar and sometimes found growing together with Sword-leaved Helleborine in southern England. It has duller, creamier flowers, blunter sepals, and its leaves, especially the lower ones, are on average shorter and broader. The best distinction is the length of the bracts, which are longer than the ovary in all White Helleborine flowers, even at the top of the spike. On Sword-leaved Helleborine the bracts are shorter than the ovary, at least in the upper part of the spike (they may be very long and leaf-like on the lowest two or three flowers), and therefore the flower spike is well-demarcated from the leafy part of the stem.

Habitat

Sword-leaved Helleborine is a 'woodland' orchid but its optimum habitat is the interface of woodland and grassland. It does best in glades, clearings, rides and on the margins of roads and tracks, in areas where the ground vegetation is not too dense. It depends on small solitary bees for pollination and these are found in species-rich grassland, visiting the sunnier parts of adjacent woodland to forage. Suitable

▲ *27 May, Hampshire. The stately, leafy stems, clearly distinct from the leafless flower spike, are characteristic.*

sunlit, open conditions are naturally transient in woods as open areas are invaded by scrub or the canopy closes overhead, increasing the level of shade. Sword-leaved Helleborine will persist and can flower well under the shade of a high, closed canopy but in the absence of successful pollination and reproduction, will eventually disappear from such sites. It can also persist in dense shade under scrub, but flowering will be very much reduced, the plants remaining in a vegetative state or even becoming 'dormant' underground. However, it can flower spectacularly if the scrub is cleared and the light intensity rises above a certain level. Notably, in Hampshire, rather than being in ancient woodland many of its sites are along ancient trackways or in secondary woods that were arable fields in the 19th century but were allowed to 'tumble down' to woodland.

In southern England, Sword-leaved Helleborine favours beechwoods on chalk, but elsewhere it grows under a variety of deciduous trees. In the Wyre Forest in Worcestershire, it once thrived in coppice cut on a relatively long, 18-year cycle. It is sometimes found in scrub and occasionally on chalk grassland, but the plants are very small on grassland with few flowers. On the coast of Co. Mayo in western Ireland, it once grew on wind-blown shell-sand overlying peat, both in stunted hazel and oak scrub and on an exposed summit (where the plants were even smaller, just 5-7.5cm high with only one or two flowers). It has also been found in pine plantations at Newborough Warren on Anglesey.

Many sites for Sword-leaved Helleborine are on calcareous soils overlying chalk and limestone, but in the north and west it is found on a variety of other soils, although probably still with an alkaline influence. It is tolerant of both wet and dry conditions, from damp woods or wet scrub in the north and west to dry chalky slopes in southern England. Sword-leaved Helleborine is confined to the lowlands.

Flowering period

Mid-May to mid-June, being at its best in the last two weeks of May, even in Scotland, although sometimes still in flower in early July at exposed sites in the north.

▲ *27 May, Hampshire. Although sadly much reduced, Sword-leaved Helleborine responds very favourably to appropriate management, especially good levels of light combined with grazing.*

Range

Sword-leaved Helleborine has always had an unusually scattered distribution in the British Isles but is now very much reduced. The strongholds are in Hampshire and Argyll, each with around a dozen sites. Other minor concentrations are found in Worcestershire (the Wyre Forest holds a few small populations), Merionethshire and Cumbria. There are one or two sites each in West Sussex, Surrey, west Gloucestershire, Warwickshire, Montgomeryshire, Caernarvonshire, Anglesey and, in Scotland, Perthshire, Inverness-shire, Ross & Cromarty and west Sutherland, and also Arran, Islay, Jura and Skye in the Inner Hebrides. In Ireland it is very scattered, with a handful of sites in Co. Kerry, Co. Clare, Co. Wexford, Co. Galway, Westmeath and Co. Donegal. **World range:** Essentially a European species but with scattered records to the east, in northern Iran, the mountains of Central Asia and through the Himalayas to southwest China. In Europe it occurs north to 63°N in Scandinavia, southern Finland and the Baltic States, east to western Russia (around Moscow) and south to the Mediterranean, including the Balearic Islands, Corsica, Sardinia and Sicily, and also to the Crimea and Caucasus. It is found in North Africa in Morocco, Algeria and Tunisia, in a few places in Turkey and in Lebanon and Israel.

▲ 27 May, Hampshire. The lower flowers can have very long bracts, but they are always very short on the upper flowers, a clear distinction from White Helleborine.

How to find it

The Hampshire Wildlife Trust reserve at Chappett's Copse holds by far the largest British population (2,185 flowering plants in 2003) and is undoubtedly the best place in southern England to look for this stunning orchid. In Scotland it can be found at Knapdale and at Ballachuan Hazelwood (both Argyll & Bute).

DESCRIPTION

Height: 15-65cm but can be as short as 5cm in very exposed situations.

Stem: Green, with some short hairs on the upper part and two to four whitish, often green-tipped sheaths at the base. Stems grow singly.

Leaves: Clear 'grass' green with fairly prominent

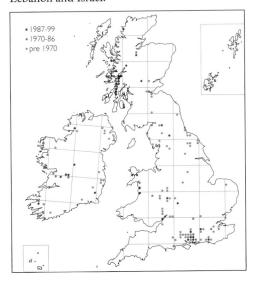

- 1987-99
- 1970-86
- pre 1970

veins, strap-shaped, keeled, long and rather narrow, the upper ones with a pointed tip, the lowermost shorter, broader and blunter. The seven to 20 leaves are spaced alternately up the stem and arranged in two variably defined opposite rows that may twist around the stem in a spiral pattern. They are held at 30°-60° above the horizontal and arch gracefully outwards.

Spike: Rather loose, with three to 15 flowers, sometimes 25 or very exceptionally even 40, the lower are held at 30°-45° above the horizontal, the unopened upper buds tending to be nearer the vertical.

Bract: Green, narrow and pointed. On the lowest few flowers the bract can be either very long and leaf-like or much shorter, only half to two-thirds the length of the ovary, but on all plants the bracts are very short at the tip of the spike.

Ovary: Green, long and slender, prominently twisted and boldly six-ribbed, with short hairs; the very short stalk is minutely hairy.

Flower: Large and white with a golden-yellow patch on the lip. The sepals and petals are a delicate white, the sepals lanceolate and pointed and the petals slightly shorter and broader. The vast majority of flowers do not open widely, the sepals and petals cupping the lip with the tips of the sepals flared outwards, but in some plants the lateral sepals are held spreading. The lip is white, short and broad and divided into inner (hypochile) and outer (epichile) halves by a distinct narrowing or 'waist'. The hypochile and base of the epichile are held parallel to the column with their sides curved upwards and inwards to form a deep gutter. The epichile is spade-shaped with a projecting central lobe or 'tooth'. The base of the hypochile is washed a rich golden-yellow, and towards the tip of the epichile there is an extensive patch of dense papillae with a golden-yellow frosting, although the fringe of the lip remains white. Towards the base of this golden-yellow patch there are five to six (rarely seven) parallel longitudinal ridges that are also washed golden-yellow. The column is whitish, long and projects forward (like a boat's figurehead) and the anther is tinged pale-yellowish. There is no scent.

Subspecies
None.

Variation and varieties
None.

BIOLOGY
Pollination and reproduction
The flowers are pollinated by solitary bees. Sword-leaved Helleborine produces no nectar and relies on deceit to attract its pollinators; the golden-yellow pseudopollen on the lip may be especially important in luring insects. However, for the deceit to function effectively there must be a good supply of genuinely nectar-producing flowers in the vicinity. Furthermore, bees will only visit flowers in bright sunlight and forage mostly between 10am and 3pm, and both the helleborines and the surrounding nectar-producing plants have to be in sunlight for some of that period; sites that catch the morning sun may be especially favoured. Pollination rates in Britain are very variable, and a study in Hampshire found that an average of 35% of flowering plants in sunny glades produced at least one seed capsule; under a high canopy this fell to 16% and in scrub to just 7%. The maximum recorded in any one season was 56% of flowering plants in a

▲ *27 May, Hampshire. The flowers sometimes open more widely, showing the yellow pseudopollen on the lip.*

◀ *27 May, Hampshire.*

▲ *27 May, Hampshire. Some plants are very robust.*

sunny glade, although many of these may have produced just one seed capsule. As well as sunlit sites, higher rates of pollination are associated with larger congregations of flowers, and it may be that the spectacle of many helleborines in flower is more attractive to bees. Conversely, at many sites, especially where there are very small populations, virtually no seed is produced. Self-pollination has not been recorded and is unlikely due to the structure of the flower.

Development and growth
Poorly known. The aerial stems grow from a rhizome that produces long and sparsely branched roots, with fungi concentrated in the tips of the roots and in the few short side roots. Plants are able to remain 'dormant' underground for about one year. Nothing specific is known about its fungal associates but it seems probable that like Red and White Helleborines it acquires a substantial proportion of its nutrients via a fungal route.

There is no information from wild plants on the length of the period between germination and the first appearance above ground but it may be four or more years. In the laboratory the interval is two and a half years. Plants need to have reached a certain height and minimum leaf area before they can flower but do sometimes bloom in their first year above ground.

Sword-leaved Helleborine is thought to lack any method of vegetative propagation.

Hybrids
C. x *schulzei*, the hybrid with White Helleborine, has been recorded very rarely from Hampshire and West Sussex.

Name and classification
The specific name *longifolia* means simply 'long-leaved'.

HISTORY AND CONSERVATION
The first British record was published by Christopher Merrett in 1666 in his *Pinax Rerum Naturalium Britannicarum* ('A picture of British natural history'): 'In Helk wood in Yorkshire, not far from Ingleborough'.

Sword-leaved Helleborine is Nationally Scarce in Britain and specially protected in Eire under the Flora (Protection) Order. It is the only orchid to be the subject of a Plantlife International 'Back from the Brink' project.

Past and present occurrence of Sword-leaved Helleborine in Britain and Ireland (based on presence or absence in 10km squares of the National Grid; data from the New Atlas).

	Britain	Ireland
total historical range, 1500-1999	131	31
current range	34 (1.2%*)	7 (0.7%*)
% lost, 1500-1969	60.5%	68%
% lost, 1970-1986	13.5%	9.5%
% lost, total	74%	77.5%

* current range as a % of the total number of 10km squares

Sword-leaved Helleborine has been in decline throughout the 19th and 20th centuries, initially due to woodland losses and the replanting of woodlands with conifers. At a few sites, small populations were given the final death-knell by collectors. The decline has continued in the last 30 years, probably due to the lack of woodland management. This has led to the disappearance of glades and rides and the development of a denser canopy, and the management that does take place often involves clear-felling large areas at once. The loss of nearby hedgerows and permanent pastures may have indirectly affected the species too, reducing the populations of suitable pollinating bees. Other threats include heavy browsing by deer, now commoner in Britain than since the time of William the Conqueror.

Sword-leaved Helleborine can now be found at less than 50 sites, with around 20 each in England and Scotland and five in Wales. Research in the 1990s showed that 31% of sites supported just one plant and 61% held less than ten. Many are likely to be long-lived individuals clinging on at a site no longer suitable for reproduction, and the prospects of such tiny populations surviving are bleak. By 2003 only nine sites in Britain held more than 50 plants, and in Ireland the species was formerly recorded from 15 counties but is now extinct in ten of them.

It is difficult to fashion effective conservation measures for this orchid. Its long-term survival depends on adequate levels of flowering and fruiting and the subsequent recruitment of enough new plants to the population. It will flower well once the light levels reach a critical threshold (which is rather lower than the levels produced, for example, by coppicing). Its pollinating bees require higher levels of sunlight, however, and at these higher light levels there is a tendency for rank vegetation and scrub to take over and this will overwhelm the helleborines. 'Nutrient creep' from surrounding agricultural land can also promote the growth of rank vegetation that can smother the orchids.

The most effective management regime probably comprises limited felling to produce a mosaic of woodland and glades, winter grazing

EXTINCT?
(the date of the last record is given where known)

Devon (before 1939)
Dorset (1876)
Wiltshire (1958)
East Sussex (1982)
Kent (1980s)
Oxfordshire (1970)
Norfolk (1883)
Herefordshire (1986)
Shropshire (last date uncertain)
Staffordshire (before 1901)
Derbyshire (before 1903)
Nottinghamshire (before 1839)
Lancashire (1898)
Yorkshire (1941)
Co. Durham (1882)
Northumberland (1841)
Monmouthshire (1987)
Cardiganshire (1985)
Montgomeryshire (1978)
Dumfries-shire (1854)
Ayrshire (1972)
Midlothian (1892)
Fife (1847)
Co. Cork
Co. Carlow
Co. Wicklow
Co. Dublin
Co. Tipperary
Co. Roscommon
Co. Mayo
Co Down
Co. Antrim (prior to c. 1840)

to suppress rank vegetation and protection from deer and rabbits when flowering and fruiting. Recent successes give hope for this very special orchid: at the Little Shoulder of Mutton in Hampshire, 31 plants were found in 1987 after Beech trees and scrub were cleared to increase the size of an existing small patch of chalk grassland. A programme of further scrub control, mowing and protecting individual plants with wire netting resulted in a negligible increase, but dramatic results came when winter grazing was introduced, with a jump to 240 plants by 2004. It now seems to be the 'perfect' site with a sunny, south-facing scrubby edge adjoining chalk grassland (which can provide nectar and nest sites for the pollinating bees).

WHITE HELLEBORINE

Cephalanthera damasonium

This subtly attractive orchid is relatively common in beechwoods in southeast England and is sometimes almost the only flowering plant to be found beneath the dense canopy of the trees. It has recently been found to have a special relationship with nearby trees, extracting nutrients from them via a mutual fungal 'partner'.

▲ 26 May, Cambridgeshire. The flowers are usually creamy and egg-shaped, with the sepals and petals hardly opening at all.

Identification

The loose spike of rather egg-shaped, upward-pointing, creamy-white flowers, most of which do not open widely, is very distinctive. Most flowers set seed, and the stout, elongated capsules, held upright, can identify the species late in the season, well after the flowers have withered.

Similar species

Sword-leaved Helleborine is much rarer but is sometimes found together with White Helleborine. The flowers of Sword-leaved Helleborine are always pure white and tend to open more widely. In addition, the sepals have more pointed tips, and the leaves, especially the lower ones, are on average rather longer and narrower. The best distinction is the length of the bracts: on Sword-leaved Helleborine these are shorter than the ovary, at least in the upper part of the spike (on the lowest two or three flowers they may be very long and leaf-like); on White Helleborine the bracts are all longer than the ovary.

Habitat

Strictly confined to well-drained calcareous soils on chalk and limestone and found in woodland and shelter belts, sometimes in scrub and occasionally on nearby grassland (especially on north-facing slopes). It tolerates quite deep shade, but the most robust plants are found where the shade is not too intense. It is strongly associated with Beech, even solitary trees, and can happily grow in the dense shade cast by this species. Its truly classic habitat is a beech hanger on a steep slope with a sparse or non-existent ground cover, the helleborines growing through a carpet of dead leaves or on bare stony or mossy ground.

Flowering period

Mid-May to late June, exceptionally from late April or to mid-July, with flowers in the open or in very dry woods being the earliest.

Range

Southern England, especially the North and South Downs, the chalk of Hampshire and Wiltshire, and the Chilterns and Cotswolds. Ranges west to Dorset, Somerset and Gloucestershire, south to the Isle of Wight and north to Herefordshire, Worcestershire, Northamptonshire and Cambridgeshire. **World range:** Almost confined to central and southern Europe, extending north to Denmark, Gotland in southern Sweden and the Baltic States, east to Belarus and the western Ukraine and south to the Mediterranean, including the Balearic Islands, Corsica, Sardinia, Sicily and Crete, and to the Crimea and Caucasus. Also found in Turkey, Syria, Israel and northern Iran.

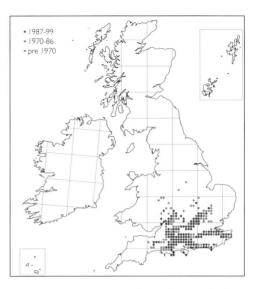

- 1987-99
- 1970-86
- pre 1970

How to find it

Usually an easy species to find in suitable habitat, although often growing well away from paths and tracks in heavy shade in the depths of the forest. Notable sites away from its heartland in the southeast include Beechwood in Cambridgeshire and Brown's Folly in 'Avon', and at Friston Forest in East Sussex it is rapidly colonising a large area of beech plantations.

DESCRIPTION

Height: 8-67.5cm but typically 15-40cm, and many are just 13-18cm tall with only one or two flowers.

▲ *26 May, Cambridgeshire. White Helleborine has a special association with Beech trees, extracting nutrients via a mutual fungal link; it may occur in large numbers where little else can grow.*

Stem: Green, the upper part is ridged and either hairless or slightly hairy. There are one to three brownish, membranous sheaths at the base, the upper of which is sometimes tipped green. Stems grow singly.

Leaves: Oval to broadly lanceolate, tapering to a moderate point and becoming narrower and more bract-like towards the spike; the lowest leaf is rather short and cowl-like. The three to five leaves are placed alternately up the stem, more or less in two opposite rows, and curve gracefully upwards to lie horizontally. They are greyish-green, sometimes with a bluish tinge, and have prominent veins (especially on the underside).

Spike: Loose, with one to 12 relatively large flowers, sometimes as many as 16, most pointing vertically upwards.

Bract: Greenish, narrowly lanceolate and relatively long, often much longer than the flower, but becoming shorter towards the tip of the spike, although still longer than the ovary.

Ovary: Pale green, either not twisted or only moderately so, slender, cylindrical and boldly six-ribbed.

Flower: Relatively large and creamy-white. The sepals are white to creamy-white with a hint of green. They are tear-shaped to oval-lanceolate with the broader end at the base and a blunt tip. The petals are slightly shorter and more oval in shape. The lip is short and broad and divided into inner (hypochile) and outer (epichile) halves by a distinct narrowing or 'waist'. The hypochile and base of the epichile are held parallel to the column with their sides curved upwards and inwards to form a gutter, the base of which is washed golden-yellow. The epichile is heart-shaped, rather broader than long, with the tip curving gently downwards. Towards the tip of the epichile there is an extensive patch of golden-yellow frosting that has three to five longitudinal ridges and furrows towards its base; these ridges are also washed golden-yellow. The column is long, slender and whitish, with the anther tinged pale yellow. The flowers do not normally open widely, the sepals, petals and lip forming an egg-shape around the

▲ 31 May, Cambridgeshire. Although often forming a tall spire, the shape of the spike is variable.

◄ 27 May, Hampshire.

column, but in a few plants the lateral sepals spread apart like outstretched arms and the upper sepal and petals then form a loose hood. There is no scent.

Subspecies

None.

▲ *31 May, Cambridgeshire. The spout-like tip of the lip is revealed.*

Variation and varieties

Var. *chlorotica* is deficient in chlorophyll, and its stem and leaves are very pale green or even yellowish-white. It has rarely been recorded.

BIOLOGY

Pollination and reproduction

Probably largely self-pollinated in a process that was described by Charles Darwin. The anther opens while the flower is still in bud and releases the pollinia, which sit on top of the column (the flower is held pointing upwards) with their front edge resting against the stigmatic zone. The pollinia are very friable and at least some of the pollen adheres to the stigma and effects pollination. Once the flower is mature, however, the outer part of the lip folds down to form a landing platform for insects, especially bees. These are attracted by the golden-yellow mass of pseudopollen on the tip of the lip (the ridges are said to taste of vanilla and are often gnawed by some creature; Darwin found minute, bitten-off fragments but could not be sure of the culprit). It seems that visiting insects may not only spread more pollen onto the stigma within the flower but also sometimes transfer pollen from flower to flower, thus causing cross-pollination. But, once the

flower is fully fertilised, the lip folds up again to shut the 'door'. The mechanism is very efficient, unlike Red and Sword-leaved Helleborines, and almost all flowers produce seed. Vegetative propagation also occurs. The roots produce buds, and these develop into new aerial shoots.

Development and growth

The aerial stem grows from a deeply buried, short, woody rhizome. This sends up to 95 roots vertically down into the soil; these are thick, corky and 30-60cm long. The mature plant was thought to be independent of fungi, but recent isotope studies have shown that it acquires the majority of its nitrogen and roughly half its carbon from a fungal 'partner'. This undoubtedly explains the ability of White Helleborine to thrive in densely shaded sites where it is sometimes the only green plant present. Albino, chlorophyll-less White Helleborines are sometimes found and these must be fully mycotrophic and completely dependent on their fungal 'partner'.

Although it appears to form relationships with a wide range of fungi,

▲ *31 May, Cambridgeshire. Rather rarely, the flowers open widely, showing the yellow pseudopollen and raised ridges on the lip and the long column projecting into the flower.*

White Helleborine preferentially forms associations with ectomycorrhizal fungi, especially Basidiomycetes; these in turn have a relationship with nearby trees. Thus, like Coralroot and Bird's-nest Orchids, it gets nutrients from the roots of these trees via the fungi but unlike the trees, it 'cheats' the fungus by giving nothing in return. In view of this, the well-known association of White Helleborine with Beech takes on a more sinister significance.

After germination the seedling is reported to spend eight years underground before sending up aerial shoots, and flowers are not produced for another two or three years. There is, however, probably little direct evidence for these timings.

Hybrids

C. x schulzei, the hybrid with Sword-leaved Helleborine, has been recorded rarely from Hampshire and West Sussex.

Name and classification

The origin of the specific name *damasonium* is obscure. The usual derivation has no connection whatsoever with orchids: '*damasonium*' was used by Pliny (AD 23-79, author of the encyclopedic *Natural History*) for '*Alisma*', which in turn was a name given by Dioscorides in around AD 64 to a 'plantain-leaved water plant'. An alternative derivation is from *damaso* meaning to 'subdue', i.e. subdue evil, as the plant was considered an antidote to the venom of toads.

HISTORY AND CONSERVATION

The first British record was published in 1670 when John Ray noted this species in his *Catalogus Plantarum Angliae et Insularum adjecentium* ('A catalogue of plants found around Cambridge'), 'In the woods near Stokenchurch, Oxfordshire...'

White Helleborine has been lost from over 40% of its historical range, largely due to woodland clearance and the replanting of woodlands with conifers. Many of the losses have been on the edges of the range, and it is now extinct in southern Yorkshire, Shropshire, Nottinghamshire, Derbyshire, Warwickshire, Essex and Devon. This species is still, however, relatively common within its range and can occur in large numbers. Furthermore, it can colonise newly available habitats, such as maturing beech plantations.

Past and present occurrence of White Helleborine in Britain and Ireland (based on presence or absence in 10km squares of the National Grid; data from the New Atlas).

	Britain	Ireland
total historical range, 1500-1999	233	0
current range	136 (4.8%*)	0
% lost, 1500-1969	33%	
% lost, 1970-1986	8.5%	
% lost, total	41.5%	

* current range as a % of the total number of 10km squares

▲ *31 May, Cambridgeshire. Plants may be tiny, with just one flower (this was 11cm high).*

GENUS *NEOTTIA*
BIRD'S-NEST ORCHIDS
AND TWAYBLADES

This genus contains two apparently very different groups, the bird's-nest orchids and the twayblades, but they are united by a very similar flower structure and almost identical pollination mechanism.

Distribution

Europe, temperate Asia and North America, just creeping into North Africa. There are *c.* 33 species in this genus, but only three occur in Europe, all of which are found in Britain and Ireland.

Classification

The genus can be conveniently divided into two groups. There are nine species of bird's-nest orchids from Europe and Asia, all of which lack green leaves and are fully dependent on fungi throughout their life, and 25 species of twayblades, all of which have a pair of green leaves held opposite each other roughly midway up the stem. Until very recently the twayblades were placed in a separate genus, *Listera*, although they had long been considered close to the bird's-nest orchids (the original *Neottia*), due to their very similar flower structure and pollinating mechanism. Recent genetic research has shown that the two groups are so closely related that they should all be in the same genus, which takes the name *Neottia*, the older and more senior of the two names available.

Floral structures

The column has a wide flat rostellum and there are two stalkless pollinia. There is, however, no detachable viscidium, rather the rostellum expels its contents in a sticky drop when triggered. There is no spur, and nectar is produced in a central groove or slight hollow at the base of the lip. The pollen is grouped into tetrads and these are loosely connected by a few weak threads. The pollen is rather powdery.

Pollination

All three British species produce nectar and have a 'hair-trigger' mechanism. This fires a drop of glue onto the head of a visiting insect, and at the same time the pollinia are released. Pollination is efficient and seed-set is high.

Growth pattern

The aerial stem grows from a rhizome that puts out numerous roots. The growth pattern is sympodial, and each year the rhizome grows upwards to form a new aerial stem that may flower and always dies off. Underground the rhizome continues to grow from a lateral bud at the base of the aerial stem.

Fungal partners

In adult plants the roots have a heavy fungal 'infection', and Bird's-nest Orchid is dependent on fungi throughout its life and is fully mycotrophic.

Vegetative reproduction

The roots are heavily 'infected' with fungi and are nutritionally independent. They are also able to form buds at their tips (a facility that is unique to orchids) and these can develop into new rhizomes. Thus, if the central rhizome dies after flowering (as in Bird's-nest Orchid) or is otherwise fragmented, each piece can grow into a new plant.

Name

The generic name *Neottia* means 'nest-of-fledglings', a reference to the appearance of the roots of Bird's-nest Orchid. (The genus *Listera* was named after Martin Lister (1638-1711), the English doctor and botanist.)

◀ *27 May, Hampshire. Bird's-nest Orchid can be hard to spot among the leaf-litter of the woodland floor.*

LESSER TWAYBLADE
Neottia cordata

Formerly: *Listera cordata*: Other names: Heart-leaved Twayblade (North America)
This species occurs widely on wet moorland and woodland in Scotland, as well as in northern England, Wales, Ireland and on Exmoor. It is very small and often hard to find, but it is well worth the effort. On close examination one can see that the flower is a perfect miniature, with every part reproduced exactly.

Identification

This little orchid is very distinctive. It has two heart-shaped leaves set opposite each other rather high on the stem and tiny, more-or-less reddish flowers, each sitting on a large, globular ovary. On close inspection with a hand-lens the flowers resemble a tiny elfin figure. The deeply forked lip forms the 'legs', the two hornlike projections at its base the 'arms', while the sepals and petals spread star-like around the column to form a 'hat' around the 'head'.

Similar species

None, but there are usually a significant number of non-flowering plants in any population, with the paired leaves lying at the tip of the stem. These are very like young Bilberry plants.

Habitat

Lesser Twayblade is found in two, apparently distinct, habitats, but both offer the same combination of cool, humid shade and acid soils. The first and most frequent habitat is wet moorland or peat bog, where it grows on the cushions of moss, usually *Sphagnum*, found under and between mature, leggy bushes of Heather, Bell Heather and Bilberry. The best conditions are usually found on north-facing slopes. In the oceanic climate of Shetland it is sometimes also found on short, heathy pastures. The second habitat is damp woodland, where the orchid can be found growing among a variety of mosses, sometimes in open areas and sometimes again among an understorey of Heather, Bilberry and scattered Bracken fronds. Willow, birch and alder woods are favoured but Lesser Twayblade is also found in ancient 'Caledonian' pinewoods and mature pine

▲ *7 June, Merioneth. A tiny plant, sometimes with just a few flowers in a reddish spike; no wonder they are hard to spot.*

plantations. It occurs up to 1,065m above sea level (Stob Coire Easain, Inverness-shire), and most sites are now in the hills, as those in the lowlands have largely been destroyed.

Flowering period

Mid-May to mid-July, exceptionally from late April, but generally peaking from late May. Once the flower has been pollinated the column quickly withers and blackens but the remainder of the flower sometimes persists until September.

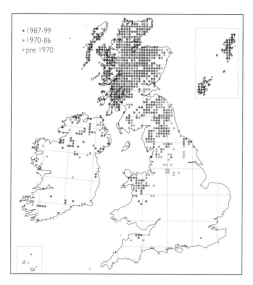

- 1987-99
- 1970-86
- pre 1970

Range

Lesser Twayblade occurs throughout Scotland, including the Outer Hebrides, Orkney and Shetland, although it is absent from the central lowlands. In England it is found from north Lancashire and Yorkshire northwards, with an isolated population in southwest England on Exmoor (Somerset/Devon). In Wales it occurs very locally from northern parts of Breconshire and Cardiganshire northwards, including Anglesey. In Ireland Lesser Twayblade is fairly widespread from Co. Sligo, Co. Cavan and Co. Down northwards but is very local in the south: in Co. Dublin and Co. Wicklow in the east, Co. Galway in the west, and from Co. Limerick and Co. Tipperary southwards.

There are a few records of Lesser Twayblade from elsewhere in southern England. In

▲ 7 June, Midlothian. Lesser Twayblade needs cool, moist conditions and is found on north-facing slopes on damp moorland or in woodland.

Hampshire it was recorded in 1853 and 1895 near Bournemouth and then it turned up in the New Forest near Brockenhurst in 1927-30 and was reported again there in the 1970s (a record from Bratley in about 1980 is suspected to have been a deliberate introduction). The species has also been recorded from Baldwin's Wood in Buckinghamshire in 1980 and from Gravetye Woods in East Sussex in about 1975 and then again in 1989. Some of these records are assumed to involve plants introduced accidentally when pines or rhododendrons were planted but wind-blown seed is a possible source and in Hampshire there could have been relict populations on the New Forest heaths.

World range: Found throughout the boreal regions of the Northern Hemisphere in Europe, Asia and North America, ranging furthest south in the mountains. In Europe it extends south to the Pyrenees, northern Italy, northern Greece, the Crimea and Caucasus and adjacent northern Turkey, and north to Greenland, Iceland and northernmost Scandinavia. In Asia it is found in Siberia eastwards to Lake Baikal and in the Russian Far East, Sakhalin and Japan. In North America it occurs south to California and New Mexico in the west and along the Appalachians to North Carolina in the east.

How to find it

Locally common in Scotland, it is worth looking for Lesser Twayblade wherever there is rank Heather on damp, north-facing slopes, as well as in suitable woodland, although the number of spikes can fluctuate markedly from year to year. It is often to be found *under* the Heather, or at least just under its eaves, and it may be necessary to move the vegetation aside to see the orchids. Scattered plants can be exceedingly difficult to find but, fortunately, the species often occurs in loose colonies and at least one or two plants may be more obvious. The key to success is patience and perseverance. Once a Lesser Twayblade is spotted, a careful search of the area will usually produce more, although a majority may be non-flowering and

even harder to spot. This species is very local in Wales but one well-known site is Roman Steps (Gwynedd).

DESCRIPTION

Height: 3-25cm but usually 5-10cm; tends to be tallest in sheltered woodland.

Stem: Green or reddish-purple, ridged towards the tip and with fine glandular hairs for a short distance above the leaves. There are one or two membranous, brownish sheaths at the base of the stem. Usually grows singly but occasionally two or three stems grow from the same rhizome.

Leaves: Two, lying opposite each other, one third to halfway up the stem and held either horizontally or at up to 45° above the horizontal. They are dark, shiny green and roughly heart-shaped, with a prominent midrib that terminates in a tiny projecting point (mucro). The leaves are also faintly net-veined (reticulate) and often have undulating margins.

Spike: Relatively open, with three to 20 flowers.

Bract: Tiny, triangular and greenish.

Ovary: Green, spherical, with six reddish ribs, held on a reddish or greenish stalk that is a little longer than the ovary, ribbed and twisted.

Flower: Very small and variable in overall coloration; it usually has a pronounced reddish tone but can be much plainer and greener. The

▲ *7 June, Midlothian. The flowers form tiny, elfin figures.*

◄ *7 June, Merioneth.*

sepals are greenish, variably washed reddish in the centre and around the edges, and are oval with blunt tips. The petals are narrower and more strap-shaped and tend to be redder. Both sepals and petals are widely spread and form a star-like pattern around the column. The lip is coppery or pale green, washed red, relatively large and triangular and divided more than halfway to the base into two sharply pointed lobes. Tiny amounts of nectar are produced

▲ 7 June, Midlothian. The ovary is roughly spherical and almost as big as the flower.

in a disc-shaped nectary at the base of the lip just below the column; there are two very short horn-shaped lobes on either side of this nectary and a longitudinal nectar-filled groove running from it to the base of the fork. The lip is held pointing downwards, more or less at right angles to the column. The column is short, stubby and whitish, with a large, thin, leaf-like rostellum that extends forward over the base of the lip, above which lie the yellow anther cap and yellow pollinia. The pollinia are shed by the anther when the flower is still in bud and lie loose on top of the rostellum, held in position by its incurved margins. The flowers have a faint but unpleasant foetid odour, probably originating from the nectar.

Subspecies
None.

Variation and varieties
Var. *trifoliata* has a third leaf above the usual two. It is rare, but has been recorded in Scotland.

BIOLOGY

Pollination and reproduction
The flowers are pollinated by a variety of small insects, including flies and gnats, attracted by the nectar. Three pressure-sensitive hairs project from the tip of the rostellum and these act as a trigger. The slightest touch by an insect causes a droplet of 'glue' to be squirted explosively onto the insect's head, and the pollinia are simultaneously released and fall onto this 'glue'. The glue dries in just a few seconds and the pollinia are carried off by the startled insect.

When the flower first opens the flap-like rostellum physically blocks access to the stigma and any insect visitor will trigger the mechanism the moment it touches the hairs on the rostellum. The rostellum remains in place once the pollinia have been removed but is now spread flat, having released the pollinia. This prevents self-pollination should the pollen-carrying insect return to the flower immediately after it has left. About 24 hours later the rostellum slowly moves upwards, allowing insects to deposit pollen from other flowers onto the stigma, which has now become very sticky. Insects are reported to work upwards from the bottom of the spike towards the top. They therefore start with the lowest and most mature flowers (i.e. those likely to have receptive stigmas), before moving on to younger flowers that still have pollinia waiting to be removed. If this is so, an insect cannot pollinate flowers on the same plant. If by any chance the pollinia are not removed by an insect, the rostellum lifts upwards anyway after a few days, allowing the flower to be fertilised.

The individual flowers of Lesser Twayblade are self-compatible and artificial self-pollination will produce viable seed, but studies in California suggested that it is not usually self-pollinating. However, it is possible that, as in Common Twayblade, small quantities of pollen may occasionally fall from the pollinia on to the stigma or be carried there by tiny insects.

Seed-set is very efficient and the capsules mature and split open within five weeks. The lowest, oldest capsules on a spike may be ripe and shedding seed before the uppermost flowers are even pollinated. Indeed, the capsules swell so quickly and seed is produced so efficiently that some authors suggest that self-pollination must occur routinely.

Lesser Twayblade also reproduces vegetatively, from buds on the roots.

Development and growth

The aerial stem grows from a slender, creeping rhizome that lies near the surface of the soil. This puts out a few long, slender, hairy roots. Usually only one stem is produced, but buds can form at the tip of the roots and develop into additional aerial shoots that flower in their third year. Lesser Twayblade is apparently short-lived and there is little information on the interval between germination and flowering, although the first green leaf is reported to appear after two or three years of underground development.

Hybrids

None.

Name and classification

The specific name *cordata* means 'heart-shaped', a reference to the shape of the leaves.

Together with Common Twayblade, this species was formerly placed in the genus *Listera*, but genetic studies have indicated that *Listera* should be united with Bird's-nest Orchid in the genus *Neottia*, as it was in the past.

HISTORY AND CONSERVATION

The first British record was published in 1666 by Christopher Merrett in his *Pinax Rerum Naturalium Britannicarum* ('A picture of British natural history'): 'Neer the Beacon on Pendle Hill in Lancashire'.

Past and present occurrence of Lesser Twayblade in Britain and Ireland (based on presence or absence in 10km squares of the National Grid; data from the New Atlas).

	Britain	Ireland
total historical range, 1500-1999	822	96
current range	454 (16%*)	48 (4.8%*)
% lost, 1500-1969	25%	41.5%
% lost, 1970-1986	19.5%	8.5%
% lost, total	44.5%	50%

* current range as a % of the total number of 10km squares

Since 1666 the species has disappeared from many sites, especially in the lowlands and on the periphery of the range in northern England, where the drainage and reclamation of bogs and heaths caused many losses in the 19th century. Lesser Twayblade has gone from 44.5% of its historical range in Britain and 50% in Ireland, with a rather large proportion of the losses in Britain being comparatively recent. Given that it has been better recorded in recent years because more people are actively looking for it, the actual decline has surely been substantially greater. It is extinct in Shropshire, Derbyshire, Cheshire, Flintshire, southern parts of Yorkshire and the Isle of Man, and probably also Montgomeryshire.

COMMON TWAYBLADE
Neottia ovata

Formerly: *Listera ovata*

This rather unassuming orchid is one of the commonest and most widely distributed species in Britain and Ireland. Its small, green, inconspicuous flowers belie the fact that it is very long-lived and has an intricate and efficient means of using insects as pollinators.

Identification

Straightforward. It is green or greenish-yellow overall with two large, egg-shaped leaves held opposite each other at the base of the stem and a tall spike of small flowers, each of which resembles a tiny green figure. Non-flowering plants, with just two leaves opposite each other at the tip of the stem, are fairly frequent.

Similar species

Lesser Twayblade is rather similar but tiny, with heart-shaped leaves, and flowers that are usually reddish and have sharply pointed tips to the lobes of the lip.

Man, Frog, Fen and Bog Orchids have greenish flowers but all of these differ markedly in the structure of the lip. Man and Frog Orchids also differ in having a basal rosette of leaves and Bog Orchid has merely tiny clasping leaves at the base of the stem.

Habitat

Possibly more varied than any other British orchid. It is found on short chalk grassland, machair, dune slacks, limestone pavements, permanent pastures, road verges and fens, and also in scrub, hedgerows and moist deciduous woodland, sometimes in deep shade. It has a preference for calcareous soils but will grow in mildly acidic conditions, occasionally amongst Bracken and Heather. It can sometimes be found in relatively new habitats, such as disused railway lines, quarries and sand-pits or in plantations, even of pine. It occurs up to 670m above sea level (Ben Lawers, Perthshire).

Flowering period

Late April to early August, latest in the north, exceptionally even to September.

▲ *29 June, Hampshire. Twayblades have two leaves and the English name originates from 'tway', an archaic and obsolete word for 'two'.*

▶ *23 May, Co. Clare.*

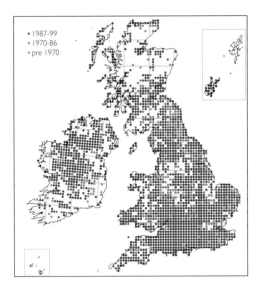

Range

Occurs almost throughout Britain and Ireland, including the Outer Hebrides and Orkney, but absent from Shetland, much of the Scottish Highlands and many coastal regions of southern Ireland. **World range:** Essentially a European species but the range extends into Asia. In Europe it occurs north to Iceland and *c.* 70° N in northern Scandinavia and south to the Mediterranean, including Corsica, Sardinia, Sicily and Crete, and to the Crimea and Caucasus. In Siberia it ranges to *c.* 95° E, and in southern Asia it is found in Turkey, northern Iran, the Altai Mountains and western Himalayas. Introduced in southern Ontario in Canada.

How to find it

One of the commonest and most widespread orchids and usually fairly easy to find, although in regions away from chalk and limestone soils it is often rather local. The best places to look will be in ancient woodlands, marshes or in grasslands that have not been 'improved', ploughed or cut too closely. Being green, including the flowers, odd plants can be inconspicuous but Common Twayblades are often found in large numbers.

DESCRIPTION

Height: 10-75cm but usually 20-60cm.

Stem: Green to mid-brown, thicker and whiter at the base with two or three membranous, scale-like basal sheaths and numerous short, white, glandular hairs. The stems usually grow singly, although not infrequently there are clusters.

Leaves: The two large, egg-shaped or elliptical sheathing leaves are held opposite each other towards the base of the stem; sometimes they lie flat and sometimes they are angled at up to 45° above the horizontal. The leaves are green in the shade and more yellowish-green in sunny places, with three to five prominent veins. There are also one to three tiny, triangular, bract-like leaves higher on the stem.

Spike: Loose to fairly compact, with 15-30 small green flowers, sometimes as many as 100.

Bract: Lanceolate and short; usually shorter than the flower stalk and sometimes much shorter.

▲ 15 May, Norfolk. The tiny green flowers look very much like a human figure.

Ovary: Green, short and rounded, with six prominent reddish-brown ribs. The reddish-brown flower stalk is twisted and a little longer than the ovary; both are variably hairy.

Flower: Small, green and vaguely man-like. The sepals are bluntly oval and dull green, sometimes tinged or fringed dull reddish or brown. The petals are dull green and narrower and more strap-shaped. Both sepals and petals curve inwards to form a very loose hood around the short, thick column. The lip is yellowish-green, long and strap-shaped, sharply folded down and backwards below the flower and divided for around half its length into two blunt-tipped lobes (the 'legs'); a shallow nectar-bearing groove runs down the centre of the lip to the base of the fork. The column is greenish. The flowers are variously described as scented (light, musky or repellent) or as odourless.

Subspecies
None.

Variation and varieties
Var. *trifoliata* has three leaves and is not uncommon. The third leaf is smaller, more pointed and placed above or, less frequently, below the main leaves.

Var. *platyglossa* has a short lip that broadens into blunt diverging lobes, sometimes with a small tooth between them. It was formerly found in dunes in South Wales.

BIOLOGY

Pollination and reproduction
Pollination was intensively studied by C. K. Sprengel (published in 1793) and later by Charles Darwin. The flowers are pollinated by small insects, especially ichneumon wasps but also by sawflies and beetles, attracted by the flowers' scent. Once it has landed the insect follows the nectar-filled groove up the lip and makes contact with the projecting rostellum. The pollinia are then stuck to its head by the sudden secretion or 'explosion' of a drop of sticky liquid that dries in just two or three seconds. The mechanism is

▲ *27 June, Norfolk. Pollination is by small insects, and the mechanism operates on a hair-trigger; it is very efficient.*

extremely sensitive and the slightest touch will trigger it. The startled insect flies away with the pollinia attached, often to another plant altogether. Meanwhile, once the pollinia have been removed, the rostellum bends forwards and downwards, thereby hindering access to the stigma and preventing self-pollination. It then slowly shrinks away upwards again to expose the stigma to visiting insects. If they are carrying pollinia these can then pollinate the flower as they try to get at the nectar at the base of the lip. The mechanism is efficient and many flowers set seed. Self-pollination may also occur occasionally; if the pollinia dry out small fragments of pollen may fall on to the stigma and effect pollination. The seed capsules each contain an average of 1,240 seeds.

▲ *27 June, Norfolk. Vegetative multiplication can produce clumps of spikes.*

Vegetative propagation also occurs, with buds on the roots producing new rhizomes, and group of clones can be formed, sometimes a dense circular cluster of dozens of plants

Development and growth

The aerial stem grows from a short, thick rhizome which has large numbers of long, fairly thick roots. Seeds are thought to germinate in spring, and early estimates of the interval between germination and flowering were seven to 20 years or more, with the seedling spending the first three or four years underground. These estimates may be rather inaccurate, however, and in the laboratory plants can produce leaves less than a year after germination.

Common Twayblade can be extremely long-lived. The remains of 24 old flower spikes have been counted on a single rhizome, and in a

study in Sweden 20 out of 29 plants were still alive after 40 years. Mature plants have been recorded spending one or two years 'dormant' underground and then reappearing.

Hybrids
None.

Name and classification

The specific name *ovata* meaning 'egg-shaped' is a reference to the shape of the leaves. Together with Lesser Twayblade, this species was formerly placed in the genus *Listera*, but recent genetic studies have indicated that this should be united with the genus *Neottia*.

HISTORY AND CONSERVATION

Together with Autumn Lady's-tresses, this was the first orchid to be recorded in Britain. In 1548 William Turner noted in his *Names of Herbes*: 'Martagon...in many places of Englande in watery middowes and in woddes'.

Common, widespread and with a very catholic choice of habitats, this species would seem to be well-placed to survive changes to the countryside. Nevertheless, Common Twayblade has vanished from almost 30% of its historical range in Britain and Ireland, with a relatively large proportion of the British losses being recent.

Past and present occurrence of Common Twayblade in Britain and Ireland (based on presence or absence in 10km squares of the National Grid; data from the New Atlas).

	Britain	Ireland
total historical range, 1500–1999	1,869	512
current range	1,354 (47.5%*)	362 (36%*)
% lost, 1500–1969	16%	22.5%
% lost, 1970–1986	11.5%	6.5%
% lost, total	27.5%	29%

* current range as a % of the total number of 10km squares

BIRD'S-NEST ORCHID
Neottia nidus-avis

Spotting a Bird's-nest Orchid in the woodland gloom is somehow very reassuring; it is a sign that you are in a special place. The species is locally common in mature woodland in parts of southern England, but in much of the remainder of the British Isles it is scarce and very local. One of the three British orchids that have no green leaves and are completely dependent throughout their life on nutrients provided by fungi, Bird's-nest Orchid only appears above ground in order to flower and set seed. Both the English and the scientific name relate to this subterranean existence, as the roots of this orchid form an untidy mass that vaguely resembles the nest of a Wood Pigeon or Rook.

Identification
The honey-brown spikes are unique among British orchids. On careful examination the flowers are typical of an orchid, with the petals and sepals forming an open, fan-shaped hood, and the lip vaguely resembling a human torso. The dried stem and open seed capsules of the previous season's blooms may be found nearby and these can remain intact for almost two years.

Similar species
Confusion is possible with Yellow Bird's-nest, a more-or-less similarly coloured but totally unrelated plant that is often found in the same habitats, although the spike of Yellow Bird's-nest is bent over and 'nodding' until it is very mature. The various broomrapes (family Orobanchaceae) also superficially resemble Bird's-nest Orchid, especially Knapweed Broomrape, which is closest in colour. These chlorophyll-less parasitic herbs are found in open, grassy habitats and could occur on the edge of woods or in woodland rides. A quick look at the structure of the flower will settle the matter, however, as neither Yellow Bird's-nest nor the broomrapes have a flower with a hood and a two-lobed lip.

Habitat
The classic habitat for Bird's-nest Orchid is the heavy shade of a mature beechwood, the orchids emerging from the leaf-litter and deep humus of a woodland floor otherwise devoid of vegetation. It also grows in mixed deciduous woodland and

▲ *2 May, Oxfordshire.*

▲ *Yellow Bird's-nest, 16 June, Norfolk. Another fully mycotrophic (fungus-dependent) species of the wood-land floor, the similarity to Bird's-nest Orchid ends with the honey colour.*

overgrown hazel coppice or sometimes under shady old hedges, shelter-belts or planted conifers, especially if there are still deciduous trees present (and in Europe it regularly grows in conifer woods). Rarely, it has been recorded from grassland just outside woods, but this is exceptional, as exposure to direct sunlight tends to dry out the ground too much. Conversely, it is not found in areas where the soil becomes waterlogged. Bird's-nest Orchid is commonest on chalk and limestone soils but also grows on clays and sands that have a chalky or limestone component, such as boulder clay. Generally it is a lowland species, but it has been recorded up to 250m above sea level in Cumbria.

Flowering period

Early May to late June, exceptionally from late April or to early July, but most are in bloom in the latter half of May. Bird's-nest Orchids have been recorded flowering and setting seed underground if the route to the surface has become blocked by a large stone or other obstacle. As no systematic searches have been made, it is not known whether this is exceptional or a regular event (Australian orchids of the genus *Rhizanthella* routinely flower underground).

Range

Found almost throughout Britain and Ireland but absent from the Isle of Man, Shetland, Orkney and the Inner and Outer Hebrides (with the exception of Skye and Mull); there are, however, only a few sites in northern Scotland, much of Ireland and in a belt from the northern parts of East Anglia through Lincolnshire and the north Midlands to north and west Wales. Its strongholds are undoubtedly southern England (especially central-southern England) and southeast Wales. **World range:** Occurs in Europe and western Siberia, reappearing in the Far East. In Europe found north to *c.* 65°N in Scandinavia and Finland and south to the Mediterranean, including Corsica, Sardinia, Sicily and the Balearic Islands, and to the Crimea and Caucasus; it is largely confined to the mountains in the south of the range and absent from the Mediterranean lowlands. In

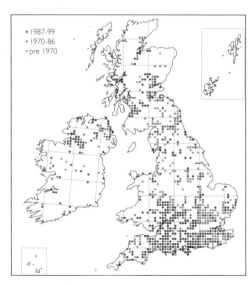

• 1987-99
• 1970-86
• pre 1970

Siberia it extends to *c.* 85°E and it is also found in Algeria in North Africa and at scattered sites in Turkey and northwest Iran. In eastern Asia it occurs in the Russian Far East, Sakhalin, Japan and Korea.

How to find it

In most of Britain and Ireland the species is rather local and only found in small numbers. It often emerges in the darker and shadier parts of a wood and this, combined with its pale-brown colour, can make it hard to find. Bird's-nest Orchid is totally dependent on the activity of its fungal 'partners' and not surprisingly does best in the warm, wet conditions beloved of fungi in general. Warm, wet springs can encourage larger numbers of plants to flower, and conversely very dry periods can result in a reduction in the above-ground population.

DESCRIPTION

Height: 15-52cm but usually 20-40cm.

Stem: Yellowish-brown, slightly glandular-hairy towards the tip. Grows singly, although two spikes occasionally develop from the same rhizome.

Leaves: No green leaves are present. The lower part of the stem is enclosed by three to five long, roughly oblong, scale-like, yellowish-brown, loosely sheathing leaves (the upper ones longer and blunter).

Spike: Cylindrical and crowded, with up to 100 flowers in large plants, but the lower flowers in the spike are usually more widely spaced and there are odd single flowers further down the stem.

Bract: Papery, lanceolate and roughly as long as the ovary and stalk together, but inconspicuous.

Ovary: Oval, subtly six-ribbed, glandular-hairy

▲ *3 June, Norfolk. Whether through seed or vegetative reproduction via division of the underground rhizome, Bird's-nest Orchid sometimes occurs in groups.*

▲ *26 May, Norfolk. Comparison of the flower structure with Common Twayblade shows how close they are.*

and held on a twisted stalk that is about half the length of the ovary.

Flower: Entirely yellowish-brown. The sepals and petals are roughly oval-spatulate in shape and form a loose fan-shaped hood over the column. The lip is slightly darker brown and has a nectar-producing bowl-shaped depression at the base (representing a rudimentary spur). The lip is divided towards the tip into two broad, rounded lobes that spread widely, especially on the lower flowers, to form a lyre-shape; there may also be a subtle point or tooth on either side of the lip half way towards the base. The lip is held pointing outwards and downwards at *c*. 90° to the column, which is pale brown, long and slender. The pollinia are yellow and project conspicuously from beneath the anther cap. The flowers have a pleasant but sickly, honey-like scent.

Subspecies
None.

Variation and varieties
Var. *pallida* has a yellowish-white stem and flowers, and white pollinia. It is rare.

BIOLOGY
Pollination and reproduction
Pollination is by insects, including flies, attracted by the nectar. The mechanism is very similar to that of Common Twayblade. The visiting insect makes contact with the projecting rostellum where there are six minute, rough, touch-sensitive points and the pollinia are stuck to its head by the sudden secretion or 'explosion' of a drop of sticky liquid. After a while the rostellum, which has hitherto blocked access to the stigma, rises to allow visiting insects, complete with pollinia attached to their heads, to make contact with the stigma. If the mechanism is not triggered, after a few days the pollinia fragment and pollen can then fall onto the stigma below, effecting self-pollination (autogamy); pollen may also be carried to the stigma by small insects such as thrips. Ants have been noted carrying pollen from one flower to another on the same spike and this may also effect self-pollination (this time geitonogamy, as it is pollen from a different flower on the same plant). Occasionally, self-pollination may take place in the bud before the flowers have even opened. Pollination is very efficient and almost all flowers will set seed.

Bird's-nest Orchid is thought to be monocarpic, that is the plant dies after flowering once. But, although the rhizome dies, the numerous roots can remain alive and go on to produce new plants from buds at their tip.

Development and growth
The aerial stem develops from a short rhizome that lies horizontally in the soil and is almost entirely surrounded by an untidy mass of short, thick, fleshy roots that stick out more or less at right-angles.

Throughout its life Bird's-nest Orchid is entirely dependent on fungi for nutrition; in adult plants fungi are found exclusively in the roots of the orchid (in the three cortical cell layers, just below the epidermis). Recent studies have shown that the orchid is very specific about its fungal 'partner' and only forms an association with a species of *Sebacina*.

This obtains its carbohydrates by forming a symbiotic ectomycorrhizal association with the roots of trees, particularly Beech: the tree produces carbohydrates through the process of photosynthesis and passes these to the fungus, which in turn contributes mineral nutrients to the tree. The orchid invades this relationship and, via the fungus, gets nutrients from the tree. Bird's-nest Orchid 'cheats' in its partnership with the fungus because, unlike the tree, it does not contribute anything to the fungus (see also p.9).

It is often stated that Bird's-nest Orchid lacks chlorophyll, but a small amount of chlorophyll is present, although no effective photosynthesis can occur. It is also often said that Bird's-nest Orchid is saprophytic and obtains its nutrients from decaying organic material. This is not correct. The orchid gets its nutrients by digesting the living fungus.

Seeds germinate in the spring and require the presence of the same fungus that supports the growth of the adult plant. The seedling initially takes the form of a torpedo-shaped protocorm a few millimetres long. It then begins to develop short, fat rootlets that stick out at about 90° and start to take on the appearance of a 'bird's nest'. At an early stage the bud that will produce the flower spike appears in the axil of a scale leaf at the tip of the rhizome. As the rhizome grows the number of roots progressively increases and the period from germination to flowering is probably three to five years.

Seed can only germinate where the *Sebacina* fungus is present and this may have a localised and restricted distribution, even within a single wood, at least partly because the fungus is entirely dependent on its host tree species and cannot grow without it. The distribution of the orchid is therefore also tied to that of suitable host trees. Adult Bird's-nest Orchids always harbour the correct fungus and form a convenient source of 'infection' for the seed, and germination is far more prolific in the immediate vicinity of adult plants. The clusters of Bird's-nest Orchids that often grow on the

▲ 13 May, Norfolk. When shoots emerge in the spring the flower buds are already fully formed.

exact spot that previously held a flowering plant may be the product of this, or alternatively, of the break-up of a single rhizome to produce several new plants.

Hybrids
None.

Name and classification
The specific name *nidus-avis* means 'bird's nest' (as the generic named *Neottia* means 'nest-of-fledglings' the scientific name is a tautology).

With a similar flower structure and pollination mechanism, the Bird's-nest Orchid is clearly related to the twayblades. DNA studies have recently shown that the relationship is a close one, and they are all now placed in the same genus, *Neottia*.

HISTORY AND CONSERVATION

First recorded from Britain in 1597 by John Gerard in his *Herball*: 'I found it growing in the middle of a wood in Kent two miles from Gravesend.'

   With its requirement for heavy shade and a stable, generally moist environment, the species has undergone a significant decline, especially in the period after 1945. This is due to the grubbing out of woodland and the conversion of deciduous woodland to conifer plantations. More subtle changes, such as the use of heavy machinery in forestry operations, could also have been detrimental. The decline has been most marked in southeast England, especially Kent and the eastern Chilterns, and Bird's-nest Orchid has gone from 54% of its total historical range in Britain and 45% in Ireland. As well as being more widespread, populations may have been larger in the past. For example, 'thousands' were recorded on the south-facing slopes of Box Hill in Surrey in 1947 at a site which nowadays only supports about 200 spikes. Bird's-nest Orchid is specially protected in Northern Ireland under Schedule 8 of the 1985 Wildlife Order (NI).

Past and present occurrence of Bird's-nest Orchid in Britain and Ireland (based on presence or absence in 10km squares of the National Grid; data from the New Atlas).

	Britain	Ireland
total historical range, 1500-1999	742	99
current range	340 (12%*)	54 (5.4%*)
% lost, 1500-1969	41%	29.5%
% lost, 1970-1986	13%	16%
% lost, total	54%	45.5%

* current range as a % of the total number of 10km squares

◀ *6 June, Norfolk. The dead spike may persist for at least a year.*

▶ *8 July, Norfolk. Marsh Helleborines.*

GENUS *EPIPACTIS* HELLEBORINES (II)

A genus of essentially woodland orchids which has diversified to occupy a variety of other situations. Recent research has shown that fungi contribute very significantly to their nutritional budgets, even as adults, with several having connections via their fungal 'partners' to neighbouring trees. As a genus, *Epipactis* is distinctive, with flowers that are rather different to those of 'typical' orchids, but it is necessary to have a good grasp of its flower structure in order to identify some of the species with confidence.

Distribution

Largely confined to Europe and Asia with single representatives in Africa and North America. The number of species is uncertain, with the most conservative authors listing around 11 species in Europe, whereas Delforge (2005) details 59. There are eight species in the British Isles, including two endemics.

Classification

Epipactis is closely related to the genus *Cephalanthera*, and, although the flowers look quite different, both have the lip divided into outer and inner portions by a narrow 'waist'. *Epipactis* differs in having more complex reproductive structures and an ovary that is not twisted; rather it has a distinct stalk which is twisted to bring the lip around to the bottom of the flower.

The genus is sometimes divided into two sections: *Arthrochilium*, which contains Marsh Helleborine, and *Euepipactis*, which contains the remainder of our species. In Marsh Helleborine the inner and outer halves of the lip are joined by a flexible hinge, whereas in all the other species the joint is rigid and the inner portion of the lip does not form such a distinct bowl.

Identification

Epipactis helleborines are relatively easy to recognise as such. They have upright stems 10-120cm tall and oval leaves with obvious parallel veins. In some species, several spikes can arise from the same rootstock. When it emerges from the soil the stem is bent double and as it grows it continues to 'weep'. Eventually, however, the stem becomes fully upright and the flowers, which remain in bud for a frustratingly long time, begin to open. In many species the flowers are relatively small and drab but they may be

▲ Violet Helleborine, 29 June, Buckinghamshire. The flower's spike is fully formed when the stem breaks through the soil surface but it may be several weeks before it elongates, becomes upright and the flowers open.

very numerous. All the helleborines bloom from mid- to late summer, later than most other orchids.

Floral structures

All the *Epipactis* helleborines have a similar flower structure. The ovary forms the apparent 'stalk' of the flower. It actually narrows into the real stalk, the pedicel, just before it reaches the main stem. Once fertilisation has occurred, the ovary swells conspicuously to form a capsule while the flower shrivels to a few brown wisps. In all species the ovary is usually obviously ribbed.

The three sepals and two petals are rather similar in size, shape and coloration; in some species they form a five-pointed star around the column and lip, in others the flowers do not open widely and form a cup or bell shape. In *Epipactis* the lip is divided into two parts. The inner section is known as the hypochile; it is cup-shaped and often contains nectar. The outer part, or epichile, is flatter, more or less triangular in shape and often reflexed (bent under) at the tip. At the base of the epichile there are raised areas known as bosses and in some species these are contrastingly coloured. The hypochile and epichile are connected by a narrow strip that is rigid in most species.

Reproductive structures

The column is a robust structure which projects from the ovary into the centre of the flower. In *Epipactis* it is often conspicuous and can be important for identification. It is topped by the anther or 'anther cap', which is attached to the remainder of the column by a short stalk or narrow flexible hinge. The two pollinia develop side-by-side within the anther. Shaped like a fat sausage, each pollinium is in turn divided into two segments by a fine groove, and the two pollinia are joined together at one end in the form of a wishbone.

Below the anther cap, the top of the column has a system of grooves, the clinandria. These form a platform on top of the main part of the column. As the pollinia mature, the anther splits open and the pollinia drop down to rest in the clinandria, which are moulded to their shape. The pollinia remain protected from above by the anther cap and are often largely hidden.

At the front of the column, separating the clinandria from the stigma below, lies the rostellum. (Literally the 'little beak', the rostellum is actually a greatly modified sterile third stigma.) The rostellum secretes a detachable white cap, the viscidium. This is a thin-skinned sack containing a sticky liquid and the slightest touch will rupture the skin and release the 'glue', which sets hard on contact with the air. Below the rostellum lies the fertile stigma. Unlike other flowers, where the stigma

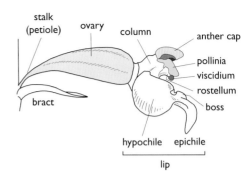

▲ *Broad-leaved Helleborine flower in profile with sepals and petals removed.*

is an obvious structure, in *Epipactis* and other orchids it is just a region on the front of the column that becomes sticky when it is receptive to pollen.

Pollination

In cross-pollinated helleborines, the clinandria or grooves on top of the column are relatively deep and the pollinia lie there securely. The rostellum functions as an additional barrier, preventing the pollinia from falling onto the stigma below. In these species the pollinia remain intact and lie with their tips in contact with the viscidium. A wasp visits the flower to drink nectar from the cup-shaped hypochile but to reach this it must rub its head or the top of its thorax against the rostellum. In doing so it ruptures the viscidium and the sticky contents glue the pollinia to the insect's head. Thus, when the wasp flies off, it carries one or both of the pollinia away with it. The wasp goes on to visit another flower, deposits parts of the pollinia on the wet surface of the stigma and pollination takes place; once pollinated, the stigma changes from whitish to brownish.

In self-pollinated helleborines, the clinandria are shallow and do not hold the pollinia securely, the rostellum is usually reduced in size and the viscidium either never develops or is present in the bud but disappears when the flowers open; there is therefore little to prevent the pollinia, or parts of them, from falling onto the stigma below. The pollinia also tend to be more friable and easily fall to pieces. The pollinia may either disintegrate where they

▲ *Broad-leaved Helleborine, 28 July, Norfolk. The viscid-ium and pollinia are conspicuous.*

▲ *Narrow-lipped Helleborine, 12 July, Buckinghamshire. This flower is freshly opened, but nevertheless lacks a vis-cidium, although the pollinia are present.*

▲ *Narrow-lipped Helleborine, 22 July, Oxfordshire. The pollinia are visibly disintegrating in situ, and there is no viscidium.*

lie (the pollen germinating in the clinandrium and the pollen tubes growing down to the stigma and ovary), or the pollen may fall on to the stigma below and pollinate it. Indeed, in some Green-flowered Helleborines the flowers never open and pollination occurs within the unopened bud. Contrastingly, it is probable that the Dune Helleborine, although self-pollinating, occasionally has a functional viscidium and is therefore sometimes cross-pollinated.

In the self-pollinated species, cross-pollination can occur from time to time, even without a viscidium. Their flowers, although typically small, dull and not opening widely, are visited by insects in order to drink nectar. The pollinia may stick to their bodies despite the lack of the viscidium as 'glue' and the insects may carry the pollinia away with them.

Separation of cross-pollinated and self-pollinated helleborines

Four of the *Epipactis* helleborines are cross-pollinated: Marsh, Dark-red, Broad-leaved and Violet. When the flowers first open they have neat, undamaged, creamy-yellow pollinia and a well-formed whitish viscidium. Although the pollinia are nearly concealed by the anther cap, they can usually be seen poking out slightly, like fat yellow sausages. After a short while it is likely that a visiting wasp will remove the viscidium and the pollinia, although the yellow anther cap remains. The flower will probably have been fertilised by this stage and the whole column will start to look tatty and brown.

Narrow-lipped, Dune, Green-flowered and Lindisfarne Helleborines are self-pollinated. They have no viscidium (if it is present, it is almost always small and vanishes before the flower opens). The pollinia are released by the anther and sit on top of the column. By the time the flower opens the pollinia have begun to swell and crumble, fragments falling over the edge onto the stigma below. The pollinia are largely hidden by the anther cap but appear to 'foam-out' from under it. The flower, having been fertilised, starts to go-over and the column turns brown.

Growth pattern

The aerial stem grows from a rhizome which puts out numerous roots, each of which can live for around three years. The growth pattern of the rhizome is sympodial; the tip of the rhizome grows upwards to form a flower spike that withers and dies off once seed has been set, while the rhizome continues to grow from one or more buds that are formed at the base of the aerial stem. These buds are formed at least a year before the next stem appears above ground but may remain dormant for one or more years, in which case the plant remains underground for a year or more. The probability of a plant appearing above ground and blooming is determined by growing conditions over the 12 months previously.

Fungal partners

There is disagreement about the extent to which adult helleborines obtain nutrients from fungi. Examination of rhizomes and roots led to a consensus that some species were 'free' from fungi, including Violet Helleborine, which thrives in deep shade. However, several species occasionally throw up variants that lack chlorophyll (including var. *rosea* of Violet Helleborine). These cannot photosynthesise but prosper nevertheless, so at least some helleborines are able to gain substantial quantities of nutrients from fungi. Recently, sophisticated techniques have been developed to identify fungi genetically and to assess their contribution to the helleborine's nutrition. The evidence produced so far suggests that fungi do play a very significant role. Several *Epipactis*, including Broad-leaved and Dune Helleborines, display consistent associations with one group of fungi, the Ascomycetes. Some *Epipactis*, such as Broad-leaved and Dark-red Helleborines, may also have an association with ectomycorrhizal fungi and therefore gain nutrients from nearby trees via their fungal 'partners', which they 'cheat'.

Development from seed

Poorly known, as the subterranean seedlings are difficult to find. The seeds have a well-developed outer shell or carapace and this slows the uptake of water and delays germination, suggesting that they have a period of dormancy. Seed probably germinates in spring, forming first a protocorm and then a mycorhizome (the earliest and most heavily infected stage in the development of the rhizome). The first roots develop in the autumn and, as the rhizome grows, fungal activity is transferred to the roots so the rhizome itself becomes 'infection-free'.

Vegetative reproduction

This may take place via several mechanisms. 1. The roots develop buds, which go on to form a secondary rhizome (recorded for Dark-red Helleborine). 2. The rhizome produces two flower spikes that each produce buds and adventitious roots below ground, and these buds go on to produce new rhizomes (recorded for Dune Helleborine). 3. The rhizome branches (as in Marsh Helleborine). In all these examples, if the central 'mother' plant dies off or the rhizome is broken up in some other way, two or more new plants may result. However, vegetative reproduction is not recorded for several of the helleborines and appears to be relatively unimportant for most species.

Name

Rather obscure. The name *Epipactis* was first given to a plant used to curdle milk by Theophrastus (*c.* 370-285 BC; often regarded as the 'father of botany'). It is not certain what he was referring to, but it may have been a *Veratrum*, a genus now known as 'false helleborines' but formerly called 'hellebores'. When the German botanist Johann Zinn described the genus *Epipactis* in 1757 he may have been struck by the resemblance of Broad-leaved Helleborine to a *Veratrum*, especially the broad, prominently veined leaves, and therefore chose to use Theophrastus's name for his new genus.

The word 'helleborine' has been used in English since the 16th century and means a plant resembling a 'hellebore'; presumably again, a reference to its similarity to a *Veratrum* (rather than the modern 'hellebores', genus *Helleborus*).

MARSH HELLEBORINE
Epipactis palustris

This is one of the most attractive orchids, and when examined closely the individual flowers are simply stunning, being miniature versions of the gaudy hothouse hybrids. Marsh Helleborine occurs widely across England, Wales and Ireland, but due to its specialised marshy habitats it is very local. It has declined significantly but can still occur in large numbers, especially in coastal dune slacks.

Identification
Distinctive. Marsh Helleborine is easily identified by its colourful, purple and white flowers, habitat and mid-summer flowering period. The flowers resemble those of the other *Epipactis* helleborines in shape but are relatively large and bright. The lip shows striking purple veins at the base, and the tip has a distinctive frilled edge.

Similar species
None.

Habitat
Marsh Helleborine is found in a wide variety of wet, marshy habitats but requires neutral to alkaline ground water and relatively short, open, vegetation to thrive. The two most typical habitats are dune slacks and spring-fed fens. In dune slacks the ground water is calcium-rich due to the presence of shell fragments in the sand. In spring-fed fens the ground water is both nutrient-poor and calcareous and such fens can be found nestled in heathland valleys or within more extensive acid bogs, as well as on more obviously chalk or limestone-rich soils. Marsh Helleborine may also be found in meadows which are seasonally flooded with chalky water, but it cannot compete with tall vegetation and such habitats must be regularly mown or grazed for it to survive. Sometimes, it may be found growing among Common Reeds, but these, too, are likely to take over and eventually crowd it out. Marsh Helleborine occasionally grows in other habitats. These include wet, slumped, clay cliffs (as in Dorset and the Isle of Wight), gravel pits and fly-ash pools. Very occasionally it is found in small numbers on 'dry' chalk grassland (as in Bedfordshire, Kent, Surrey and Wiltshire), especially where quarrying and excavations have left a compacted surface prone to becoming

◀ *8 July, Norfolk. Growing on close-cropped turf, it is possible to see the structure of the whole plant.*

waterlogged; it also grows in large numbers on the floor of an old chalk pit in Norfolk where there is standing water in the winter months.

Flowering period

Late June to early August, very exceptionally to early September but mostly in July.

Range

Widespread in England, Wales and Ireland but often very local and absent from large areas (much of Kent, Sussex, Surrey, Wiltshire, Devon, Cornwall, the Midlands, Co. Durham, Cumbria, mid-Wales, Co. Kerry, Co. Cork, Co. Waterford and Co. Wexford in southern Ireland and Co. Antrim in Northern Ireland). The strongholds are in Norfolk and Hampshire, but even in these areas it has declined significantly. Very rare in Scotland and recently only recorded from a handful of sites: Perthshire in the Central Highlands, Argyll and the Inner Hebrides on Islay and

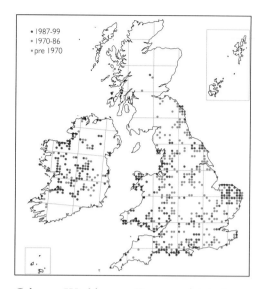

• 1987-99
• 1970-86
• pre 1970

Colonsay. **World range:** Europe and Asia. In Europe it is found north to Denmark, southern Scandinavia and the Baltic States and south to Portugal, northern Spain, southern Italy, central Greece, Bulgaria, the Crimea and Caucasus,

▲ 8 July, Norfolk. Summer rain has caused shallow flooding in this abandoned quarry.

and also Corsica and Sicily, but absent from the Mediterranean lowlands. Also found in Turkey, northern Iran, Central Asia and extends eastwards to Lake Baikal in eastern Siberia.

How to find it

This is a showy, conspicuous orchid that often grows in large numbers, especially in coastal dune slacks. Notable sites include Lindisfarne in Northumberland, Sandscale Haws in Cumbria, Ainsdale in Lancashire, Sandwich Bay in Kent and Wells-Holkham, Beeston Common and Buxton Heath in Norfolk.

DESCRIPTION

Height: Usually 20-45cm, occasionally up to 82cm. Dwarf forms, only 10cm high but with normal-sized flowers, have been recorded, especially in dry habitats.

Stem: Green, flushed with brownish-purple, especially towards the tip, prominently hairy, ridged towards the tip and with one or two purplish sheaths at the base. Several stems may grow from the same rhizome.

Leaves: Mid-green, sometimes washed purple around the base or sheaths, with three to five prominent veins. Of the four to eight leaves,

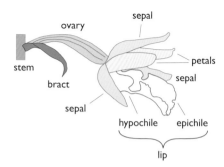

the lowest one or two are short, egg-shaped and formed into a cowl around the stem; the remainder are large, pointed, broadly strap-shaped with a distinct keel, 'papery' in texture but rather stiff; these are held erect, c. 45-60° above the horizontal, arranged in a spiral around the stem and grade into narrower and more bract-like non-sheathing leaves towards the spike.

Spike: Up to 25 flowers, although usually rather fewer, form a lax spike; all face more or less to one side and are initially held horizontally but slowly droop.

Bract: Green, lanceolate and pointed, the lowest a little longer than the ovary, the upper much shorter and also blunter.

Ovary: Brownish-purple, prominently hairy,

◄ 21 July, Norfolk. A particularly richly coloured plant.

▶ 8 July, Norfolk. The large boss at the base of the outer half of the lip (epichile) and the delicate purple veining on the interior of the cup (hypochile) are clearly visible.

cylindrical, with six fine ribs, narrowing at each end and tapering to a short, purple stalk that is twisted through 180°.

Flower: Purplish with a white, frilled lip and prominent purple veins; the flowers open widely and the lip is held projecting horizontally outwards. The sepals are oval-lanceolate, the lateral sepals asymmetrical. On the outer surfaces they are sparsely hairy and dull greenish-yellow, flushed, veined and mottled purple, especially towards the base; on the inner face they are more solidly washed purple, especially towards the tip, with a neat whitish border. The petals are slightly shorter and blunter, white, washed pinkish-purple towards the base on the outer surfaces (shining through to the inner surface) and also delicately veined with purple towards the base on the inner face. The hypochile is formed into a dish, the base of which is longer than wide and yellow, variably blotched with reddish nectar-producing swellings. The sides, including the erect, triangular side-lobes, are white with prominent purple veins on the inner surface. The epichile is white with a slight purple wash towards the edges at the base; it is more or less circular but with the sides turned upwards and strongly frilled or crimped. At the base of the epichile there is an irregular boss which is whitish with yellow edges and bisected by a deep, narrow groove; this also produces small quantities of nectar. The hypochile and epichile are connected by a narrow, flexible hinge. The column is very pale yellowish-white with a well-developed white viscidium, dull yellow anther cap and primrose yellow pollinia.

Subspecies
None.

Variation and varieties
Var. *ochroleuca* lacks brown and purple pigments and is very pallid. The stem and ovary are green, the sepals yellowish-white to pale green, and the petals and lip are white, although the interior of the hypochile still has purple veins. It is uncommon, but where it is found it occurs in large numbers.

▲ 9 July, Norfolk. Var. albiflora. *This rare variety lacks anthocyanin pigments and has a green stem, ovary and sepals and unmarked white petals and lip, lacking even purple banding.*

Var. *albiflora* is similar but lacks the purple veins. It is rare.

BIOLOGY

Pollination and reproduction
Marsh Helleborine is cross-pollinated but, despite several investigations, there is disagreement as to which insects are the most effective pollinators and what role the unusually flexible outer part of the lip plays in the mechanism.

The flowers are visited by a wide variety of insects, including flies and beetles. Some of them, such as hover flies and honeybees, groom themselves extensively and even if they pick up pollinia are not effective in delivering them to other flowers. Honeybees also feed their young on pollen. Solitary bees and wasps are probably the most efficient pollinators, the nectar on the large boss on the lip acting as a guide to entice the insect into assuming the correct position for pollination. Ants also visit the flowers and may cause self-pollination, or may carry fragments of pollinia away and pollinate other flowers on the same spike (geitonogamy). Self-pollination may also occur spontaneously as pieces of pollinia fall onto the stigma below. An average of over 80% flowers set seed.

Charles Darwin suggested that the outer part of the lip hinged downwards due to the weight of the visiting insect, allowing it to enter the flower without removing the pollinia. Once the insect was within the hypochile, however, the epichile hinged back up to its original position. The insect, as it backed out of the flower, was therefore forced upwards, allowing the pollinia to become attached to its head. Later authors suggested other functions for the hinged lip, such as causing the insects to struggle to keep their balance and this being

sufficient to bring their heads into contact with the viscidium.

Vegetative reproduction may occur if the rhizome breaks up into several sections.

Development and growth

The aerial stems grow from a relatively slender, well-branched rhizome that creeps horizontally near the surface of the soil. A single plant may have an extensive rhizome and produce several aerial stems. Indeed, it has been claimed that over 100 flower spikes may grow from the same plant (Davies *et al.* 1983). Roots are produced at many points along the rhizome, both horizontal roots that penetrate the more organic surface layers and vertical roots that often grow deep into the mineral soil. The roots are reported to have little or no fungal 'infection', except in soils deficient in nitrogen. And indeed, recent isotope studies have shown that Marsh Helleborine may acquire around 30% of its nitrogen from its fungal 'partner' but it does not appear to receive any carbohydrates via that route.

The subterranean seedling stage has never been observed in the wild and there is no information on the early development of this species.

Hybrids
None.

Name and classification
The specific name *palustris* means 'of swampy ground'.

HISTORY AND CONSERVATION

The first published record was in the 1633 edition of Gerard's *Herball*, where John Goodyer recorded it: 'within a mile of…Peters-field, in a moist meadow named Wood-mead, neere the path leading from Peters-field towards Beryton' (a record in Mathias de Lobel's *Stirpium Illustrationes* ('Illustrations of plants') dated from 1601, but this was not published until 1655).

Marsh Helleborine has declined substantially and is now gone from 60% of its historical range in Britain and 39% in Ireland. The decline has affected all areas but perhaps

▲ *8 July, Norfolk. The flower in profile, showing the two halves of the lip, connected by a flexible hinge.*

especially those away from the coast. It is extinct in the Channel Islands, Bedfordshire, Huntingdonshire, Northamptonshire, Worcestershire, Radnorshire, Dumfries and Galloway, Roxburghshire, Berwickshire, the Lothians and Fife.

Many of the losses occurred in the 19th century due to the drainage and destruction of marshes and fens. Drainage and the subtler effects of water abstraction continued to cause losses in the 20th century. More recently, eutrophication, that is the enrichment of ground water by fertiliser run-off or even the discharge of sewage, has caused suitable fens to become overgrown with more vigorous vegetation. The abandonment of grazing or mowing compounds this effect and has led to the invasion of fens by scrub, in which case they quickly become too overgrown for the helleborine to survive.

Marsh Helleborine is specially protected in Northern Ireland under Schedule 8 of the 1985 Wildlife Order (NI).

Past and present occurrence of Marsh Helleborine in Britain and Ireland (based on presence or absence in 10km squares of the National Grid; data from the New Atlas*).*

	Britain	Ireland
total historical range, 1500-1999	450	160
current range	180 (6.3%*)	98 (9.7%*)
% lost, 1500-1969	53%	29.5%
% lost, 1970-1986	7%	9.5%
% lost, total	60%	39%

* current range as a % of the total number of 10km squares

◀ *8 July, Norfolk. A rather dusty-pink plant.*

DARK-RED HELLEBORINE
Epipactis atrorubens

This orchid is found very locally in open, rocky places in the north and west of Britain and Ireland and is strongly associated with outcrops of limestone. Whether they are emerging from the grykes in a limestone pavement or set against a grassy slope, the spikes of reddish-purple flowers and rather dusky-green foliage are very striking. In Europe it is often a woodland plant, and the absence of trees in our denuded landscape may be a reason for its very scattered and local distribution in the British Isles. Dark-red Helleborine is the county flower of Banffshire.

Identification
With its attractive reddish-purple flowers, Dark-red Helleborine is easy to identify. It has very obvious yellow anthers and pollinia, and is cross-pollinated.

Similar species
Broad-leaved Helleborine is the only other helleborine to occur in the same rocky habitats, albeit only occasionally. It may sometimes have rather dark-reddish flowers and, conversely, Dark-red Helleborine may rarely have paler pinkish or greenish-red flowers, similar to those of some Broad-leaved Helleborines. However, Dark-red Helleborine can always be distinguished by its leaves, which are darker, more markedly folded and held in two opposite rows. It also has larger and rougher bosses on the lip and a very hairy ovary.

Habitat
Dark-red Helleborine is very strongly associated with limestone, growing on cliff ledges, scree slopes, rocky hillsides, in old quarries and in the shelter of the grykes of limestone pavements. It is usually found in the immediate vicinity of bare rock but sometimes also on well-drained grassy slopes with scattered scrub or even in meadows or on road verges. And, although most sites are open and sunny, it is also found in moderate shade on well-wooded limestone pavements, in open ash woodland or in pine plantations. Indeed, light woodland

▶ 17 July, Co. Durham. The leaves are clearly arranged into two opposite ranks.

and woodland edges may be the more typical habitat, as in Europe; most British sites are deforested and heavily grazed and the species has a very fragmented, 'relict' distribution. Most sites are between sea level and 270m, but it is present at 400m in eastern Cumbria, over 500m on Cronkley Fell in upper Teesdale and at 610m in Gleann Beag in east Perthshire.

Flowering period

Early June to early August, but mostly late June to late July.

Range

Very local and scattered. In North Wales recorded from Caernarvonshire and Flintshire (including the Great Orme), and in England found in the Peak District of Derbyshire, the Yorkshire Dales, in west Lancashire in the Morecambe Bay area, in Cumbria in the southern Lake District (around the Kent estuary and at Hodbarrow), the north Pennines (upper Eden Valley) and in Co. Durham. In Scotland found in the eastern Highlands in east Perthshire, in Banffshire and in the northwest on the north coast of Sutherland, in west Ross & Cromarty and on Skye. In Ireland confined to the Burren region of Co. Clare and Co. Galway. **World range:** Primarily a European species, extending a little way into western Asia. Occurs north to northernmost Norway

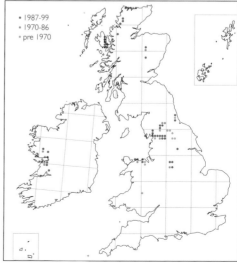

• 1987-99
• 1970-86
• pre 1970

▲ *5 July, Lancashire. Dark-red Helleborine will grow in quite wooded situations.*

◄ *5 July, Lancashire. A classic plant in the classic habitat, limestone pavement.*

and in Russia to the Arctic Circle, and south to southern Spain, southern Italy, southern Greece, Romania and patchily to the Caucasus but absent from the Mediterranean lowlands. Also found in western and northern Turkey, northern Iran, and southern Siberia to about 85°E.

How to find it

Dark-red Helleborine is usually a relatively easy species to locate when it is growing in the open. Undoubtedly the best site to see the species is Bishop Middleton Quarry in Co. Durham where it is abundant, creating a great spectacle.

DESCRIPTION

Height: 11.5-60cm, sometimes to 100cm.
Stem: Dull green, variably washed purple, especially towards the base (sometimes entirely purple), with a dense covering of whitish hairs, particularly on the upper part of the stem.

There are one to three funnel-shaped basal sheaths, the uppermost often green towards the tip. Stems usually grow singly but sometimes two or three may arise from the same rhizome.
Leaves: Around five to ten, arranged more or less in two opposite rows towards the base of the stem. The leaves are dark green, variably washed reddish-purple on the underside and are sometimes purple at the base. They are always distinctly longer than wide (the lower elongated-oval, the upper tending to be narrower and more lanceolate), strongly folded and keeled, and held stiffly at about 30° above the horizontal.
Spike: Rather lax, with six to 45 flowers set loosely to one side of the stem. Plants in sheltered localities tend to have the most flowers but there are often fewer than ten in more exposed situations. There is usually a distinct gap between the uppermost leaf and the lowermost flower.

▲ 17 July, Co. Durham. The contrasting yellow anther-cap is very noticeable; the large, rough boss at the base of the lip less so.

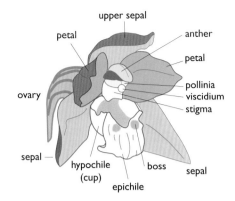

Labels on diagram: upper sepal, petal, anther, petal, pollinia, viscidium, stigma, ovary, sepal, hypochile (cup), boss, epichile, sepal

Bract: Lanceolate, green, sometimes washed purple at the base. The lower bracts may be a little longer than the flowers but they become shorter towards the tip of the spike.

Ovary: Pear-shaped, six-ribbed, green, variably washed purple (sometimes deep blackish-purple) with abundant short, pale hairs. The flower stalk is short and greenish to purplish-black.

Flower: Usually a distinctive, rich, wine red. The flowers often do not open very widely and may assume a slightly drooping, bell-like shape. The sepals are oval with slightly pointed tips and a downy outer surface. The petals are shorter and broader, more oval-triangular in shape. Both sepals and petals are deep purple, slightly paler on the inner surfaces and towards the base of the petals. The hypochile is dull green on the outer surface of the cup, becoming rich purple towards the front, with the interior pale greenish-white and mottled purple. The epichile is heart-shaped, broader than long and variably turned under at the tip. It is rich purple with two elaborate wrinkled bosses at the base which sometimes merge into a V or heart shape. The column is pale greenish-white, flushed purple, with the anther cap contrastingly yellow with a narrow brown stripe at the sides; the pollinia are also yellow. There is a functional viscidium, and the flowers have a vanilla-like scent.

Subspecies
None.

Variation and varieties
Occasionally the flowers may be paler red or even greenish, especially in sites exposed to full sunlight, but normal plants always have some traces of dark red. Two aberrant varieties have been named:

Var. *albiflora* has white or creamy flowers and has been recorded in the Kishorn area of west Ross and Cromarty.

Var. *lutescens* has yellowish or buff flowers and has been found in The Burren in Ireland.

BIOLOGY

Pollination and reproduction
This species is cross-pollinated. Both the colour and the scent of the flowers may be important in attracting suitable pollinators and wasps, bees and hover flies visit to feed on the nectar, removing the pollinia in the process.

Vegetative reproduction may take place, new plants developing from buds on the roots.

Development and growth
The aerial stem grows from a short, thick, hard rhizome that puts out 40-50 long, slender, widely spreading roots. These sometimes form irregular swellings from which fresh rootlets grow.

The roots of this species are reported to have a rather limited fungal 'infection', and it was thought to be largely phototrophic as a mature plant, depending on photosynthesis to supply its nutrients rather than fungi. Recent isotope studies have shown, however, that Dark Red Helleborines acquire about 65% of their nitrogen and 15% of their carbon from fungi. And, unexpectedly, they have an association with ectomycorrhizal fungi and thus, like Coralroot and Bird's-nest Orchids, may gain nutrients from the roots of nearby trees via these fungi (see p.8). These studies took place in Europe, where Dark Red Helleborines are often found in wooded environments. British and Irish plants may grow well away from any trees, and the absence of suitable host trees may be a limiting factor in its distribution in the British Isles.

There is no information on the length of the period between germination and flowering.

Hybrids

E. x *schmalhausenii*, the hybrid with Broad-leaved Helleborine, has been reported from several parts of the range, notably Cumbria. It is fertile and therefore very difficult to confirm because infertility cannot be used to distinguish potential hybrids from plants that are merely aberrant.

Name and classification

The specific name *atrorubens* means simply 'very dark red'.

HISTORY AND CONSERVATION

The first British record was published in 1677 in Ray's *Catalogus Plantarum Angliae et Insularum adjecentium:* 'On the sides of the mountains near Malham 4 miles from Settle in great plenty'.

Past and present occurrence of Dark-red Helleborine in Britain and Ireland (based on presence or absence in 10km squares of the National Grid; data from the New Atlas).

	Britain	Ireland
total historical range, 1500-1999	60	13
current range	42 (1.5%*)	8 (0.8%*)
% lost, 1500-1969	18%	0%
% lost, 1970-1986	12%	38%
% lost, total	30%	38%

* current range as a % of the total number of 10km squares

Dark-red Helleborine is very local and absent from many apparently suitable sites within its restricted range. In Britain it is Nationally Scarce. Most populations are small, with many non-flowering plants, and many plants that would flower are prevented from doing so by sheep, deer or rabbits. Bishop Middleton quarry in Co. Durham holds 2,000 or more plants, probably more than all the other British sites put together.

Some sites have been lost due to quarrying, and overgrazing threatens others; both the British and Irish populations may still be in decline. Extinct in Breconshire and

Denbighshire, and old records for west Gloucestershire and Herefordshire are not always accepted as valid.

▲ 17 July, Co. Durham. The leaves have been largely grazed off, but nevertheless it is able to flower well, perhaps aided by its fungal 'partner'.

◀ 17 July, Co. Durham. Usually arises singly, but two or three spikes growing together is not uncommon.

BROAD-LEAVED HELLEBORINE
Epipactis helleborine

The commonest and most widespread of the helleborines, this species is found in and around woodland and, in the north and west, sometimes also in more open habitats. But, although at heart a forest orchid, it is a species that you stumble upon in unexpected places rather than set out to find; a shady lane, a road verge, an old railway cutting – nowhere is too humble for this adaptable helleborine. It is said to be commoner in the city of Glasgow than anywhere else in Britain and has spread from coast to coast in North America since it was introduced in 1879. 'Young's Helleborine', described in 1982 and thought to be endemic to Britain, is now known to be a minor variant of Broad-leaved Helleborine.

Identification

A very variable species. Broad-leaved Helleborine can be a tall, robust, leafy plant or a small, weedy specimen with just one or two flowers. The flowers themselves can be almost entirely green or almost completely purple but are usually a mixture of pale green, pink and purple. It is said that plants in deep shade tend to be taller and greener whereas those in sunnier locations are shorter with more red or purple coloration in the flower, but the variation often seems to be random.

Typically, Broad-leaved Helleborine has several relatively large leaves which are a dull, mid to dark green, sometimes washed purple but lacking yellow tones. They are usually obviously veined or 'pleated' and placed all around the stem, in three rows or in a spiral pattern, but are sometimes arranged into two opposite ranks. As the name suggests, the leaves are broad, especially the lowest, which may be roughly as wide as they are long. The upper part of the stem and the ovaries are hairy, although hairs can be sparse on the ovaries. The outer part of the lip is heart-shaped, broader than long and usually turned under at the tip. There are two bosses at the base of the lip which are usually brownish and rough or wrinkled but can be smooth and pink. Importantly, the base of the flower stalk is washed purple. Broad-leaved Helleborine is cross-pollinated; when

◀ *28 July, Norfolk. A typical plant, with an open, rather sparsely-flowered spike.*

freshly opened, the flowers have an obvious and functional white viscidium, an important distinction from Narrow-lipped, Dune and Green-flowered Helleborines (see p.76 for a discussion of the separation of cross-pollinated and self-pollinated helleborines).

Similar species

Violet Helleborine may occur in the same woods but is typically found in densely shaded areas. It is usually distinctive. Its leaves are more greyish-green with a distinctive purple wash to the undersides, and also narrower, with the lowest leaf longer than wide. Its flowers are larger, brighter and cleaner; the sepals and petals are pale greenish-white, lacking pink or purple tones, and the lip is whitish with two smoothly pleated, pink bosses. Like Broad-leaved Helleborine, it is cross-pollinated.

Narrow-lipped Helleborine is a scarce inhabitant of southern beechwoods. It has green flowers, often with a delicate pink wash to the petals and lip (but not the sepals). As its name suggests, the tip of the lip is long, narrow and pointed, and held projecting prominently outwards. Its leaves are a paler and more yellowish-green and usually held in two opposite ranks. In combination these features should be distinctive but the tip of the lip of Broad-leaved Helleborine may not always be reflexed, especially when the flower has just opened. In Broad-leaved Helleborines with largely green flowers, this can cause confusion but the outer part of the lip (epichile) in Broad-leaved Helleborine is always broader than long. In case of any doubt, the base of the flower stalk is greenish-yellow in Narrow-lipped Helleborine and the flowers are self-pollinated and lack an effective viscidium.

Dune Helleborine is only found on Anglesey, in northern England and in southern Scotland, usually on dunes but also at inland sites; conversely Broad-leaved Helleborine is occasionally found on open dunes or under the pines that are often planted on coastal sand hills. In its typical form, Dune Helleborine can be separated from Broad-leaved by its more yellowish-green, two-ranked leaves that are held rigidly at about 45° above the horizontal. Its flowers are smaller, duller and do not open as widely. The petals and base of the lip are variably washed pink, but it never shows pink or purple tones to the sepals or a strong purple wash on the lip. At inland localities the variant of Dune Helleborine, known as 'Tyne Helleborine', is found. This is very like Narrow-lipped Helleborine and can be distinguished from Broad-leaved by the forward-pointing tip to its lip and a yellowish-green base to the flower stalk. Dune Helleborine is normally self-pollinated.

Green-flowered Helleborine typically has green flowers which are held drooping and do not fully open. Sometimes, however, its flowers may be held more horizontally and may open widely although they are still predominantly green, with any pink tones restricted to a delicate wash on the lip. Whatever, its upper stem and ovaries are hairless or there are just a few, sparse hairs on the stem, the base of the flower stalk is green and it is self-pollinating.

Dark-red Helleborine is usually rather distinctive but Broad-leaved is occasionally found in the rocky habitats beloved of Dark-red Helleborine and sometimes has rather dark-reddish flowers, too, while Dark-red Helleborine rarely has pinkish or greenish-red flowers. If there is doubt, Dark-red Helleborine can be distinguished by its leaves, which are darker, more markedly folded and held in two

▲ 26 July, Norfolk. A richly coloured flower. The pollinia have already been removed.

◀ 28 July, Norfolk. Two plants side by side, one in full flower, the other still in bud.

opposite rows. The bosses on its lip are also larger and rougher and its ovary is densely hairy.

Habitat

Broad-leaved Helleborine is essentially a plant of deciduous woodland. It favours the better-lit areas along paths, rides and roadsides, in glades and on the woodland fringe, but can grow in deep shade. Like many of the helleborines it has an affinity for Beech trees. It can also be found in suitable shady conditions in scrub, along well-grown hedges, banks, disused railways and stream-sides. Broad-leaved Helleborine will also grow in the open, on limestone pavements, cliffs, scree and grassland, but only in the cooler and damper conditions of the north and west. In Ireland and south Wales it is found in dune slacks. One of the most adaptable of the helleborines, it is an opportunist and can colonise newly available habitats, such as mature birch scrub on spoil heaps, willow and alder carr and conifer plantations (especially where conifers have replaced ancient woodland). In Glasgow and a few other cities

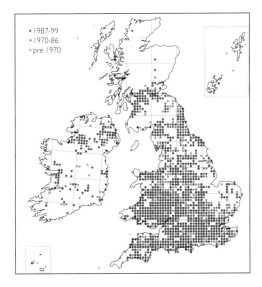

and the region around Lough Neagh in Co. Armagh, Co. Derry and Co. Antrim. **World range:** Very widespread in Europe and Asia and introduced to North America. In Europe it occurs north to *c.* 71°N in Norway and to southern Finland, and south to the Mediterranean, Crimea and Caucasus. It is absent from the Mediterranean lowlands but found on the Balearic Islands, Corsica, Sardinia and Sicily. Also scattered in Turkey, Lebanon and Israel. In Asia it also ranges through southern Siberia east to Lake Baikal and south through the mountains of Central Asia to the Himalayas. Populations from North Africa and the Far East are often now treated as different species. Introduced to North America, perhaps deliberately as a remedy for gout. It was first recorded in 1879 near Syracuse, New York, and is now widespread; it reached California by 1950 and is still spreading.

How to find it

The commonest of the helleborines but nevertheless often rather local, it is best looked for in and around undisturbed ancient woodland, especially along shady roads and tracks passing through suitable habitats. It is frequently robust but despite this the relatively small, dull flowers can be surprisingly hard to see when it is growing among brambles or Bracken.

DESCRIPTION

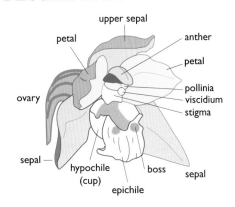

Height: 10-120cm but usually around 25-80cm.
Stem: Pale green, often washed purplish towards the base, with short, whitish hairs on the upper portion and two or three leafless

in southern Scotland and northeast England, Broad-leaved Helleborine has moved into mature gardens, as well as parks, cemeteries, golf courses, playing fields, rubbish tips, roadsides and railway embankments. It is comparatively tolerant of soil pH and will grow in slightly acid conditions but is usually commonest on calcareous soils. Recorded up to 350m above sea level (Ystradfellte, Breconshire).

Flowering period

Early July to early September but mostly from mid-July to mid-August. Like all the helleborines, it flowers earlier and more sparsely in dry summers.

Range

Widespread in England and Wales, although rather local in some areas, such as Norfolk, Suffolk, Cambridgeshire and Lincolnshire, and absent from west Cornwall and some upland areas in northern England. In Scotland it is well distributed in the Central Lowlands and scattered in the Borders but to the north is extremely local, with a few sites in southern Perthshire, Angus, Banffshire, Sutherland, west Ross & Cromarty, Argyll and Kintyre, and on the Inner Hebrides on Skye. Widespread in Ireland but mostly found in the west and the north and rather local away from The Burren (Co. Clare and Co. Galway), Co. Fermanagh

▲ | August, Northumberland. A spike of rather purple flowers. Broad-leaved Helleborines, when inspected closely, all too often appear rather dishevelled.

sheaths at the extreme base. Usually grows singly but clumps of two or three are quite frequent and five or more may occasionally grow from the same rhizome. Non-flowering stems are frequently produced.

Leaves: Four to ten, more-or-less spirally arranged around the stem. They are oval to oval-lanceolate and less than twice as long as wide; the lowest leaf is sometimes almost rounded, but they become narrower and more bract-like towards the flower spike. The leaves are dull, mid to dark green, sometimes tinged purple, with several prominent veins.

Spike: Up to 60 flowers, rarely as many as 100, are arranged into a roughly one-sided spike that is sometimes very dense but on other plants rather lax.

Bract: Dull green, lanceolate, with a pointed tip. The lowest are significantly longer than the flower but they become shorter, roughly the length of the ovary, towards the tip of the spike.

Ovary: Green, hairless or with a few short hairs, boldly six-ribbed and rather pear-shaped, tapering into a long, twisted stalk which is washed purple at the base.

Flower: Very variable in colour but usually with some purple tones and opening widely. The sepals are oval, tapering to a point, with their outer surface green mottled with variable amounts of dull purple or pink (sometimes none) and a prominent green midrib; their inner face varies from pale green to dull, dusty purple. The petals are similar but slightly shorter and less tapering and tend to be paler, 'cleaner' and often pinker. They vary from pale, dusty pink to purple and are often whiter towards the centre; they also have a green midrib on the outer face. The hypochile is pale greenish-white, variably washed pink or purple, with the interior of the cup purple to mid-brown, glistening with nectar. The epichile is heart-shaped, broader than long, with the major part strongly curled down and under. There are two bosses at the base of the epichile, usually purplish-brown and wrinkled, but they may be green or pink, and are sometimes smooth. The epichile varies in colour from dull greenish-white, washed pink, to pale pink or dull purple. The column is greenish-white, the anther cap dull pale yellow with brown stripes at the side, and the pollinia are creamy-yellow. There is an obvious and functional white viscidium. The flowers usually have no scent.

Subspecies

E. h. neerlandica **'Dutch Helleborine'** Overall deep green and rather short (15-40cm), with short, stiff, rounded leaves that are held more-or-less erect and grouped at the base of the stem, which they closely sheathe. The leaves have a border of tiny teeth that are irregular and fused at the base (use a 20x hand-lens; typical Broad-leaved Helleborines have more regular teeth). The spike is dense and the flowers are dull purplish-pink, bell-shaped and do not open widely. Confined to dune slacks in south Wales, where it grows among Creeping Willow. Otherwise, it is only found along the coast of the North Sea from Pas-de-Calais in northeast France to Denmark and on the Baltic coast of northern Germany. Although it is treated as a distinct species, *E. neerlandica*, by some Continental authors, genetic studies reveal little difference between it and typical Broad-leaved Helleborines.

Variation and varieties

Var. *monotropoides* (also known as var. *albifolia*) lacks chlorophyll and is pale pink or straw-coloured with white or rosy flowers. It is very rare.
Var. *viridiflora* lacks anthocyanins and has pale green flowers with a greenish-white lip and shows no trace of red or purple. It is rare.
Var. *purpurea* has especially dark purple or reddish-violet flowers. It is rare.

'Young's Helleborine *E. youngiana*'

This was described in 1982 from plants found in Northumberland and was subsequently identified in Scotland and, more controversially, in Yorkshire and south Wales.

'Young's Helleborine' was reported to differ from Broad-leaved Helleborine in a number of ways. Its wavy-edged, more-or-less two-ranked leaves are on average paler and more yellowish-green. The lowest leaf is usually longer than

▲ *I August, Northumberland. A 'Young's' type, with rather yellowish-green leaves and bright flowers.*

wide, rather than wider than long. Its ovary is sparsely hairy to hairless (only rarely hairless in typical Broad-leaved Hellebrines). The flowers are similar to some Broad-leaved Hellebrines but relatively large, clean and bright. The critical difference, however, was to be found in the reproductive structures; in 'Young's Helleborine' the viscidium is very small and disappears rapidly. The pollinia remain in the flower and disintegrate onto the stigma causing self-pollination. The column has a long rostellum (as long as the anther cap) which, together with two pointed bosses at the base of the stigma, forms a distinctive 'three-horned' shape.

Some botanists were, however, always sceptical about the distinctiveness of 'Young's Helleborine' and recent genetic studies have shown that it does not exist as a distinct entity. At each site investigated, the 'Young's Hellebrines' were genetically closer to the local Broad-leaved Hellebrines than they were to 'Young's Hellebrines' at other sites. Also, rather than being self-pollinated, it has a high level of genetic diversity and a population genetic structure that indicates that it is cross-pollinated. Plants matching the description of 'Young's Helleborine' in terms of their leaves, ovaries and flowers are found at its classic sites (for example, Settlingstones in Northumberland) but almost all appear to have a large and fully functional viscidium and are presumably cross-pollinated, supporting the genetic studies. With the claimed differences in reproductive biology gone, the remaining distinctions between 'Young's' and Broad-leaved Helleborine are very subtle and it is hard to justify even the status of 'variety' for 'Young's', especially given the wide variation in Broad-leaved.

BIOLOGY

Pollination and reproduction
Broad-leaved Helleborine is pollinated by wasps, especially long-headed species of the genus *Dolichovespula*. Wasps have short

◀ *28 July, Norfolk. A beautiful, richly-coloured plant with wine red petals and lip. The pollinia have already been removed from all the flowers.*

mouthparts but can nevertheless easily reach the nectar produced in the hypochile; in the process they rupture the viscidium and the pollinia are stuck to their heads. Other insects, including short-headed wasps, bees, hover flies and beetles, may visit the flowers but are the wrong size or shape to act as efficient pollinators. Fermentation of the nectar in the helleborine's flowers may produce ethanol and this can have a narcotic effect on visiting wasps, which become slow and sluggish and may even fall to the ground 'drunk'.

The flowers are self-compatible and are frequently pollinated by wasps carrying pollinia from flowers of the same spike (i.e. geitonogamy). It is sometimes stated that Broad-leaved Helleborine may be self-pollinated (i.e. fertilised by pollen from the same flower). The evidence for this is contradictory but experiments have shown that in normal circumstances self-pollination either does not occur or only takes place rarely when small insects carry pieces of pollinia onto the stigma below. It has also been reported that in drought conditions the flowers shrivel without opening and may be cleistogamous and self-pollinate in the bud (Ettlinger 1997). Seed-set is usually good and almost all the flowers may produce ripe capsules, each containing up to 3,000 seeds.

Development and growth
The aerial stem grows from a small, woody rhizome which sends numerous cordlike roots deep into the soil. The degree of fungal 'infection' of the roots is reported to vary, being high in plants growing in humus-rich soils and negligible in mineral soils, but at least some Broad-leaved Hellebrines are heavily dependent on their fungal 'partner'. Recent isotope studies have shown that they acquire around 60% of their nitrogen and about 14% of their carbon via fungi. Unexpectedly, Broad-leaved Helleborine has an association with ectomycorrhizal fungi and thus, like Coralroot and Bird's-nest Orchids, may gain nutrients from the roots of nearby trees via these fungi (see p.8). It is probably not very fussy about its

▲ *28 July, Norfolk. A very pallid plant, with just a hint of purplish-pink in the sepals and lip. The pollinia and viscidium have already been removed.*

fungal 'partners' but might have a preference for Ascomycetes, including ectomycorrhizal fungi of the genus *Tuber*, better known by their English name 'truffle'.

Broad-leaved Helleborine, presumably supplied by its fungal 'partner', may spend a significant proportion of the time underground. Plants may flower and then spend one or, rather less often, two or even three years 'dormant' before appearing again. In a study in America, 25%-50% of the population appeared above ground each year and around a third of these flowered. Very few plants flowered every year, however, although annual flowering may be more frequent where the soil is reasonably moist.

The interval between germination and flowering can be as little as 18 months, although periods of eight or nine years, including several years above ground as a non-flowering plant, are also quoted.

Hybrids

E. x schmalhausenii, the hybrid with Dark-red Helleborine, has been reported from several parts of the range, notably Cumbria. It is fertile and very difficult to confirm.

E. x schulzei, the hybrid with Violet Helleborine, has been recorded quite frequently but, like *E. x schmalhausenii*, is fertile and hard to confirm.

x Dune Helleborine has been found in

Scotland and confirmed by genetic analysis. This hybrid has no scientific name.

Name and classification

The specific name *helleborine* means 'like a hellebore'. The leaves of Broad-leaved Helleborine do indeed look like those of *Veratrum album*, a plant that was once called 'White Hellebore' but is now, rather ironically, known as 'White False Helleborine'. (Broad-leaved Helleborine bears no resemblance to the plants now called 'hellebores', quite unrelated flowers belonging to the buttercup family.)

HISTORY AND CONSERVATION

The first British record was in 1562 when William Turner stated in his *Herball*: 'I have seen it…in England in Soffock'.

Past and present occurrence of Broad-leaved Helleborine in Britain and Ireland (based on presence or absence in 10km squares of the National Grid; data from the New Atlas).

	Britain	Ireland
total historical range, 1500-1999	1,218	161
current range	840 (29.5%*)	107 (9.7%*)
% lost, 1500-1969	19%	24%
% lost, 1970-1986	12%	9.5%
% lost, total	31%	33.5%

* current range as a % of the total number of 10km squares

The *New Atlas* states that the 'overall distribution is stable' but although the boundaries of the range may be largely unchanged there has been a significant decline, with the loss of around a third of the historical range. Losses have been concentrated in the Midlands and northern England, where the distribution is now rather fragmented, and more recently in the Home Counties. The clearance or 'coniferisation' of woodland, increase in dense shade due to a lack of woodland management, ground disturbance by machinery and horses, and grazing by deer may all have contributed to the decline, and losses seem to be ongoing.

VIOLET HELLEBORINE
Epipactis purpurata

Thought to be a long-lived orchid, older and more mature plants may produce several flowering spikes from the same rootstock, and a group of Violet Helleborines blooming in the cathedral-like gloom of a late summer beechwood certainly makes a dramatic sight. Among the last orchids to come into flower, it is endemic to western and central Europe and in Britain is confined to the southern half of England, but it is always rather local and uncommon.

Identification

Relatively distinctive. The flowers are pale green or whitish with the lip faintly washed pink and bearing two pink bosses; the petals and sepals spread widely and the large, pale flowers contrast strongly with the dark purplish stem and the rather small, dark leaves. It is cross-pollinated, and the flowers have an obvious and functional viscidium, a useful distinction from Narrow-lipped and Green-flowered Helleborines (see p.76 for a discussion of the separation of cross-pollinated and self-pollinated helleborines).

Similar species

Broad-leaved Helleborine is much commoner than Violet Helleborine. It has broader leaves, with the lowest more-or-less wider than long (longer than wide in Violet Helleborine). Its leaves are also a cleaner and brighter green (duller, more greyish-green in Violet Helleborine, with a distinctive purplish wash to the underside). Its flowers are smaller and often duller and darker with a purplish wash, with the bosses on the lip usually rougher and browner. In Violet Helleborine the flowers are cleaner, brighter and paler, with two smoothly pleated, pink bosses. Like Violet Helleborine, it is cross-pollinated.

Narrow-lipped Helleborine is also found in densely shaded beechwoods in southern England but is easily separated by its long, pointed lip and much paler stem, flower stalks and leaves.

▶ *11 August, Suffolk. Summer 2003 was hot and dry, and the helleborines were small and few in number.*

▲ *11 August, Suffolk. Growing on a relatively bare wood-land floor in old hazel coppice, a typically shady spot.*

woodland relics and in wild gardens. Although it can tolerate acid soils, it is strongly associated with areas of calcareous bedrock, especially chalk, and its deep root system requires a substantial thickness of soil. It can grow on sands and gravels but is particularly associated with clays, especially the 'clay-with-flints' found on plateaus and hilltops overlying chalk. Within woods, it is often found in areas of deep shade where little else can grow; it can flourish in much darker situations than Broad-leaved Helleborine but may share its dimly-lit haunts with Narrow-lipped Helleborine.

Flowering period

Mid-July to early September, exceptionally late June to late September, but typically peaking in early August. It tends to flower earliest in more open situations and will be especially early in a dry season.

Range

Found in southeast England (including the Isle of Wight) and the Midlands, occurring west to Dorset, north Somerset, Gloucestershire, Herefordshire and Shropshire, and north to south Staffordshire, Leicestershire, south Lincolnshire, Huntingdonshire, Hertfordshire and southern Suffolk. Also recorded from Denbighshire. The species is commonest in Kent, Surrey and the Chilterns. **World range:**

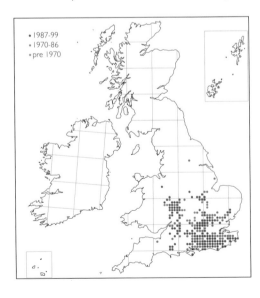

Green-flowered Helleborine may be in bloom late in the summer, like Violet Helle-borine, but is easily separated by its more-or-less hairless, green stem and ovaries, green flower stalks and rather smaller flowers which are usually held drooping and seldom open widely.

Habitat

Violet Helleborine is very much a woodland orchid, favouring beech, hornbeam and oak woods as well as overgrown hazel coppice. It is occasionally found in hedgerows that are

Confined to western and central Europe where it occurs north to Denmark, west to France (to a line between Mont St Michel and Grenoble), south to the Alps, Balkans and Transylvanian Alps in Romania, and east to the Baltic States.

How to find it

Despite its size and showy flowers, this can be a tricky species to find. Like other helleborines, it is loosely colonial, and although the colonies sometimes grow alongside paths and roads or on the edges of glades and clearings, they are equally at home in deep shade and can easily be missed. It is best looked for in wet seasons, as the species is affected by drought and in dry summers the size and number of spikes may be greatly reduced.

DESCRIPTION

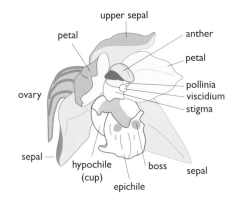

▲ 10 August, Suffolk. Of all the woodland helleborines, Violet has the brightest and cleanest flowers.

Height: 20-90cm but usually less than 70cm.
Stem: Greyish-green, variably but often heavily washed purple, with dense, short, grey hairs on the upper part of the stem and one to three small, purplish-brown sheathing scales at the base (the uppermost scale often tipped green). Stems usually grow singly but multiple stems are fairly common, groups of six to eight not unusual, and a cluster of 38 has been recorded.
Leaves: Well-spaced up the stem and arranged spirally (or sometimes in two opposite rows), the four to 14 leaves are relatively small, more-or-less oval in shape and taper to a point. They are usually rather more than twice as long as wide, with the upper leaves narrower and more bract-like and the lowest leaf short and cowl-like. The leaf posture is variable; they may be held horizontally with the tips slightly drooping or at about 30° above the horizontal. They are a rather dull, 'cold', greyish-green and may be washed purple towards the tips. The undersides have a diagnostic purple wash and the leaf sheaths are also frequently tinged purple.
Spike: Slightly to moderately one-sided, there are usually seven to 40 flowers but some well-grown plants can carry over 100 blooms.
Bract: Green, variably washed purple. The bracts are narrow, lanceolate, held roughly horizontally and are longer than the flower in the lower part of the spike, becoming shorter in the upper part.
Ovary: Green, with six prominent ribs, which

may be washed purple, and sparsely hairy. The flower stalk is purplish and variably twisted.

Flower: Rather large, opening widely, and overall greenish-white with a pinker lip. The sepals are triangular-oval, rather large and pale green, becoming paler towards the edges and with a prominent green midrib on the outer surface. The petals are smaller, whitish, becoming slightly greener towards the centre, with a fine green midrib. The hypochile is translucent-whitish, slightly greener towards the base of the cup, with the interior variably washed pale purplish-rose to pale brown or pale greenish. This colour shines through to the outside. The epichile is short, triangular or heart-shaped with the tip strongly folded downwards. It is whitish with two prominent, smoothly pleated, pink bosses at the base. The column is whitish and the large, conspicuous anther cap is very pale yellowish-white with narrow brown stripes at the sides. The viscidium is whitish and the pollinia are pale yellow. The flowers are faintly scented.

Subspecies
None.

Variation and varieties
Plants may sometimes have variegated leaves, and some may have the leaves very extensively streaked violet. One variety has been named:

Var. *rosea* is rare but stunning. It lacks chlorophyll and the entire plant is a rosy pink with whitish flowers.

BIOLOGY

Pollination and reproduction
Routinely cross-pollinated, often by wasps which are attracted to the nectar. As with Broad-leaved Helleborine, the nectar is reported to have a narcotic effect, with 'drunken' wasps falling to the ground. Pollination is efficient and most or all of the flowers on a spike will set seed. There are no reports of vegetative reproduction.

◄ *11 August, Suffolk. A multi-stemmed plant (the record is 38 spikes growing together).*

Development and growth
Violet Helleborine grows from a rhizome which lies more-or-less vertically in the soil and has up to 50 fleshy roots, each up to 70cm long (exceptionally 120cm), growing vertically downwards. It is reported that the roots are fungus-free and therefore the mature plant is phototrophic, depending on photosynthesis rather than fungi for nutrition. However, given the dense shade in which it grows, it seems much more likely that fungi contribute a large part of its nutritional budget; the rare var. *rosea* lacks chlorophyll but nevertheless is able to flower and fruit successfully and must depend entirely on fungi.

Violet Helleborine is long-lived and only appears above ground when mature enough to flower. Immature, non-flowering plants are very rarely seen. A single-stemmed plant may be 30 years old, and it has been suggested that large, multi-stemmed plants are probably hundreds of years old.

There is no information on the duration of the period between germination and flowering.

Hybrids
E. x schulzei, the hybrid with Broad-leaved Helleborine, has been recorded widely but this hybrid is fertile and therefore very difficult to confirm. (Infertility and the failure to produce viable pollen and seed are a standard means of confirming a hybrid.)

Name and classification
The specific name *purpurata* means purplish.

HISTORY AND CONSERVATION
This species was discovered by Rev. Dr. Abbot 'parasitical on the stump of a maple or hazel in a wood near the Noris farm at Leigh, Worcestershire, in 1807' and was described scientifically from English specimens in 1828 by Sir J.E. Smith in *The English Flora*. Notably, the type specimen was probably the rare variant *rosea*.

Violet Helleborine has declined steadily over the last 150 years as ancient woodlands have been destroyed or replanted with conifers, although most sites should now be safe from this particular threat. It has vanished from the edge of the range and is extinct in Devon, Cambridgeshire, Norfolk and southwest Yorkshire, and is reduced to one site in south Lincolnshire.

Favouring the dense shade of closed-canopy woodland, this is perhaps the only species of orchid to have benefited from the abandonment of coppicing in many British woods during the 20th century. Conversely, the great storms of 1987 and 1990 devastated many woods, opening up the canopy and leading to a great reduction in the numbers of Violet Helleborines in affected areas. Another threat is deer, and whole populations of orchids can be grazed off in some woods. The species can be very persistent, however, and has even been recorded pushing its way through newly laid tarmac.

Past and present occurrence of Violet Helleborine in Britain and Ireland (based on presence or absence in 10km squares of the National Grid; data from the New Atlas).

	Britain	Ireland
total historical range, 1500-1999	235	0
current range	145 (5%*)	0
% lost, 1500-1969	28.5%	
% lost, 1970-1986	10%	
% lost, total	38.5%	

* current range as a % of the total number of 10km squares

◄ 10 August, Suffolk. Violet Helleborine is cross-pollinated, mainly by wasps.

NARROW-LIPPED HELLEBORINE
Epipactis leptochila

Other names: *E. muelleri*

This enigmatic orchid is confined to southern England with an outpost in south Wales. It is a characteristic species of the beechwoods of the Cotswolds and Chilterns but is scarce and local and has declined markedly in recent years. For a while, a case of mistaken identity allayed fears about this decline, but it is now clear that this surprisingly attractive helleborine is in need of friends.

Identification

Narrow-lipped Helleborine looks almost uniformly green and has relatively large, clean, pale-green flowers with purplish-pink confined to a wash around the base of the lip and a variably obvious tinge on the petals. The flowers are held drooping and the tip of the lip projects forward rather than being turned under as in most other helleborines; the lip appears long and pointed, hence the English name. The upper stem and ovaries are hairy (use a hand-lens to check this), and the base of the flower stalk is greenish-yellow. The leaves are usually carried in two opposite ranks and are fresh green, sometimes tinged with yellow. The flowers are self-pollinated and lack a viscidium, the pollinia crumbling apart where they lie and falling piecemeal onto the stigma. This is a useful distinction from Broad-leaved and Violet Helleborines which are cross-pollinated (see p.76 for a discussion of the separation of cross-pollinated and self-pollinated helleborines).

Similar species

Broad-leaved, Violet and Green-flowered Helleborines may be found in the same woods although only Violet Helleborine is frequent in the deep shade beloved of Narrow-lipped Helleborine.

Broad-leaved Helleborine can have largely green flowers, but they are usually extensively

▶ *22 July, Oxfordshire. This can be a very stately helleborine but all too often its flower spikes are grazed off by deer.*

washed with dull pink or purple, and the tip of the lip is almost always turned down and backwards to give the lip a very short, blunt-ended appearance. Even if the lip is not reflexed, the heart-shaped epichile is always broader than long. The base of the flower stalk is tinged with purple, and, in most Broad-leaved Helleborines, the leaves are a darker and duller green and are usually carried spirally around the stem.

Violet Helleborine has flowers that are closer in coloration to Narrow-lipped, but they are held more erect and face outwards, giving the spike a different character. The flower stalk is purple and the leaves are a far duller greyish-green and often have a faint purple wash on the underside.

Green-flowered Helleborine is self-pollinated, like Narrow-lipped Helleborine, and can be rather similar to it (especially var. *vectensis* of Green-flowered), with drooping, bell-like green flowers and a green flower stalk. However, it has a hairless, or almost hairless,

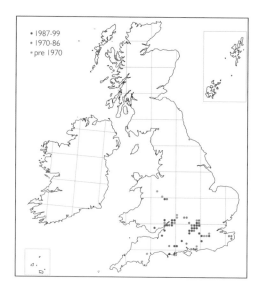

upper stem and ovaries, and the interior of the cup at the base of the lip is pale greenish. In many cases, the flowers of Green-flowered Helleborine are very distinctive as they often hang down almost vertically and in some populations hardly open at all.

▲ 22 July, Oxfordshire. *Growing on a typically bare woodland floor below Beeches.*

Habitat

Narrow-lipped Helleborine is always found on calcareous soils derived from chalk or limestone, especially on the steeper slopes where the soil is very thin and 'skeletal'. It is strictly a woodland orchid and usually to be found in ancient woodland. The classic habitat is a beechwood on chalk, sometimes with a mixture of Yew, but occasionally it is found under a variety of other deciduous trees, including overgrown ash-hazel coppice. Whatever the type of woodland, Narrow-lipped Helleborines will be found in areas of deep shade where the ground cover is sparse or absent. It is intolerant of direct sunlight.

Flowering period

Rather short, from the second week in July to mid-August (exceptionally from late June) but mostly in the last half of July.

Range

Highly localised. The strongholds are the Cotswolds in Gloucestershire and the Chilterns in Berkshire, Oxfordshire and Buckinghamshire. Away from these areas it is rare with just a few widely scattered populations in Surrey, Hampshire, Dorset, south Wiltshire, north Somerset, Shropshire and Glamorganshire. The species is inconspicuous, however, and could still be found at new localities. Delforge (1995) reported the presence of an unidentified helleborine of the 'leptochila group' from the Burren in Co. Clare. **World range:** Although once thought to be endemic to Britain, the species has now been found in Europe, north to Denmark, east to Slovakia, Hungary and Yugoslavia, and south to Italy and the Pyrenees.

How to find it

With a restricted distribution, specialised habitat and short flowering period, this can be a hard species to find. It is also superficially rather anonymous, although well-grown plants are very attractive. The apparent size of colonies can vary dramatically from year to year but the underground population may be much more stable and rather larger. One of the places to see

▲ 12 July, Buckinghamshire. This species has largely green flowers but with a pinkish-purple tinge to the lip and sometimes also the petals.

the species at its best is the Warburg Reserve at Bix Bottom in Oxfordshire where a strong population is protected from deer.

DESCRIPTION

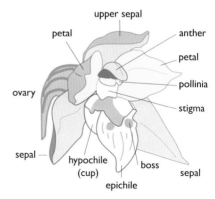

Height: 15-75cm but usually 30-60cm.
Stem: Green, with the upper part hairy. Usually grows singly but sometimes there are two together and rarely up to five or six stems may arise from a single rootstock.
Leaves: Three to seven, fresh green and arranged in two opposite rows up the stem, although

▲ 22 July, Oxfordshire. A particularly crowded spike on a robust plant.

Bract: Pale green and lanceolate; in the lower part of the spike the bracts are very long, project well beyond the flower and often hang downwards, but towards its tip they are shorter.

Ovary: Pale green, variably hairy, prominently six-ribbed but not twisted; the flower stalk is greenish-yellow.

Flower: Overall greenish, relatively large and usually opening fairly widely, although occasionally some flowers may not open fully, especially towards the tip of the spike. The sepals are oval-triangular and elongated into pointed tips, pale green on the outer surface and slightly paler and more whitish-green on the inner. The petals are similar in shape but slightly smaller. They are also paler, more greenish-white, becoming even paler towards the edges but greener towards the midrib (which is prominent on the outer face) and variably flushed pale pink with faint pink veins. The hypochile is whitish-green on the outside of the cup, variably flushed purplish-pink at the sides, and similarly pale on the inside but with a wine-red or chocolate-brown rear wall; it contains nectar. The epichile is whitish-green, sometimes delicately flushed pink, shaped like an arrowhead, longer than wide, and its pointed tip projects outwards. It has two relatively small, smooth bosses at its base and these are washed purple or purplish-pink; they flank a longitudinal central groove connecting the hypochile and epichile. The column is greenish-white, the pollinia creamy-yellow and the anther cap pale greenish-yellow with a narrow cream and broad chocolate-brown stripe on either side; it is attached to the column at the rear by a projecting spur or stalk (and in profile looks a little like the 'leaping jaguar' motif of the famous sports car, a distinction from Broad-leaved Helleborine where the anther is unstalked). The rostellum is reduced in size (less than half as long as the anther) and the viscidium, although present in the bud, vanishes by the time the flower opens.

Subspecies

None.

sometimes not obviously so. The leaves are elliptical and mostly more than twice as long as wide, with the uppermost long, narrow and grading into the lowest bracts. They are rather 'floppy' and held more-or-less horizontally but the uppermost, bract-like leaves are pendant.

Spike: Usually rather lax, with four to 35 flowers, often facing to one side. Initially held horizontally, they droop to a variable extent as they age.

▲ 22 July, Buckinghamshire. Showing the pointed tip to the lip, which is not bent back underneath the flower, and the relatively small, smooth bosses at it base.

Variation and varieties

Var. *cleistogama* was described from plants found in Gloucestershire on the steep western escarpment of the Cotswolds near Wotton-under-Edge, but this population is apparently now extinct. It had pendulous bracts, flowers that did not open and, within the flower, a greener lip. It has been treated as a distinct species but the upper flowers of some normal plants may never open, and it seems much more likely to have been a minor variant.

Var. *cordata* has a shorter, less pointed and more heart-shaped lip but has not been recorded for many years.

BIOLOGY

Pollination and reproduction

Narrow-lipped Helleborine is routinely self-pollinated but occasionally the flowers may have a functional viscidium. Visiting insects will then carry away the pollinia, and some cross-pollination is therefore possible. Seed-set is good and each capsule forms 1,000-2,000 seeds.

Development and growth

The rootstock lies rather deeply in the soil and numerous roots grow from it. Otherwise, there is no information on this species. A plant lacking chlorophyll, with a lemon-yellow stem and flowers, and pale greenish-yellow leaves, has been recorded (Young 1962b). It apparently thrived and flowered. This observation, together with the dense shade of its normal habitats, suggests that Narrow-lipped Helleborine must be able to acquire a large proportion of its nutrients from fungi.

Hybrids

None. (*E. x stephensonii*, the hybrid with Broad-leaved Helleborine, has been reported, but not confirmed, in southern England.)

Name and classification

The specific name *leptochila* means 'with a slender lip'.

Initially confused with variants of Broad-leaved Helleborine, it was not until 1921 that Narrow-leaved Helleborine was described as a distinct species. It was then confused with Green-flowered Helleborine until the British botanist Donald Young resolved the identity and characteristics of the two species in the 1950s and early 1960s. Confusion then arose again in the mid-1970s when plants resembling Narrow-lipped Helleborine were found inland in northern England (the 'Tyne Helleborine', see p.97). In some places these 'Tyne Helleborines' were found together with Dune Helleborines and intermediates were reported, leading to the conclusion that Narrow-lipped and Dune Helleborines must be one and the same species. However, more recent genetic studies have shown that all the plants in northern England are Dune Helleborines, and that they are genetically distinct from the true Narrow-lipped Helleborine, which is once again restricted to its classic habitat, the southern beechwoods.

Narrow-lipped Helleborine is one of a group of self-pollinating helleborines found in Europe, all of which have evolved independently from within the cross-pollinated Broad-leaved Helleborine complex. Being self-pollinated, they have a restricted genetic diversity but some, such as Narrow-lipped Helleborine, are successful species which have spread widely.

These self-pollinating species have long caused problems for both taxonomists and botanists, and their identification and correct classification is only now being resolved by genetic and biochemical techniques. For example, it has been suggested that Narrow-lipped and Dune Helleborines are the same as *Epipactis muelleri* of Continental Europe (most recently by Stace 2004). Recent genetic research shows that this is not the case.

HISTORY AND CONSERVATION

The first British record comes from 'Woods at Bosmere pool, Salop' in 1841. This was published in Leighton's *Flora of Salop* and was later identified as Narrow-lipped Helleborine.

It is Nationally Scarce, generally rather localised and declining. Indeed, following the clarification of the status of Narrow-lipped and Dune Helleborines, it is now known to be much scarcer than was reported in *Scarce Plants* in 1994.

Past and present occurrence of Narrow-lipped Helleborine in Britain and Ireland (based on presence or absence in 10km squares of the National Grid; data from the New Atlas*).*

	Britain	Ireland
total historical range, 1500-1999	58	0
current range	29 (1%*)	0
% lost, 1500-1969	26%	
% lost, 1970-1986	24%	
% lost, total	50%	

* current range as a % of the total number of 10km squares

The *New Atlas* records Narrow-lipped Helleborine from just 29 10km squares from 1987 onwards, and it has vanished from 50% of its historical range, with many of the losses being comparatively recent. It is now extinct in Devon, West Sussex and Monmouthshire, has not been seen in Kent and Hertfordshire for some years and was recorded for the first time in Herefordshire in 1970 only to disappear again.

Direct threats include the destruction of

▲ *22 July, Oxfordshire. Two stems growing together.*

its woodland habitat and the conversion of suitable woods to conifer plantations, although these practices have largely ceased. The loss of suitable shaded woodland due to the opening up of the canopy by severe gales, such as the great storms of 1987 and 1990, is a subtler threat. The compaction of woodland soils by the use of heavy machinery in forestry operations, horse riding, mountain biking and the spread of wild boar are other potential hazards. However, the most obvious is the widespread damage to flowering plants by the ever-increasing population of deer. Unlike Violet Helleborine, it does not seem to have benefited from the abandonment of coppicing during the 20th century, perhaps because it is slow to move into overgrown coppice.

DUNE HELLEBORINE
Epipactis dunensis

Other names: *E. muelleri*

Often considered to be one of the less attractive helleborines due to its relatively small, dull flowers, Dune Helleborine has the distinction of being endemic to the British Isles and has a very curious distribution and ecology. Typical plants are found in damp dune slacks on the coasts of north Wales and northwest England, and a distinct variety, the 'Tyne Helleborine', is found inland at scattered sites in northern England and southern Scotland, usually on old spoil heaps and in areas contaminated with heavy metals. 'Tyne Helleborine' differs genetically, albeit only slightly, from typical dune slack populations, and it may prove necessary to treat it as a distinct species. Dune Helleborine is the county flower of Lanarkshire.

Identification

Dune Helleborine has yellowish-green, two-ranked leaves which are held rather stiffly at about 45° above the horizontal. The upper part of the stem is distinctly downy, and the flowers are relatively small, do not open very widely and are yellowish-green with the petals and base of the lip washed with pink. The outer part of the lip (epichile) is heart-shaped, usually broader than long, and its tip folds downwards to a variable extent as the flower ages. The base of the flower stalk has a violet tinge. 'Tyne Helleborine' is found at inland sites and has greener flowers with an epichile that is longer than broad and not folded downwards. The base of its flower stalk is yellowish-green. Both forms are usually self-pollinated (see p.76 for a discussion of the separation of cross-pollinated and self-pollinated helleborines).

Similar species

Broad-leaved Helleborine typically has broader, darker and greener leaves, arranged all around the stem and not held rigidly erect. It has larger and more widely opening flowers, often with pink or purple tones on the sepals and a distinctly purple tinge to the lip. Unlike 'Tyne Helleborine', the outer part of its lip is almost always strongly bent down and under;

▶ *6 July, Lancashire. A typical Dune Helleborine among Creeping Willow, with small, slightly 'sickly', yellowish-green leaves that are held stiffly erect.*

▲ 17 July, Northumberland. 'Tyne Helleborine' typically appears neat and clean-cut.

usually self-pollinated, only very occasionally showing a functional viscidium.

Green-flowered Helleborine is, like Dune Helleborine, self-pollinating and potentially more confusing. However, its upper stem and ovaries are either hairless or have a few sparse hairs. Its leaves are a clean apple green and often short and rounded, and its flowers hang more-or-less downwards, both in bud and when open. A feature to check in difficult cases is the fringe on the edge of the leaves (use a 20x hand-lens). In Green-flowered Helleborine the tiny, transparent, whitish teeth (cilia) are arranged into irregular groups separated by gaps, but in Dune Helleborine there is an even fringe of minute teeth.

Narrow-lipped Helleborine is very similar to 'Tyne Helleborine', and indeed, for almost 30 years after its discovery, 'Tyne Helleborine' was thought to be Narrow-lipped Helleborine. Fortunately, separation of the two is academic, as Narrow-lipped Helleborine is confined to southern England, with a few colonies on the Welsh Marches and in south Wales. The sepals and petals of Narrow-lipped Helleborine are on average larger and slightly broader, its lip is a little more attenuated into a point, the bosses at the base of the lip are washed pink and the groove between them is rather broader.

Habitat

Dune Helleborine is typically found in damp dune slacks where it grows on the slightly higher and drier areas among and through a carpet of low, scrubby Creeping Willow. It has also spread into nearby pine plantations. 'Tyne Helleborine', on the other hand, is found at inland sites, in light, regenerating woodland, especially birchwoods, where the ground is kept relatively open by the presence of heavy metals, mine waste or clinker. For example, in Northumberland most of the populations grow along the River South Tyne on well-drained gravel soils that are heavily contaminated by

'Tyne Helleborine' can also be separated by the yellowish-green base to its flower stalk (washed violet in Broad-leaved). However, Broad-leaved Helleborine is very variable and in northern England and southern Scotland some have more yellowish-green, two-ranked leaves, although they still have large, widely opening flowers (these are the so-called 'Young's Helleborine', see p.97). In tricky cases it is worth checking the reproductive structures within the flower as Broad-leaved Helleborine is cross-pollinated and Dune Helleborine

▶ 17 July, Northumberland. A group of 'Tyne Hellebo-rines' growing under birches and willows by the River South Tyne.

▲ *6 July, Lancashire. A typical Dune Helleborine growing up and through the pink flowers of Restharrow.*

habitats as all the inland sites are of recent origin and are man-made. And, although seemingly very different, adaptations which allow the species to grow in dune slacks prone to the stresses of summer drought and salt spray may be similar to those needed in habitats stressed by the presence of toxic metals.

Flowering period

Late June to mid-August, usually peaking in the second week of July in the dune populations but a little later in adjacent conifer plantations and at inland sites. The flowers are short-lived and can be badly affected by drought.

Range

Dune Helleborine is found on Anglesey, the coasts of Merseyside and Lancashire and by the Duddon Estuary at Sandscale Haws in Cumbria. It has also been reported from the coast of Co. Dublin. 'Tyne Helleborine' occurs in Northumberland, Cumbria, Co. Durham and northwest Yorkshire. Scattered populations of typical dune-type plants have also been recorded at inland sites in north Lincolnshire, southeast Yorkshire, Co. Durham, Cumbria, and in southern Scotland in Lanarkshire, Midlothian and West Lothian. However, the features that separate these from 'Tyne Helleborine' (especially the colour of the base of the flower stalk) have only recently been clarified and all the records of 'Dune

zinc and lead tailings, but it is also found on wooded spoil-heaps contaminated with lead. In Scotland 'Tyne Helleborine' is found on the wooded slopes of old 'pit bings' (the shale-rich spoil heaps produced by coal mining), and at Almond Bing (Falkirk) and Carlisle (Cumbria) it is also found on and around old railway lines, both in deep shade and in more open areas.

It seems likely that Dune Helleborine has spread inland from its semi-natural coastal

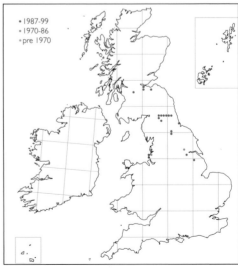

• 1987-99
• 1970-86
• pre 1970

Helleborine' at inland sites merit re-examination. **World range:** Endemic to Great Britain.

How to find it

Usually easy to find in dune slacks, although often hidden among Creeping Willow. The dune populations are all protected on reserves, including Newborough Warren on Anglesey, Ainsdale in Lancashire and Sandscale Haws in Cumbria. Inland, the most accessible sites for 'Tyne Helleborine' are the tiny Williamston Reserve and Beltingham River Gravels (both Northumberland).

DESCRIPTION

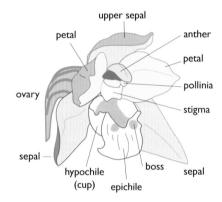

Due to the significant differences between the two varieties, they are described separately.

1. 'Typical' Dune Helleborine

Height: 20-40cm, sometimes to 50cm, with the tallest plants occurring in sheltered sites.
Stem: Pale green, tinged violet towards the base and downy towards the tip, with fine, pale hairs. Usually arises singly, although sometimes there may be two or three together.
Leaves: Three to ten, arranged in two opposite rows up the stem and held stiffly at about 45°. The leaves are oval-lanceolate, mostly more than twice as long as wide and become relatively narrower towards the flower spike, but the lowest is very short, broad and rounded and forms a cowl-shaped sheath. They are yellowish-green, deeply veined and their margins have fine, regular, whitish

▲ *6 July, Lancashire. A typical Dune Helleborine. The outer part of the lip (epichile) is broader than long and, in this case, strongly washed pink.*

teeth (cilia) 0.03-0.06mm wide. The leaves are often damaged by wind or drought by flowering time.
Spike: Rather lax, with six to 20 flowers, sometimes as many as 30, set to one side of the stem. The flowers are initially held horizontally (patent) but often droop and become pendant as they go over. At the Scottish sites the flowers are characteristically held in a drooping position, but this could be evidence of hybridisation.
Bract: Strap-shaped with a pointed tip; the lower bracts are slightly longer than the flowers, but they become shorter towards the tip of the spike.
Ovary: Green, hairy, six-ribbed (but not

▲ *6 July, Lancashire. A typical Dune Helleborine with the tip of the lip bent down and under.*

twisted) and pear-shaped, tapering into a short stalk that is washed violet at the base.

Flower: Relatively small, dull and not opening widely, the flower is cup-shaped. The sepals are yellowish-green, oval-triangular, relatively short and blunt with a prominent midrib on the outer surface. The petals are similar in shape but slightly smaller and very pale green, often washed pink. At the base of the lip, the interior of the hypochile is reddish-brown to dark brown and contains nectar; the exterior of the hypochile is whitish, variably flushed pink (the colour shining through from the inside). The epichile is whitish, sometimes with a pink flush in the centre, with a greener tip. Heart-shaped, it is usually broader than long and the tip is sometimes folded under, especially as the flower matures; often the entire epichile is bent downwards near the join with the hypochile. At the base of the epichile there are two smooth, pink or greenish bosses, and these frame a

distinct notch running between the epichile and hypochile. The anther is yellowish-green and is variably stalked. The pollinia are crumbling and whitish. The viscidium, although present in the bud, usually disappears as the flowers open.

2. 'Tyne Helleborine'

Height: 17-52cm.

Stem: Green, with fine, whitish hairs on the upper part. Usually grows singly but fairly frequently two stems arise together.

Leaves: The three to seven fresh green leaves are arranged in two opposite rows up the stem, although sometimes not obviously so. They are rather floppy and not held as rigidly erect as in typical dune slack plants; indeed, the uppermost leaves and lower bracts may be held horizontally. The leaves are deeply veined but not sharply folded, the lower elliptical, mostly more than twice as long as wide, the uppermost long, narrow and grading into the lower bracts. The leaf margins have very fine, regular teeth (cilia) 0.01-0.05mm wide, sometimes imperceptible.

Spike: Usually rather lax, with five to 35 flowers (mostly between ten and 25), often facing to one side. Initially held horizontally, they droop as they age.

Bract: Fresh green, lanceolate and several times the length of the flower in the lower part of the spike but shorter at its tip.

Ovary: Green, hairy, ribbed (but not twisted) and tapering into a yellowish-green stalk.

Flower: Greenish and relatively small but opening quite widely. The sepals are narrowly oval in shape, elongated towards the bluntly pointed tip. They are pale green on the outer surfaces, paler and more whitish-green on the inner surfaces with a diffuse whitish margin. The petals are similar but slightly smaller and proportionally shorter, paler and whiter. The hypochile is transparent-whitish with its interior washed dirty chocolate-brown at the base and rear, this colour shinning through to the exterior of the cup. The epichile is heart-shaped, variably longer than broad, with a pointed tip that projects forward. At its base there are two small, smooth bosses that frame a narrow, longitudinal groove. The epichile, including the basal bosses, is whitish with a faint cream or greenish wash. The column is greenish-white, the pollinia cream-coloured, and the anther cap is dull pale ochre with a brown stripe on either side. The rostellum is short, around half as long as the anther. The clinandrium (depression on the top of the column) is much smaller than 'typical' Dune Helleborine, and the viscidium is always absent.

Subspecies
None.

Variation and varieties
Typical Dune Helleborine and the 'Tyne Helleborine' (which has no formal scientific name) are described above. At some inland localities intermediates between the two have been reported.

Among dune populations, those growing in the open have a distinctive, almost 'sickly' yellow cast and often look rather wind-blasted, whereas those growing nearby in the shelter of plantations are taller, have more flowers and both the leaves and flowers are greener and 'healthier'. Dune-slack type plants growing at inland sites are also reported to be greener and more robust.

BIOLOGY

Pollination and reproduction
Dune Helleborine is self-pollinated and even in bud, fragments of the pollinia may fall onto the stigma and effect pollination. However, in some plants the viscidium may persist until the flower has opened, allowing the pollinia to be removed by insects and cross-pollination to take place. Even when no viscidium is present, plants may be cross-pollinated, wasps or other insects carrying away the pollinia that stick to their bodies regardless. In one case, around two-thirds of the flowers in a population of 'Tyne Helleborine' had their pollinia removed (Richards 1986). At a site near Glasgow, genetic studies have shown that Dune

▲ 17 July, Northumberland; 'Tyne Helleborine'. The pale, nearly whitish, tip of the lip contrasts with the sooty-brown interior of the cup at its base (the hypochile).

Helleborine is interbreeding with Broad-leaved Helleborine to form a hybrid swarm.

Vegetative reproduction may also take place, the rhizome producing two flower spikes and these in turn producing buds and roots.

► 17 July, Northumberland; 'Tyne Helleborine'. *The tip of the lip is pointed and does not bend down and under; it is also rather narrow and usually longer than broad.*

Development and growth

The rhizome is short, slender and woody. It lies deeply buried in the soil and bears up to ten thin, wiry roots. There is no information on the period between germination and flowering.

Hybrids

x Broad-leaved Helleborine has been found in Scotland. Although confirmed by genetic analysis, this hybrid has no scientific name. At Bardykes Bing near Glasgow there is a hybrid swarm of Dune and Broad-leaved Helleborines and the individual plants are very difficult to identify.

Name and classification

The specific name *dunensis* means 'of dunes'.

The taxonomy of Dune Helleborine is complex and confusing, and is best understood in seven stages:

Stage 1: In 1921 Dune Helleborine was first recognised as something different and described as a subspecies of Narrow-lipped Helleborine, using the name *E. leptochila dunensis*.

Stage 2: In 1926 Dune Helleborine was elevated to the status of a full species, *E. dunensis*, known only from coastal dune systems on Anglesey and in northwest England.

Stage 3: Colonies of plants identified as Narrow-lipped Helleborine, a species hitherto known only from mature woodland on chalk and limestone in southern England, were found at inland sites in Yorkshire in 1967, Northumberland in the early 1970s and subsequently more widely in northern England. (These would eventually become known as the 'Tyne Helleborine'.)

Stage 4: From the late 1970s onwards a few colonies of Dune Helleborines were discovered at inland sites, from Lincolnshire northwards.

Stage 5: The discovery at a few sites in northern England of populations apparently intermediate between Dune Helleborine and Narrow-lipped Helleborine led to the conclusion that they must be one and the same species, and that Dune Helleborine should therefore be treated as a variety of Narrow-lipped Helleborine, named *E. leptochila* var. *dunensis*.

Stage 6: More recently, research, based in part on DNA studies, has led to the conclusion that *all* the populations in northern England, both 'Dune' and 'Narrow-lipped', are closely related, but *not* the same species as Narrow-lipped Helleborine in southern England. These northern helleborines take the name *E. dunensis*, a species endemic to Great Britain.

Stage 7: There have been tentative suggestions that 'Tyne Helleborine' should be treated as a distinct species. There is some support for this from genetic studies, which do show some differences between 'Tyne Helleborine' and typical dune slack plants. However, they also indicate that they are probably each other's closest relatives, have the same ancestor and have only recently separated into two slightly different entities.

Note that the helleborines on Holy Island off Northumberland, once thought to be Dune Helleborine, have now been separated as a distinct, endemic species, Lindisfarne Helleborine (see p.122). Delforge (1995) suggested that 'Tyne Helleborine', together with Lindisfarne Helleborine, were the British representatives of a European species, Muller's Helleborine *E. muelleri*. The genetic evidence shows that this is not the case, but this name has nevertheless been used in some recent publications.

HISTORY AND CONSERVATION

Dune Helleborine is Nationally Scarce and recorded from just 26 10km squares in the *New Atlas*.

Dune slack populations are confined to a small number of sites but at these localities Dune Helleborine is often common, for example, at Sandscale Haws in Cumbria over 1,000 flowering plants have been counted. It is, however, sensitive to the level of grazing, especially by rabbits. If this is too intense the spikes are all nipped off and the plants fail to set seed. Conversely, if grazing is too light, scrub invades the habitat and may eventually shade it out.

The inland populations in northern England were found in the 1960s and 1970s. Some were large, with colonies of over 1,000 flowering plants. All these sites are in young, 'secondary' woodland, however, and as this matures the accumulation of humus seems to buffer the effects of the toxic metals and the ground cover increases; such changes may lead to the disappearance of the helleborines.

Past and present occurrence of Dune Helleborine in Britain and Ireland (based on presence or absence in 10km squares of the National Grid; data from the New Atlas*).*

	Britain	Ireland
total historical range, 1500-1999	26	1?
current range	24 (0.8%*)	0
% lost, 1500-1969	0%	0
% lost, 1970-1986	8%	0
% lost, total	8%	0

* current range as a % of the total number of 10km squares

LINDISFARNE HELLEBORINE
Epipactis sancta

For almost 50 years after their discovery, the helleborines on Holy Island in Northumberland were considered to be Dune Helleborines. However, studies in the 1980s highlighted some apparently minor differences, and recent genetic work has confirmed that they are not the same as the helleborines growing in the dune slacks along the coasts of northwest England and Anglesey. Rather they are a distinct species, endemic to this one small island.

Identification
Straightforward, due to its extremely limited distribution, although this species is very similar to Dune Helleborine, with yellowish-green leaves held in two opposite ranks and rather dull, greenish flowers which are normally self-pollinated.

Similar species
Dune Helleborine is very close in appearance, but typical dune slack plants have slightly larger flowers and the base of the flower stalk is washed violet (greenish in Lindisfarne Helleborine); the details of the column also differ. Lindisfarne Helleborine is even closer to 'Tyne Helleborine', which also has a greenish-yellow flower stalk and a similar column structure, but the lip of 'Tyne Helleborine' tends to be slightly longer and narrower, and does not turn under at the tip.

Habitat
Dunes and dune slacks, especially the slightly raised and more steeply sloping zone around the perimeter of the slacks. It grows among Creeping Willow and various grasses or, just as frequently, on bare sand among Marram grass. It may be associated with the disturbed ground around rabbit burrows.

Flowering period
Late June and the first three weeks of July but usually at its best early in July. Self-pollinated; the flowers go over quickly.

▶ 16 July, Northumberland. Towards the end of the flowering period, with the lower flowers withered, but in this robust plant the leaves are unusually undamaged.

Range

Only found on the island of Lindisfarne off the coast of Northumberland, growing at the Snook at the western end of the island. **World Range:** Endemic to England.

How to find it

Found singly and in small groups scattered through the dunes of the Snook, although scarce and rather scattered, and absent from much apparently suitable habitat. The species is prone to drought and may not flower if it is too dry, or the buds will shrivel before opening.

DESCRIPTION

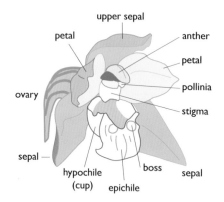

Height: 15-31cm.

Stem: Yellowish-green, finely hairy towards the tip.

Leaves: Yellowish-green, arranged in two ranks on either side of the stem and held at around 45°. The lowest leaf is rather short, broad and rounded and forms a cowl-shaped funnel near the base of the stem. The two to four higher leaves are elongated-oval in shape, becoming narrower and more lanceolate towards the spike. They are clearly veined and longitudinally folded but not sharply keeled. The leaf margins have tiny, very fine, regular teeth (cilia), 0.01-0.05mm wide (sometimes imperceptible). By flowering time many leaves are wind-burnt, grazed or otherwise damaged.

◀ *16 July, Northumberland. A small plant, growing as usual from bare sand.*

▲ *16 July, Northumberland. The stem and ovary are distinctly hairy, and the pollinia have apparently been removed.*

Spike: Fairly loose, with most flowers facing to one side and held roughly horizontal or just below the horizontal, although the flowers droop as they age. The spike consists of five to ten flowers, although large plants may have as many as 21.

Bract: Yellowish-green, lanceolate, longer than the flowers in the lower part of the spike but rather shorter than the uppermost leaves and becoming shorter towards the tip.

Ovary: Green, ribbed, hairy and quickly inflating as the flower self-pollinates. The flower stalk is green or yellowish-green.

Flower: Rather small and drab but opening fairly widely. The sepals are greenish and roughly triangular with the petals smaller and paler. The hypochile is whitish with a chocolate-brown inner rear wall to the cup and sometimes a pink wash to the exterior. The epichile is heart-shaped with the tip variably deflexed and whitish, washed green in the

▲ 16 July, Northumberland. The lip is typically whitish, becoming green towards the tip.

centre towards the tip. The column is whitish, the anther cap yellow with a narrow brown stripe at the side, and the pollinia are ochre-yellow. The clinandria (depressions on the top of the column) are very reduced and the rostellum is short, around half the length of the anther.

Subspecies
None.

Variation and varieties
None.

BIOLOGY

Pollination and reproduction
Self-pollinated.

Development and growth
No information.

Hybrids
None.

Name and classification
The specific name *sancta* means 'holy' or 'sacred', a reference to Holy Island.

Holy Island plants were initially identified as Dune Helleborine, but the colour of their flower stalks and details of the flower structure led to suggestions from the 1980s onwards that they were not the same as the Dune Helleborines growing on the coast of northwest

England and Wales. Delforge & Gévaudan (2002) went on to propose the name *Epipactis sancta* for the species. Genetic studies show that not only are Holy Island plants distinct from both classic dune slack populations and the 'Tyne Helleborine' but also that they probably evolved independently of both of these.

HISTORY AND CONSERVATION

These helleborines were first found on Holy Island in 1958. In recent years there has been an increase in the number of flowering plants due to a reduction in the number of rabbits (which nip off the stems) and around 150-300 spikes appear annually. The presence of rabbits may be important, however, despite their impact on flowering numbers; they prevent scrub from invading the dunes and the bare ground created by their scrapings may help in the establishment of seedlings.

▲ 16 July, Northumberland. The yellow pollinia are still intact on this plant.

GREEN-FLOWERED HELLEBORINE

Epipactis phyllanthes

Formerly: *E. pendula, E. vectensis*. Other names: Pendulous-flowered Helleborine
This mysterious orchid has a habit of coming and going at its known sites and of popping up unexpectedly in new places, so is always worth looking out for in almost any type of woodland in England and Wales. It is also one of the most variable orchids, and this has caused a great deal of confusion over the years.

Identification

Green-flowered Helleborines come in a wide variety of sizes and shapes. Some are diminutive plants with large, swollen, pear-shaped ovaries and small flowers which hang vertically downwards and never really open. Others are rather robust, with wide-open, saucer-shaped flowers that can be held facing more outwards than downwards (with such well-developed plants being commonest in northern England). However, despite this diversity, this species often has a fairly distinctive 'feel'.

Green-flowered Helleborine is typically relatively slender with short leaves which are a fresh apple-green colour. Leaf shape and posture are variable, but some plants have characteristically well-spaced leaves that are very rounded and held stiffly horizontal. The flowers are green with a whitish or sometimes pinkish lip and often do not open widely or, indeed, may not open at all; such plants appear to be permanently in bud, although the large ovaries swell conspicuously. The base of the flower stalk is greenish, and in most plants the flowers hang vertically downwards. The lip shape is very variable. In some populations it is almost identical to the petals (a feature shown by no other British helleborine) and in others the lips are fully formed and divided as normal into a cup-shaped hypochile and

◀ *1 August, Northumberland, var. pendula. A typically small, few-flowered plant, with very rounded leaves held horizontally and flowers that do not open widely.*

▶ *12 July, Northumberland, var. pendula. A robust plant, with many flowers, but almost all of them, as usual, are drooping.*

heart-shaped epichile. The flowers are generally self-pollinated, the pollinia crumbling within the flower onto the stigma.

Whatever the appearance of the flowers, three features will confirm an identification. First, the upper part of the stem and the ovaries are either hairless or, rather less frequently, the upper stem may be sparsely hairy (use a hand-lens). Second, the hypochile is greenish-white, lacking an obvious dark brown or purple lining. Third, in difficult cases look at the edge of the leaves (a 20x hand-lens is best for this). In all the other helleborines there is an even fringe of tiny, whitish, hair-like projections, but in Green-flowered Helleborine these cilia are unevenly distributed in groups.

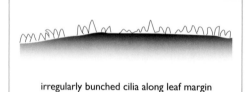

irregularly bunched cilia along leaf margin

Similar species

Narrow-lipped Helleborine is found in beechwoods in southern England and south Wales and is also greenish overall. At all times it can be distinguished by its rather hairy upper stem and ovaries.

Dune Helleborine occurs on coastal dunes in Anglesey and northwest England, and as the distinct variety known as 'Tyne Helleborine' at inland sites in northern England and southern Scotland. It always has a hairy upper stem and ovaries and a dark lining to the hypochile at the base of the lip. In addition, typical dune slack plants have a violet wash to the base of the flower stalk (yellowish-green in 'Tyne' and Green-flowered Helleborines).

Broad-leaved Helleborine sometimes has greenish flowers but always has a densely hairy upper stem and slightly hairy ovary. It is also cross-pollinated (see p.76 for a discussion of the separation of cross-pollinating and self-pollinating helleborines).

▲ *26 August, Norfolk, var. degenera. Very typically, growing through a carpet of Ivy. In this season the flowers hardly opened at all.*

Habitat

Very varied, and although the species favours alkaline soils, it is not confined to areas of chalk or limestone and will grow on calcareous to mildly acidic sands and clays and in silty river valleys. It is mostly found in light to moderate shade but can occur in densely shaded situations, although it is often rather small and slight in such places. Green-flowered Helleborine frequents a wide variety of woodlands but has a definite preference for beechwoods in southern England and overall favours smaller woods, copses, belts of trees or tall hedges next to woodland, or the better-lit edges of larger woods; it is often found on road verges. It prefer areas where the ground cover is rather sparse or low, no taller than 15-20cm, and is characteristically found growing through a carpet of Ivy.

Rather than having an association with ancient woodland, many of its sites are relatively recent in origin, such as beech and pine plantations and shelterbelts and, in Northumberland, the maturing birch and hawthorn scrub found on old waste tips contaminated with zinc and lead. Another favoured habitat is thickets of willows and other trees alongside rivers and streams that are subject to occasional flooding, the helleborines growing on the better-drained ridges and banks. Indeed, this may be the 'natural' habitat of the species and it has even been found in Hampshire growing among reeds and willows in the tidal part of the River Itchen. Conversely, Green-flowered Helleborines also occur in very dry woods. At a few sites in Wales, northwest England and Co. Dublin, it grows in the open on sand dunes, coming up through a blanket of Creeping Willow on the drier hummocks. However, it tends to look yellow and 'sickly' in this habitat, appearing rather healthier where it has spread into adjacent conifer plantations.

Flowering period

Late June to early or even mid-September but mostly from mid-July to mid-August, with dune populations typically earliest.

Range

In England rather scattered and local but found west to Dorset, Gloucestershire and Herefordshire, east to Kent and Norfolk and north to south Cumbria and Northumberland. The bulk of the population is found in central and northern Hampshire, Wiltshire, West Sussex and Surrey, where Green-flowered Helleborine can be locally frequent. In Wales there are scattered sites in coastal dunes in Glamorganshire (including Kenfig and Whitford Burrows) and Merionethshire (Morfa Dyffryn), but it is otherwise only found in Flintshire. There are also a handful of sites in Ireland, in Co. Dublin, Co. Leitrim and Co. Ferrmanagh. **World range:** Restricted to western Europe, from northern Spain through France and Belgium to Denmark. May occur more widely but the taxonomic confusion surrounding the species and its close relatives in Europe has clouded an understanding of its true range.

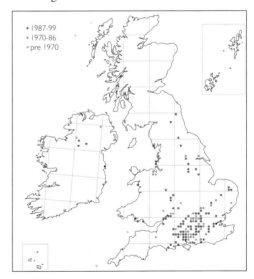

How to find it

Its overall green coloration, relatively small size, habitat and flowering period can make this a hard species to find, although the apple-green, rounded leaves, which are held horizontally, and the mass of large, drooping buds often catch the eye. Colonies are often small, and numbers can fluctuate, with fewer plants in dry years. Most of the sites for the species in southern England are anonymous and have little or no other orchid interest, and the most accessible sites to see the species at its best are the dunes on the Lancashire and Cumbrian coasts.

DESCRIPTION

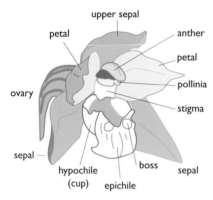

Height: 5-75cm but mostly 15-50cm; taller plants are commonest in northern England.
Stem: Robust, purple-brown at the base (where there are one to three similarly coloured sheaths) but becoming apple-green for most of its length. The stem, including the upper part, is hairless or has sparse, short hairs. Usually grows singly but occasionally two or three stems may arise together. We have seen a photograph of a group of nine (Killick *et al.* 1998), although such a large cluster may have resulted from the rhizomes of several plants growing together.
Leaves: There are three to seven, exceptionally as many as 16, apple-green leaves which are well spaced but often rather high up on the stem. They are very variable in shape and posture but usually relatively small. Many plants have leaves that are broadly oval or egg-shaped but on others they are longer, narrower and more pointed. On all plants, the upper leaves are usually narrower and more bract-like, and the lowest green leaf is often rather small and frequently funnel-like, partially sheathing the stem. The leaves may be arranged in two ranks on either side of the stem and on some plants are held flat in a very characteristic horizontal plane. On others they may be held lightly folded and positioned nearer to 45°. The margins

have tiny, whitish teeth (cilia) arranged into irregular groups.
Spike: The buds may be held upright, horizontally or drooping, but, once open, the flowers usually hang down near to the vertical. The spike contains between two and 25 flowers, exceptionally as many as 35, and is often fairly crowded. The flowers often face in the same direction, and the uppermost buds in the spike may fail to open.
Bract: Green and lanceolate; the lowest bracts are much longer than the flowers but they become progressively shorter, with the uppermost a little shorter than the flowers. The bracts are usually horizontally, especially on less densely crowded spikes.
Ovary: Swells rapidly and becomes large and pear-shaped. It is shiny, virtually hairless but with six prominent ribs, tapering into the short, curved and twisted green stalk.

▲ 12 July, Northumberland, var. pendula. *The ovary is boldly-ribbed but hairless, and the base of the flower stalk is green.*

Flower: Var. *pendula* (see below for other flower shapes). Overall greenish. The sepals are elongated-ovals, variably tapering to a pointed tip, and pale green with a prominent green midrib on the outer surface. The petals are a little smaller, paler and more greenish-white. The hypochile is whitish or dull olive-white, almost translucent, with the interior of the cup pale greenish (sometimes lightly washed brown). The epichile is heart-shaped with a pointed tip which is strongly turned under, and there are two rough bosses at the base with a central groove between them. It is whitish and tinged with green or sometimes pale pink in the centre or towards the tip, especially the bosses. The column is whitish and the anther cap dull yellowish-white with narrow brown stripes at the side. The pollinia are cream or whitish, quickly crumbling and inconspicuous in the anther. A small and not very sticky viscidium may be present in the bud, but this withers by the time the flower opens.

Subspecies

None.

Variation and varieties

Green-flowered Helleborine is very variable, both in terms of the structure of the flowers and in the overall size and shape of the plant. The flowers range from those where the lip is well developed, with a clear distinction between the basal cup (hypochile) and the heart-shaped tip (epichile), to those where the lip is simple and petal-like. There are also parallel differences in the shape of the anther. Between the two extremes the range of variation is almost continuous. There are four named varieties, although due to the variation it can be difficult to identify plants. Notably, there is no real dividing line between var. *pendula* and var. *vectensis*, and flowers with mixed characters can be found. It would probably be better to unite the two varieties as var. *vectensis*.

There are broad geographical trends in lip shape, with populations in the north and west having the most robust plants, the best developed lip structure and widely opening

▲ *I August, Northumberland, var.* pendula. *The lip is well-formed in this variety and, on this plant, the flowers have opened extraordinarily widely.*

flowers (var. *pendula*), whereas those in the south tend to be smaller, with incompletely developed flowers that open only partially. Even in the same region, however, there can be a good deal of variation, and at a few sites a mixture of lip shapes can be found in the same colony.

Var. *pendula* The lip is large and fully developed. The hypochile is well formed and around 4mm long. The epichile is heart-shaped, as long as the hypochile or only slightly longer, with a pointed tip that is normally strongly reflexed. The epichile is wrinkled at the base or has two bosses. The flowers open widely and cleistogamic flowers are rare. This is the commonest variety in north Wales and northern England but it has been found further

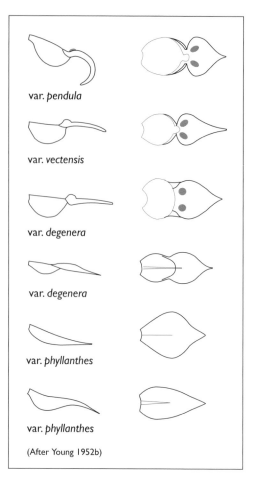

var. *pendula*

var. *vectensis*

var. *degenera*

var. *degenera*

var. *phyllanthes*

var. *phyllanthes*

(After Young 1952b)

▲ 17 July, Norfolk, var. *vectensis*. In this variety the lip is well formed and it can, as here, have a pink tinge.

south and intermediates with var. *vectensis* are not infrequent.

Var. *vectensis* As var. *pendula* but the hypochile is smaller, 2.5-3.5mm long, and more hemispherical so that it embraces the column closely. The epichile is distinctly longer than the hypochile, sometimes markedly so, and the tip is generally not reflexed so that the whole lip points forwards. The flowers open to a variable extent and are often cleistogamous. Mostly found in southern England and the Midlands but has been recorded north to Yorkshire. Plants growing in the dunes of south Wales are sometimes separated as var. *cambrensis* but differ only slightly from var. *vectensis*. They were once tentatively placed with Dune Helleborine and then described as a distinct species, *E. cambrensis*.

Var. *phyllanthes* The lip is not divided into hypochile and epichile and is oval or lanceolate with a central midrib, resembling a petal in size and shape. The flowers rarely open widely and are usually cleistogamous. This form is commonest in southern England.

Var. *degenera* This is intermediate between var. *vectensis* and var. *phyllanthes*. The hypochile is reduced to a shallow depression at the base of the lip and although there may be small bosses at the sides of the base of the 'epichile', the lip has either no waist at all or only a rudimentary one and always lacks the central groove between the two bosses. The flowers rarely open widely and are usually cleistogamous. It is mainly found in southern England.

The size and shape of the plants and their overall colour also varies, especially the size and shape of the leaves. This variation seems to be determined by the local environment (for example, on exposed dunes the plants are dwarfed and yellowish). In addition, individual plants and whole populations vary in the degree to which the flowers open and how pendulous they are, although this can change from season to season; plants in which the flower buds never open are commonest in dry seasons, whereas in very wet years more plants than normal may show widely opening flowers.

BIOLOGY

Pollination and reproduction

Green-flowered Helleborine is always self-pollinated. In some plants this occurs when the flowers are still in bud (the flowers are cleistogamous); the buds may or may not open subsequently. Following pollination the whole column, together with the lip, withers rapidly but the sepals and petals can remain intact for a long time.

Development and growth

The aerial stem grows from a rhizome which varies from nearly horizontal to nearly vertical, with numerous thick, fleshy roots, both long and short. There is no information on the period between germination and flowering.

▲ 14 August, Norfolk, var. degenera. *The flowers have opened as much as they are going to, and the ovaries are all swollen (they were presumably self-pollinated in bud).*

Hybrids

None.

Name and classification

The specific name 'phyllanthes' may celebrate Phillis Wood near Treyford in West Sussex, the site from which the first specimens were collected in the 1830s, but is more probably from a compound of Greek words meaning 'leaf-like flower'.

This species was misunderstood for a long time and widely confused with Narrow-lipped Helleborine. It was not until 1952 that *E. vectensis* (described as a variety of Narrow-lipped Helleborine in 1918 and then as a distinct species in 1940) and *E. pendula* (described in 1942) were shown by the British botanist Donald Young to be the same as *E. phyllanthes*, a species described in 1852 in the *Gardeners' Chronicle* but ignored for a hundred years. 'Epipactis cambrensis' (described in 1950) has since been added to the pot-pourri.

HISTORY AND CONSERVATION

Nationally Scarce in Britain and specially protected in Northern Ireland under Schedule 8 of the 1985 Wildlife Order (NI). A better awareness of the species has led to an increase in the number of records in recent years but this is offset by the loss of known sites. It is extinct in the Isle of Wight, Somerset, Suffolk, Warwickshire, Derbyshire, Co. Antrim, Co. Derry and Co. Wicklow.

Losses may be due to the grubbing-out or coniferisation of woodland, but some of its habitats are ephemeral in nature and become unsuitable as the woodland matures and becomes more shaded. In general, there has been a decrease in numbers in southern England but some spread on the edges of the range. For example, it was first found in Norfolk in 1969 at Santon and subsequently a number of colonies were discovered in the 1990s along the banks of the Rivers Yare and Wensum in Norwich.

Past and present occurrence of Green-flowered Helleborine in Britain and Ireland (based on presence or absence in 10km squares of the National Grid; data from the New Atlas).

	Britain	Ireland
total historical range, 1500-1999	134	9
current range	86 (3%*)	4 (0.4%*)
% lost, 1500-1969	21%	44.5%
% lost, 1970-1986	15%	11%
% lost, total	36%	55.5%

* current range as a % of the total number of 10km squares

Distribution

There are around five species in this genus, distributed in Europe, Asia, Africa and through the Pacific Islands to Australia. All are fully mycotrophic and depend on fungi throughout their life.

Name

The generic name *Epipogium* derives from the Greek and means 'overbeard', a reference to the position of the lip, uppermost in the flower.

GENUS *EPIPOGIUM*
GHOST ORCHIDS

GHOST ORCHID
Epipogium aphyllum

This may be the rarest wild plant in Britain. It has only been recorded in two widely separated regions: the Chilterns and around Herefordshire and Shropshire. Fully dependent on fungi throughout its life, it only appears above ground to flower and fruit. There have, however, been no documented sightings in England for almost 20 years and it has become the Holy Grail for many orchidophiles. Once known as 'Spurred Coralroot', the English name Ghost Orchid much more accurately reflects its elusiveness. Its small size and pallid, ethereal appearance make it extremely hard to find in its gloomy woodland haunts – truly 'ghostly' qualities.

Identification
Very distinctive, it is pale and 'waxy' with relatively large, pinkish flowers and no green leaves.

Similar species
None.

Habitat
In Herefordshire and Shropshire it has been found in oak woodland on clay soils. The Chiltern sites are in beechwoods on chalk or clay-with-flints. Ghost Orchid often grows where the soil is slightly deeper, in hollows or on the top and sides of ditches (but not, apparently, in the bottom of a ditch). The margins of roads and tracks appear to be favoured but this may reflect the fact that it is easiest to search for the plants in such places. It often grows in a deep mat of decaying leaves but may also be found in areas with almost no leaf mould, the rhizome lying in the mineral soil itself. Several times it has been found growing out of old tree stumps, and one has even been recorded growing through a rotten mattress in a roadside ditch.

Ghost Orchid is often said to grow in heavily shaded woodland where the ground is otherwise bare. In 1953, however, having discovered the largest ever colony in Britain, Rex Graham stated, 'The canopy, locally heavy, is on the whole rather more open than what one might have expected to be ideal for this orchid, and a few plants grew in comparatively light conditions and amongst the type of ground

▲ 14 August, Buckinghamshire (Nigel Redman). With three flowers, this is typical of British plants.

◀ 14 August, Buckinghamshire (Nigel Redman). A ghostly apparition on the beechwood floor.

vegetation that invades these woods whenever light gives a chance'.

Flowering period
April to mid-October but mostly mid-July to mid-September. Plants in Buckinghamshire tend to flower from mid-July to the third week of August and those in Oxfordshire a little later, from mid-August to mid-September.

Flowering is said to follow a wet spring. This allows the plant to store up water prior to developing an aerial stem. The flower bud is, however, initiated in the year prior to flowering, so the conditions in two consecutive years may be critical in determining whether the plant is able to bloom. The Ghost Orchid may even flower underground, buried in the leaf-litter.

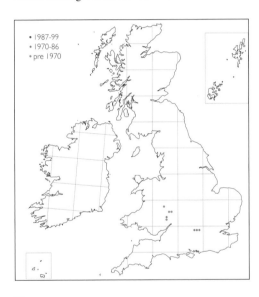

Range
Confined to England, where it has been found in Oxfordshire, Buckinghamshire, Herefordshire and Shropshire. **World Range:** Central and northern Europe and through northern Asia to the Far East, with a few scattered sites south to the Himalayas and China. Occurs north to northern Scandinavia and south to the Alps, central Italy, northern Greece, Crimea and Caucasus; also found on Corsica. Largely absent west of the Alps and Massif Central, but there are odd sites, including the Pyrenees. In Siberia it ranges east

to the Kamchatka Peninsula, Russian Far East, Sakhalin, Japan, northeast China and Korea and is also found to the south scattered through the Himalayas and southern China, including Taiwan.

How to find it
Ghost Orchid is probably the hardest plant to find growing wild in Britain. Its small size makes it extremely inconspicuous and very difficult to see in the deep leaf-litter of the woodland floor. Plants may even be hidden under wind-blown leaves. Some ingenious techniques have been used to try to locate it, including night forays where a powerful torch is shone parallel to the ground in the hope of highlighting the tiny spikes. The prolonged period during which it may bloom does not help, nor does the fact that slugs so often destroy the flower spikes; even if they survive, the flowers do not last more than a few days. Knowledge of the precise location of previous records is of only limited use, as they seldom reappear in exactly the same spot. Finally, even in the right place at the right time few flower spikes are produced, with one to four, exceptionally seven, at any one site in any one year. The total of 25 near Marlow in 1953 was quite unique.

DESCRIPTION
Height: Usually 5-10cm but sometimes to 12.5cm and exceptionally to 24cm.
Stem: Swollen at the base, thick but fragile and translucent-white, washed dull rose-pink or pinkish-brown and variably streaked pinkish. Above the uppermost flower the stem continues as a short, narrow projection (like an aborted flower stalk). Stems arise singly but occasionally two spikes grow from the same rhizome.
Leaves: There are no green leaves, merely two or three brown, sheathing scales at the base of the stem and one or two longer, often dark-edged, tightly clasping, scale-like leaves higher on the stem.
Spike: Most plants carry one or two flowers, but the more robust bear three or four blooms,

which are held pointing outwards or nodding downwards on short stalks. Neither the stalk nor the ovary is twisted, hence the spur points more-or-less upward and the lip similarly lies at the top of the flower.

Bract: Roughly equal in length to the flower stalk and ovary together, papery and translucent with a yellowish-straw wash.

Ovary: Bag-like, pale straw, veined or spotted with pink or violet; the flower stalk is noticeably slender and curves to hold the ovary hanging downwards.

Flower: The spur and lip lie at the top of the flower, with the lip facing downwards and outwards. The lip is whitish or very pale pink and divided into two sections: at the base the hypochile is short with two broad, spreading, triangular side-lobes flanking the entrance to the spur; the epichile is longer, broadly tongue- or heart-shaped and deeply concave with crimped margins and several rows of raised magenta ridges. The lip is strongly curved to lie parallel with the spur, which it may touch. The spur is relatively large, sack-shaped, slightly curved, pale pink and filled with nectar. The sepals and petals are very pale yellowish-straw with fine reddish dots or streaks; they are narrow and strap-shaped with their edges curled inwards, making them appear even narrower. The 'upper' sepal and two petals hang down below the rear of the flower, and the two lateral sepals project downwards and variably outwards at the sides. The column is pale yellow and short with a well-developed rostellum; the anther is pale yellow and the two pollinia are connected by a stalk at their base to the two distinct viscidia. The nectar is said to smell of fermenting bananas or vanilla but it is also described as foetid.

BIOLOGY

Pollination and reproduction

Possibly pollinated by bumblebees and wasps. The insect lands on the lip and moves towards the spur to access the nectar. As it backs out, it ruptures the rostellum, pushes the anther

▲ 14 August, Buckinghamshire (Nigel Redman). The spur of the flower lies at the top and the lip faces downwards. The magenta ridges on the lip have presumably evolved to guide a pollinator, but the mechanism is obscure.

cap aside, and the slender stalks of the pollinia are glued to its back or head. However, it has been suggested that bees, although they do visit the flowers, are unlikely pollinators. They are the wrong shape and size, especially given that the flowers are 'upside-down' (and all references to bees as pollinators may originate with the observations of a Dr Rohrbach in the 19th century); if this is so, the mechanism of pollination is a mystery. Self-pollination in flowers in the normal pendant position is prevented by the position of the stigma, above the anther, because pollen cannot fall upwards. However, self-pollination may be possible while the flowers are upright when still in bud.

Whatever the mechanism, few flowers produce capsules, perhaps because of the lack of suitable pollinators in the dark woods where Ghost Orchids are found, or because of a lack of other simultaneously flowering Ghost Orchids to cross-pollinate the flower.

The species certainly reproduces vegetatively and this may be the major means of propagation, although the literature is contradictory about the mechanism. Some sources state that new plants grow from buds at the tip of the roots. Others state that some of the branches of the rhizome become slender, attenuated and thread-like, and function as underground runners. Bulbils are formed at intervals along these runners and these may become detached and grow into independent new plants. After flowering, the major part of the rhizome usually dies, leaving the runners to form new plants.

Development and growth

Throughout its life Ghost Orchid is entirely dependent on fungi for its nutrition (that is, fully mycotrophic). It is often stated that Ghost Orchid is 'saprophytic' and gets its nutrients from decaying organic material, but this is not correct, as it feeds by consuming a living fungus. It seems likely that, like Bird's-nest and Coralroot Orchids, its fungal 'partner' will prove to be ectomycorrhizal and have a symbiotic association with the roots of trees. This would allow the Ghost Orchid to acquire nutrients, via its fungal 'partner', from the trees.

The aerial stem grows from a whitish rhizome which has many branches. In turn, these are forked or tri-lobed. The lobes are rounded at the tip and often spread fanwise. The much-branched rhizome is said to look like certain types of coral, hence the old name, 'Spurred Coralroot'. There are no roots, rather the rhizome has a sparse covering of fine, long hairs. Once the plant is mature enough to flower, a bud appears in the autumn and swells as the food and water reserves from the rhizome are transferred to it. If the following season is sufficiently wet, a flower spike may be produced.

Seed probably germinates in the autumn, and up to ten years, possibly even twenty, may elapse before flowering, although no one has performed a long-term study of marked plants to confirm this.

Subspecies
None.

Variation and varieties
None.

Hybrids
None.

Name and classification
The specific name *aphyllum* derives from the Greek and means 'without leaves'.

HISTORY AND CONSERVATION

A *Red Data Book* species that is classified as Critically Endangered, it is fully protected under Schedule 8 of the Wildlife and Countryside Act 1981.

The first British record dates from 1854, when Ghost Orchid was found by the Sapey Brook on the border of Herefordshire and Worcestershire, as detailed in the *Journal of Botany*: 'The discovery was communicated … on the 9th of this month [September], by the Rev. W. Anderton Smith, of Tedstone, from the Rectory, Delamere, Bromyard: - "…a few weeks since, Mrs. Anderton Smith found a specimen… For some time we looked in vain for other specimens; but, on the 23rd ult., I was fortunate in detecting a considerable mass of it. All were found at the foot of a very steep woody bank, close to a brook; the soil very wet and stiff. As the banks are very much trampled on at present (timber and faggots being drawn along), I decided on digging it up, and planting it in a similar spot in our own grounds."'

The next records of Ghost Orchid came from Bringewood Chase near Ludlow (then in Shropshire, the area is now in the administrative county of Herefordshire). It was found by a Miss Lloyd in 1876 and again in the same wood by a Miss Peel in 1878, with a third record from a different part of the wood in 1892. A Ghost Orchid was also recorded from the Wye Valley near Ross-on-Wye, Herefordshire, in July 1910.

There was then a gap of 13 years before the species was seen again in Britain, this time in Oxfordshire. In June 1923 two plants were found just north of Henley-on-Thames. After a prolonged search, Dr. G. C. Druce, perhaps the most eminent botanist of the day, succeeded in tracking down a third plant in July. In late May of the following year two more plants were found there. Then, on 30 June 1931,

Ghost Orchid was found a few miles to the west by Mrs Vera Paul (then a schoolgirl), in beechwoods towards Stoke Row. There was a single large spike, 24cm high with three flowers, growing from the middle of an old tree stump. A single spike was also seen nearby in 1933.

The trail went cold again for 20 years and it was not until 1953 that Ghost Orchid appeared again, this time in Buckinghamshire (around ten miles from the Oxfordshire sites). Rex Graham had been searching for Ghost Orchids for 20 years and on 18 July 1953 was in woods west of Marlow. He was lighting his pipe when, over the bowl of it, he saw a Ghost Orchid growing among the beech leaves. There proved to be a scattered colony of 25 spikes belonging to 22 plants. Three specimens were collected and at least three more spikes were felled by slugs. It was found there again the following year but not in such great numbers. These woods went on to become the most productive area for the species, although the number of plants never matched the 1953 total. Spurred on by the events in Buckinghamshire, Vera Paul searched the woods near Stoke Row in 1953 and two spikes were found. Plants were seen there in 1954 and 1956, too, while on 17 September 1963 five spikes were found close to the stump where the species had been first found in 1931. Sightings in this complex of woods have continued, with reports up to and including recent years.

On 19 September 1982, after a gap of 62 years, the Ghost Orchid reappeared in Herefordshire, when a single spike was found in a cart track under oak and pine in a wood far removed from its old localities. By 1 October the stem had rotted, probably due to slug damage.

The *Red Data Book* states flatly that Ghost Orchid has not been seen since 1986, but there were reliable reports from near Marlow until 1989 and several reports since from both Buckinghamshire and Oxfordshire, covering almost every year up to 2003. The evidence for some of these is certainly limited, however, and the finders have displayed a great reluctance in coming forward and allowing the record to be confirmed, probably to the detriment of the plant. The relative lack of records in recent years may merely be part of the natural cycle of a small population or more likely reflects a genuine decline. It has been suggested that the opening of the canopy following tree falls after the great storms of 1987 and 1990 may have resulted in the exposure of the woodland floor to too much sun, conditions becoming too dry for the species (but see Habitat).

Ghost Orchid is on the very edge of its range in England and is naturally rare. Its position here has not been helped by the unsympathetic management of ancient woodland, which has been cleared or replanted with conifers (for example, Bringewood Chase in Shropshire has largely been 'coniferised', with little ancient woodland remaining). Other more immediate threats include horse riders and cyclists who create paths through areas where the plants have flowered in the past, and forestry operations which involve the use of heavy machinery and the dumping of materials. Some of these problems could be avoided if the responsible authorities knew the location of the plants, but there is such secrecy surrounding Ghost Orchid that many sightings are 'hushed up'. Humans can be a direct threat, too, with photographers trampling the area around flower spikes, and in 1978 and 1979 collectors apparently dug up several plants. Finally, there are natural hazards, with deer and slugs taking a toll. Well-meaning naturalists have advocated surrounding plants with slug pellets, but even a moribund slug may cause damage and there is no information on the effect of molluscicides on the plant or its fungal 'partner'.

▶ *16 June, Norfolk. Fen Orchid, a relatively robust plant.*

GENUS *LIPARIS*
FEN ORCHID

Distribution

This small, green-flowered orchid
grows from a pseudobulb, a structure
commonly found in tropical epiphytes
and, although *Liparis* has an almost
worldwide distribution, it is essentially
tropical. There are 300 or so species but
just one is found in Britain and Europe.

Name

The generic name *Liparis* is from the
Greek *liparos* and means 'fatty', 'greasy' or
'shiny', a reference to the appearance of
the leaves.

FEN ORCHID
Liparis loeselii

Other names: Loesel's Twayblade (North America)

This small and rather drab orchid has always been very localised in Britain and is now confined to just a handful of sites in Norfolk and South Wales. Indeed, it is threatened throughout its range in Europe and has declined in much of North America, too. Surprisingly, studies of its life history suggest that it is a 'weedy' species, well-adapted to colonising and rapidly filling newly available habitats, and that it thrives on disturbance.

▲ 18 June, Norfolk. The aerial stem grows from a pseudo-bulb, a swelling in the stem that is concealed by the base of the leaves.

Identification

Very rare and localised, this is an orchid highly unlikely to be stumbled upon by chance. When in flower, Fen Orchid is distinctive. The small, pale green flowers appear to be a jumble of thin, spidery projections and are unique. Importantly, they are usually held facing upwards, with the column vertical, and the three strap-shaped sepals, two thread-like petals and the lip all held more-or-less horizontally in a cross; two of the sepals lie parallel, close together under the tongue-like tip, to form one 'arm' of the cross.

Similar species

Non-flowering plants may form the bulk of the population. They could be confused with Common Twayblade or Lesser Butterfly Orchid but are much smaller and their leaves sheathe the swollen base of the stem to form a pseudobulb.

Habitat

Fen Orchid is found in two distinct habitats; marshes in the Norfolk Broads and damp dune slacks on the coast of South Wales. Although superficially very different, both offer the same combination of bare ground which is kept damp or wet by neutral or calcium-rich ground water.

In the Norfolk Broads, Fen Orchid occurs as a member of a particularly species-rich community in areas of wet, peaty fen dominated by Common Reed or Great Fen Sedge. It grows on the mossy carpet at the base of the reeds, on the sides and tops of sedge tussocks, or on the bare peat itself. It is

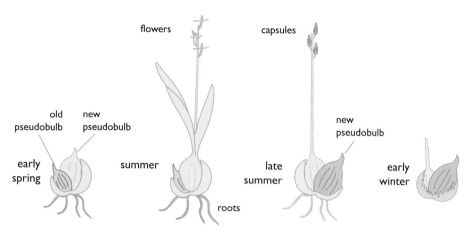

▲ *Annual replacement of pseudobulbs in Fen Orchid.*

extremely fussy, however, and an analysis of its current and former sites in East Anglia reveals that they have several features in common: 1. All are wet, with a water table which is typically just below the surface and relatively stable. Fen Orchid does not necessarily require waterlogged conditions and, indeed, may grow on tussocks up to 15cm above the water level, but the presence of surface water could be important in protecting it from slugs and snails. 2. The ground water is neutral to mildly alkaline and very low in nutrients. 3. Most sites were cut for 'sedge' (Great Fen Sedge was used for thatching) or 'litter' (hay). The cutting and removal of reed and sedge, combined with infertile ground water, slow the development of scrub and keep the vegetation relatively sparse and open. 4. Most of the sites in the Broads are on abandoned turbaries where peat was cut as fuel in past times. These cut-over areas then flooded, and gradually the resultant 'turf ponds' were colonised by vegetation to form semi-floating mats or 'hovers'. These mats are able to rise and fall with changing water levels, and this may be important in keeping the Fen Orchids at roughly the same level relative to the water table. (As more peat accumulates, however, and despite continued cutting or grazing, the vegetation inevitably changes, and Fen Orchid will eventually disappear.)

In South Wales (and formerly north Devon) Fen Orchid is found in dune slacks, growing with Creeping Willow, Marsh Pennywort and a variety of mosses. As in the Norfolk Broads, the species has very specific habitat requirements: 1. The slacks must be calcareous; calcium is provided by fragments of seashells in the sand. 2. The slacks must be moist (although they may be flooded in the winter, sometimes for as long as five months, the water table can fall to more than 50cm below ground level in August and September). 3. The slacks must be young.

Fen Orchid can colonise newly formed slacks very quickly, within a few years of the slack developing from bare sand. Indeed, establishment from seed seems to be most successful in these young slacks, perhaps because some bare ground remains, and completely new populations of Fen Orchid are only found in such new slacks. As the vegetation becomes more established, however, it is less able to compete; fewer new plants appear and eventually there are no new recruits to the population. Fen orchid will usually die out in a slack about 50 years after its formation.

Flowering period

In south Wales, early June to late July, exceptionally as late as mid-September. In Norfolk, early or mid-June to early July, with a few appearing later, to late July. In dry seasons few plants flower, whereas flowering tends to be retarded in wet years if surface water lingers. The individual flowers are rather short-lived.

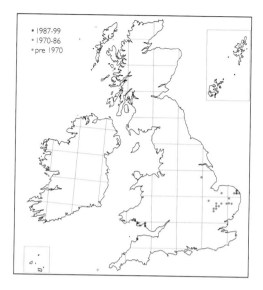

Key:
• 1987-99
• 1970-86
• pre 1970

Non-flowering plants, which may be much more numerous, are exceedingly hard to spot. Visitors are asked to keep way from the Norfolk sites but are welcome at Kenfig in Glamorganshire. Detailed and up-to-date directions are required to find Fen Orchid at this site, and it is best to contact the visitor centre in advance.

DESCRIPTION

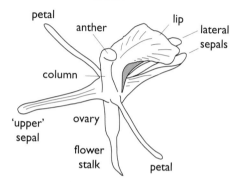

Height: 3-18cm, exceptionally to 30cm.
Stem: Green and three-angled, becoming almost winged towards the tip. The base of the stem is enlarged and this elliptical, green, shiny swelling is enveloped by the bases of the leaves to form a pseudobulb, the top of which is sometimes visible.
Leaves: Two or very occasionally three, strap-shaped, tapering both towards the base and the pointed tip. They are held erect and nearly opposite each other. The leaves are pale green, shiny and prominently keeled. Immature, non-flowering plants, with just one leaf, are common.
Spike: Up to 12 flowers form a loose spike, but there are usually rather fewer, sometimes just one, although as many as 17 have been recorded.
Bract: Green, minute, lanceolate.
Ovary: Green, narrow and tubular, six-ribbed, straight or slightly twisted at the base; the flower stalk is around half the length of the ovary, three-angled and twisted.
Flower: The flowers are entirely greenish-yellow and face upwards so that all the petals and sepals lie more-or-less horizontally and the ovary and column point upwards. The sepals

Range
Much reduced in Britain and now found at only three sites in the Norfolk Broads and at three sites in South Wales, in Glamorganshire and Carmarthenshire, but only in significant numbers at Kenfig. **World range:** Temperate Europe, Asia and North America. Found north to *c.* 61°N in southern Scandinavia, Finland and the Baltic States and south to northernmost Spain, southern France (including Corsica), northern Italy, Bosnia and Romania (and formerly also Bulgaria). In Asia the range extends eastwards to *c.* 80°E in central Siberia and also recorded in far eastern Siberia and southeast Kazakhstan. In North America widespread in the northeast, from Nova Scotia and New England to Saskatchewan and Minnesota, ranging south to North Carolina, Illinois and Iowa. There are also other scattered populations west to the Northwest Territories, British Columbia and Washington, and south to Alabama.

How to find it
This small, green orchid is hard to find. It often grows in fairly dense vegetation and even flowering plants can be very inconspicuous.

◀ 16 June, Norfolk. The whispy petals and upward-pointing column and lip result in a flower that does not resemble other orchids and is hard to make sense of.

are long and narrow (*c.* 5.5mm long x 1mm wide) with their edges rolled under, making them appear even narrower; the lateral sepals lie parallel below the lip and are often twisted. The petals are even finer (*c.* 4.5mm x 0.5mm) and are usually curved, both downwards in a gentle bow and forwards in the direction of the lip. The lip is tongue-shaped, rather broader than the sepals (*c.* 5mm x 2.5mm), with a wide longitudinal groove that is deepest towards the base, and has slightly wavy or frilly margins. It points upwards, parallel with the column, and then bends sharply over at right angles to lie in

▲ *29 June, Norfolk. A relatively few-flowered plant. The cause of the leaf-blotching is unknown.*

a horizontal plane. The column is pale green, relatively large and prominent, slightly curved towards the lip (like an erect cobra), with the anther cap sitting on top and pointing forwards. There is a minute rostellum and two waxy, yellow pollinia, each of which is divided into two flat plates and attached to one of the two viscidia.

Subspecies

L. l. loeselii is found in Norfolk and has up to 12 flowers and pointed, relatively narrow leaves which are at least four times as long as broad. It is widespread in Europe, where it may also be found in dunes.

L. l. ovata occurs in South Wales and formerly also in north Devon. On average it is shorter and has fewer flowers (usually up to six, rarely as many as ten). The leaves are rather more broadly elliptical or egg-shaped, blunter and more hooded at the tip and held more consistently erect. It also occurs in Brittany and in the early 1900s was present in the Dutch and German Waddenzee.

There has occasionally been speculation that the two subspecies should be treated as distinct species, but recent genetic analysis has shown virtually no difference between them.

Variation and varieties

None. (Subspecies *ovata* is sometimes treated as var. *ovata*.)

BIOLOGY

Pollination and reproduction

The Fen Orchid is probably routinely self-pollinating, the process being assisted by rain. Raindrops hit the anther cap, which lies on top of the column like a tiny 'lid'. This in turn knocks the pollinia towards the stigma. The upturned lip may function to deflect raindrops towards the anther. The prolific numbers of seedlings recorded suggest that seed is the major means of reproduction; in South Wales up to 128 shoots have appeared in a 0.25m² plot.

Vegetative reproduction also occurs but its importance relative to seed is unknown.

▲ 16 June, Norfolk. The flowers are self-pollinated and the lip is thought to deflect raindrops onto the column to knock-out the pollinia.

'Buds' (detachable propagules) are formed on the swollen stem of the pseudobulb, and these are dispersed in the autumn, already carrying a fungal 'infection'.

Development and growth

The aerial stem grows from a pseudobulb, the swollen tip of the rhizome which acts as a storage organ and is surrounded by the leaf sheaths. Each summer, the rhizome continues its growth from a bud at the base of the existing pseudobulb, and this new section swells in turn as it stores nutrients. Normally, only the two youngest sections of the rhizome, representing the last two year's growth, are alive at any one time, and so there are two pseudobulbs lying side-by-side.

► 16 June, Norfolk. Flowers from above, showing the thread-like petals, which, together with the sepals and lip, form a cross shape.

Fen Orchid remains partially dependent on fungi as an adult plant, fungal 'infection' being concentrated in the rhizome; the pseudobulb is always fungus-free. A few short, thick, hairy roots, largely free of fungi, develop in the spring from the base of the pseudobulb.

Seed germinates in the autumn and the protocorm produces the first green leaf by the following August. The first small pseudobulb develops in the autumn of that year and the protocorm starts to wither away. No roots are developed in this first year and all the plant's requirements for water must be met by its minute root hairs or by its fungal 'partner'. In the summer of the second year both roots and small leaves develop and a new pseudobulb is formed. Fen Orchid can flower in the fourth year after germination (perhaps as early as the second year), and plants reach their maximum size from the seventh year onwards. However, there is a high mortality among immature plants, and the vast majority disappear before they can flower. But, once mature, most flowering individuals reappear the next season, and they may flower for several years in succession; the average lifespan of mature Fen Orchids is ten years. Occasionally, plants may remain underground for one year, very rarely two, although it is hard to be sure in such cases that the leaves have not appeared and been rapidly grazed off.

Hybrids
None.

Name and classification
The specific name *loeselii* celebrates Johann Loesel (1607-1657), a Prussian professor of medicine and a botanist.

HISTORY AND CONSERVATION
The first British record was published in 1660, when John Ray found it 'in the watery places of Hinton & Teversham Moors' in Cambridgeshire (*Catalogus Plantarum circa Cantabrigiam nascentium*; 'Catalogue of plants found around Cambridge').

A *Red Data Book* species, it is considered Endangered and included in Schedule 8 of the Wildlife & Countryside Act 1981. It has always been scarce and localised in Britain but was formerly known from 34-36 sites in eastern England, one in Devon and a further nine in South Wales. Fen Orchid is now reduced to three sites in the Norfolk Broads where the overall population is stable: two in the Ant Valley, one holding a few hundred plants, the other about a thousand, and a much smaller colony in the Bure Valley, typically with about 10 plants but up to 40 can appear in a very good year. There are also three sites in South

◀ 16 June, Norfolk. The flower in profile, showing the erect column and horizontal lip.

Wales where the population totalled over 10,000 plants until recently but has declined to an unknown extent.

In Norfolk, always the stronghold of the species, in addition to the three surviving localities, there were formerly eight more sites in the Broads, with a further eight colonies scattered elsewhere in the county, especially the Waveney-Ouse Valley on the Norfolk-Suffolk border. In Suffolk there were four or five sites but the species was last recorded in 1974 at Thelnetham. In Cambridgeshire there were eight sites, six of which were drained long ago, but Chippenham Fen and Wicken Fen remain intact, although Fen Orchid was last recorded at these sites in 1928 and 1945 respectively. In Huntingdonshire there were two sites, the last record coming from Whittlesea Mere in 1849, but this too was subsequently drained. Elsewhere in eastern England, Fen Orchid was recorded from Ham Fen in Kent in 1802 and was reported in 1884 near Lincoln.

Early losses in East Anglia were largely due to the drainage of the fens and their conversion to agriculture. Although drainage and water abstraction continued to cause extinctions, most of the more recent losses have been caused by the decline of peat and turf-cutting, reed and sedge harvesting and grazing, all traditional land uses. Even in areas protected as reserves

(indeed, probably especially in 'protected' areas such as Wicken Fen) this resulted in the development of rank vegetation, scrub and in some cases the eventual transformation of the fen into wet carr woodland. Thus, although quite a few of the old sites still exist as 'fens', changes in the vegetation have rendered them totally unsuitable for Fen Orchid. Collecting also took its toll, as demonstrated by this account of a club outing to Burwell Fen, Cambridgeshire, in 1835: 'We had very good sport both in plants and insects. *Ophrys loeselii* was found in great plenty. Between four hundred and five hundred specimens were brought home. It was growing in the grass and moss among the pits where they cut turf. There were two bulbs to each plant, and the bulbs were scarcely in the ground at all, so that we picked them out easily with our fingers' (quoted in Marren 1999). As with most orchids, however, such wanton destruction was a minor factor in its decline compared with changes in its habitat.

In South Wales, Fen Orchid was first recorded in 1897 from dunes at Pembrey in Carmarthenshire and was eventually found at a further eight 'Burrows' (Kenfig, Margam, Baglan, Crymlyn, Oxwich, Whiteford, Tywn and Pendine/Laugharne). It was still present in seven dune systems in the early 1970s but by 2001 was reduced to just three: Kenfig, which still holds a substantial population and, although there has been some decline, concerted management efforts have stabilised numbers; Whiteford, where it is on the point of extinction, with just two plants in 2004; and Pendine/Laugherne, where 76 plants were counted in 1997 but just one was found in 2000. The other sites have either been buried by sand, dried out, become overgrown or have been reclaimed for heavy industry.

The dune slack subspecies *ovata* was also found at Braunton Burrows in north Devon in 1966, when two flowering spikes were found in a slack that had been virtually bare of vegetation in 1953. Fen Orchid was last seen there in 1987.

Fen Orchid has declined in South Wales as the habitat has become unsuitable. Over-stabilisation of the dunes has meant that few new slacks have been formed and a lack of grazing, exacerbated by a decline in the rabbit population due to myxomatosis, has hastened the ageing process in the existing slacks. At Kenfig there was a large amount of mobile sand after World War Two and many new slacks were formed. It is this era of slack formation which has provided the current supply of suitable habitat: in 1946 40% of the area was bare sand but this had declined to 2% by 1992 and inevitably there will soon be a sharp decline in suitable habitat as the existing slacks mature and are not replaced.

In both Norfolk and South Wales the problems of Fen Orchid conservation are similar and so are the solutions. Fen Orchid is a 'weedy' species adapted to grow in dynamic, changing environments. It is able to colonise wet, calcareous habitats with plenty of bare ground and multiply quickly but is eventually crowded out as the vegetation matures. There is a high rate of turnover of individual plants, with considerable ups and downs in overall numbers. Many plants are short-lived but large numbers of seedlings can be produced, and to maintain a population conditions need to be right for seedlings to become established.

A variety of conservation measures are being employed, such as reed and sedge harvesting in the Broads and scrub removal, grazing, close mowing and turf stripping in South Wales. These should provide the plants, both adults and seedlings, with the appropriate niche. Many of these techniques are only possible on a relatively small scale, however, and are interim measures which will slow but not stop the inevitable succession to unsuitable habitats. The only real hope for the Fen Orchid's long-term survival is more radical action: digging peat from the Norfolk Broads to create fresh turf ponds; and the destabilisation of the dunes in South Wales to create a succession of young slacks. If the right conditions were available, reintroduction also becomes an option. There have been small-scale experimental trials at sites in Norfolk and Suffolk but so far no full programme has been attempted.

Past and present occurrence of Fen Orchid in Britain and Ireland (based on presence or absence in 10km squares of the National Grid; data from the New Atlas*).*

	Britain	Ireland
total historical range, 1500-1999	26	0
current range	7 (0.25%*)	0
% lost, 1500-1969	61.5%	
% lost, 1970-1986	1.5%	
% lost, total	63%	

* current range as a % of the total number of 10km squares

▶ *13 July, New Forest. Bog Orchids often grow from tiny bulbils which develop on the edge of the leaf and can thus form small groups.*

GENUS
HAMMARBYA
BOG ORCHID

Distribution
Bog Orchid is the only member of this genus, which has a circumpolar distribution in Europe, Asia and North America.

Name
The generic name *Hammarbya* has an auspicious history. In the mid-18th century the great Swedish naturalist Linnaeus gave Bog Orchid the name '*Ophrys paludosa*'. As the relationships between the various orchids came to be better understood, Bog Orchid was moved from *Ophrys* to its own genus by Otto Kuntze in 1891. He named the new genus '*Hammarbya*' in honour of Hammarby, Linnaeus's summer residence near Stockholm.

BOG ORCHID
Hammarbya paludosa

Formerly: *Malaxis paludosa*. Other names: Bog Adder's-mouth (North America)
This tiny green orchid is the exact opposite of the classic big, bright and blousy hothouse hybrid. Indeed, it is the smallest orchid in the British Isles and one of the hardest to find. But, despite its rather dull flowers and diminutive stature (or perhaps because of these), it holds a particular fascination for botanists and is always a delight to see. It is still fairly common, at least locally, in northwest Scotland but has declined markedly in the lowlands and in England is now only frequent in the New Forest.

Identification
The small size, tiny green flowers and habitat make this orchid distinctive – when and if you can find it.

Similar species
Of the plants found in its boggy habitat, Marsh Arrowgrass is closest in general appearance but has very different flowers.

Habitat
As its name suggests, this species is found in bogs. It is associated with a good cover of *Sphagnum* (bog-mosses) and grows alongside sundews, butterworts, cottongrasses, White Beak-sedge and Cross-leaved Heath. Importantly, it requires a bog which has a flow of water through the peat, and it does not like stagnant conditions; as well as streams and runnels, the slow flow of water may even be evident on the surface of the peat. Bog Orchid is often found in the vicinity of such moving water and also close to the shores of lakes and lochs. The ground water is usually moderately acidic but in parts of Wales the species is also recorded from areas flushed with alkaline water. Another essential requirement is that the bog must not dry out, even in a hot summer. Bog Orchids often grow on carpets of *Sphagnum* but can also be found on bare peaty mud or in denser vegetation amidst sedges, grasses and

◀ *13 July, New Forest. The flower spike continues to grow as the flowers open and becomes significantly taller. This plant was 12cm high.*

small shrubs. Generally found in the lowlands but it has been recorded up to 500m above sea level (Llyn Anafon, Caernarvonshire).

Flowering period

Late June to mid or even late September but perhaps most reliably from early July to mid-August. It tends to flower early in a hot summer and later in a cool, wet season. Numbers are erratic, with wide variations between years. Flowering at any one site is not necessarily synchronised, however, and the flowers themselves are long-lasting, and thus larger colonies may have at least some plants in bloom over a lengthy period.

Range

Bog Orchid is widespread in Scotland. There are a few sites in the southwest, in Dumfriesshire and Kircudbrightshire, and in the eastern Highlands in Angus and south Aberdeenshire. The majority are, however, in the northwest where it is found north to Sutherland and extends to the Inner and Outer Hebrides and to Yell in Shetland. In Ireland, Bog Orchid is

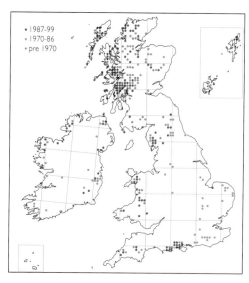

• 1987-99
• 1970-86
• pre 1970

known from relatively few, scattered localities; in the west in Co. Clare and from Co. Mayo to Co. Donegal; in the east in Co. Carlow, Co. Kilkenny, Co. Wicklow and Co. Dublin, and in Northern Ireland in Co. Armagh, Co. Down and Co. Antrim. In Wales it is also recorded at just a few, scattered sites, mostly in the west, from Breconshire, Carmarthenshire

▲ *29 June, New Forest. Although often hard to find, Bog Orchids can be conspicuous at times, contrasting as here with a carpet of russet Sphagnum.*

and Pembrokeshire north and west to Caernarvonshire, but often there are just one or two sites in each county. In England the species is now very local, occurring in Cumbria, at a handful of sites in northwest Yorkshire and Northumberland and at one site in Norfolk. In southern England it is known from a very few localities in Cornwall and Devon (including Dartmoor, although it is very rare there) but occurs much more commonly in the Purbeck region of Dorset and especially in the New Forest in Hampshire. **World range:** In Europe it occurs north to the Faeroe Islands and to *c.* 69°N in Scandinavia, and south in the mountains to France, the Italian Alps, the former Yugoslavia and Romania. In Asia there are scattered records from across southern Siberia to Sakhalin and Japan. In North America it occurs from Alaska eastwards to western Ontario and south to Minnesota.

How to find it

This tiny green plant is one of the hardest British orchids to find. It is so inconspicuous that it is easy to tread on it unawares, and the pseudobulbs, often only half-buried in the moss, can easily be dislodged. All in all, it is best not to look for it until you are an experienced orchid hunter.

Faced with a large area of apparently suitable habitat, the task of searching for Bog Orchid may be daunting. It is best, however, to concentrate on the most suitable areas. These are likely to be along the edges of streams and runnels or where there is some obvious movement of surface water and away from dense stands of shrubs such as Cross-leaved Heath and Bog Myrtle. Like all our smaller orchids, Bog Orchid is difficult to see from a walking height and becomes much more obvious when viewed from a low vantage point. On open, flat *Sphagnum* carpets or 'lawns' it can then be fairly conspicuous, but plants may grow among grasses and sedges and these are extremely difficult to see; dense hummocks of

◀ *29 June, New Forest. Growing as usual on a carpet of* Sphagnum, *minute bulbils are starting to appear on the margins of the leaves.*

Sphagnum are not favoured but the orchids can be found around their edges, especially if they are close to water.

Once a Bog Orchid has been seen, before diving in for a closer look, it is wise to make a very careful inspection of its immediate surroundings. This species often grows in scattered groups, and one or two relatively obvious plants may be accompanied by several others hidden in the vegetation at one's feet.

DESCRIPTION

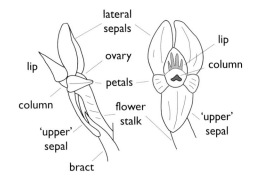

Height: 2-15cm but usually 4-8cm.
Stem: Yellowish-green and three to five angled. The stem grows from a pea-sized pseudobulb which is covered by the leaves and often only half-buried in the moss.
Leaves: There are two or three (occasionally four) oval to oblong, fleshy, pale-green or yellowish-green basal leaves. They are prominently veined, sheathe the pseudobulb at their base, and their margins and tips are strongly curved inwards giving them a hooded appearance. One to three minute, triangular, scale-like leaves are scattered higher along the stem.
Spike: Up to 25 flowers are carried in a spike which is dense at first but elongates and becomes much more open as it matures.
Bract: Green, narrow and pointed, about as long as the ovary.
Ovary: Green, ovoid and just a little fatter than the flower stalk, which is about three times its length and twisted through 360° (therefore the lip is held uppermost and the flower is hyper-resupinate).

▲ *7 July, Norfolk. The lip is uppermost (the flower stalk is twisted through 360°), and the lateral sepals wrap around the back of the flower.*

Flower: Greenish and tiny, about 2mm wide by 4mm tall. The sepals are yellowish-green and tongue-shaped; the dorsal sepal points downwards and is slightly longer than the lateral sepals, which point upwards. The petals are rather smaller and narrower, strap-shaped and green. They are held spreading horizontally but curve sharply back around the sepals to clasp the flower. The lip is dark green with paler green longitudinal stripes and is rather shorter than the petals, triangular and curled upwards at the sides. It is held erect, pointing upwards and forwards between the two lateral sepals and clasping the column at its base. There is no spur, and the very short, broad, green column projects horizontally from the centre of the flower, with the lid-like anther shrivelling to expose the pollinia shortly after the flower opens. The two pollinia are each made up of two thin plates of waxy pollen, and the minute rostellum is topped by a small, sticky mass. The flowers are said to have a sweet, cucumber-like scent.

Subspecies
None.

Variation and varieties
None.

BIOLOGY

Pollination and reproduction

The flowers are probably pollinated by gnats and tiny flies, attracted to the nectar at the base of the lip, and the pollinia are usually removed. Seed-set is good. Perhaps more importantly in terms of reproduction, the leaves are often fringed with numerous, minute, protocorm-like buds, called bulbils. These drop off and can develop into new plants if they are 'infected' from the soil by fungi of the right species (unlike the propagules of Fen Orchid, they do not carry fungi from the mother plant). This may account for the frequency with which Bog Orchid is found in small groups.

Development and growth

The rhizome lies almost vertically in the peat or *Sphagnum*, and a swelling is formed each year at its tip. In the spring leaves develop around the base of this swelling and the flower spike grows from a bud on the top; the swollen stem and leaf sheaths combine to form a pseudobulb 4-8mm in diameter. After it has flowered the aerial stem dies off, but the rhizome continues to grow from a bud at the base of the pseudobulb and at the end of the growing season again terminates in a swollen internode. Although in theory a whole string of pseudobulbs could be produced (as seen in many epiphytic orchids), in practice only the two most recent are alive; the older, lower, pseudobulb is buried in the moss and surrounded by the remains of the previous year's leaves. Unusually, the rhizome of Bog Orchid grows vertically with the two pseudobulbs one above the other. This vertical growth pattern presumably allows the orchid to adjust to the changing level of the bog's surface due to, for example, the growth of *Sphagnum*.

There are no roots, merely root hairs, and Bog Orchid is largely dependent on fungi throughout its life cycle; the rhizome and leaf bases are 'infected' at all times. The pseudobulb, which acts primarily as a storage organ, is separated from the older parts of the rhizome

▲ 13 July, New Forest. The lip, which is much smaller than the sepals, is boldly striped with pale and dark green.

The specific name *paludosa* means 'growing in boggy ground'.

Bog Orchid is sometimes placed in *Malaxis*, a genus of rather similar orchids. It is also closely related to Fen Orchid and could easily be united with it in the genus *Liparis*, but the current evidence is that it is sufficiently distinct to justify its continued separation in its own genus, *Hammarbya*.

HISTORY AND CONSERVATION

The first British records, from Hertfordshire and Kent, were published in John Parkinson's *Theatrum Botanicum* ('Botanical exhibition') of 1640: 'Bifolium palustre.... In the low wet grounds between Hatfield and S. Albones; in divers places of Romney Marsh'.

Nationally Scarce in Britain and specially protected in Northern Ireland under the 1985 Wildlife Order (NI) and in Eire under the Flora (Protection) Order. Bog Orchid is threatened and declining throughout its European range due to loss of habitat, and some of the largest populations are now found in western Scotland and the New Forest.

Past and present occurrence of Bog Orchid in Britain and Ireland (based on presence or absence in 10km squares of the National Grid; data from the New Atlas).

	Britain	Ireland
total historical range, 1500-1999	302	44
current range	118 (4%*)	15 (1.5%*)
% lost, 1500-1969	47%	59%
% lost, 1970-1986	14%	7%
% lost, total	61%	66%

* current range as a % of the total number of 10km squares

Systematic searches have produced records from many new localities in recent years but, despite this, Bog Orchid has vanished from 61% of its historical range in Britain and 66% in Ireland. It is now extinct in most of England, including Kent, East and West Sussex (where it was formerly found in several areas,

by a band of lignified tissue. This effectively cuts off one year's growth from the next and prevents fungi from reaching the pseudobulb and its store of nutrients. An internal root is produced at the base of the new segment of the rhizome, and this grows down through the lignified barrier into the older segment, apparently reabsorbing nutrients and water from the decaying tissue and, bypassing the pseudobulb, carrying the fungal 'infection' into the new segment.

Life expectancy and the period between germination and flowering are unknown.

Hybrids
None.

Name and classification

◀ 29 June, New Forest. As in Fen Orchid, the aerial stem grows from a pseudo-bulb, a swelling in the stem concealed by the base of the leaves; a second, non-flowering plant is growing alongside.

especially Ashdown Forest, but was last seen in 1956), Surrey, Hertfordshire, Bedfordshire, Cambridgeshire, Suffolk, Lincolnshire, Staffordshire, Cheshire, Lancashire and Co. Durham. The dramatic decline in lowland Britain started with the Enclosure Acts of the late 18th and early 19th centuries and the consequent reclamation of bogs and wet heaths. Habitat destruction has continued to the present day, and in the lowlands the remaining areas of mire and heath have also suffered from a lack of grazing, necessary to maintain the open sward that the Bog Orchid requires. Conversely, in the uplands, overgrazing may have caused suitable habitats to be degraded.

Many of the remaining colonies are small, with just a few plants. Even in its strongholds Bog Orchid is uncommon to rare; in Cumbria there are around ten sites, with just two populations regularly exceeding 100 spikes. In the New Forest there are around 30 populations, with over 200 spikes appearing in good seasons at two or three of the largest, and in Dorset there are nine recorded sites. In Norfolk, which holds the only remaining population in eastern England, there is now just one site, and in recent years there have been only one to four flowering plants in an area where 117 were counted in 1910; to add insult to injury all the flowering plants were stolen in 2000.

Distribution
A genus of 11 species, exclusively found in North and Central America with the exception of Coralroot Orchid *C. trifida*, which extends to the boreal zone in Europe and Asia. All *Corallorhiza* are largely or totally dependent on fungi as a source of nutrition throughout their life.

Name
The generic name *Corallorhiza* derives from the Greek *korallion* 'coral' and *rhiza* 'root', thus 'coralroot'; there are no roots, however, only a rhizome, and this does not resemble coral in all species.

GENUS *CORALLORHIZA*
CORALROOT ORCHIDS

CORALROOT ORCHID
Corallorhiza trifida

Other names: Early Coralroot (North America)
This tiny orchid lacks green leaves and throughout its life is largely parasitic on its fungal 'partner', living entirely underground apart from the brief period during which the flower spikes are produced. It is found throughout the Northern Hemisphere, and its generally northerly distribution is reflected in Britain where it is confined to Scotland and northern England. Both the English name and the generic name *Corallorhiza* refer to the shape of the underground rhizome, which is said to be coral-like. Coralroot Orchid is the county flower of Fife.

Identification
With no leaves (merely scale-like sheaths on the stem) and tiny greenish-white flowers, this species is very distinctive.

Similar species
None. Bird's-nest and Ghost Orchids also lack green leaves but are very different. Bird's-nest Orchid is usually taller and always more robust, with large, honey-coloured flowers, and Ghost Orchid has a proportionally much larger flower with the lip uppermost and is only found, very, very rarely, in southern England.

Habitat
Coralroot Orchid is found on permanently damp ground with a good layer of peaty organic matter or moss, including *Sphagnum*. It can grow both in full sunlight and in the shade, even heavy shade, and favours mildly acidic soils which are low in nutrients. It is commonest in wet willow and alder carr growing on raised bogs and around lochs. Its other favoured habitat is a damp dune slack with a carpet of Creeping Willow but Coralroot Orchid appears to have rather exacting requirements regarding the level of the water table and does not like prolonged flooding (for example, on

▶ *7 June, Northumberland. Among Creeping Willows in a dune slack; Coralroot Orchid extracts nutrients from the willow, via its fungal 'partner'.*

◀ *7 June, Northumberland. In dune slacks Coralroot Orchid usually has a stout, mahogany-brown stem. Like all orchids growing in dunes, it often has a 'scorched' look, in this case with the tips of the sepals blackened.*

Lindisfarne in Northumberland a slack that regularly held 150 flower spikes now supports only 20 after several wet years). Rather less frequently, Coralroot Orchid is found in birch and pine woodland, including plantations, and in overgrown scrubby fens with a mixture of *Sphagnum*, sedges and willows. It is found up to 365m above sea level (Braemar, Aberdeenshire).

Coralroot Orchid is parasitic on a group of fungi that form mycorrhizal relationships with birches and willows (also pines in North America and presumably also in Scotland). The presence of both the correct fungal 'partner' and one of these trees is essential and may explain the very local occurrence of Coralroot Orchid.

Flowering period
May to August. In dune slacks it flowers in May and early June, increasingly in recent years from early May onwards, and emerging earlier in drier slacks compared to wetter ones. Woodland plants are mostly in bloom from early June to late July.

Range
Widespread in eastern and central Scotland, from the Borders north to Caithness. However, it is absent from the west, apart from Ayrshire and Renfrewshire. In England it is very local, occurring in Northumberland and in Cumbria, where it is found in dune slacks at Eskmeals, North Walney and Sandscale. The

▲ *6 June, Cumbria.*

southernmost records come from Ribblesdale in Yorkshire. **World range:** This species has a circumpolar distribution, occurring very widely in northern Europe, Asia and North America, ranging southwards locally where mountains provide a suitable habitat. It occurs north to Greenland, Iceland and northernmost Scandinavia and south to the Pyrenees, Massif Central, Alps, Apennines and Balkans, also Corsica, the Crimea and Caucasus. In Asia, primarily boreal but with isolated outposts in the mountains of Central Asia and China. In North America occurs from Newfoundland east to Alaska and south in the mountains to California, New Mexico and West Virginia.

How to find it
Small and leafless, this is an inconspicuous orchid and very hard to spot. The number of flowering spikes can also vary greatly from season to season. As with all such diminutive orchids, scanning from a low level can be productive. Dune slack populations are the easiest to localise, with one of the biggest at Sandscale in Cumbria.

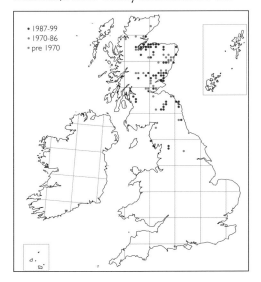

• 1987-99
• 1970-86
• pre 1970

▲ *In woodland Coralroot Orchid has a green stem and ovaries and is relatively slender (Paul Sterry/Nature Photographers Ltd).*

DESCRIPTION

Height: 5-30cm, usually 10-13cm.

Stem: Usually yellowish-green in woodland plants but tends to be mahogany-purple in dune populations. Frequently found in small groups and up to ten spikes may develop from one rhizome.

Leaves: There are no green leaves, merely two to four long, membranous, sheathing scales on the lower half of the stem, and these may be brown, whitish or green.

Spike: There are four to nine flowers (occasionally as many as 13) held pointing outwards and slightly drooping in an open, lax spike.

Bract: Green, minute, triangular and pointed.

Ovary: Green or mahogany-purple, spindle-shaped, six-ribbed, on an extremely short, twisted stalk.

Flower: The sepals and petals are strap-shaped, with the petals slightly smaller; both are greenish-yellow, often tinged reddish-brown around the fringes and tip and thus apparently 'browned off'. The interior of the petals may also be blotched with reddish-brown. The lateral sepals curve inwards and are held forward and slightly drooping on either side of the lip. The upper sepal and petals form a loose hood. The lip is tongue-shaped, shorter and broader than the petals and sepals, with a ruffled margin. A central groove, which may produce nectar, runs between two raised longitudinal ridges and there is a very short spur. The lip is kinked downwards towards the base and, although technically 'three-lobed', the tooth-like side-lobes near the base are very small. It is white, spotted with crimson at the base, and these spots may occasionally coalesce into a larger blotch. The column is long, green and curved, the lid-like anther lies on the top and there are four waxy yellow pollinia, a small rostellum and two distinct viscidia. The flowers are slightly scented, with the perfume reported to be 'musk-like'.

Subspecies

None.

Variation and varieties

Plants growing in dune slacks tend to be shorter than those in woodland, with reddish rather than greenish stem and ovaries, but there are no named varieties.

BIOLOGY

Pollination and reproduction

The flowers are routinely self-pollinated. The rostellum is small and degenerates quickly, and the pollinia crumble apart, falling onto the stigma below; 85-100% of flowers set seed. Small insects, including flies, wasps and beetles, visit the flowers, but the pollinia, although easily detached, do not readily stick to the insects and any cross-pollination is purely accidental; visiting insects are probably more effective in nudging fragments of the disintegrating pollinia onto the stigma below. Vegetative reproduction may also occur, via fragmentation of the rhizome, the side-branches elongating and producing new plants.

Development and growth

The aerial stems grow from a creeping, horizontal, underground rhizome. This is a much-branched mass of cream-coloured, fleshy, coral-like knobs. There are no roots and water must be absorbed either through tufts of root hairs or via the fungal 'partner'.

The rhizome is permanently 'infected' with fungi and, throughout its life, Coralroot Orchid is almost completely dependent on its fungal associate for nutrients. Like Bird's-nest Orchid, it is very fussy and only forms a relationship with the *Thelephora-Tomentella* complex of fungi (family Thelephoraceae). This group of fungi, apart from its relationship with orchids, is exclusively ectomycorrhizal, forming symbiotic relationships with the roots of trees (see p.8). The fungi that Coralroot Orchid 'partners' are species that simultaneously attach themselves to the roots of willows, birches and pines. It has been shown in the laboratory that the orchid obtains carbohydrates from the trees via their mutual fungal 'partner', but the orchid undoubtedly 'cheats' in its relationship with the

▲ *The tiny flowers are usually self-pollinated and most flowers set seed (Bob Gibbons/Natural Image).*

fungus-tree partnership, receiving nutrients but giving nothing in return. It is therefore parasitic. (Coralroot Orchid is not a saprophyte; it gets its nutrients from a living fungus, not dead organic matter.)

Coralroot Orchid does have a limited ability to photosynthesise as the stem, ovary and scale-like leaves on the stem contain chlorophyll. Even in diffuse daylight such photosynthesis can contribute in a small way to its overall nutritional budget.

Seed germinates from the spring onwards but may remain dormant until the spring of the second year, perhaps even longer. Germination will, however, only take place when the seeds have been colonised by the appropriate fungi. The seedling is initially a globular protocorm which develops scattered root hairs. It then elongates and starts to branch; each time the rhizome branches, the main rhizome bends in one direction and the side branch goes off in another, producing the 'coralloid' growth

▶ *6 June, Cumbria. The lip has a central groove that may produce nectar; this would attract insects but despite this the flowers are usually self-pollinated.*

pattern. After as little as nine months, some seedlings have developed into a branched rhizome 15-25mm long with the bud for the aerial shoot already well-developed. Flower spikes may be produced two to five years after germination but there is a little uncertainty about the exact timing. Some related species of *Corallorhiza* are monocarpic and die after flowering once.

Hybrids
None.

Name and classification
The specific name *trifida* comes from the Latin for 'split into three', a reference to the shape of the lip. This is barely appropriate, as the lip is only very slightly three-lobed.

HISTORY AND CONSERVATION
The first British record was published in 1777 by the Rev. John Lightfoot, curate of Uxbridge. In *Flora Scotica* he noted: 'Ophrys Corallorhiza… In a moist hanging wood near the head of Little Loch Broom on the western coast of Ross-shire'.

Nationally Scarce. This small, inconspicuous orchid is hard to find, and the true picture of its status and distribution is still emerging. Efforts have been made to seek it out in recent years (especially for the *New Atlas* scheme), and these

have turned up many new sites. But, despite these new records, there has been a net loss of 46% of the total historical distribution and many of the losses are relatively recent. Many of its habitats seem relatively secure, however, and importantly many are not affected by changes in agricultural practices. It is possible that climate change could be responsible as many 'northern' plants are currently in retreat.

Woodland populations are usually small, scattered and hard to find but in some dune slacks there can be large numbers; at Sandscale in Cumbria at least 3,000 plants were counted in five slacks in 1991, making it the largest English population.

Past and present occurrence of Coralroot Orchid in Britain and Ireland (based on presence or absence in 10km squares of the National Grid; data from the New Atlas*).*

	Britain	Ireland
total historical range, 1500-1999	102	0
current range	55 (1.9%*)	0
% lost, 1500-1969	17%	
% lost, 1970-1986	29%	
% lost, total	46%	

* current range as a % of the total number of 10km squares

GENUS *GOODYERA*
LADY'S-TRESSES (I)

Distribution
A genus of 40-100 species, nearly worldwide in
distribution although most are found in South-East
Asia. Some are called 'jewel orchids' and are known
for their beautiful foliage. Only two species occur
in Europe, the widespread Creeping Lady's-tresses
and G. *macrophylla*, endemic to Madeira.

Name
The genus *Goodyera* is named in honour of John
Goodyer (1592-1664), a manorial steward at
Petersfield, Hampshire, who has been dubbed the
'first amateur naturalist' and 'the Cavalier botanist'.

CREEPING LADY'S-TRESSES
Goodyera repens

Other names: Lesser Rattlesnake Orchid, Lesser Rattlesnake Plantain (North America)
This small, white-flowered orchid is almost always found growing under pine trees and is
locally common in Scotland, the home of the only native pine woodland in the British Isles.
A few colonies in old pine plantations in Norfolk represent an enigma. The lady's-tresses
could have been introduced accidentally with the pine seedlings, could be indigenous to the
area and have simply moved into a congenial new home, or could have arisen from wind-
blown seed.

Identification

The spikes of small, densely hairy, white flowers
are distinctive. Creeping Lady's-tresses is
evergreen and can be found and identified all
year. Indeed, it is often easier to locate in winter
when much of the other vegetation has died
down. It forms small patches of rosettes which
are composed of small, oval, dark-green leaves
rather like Garden Privet in size, shape and
colour. Notably, the veins on the leaves form
a faint net over the surface; almost all other
British orchids have veins that are parallel.

Similar species

The other species of lady's-tresses belong to
the genus *Spiranthes* but are nevertheless rather
similar. They have small white flowers which
have a covering of glandular hairs, although
none of them are as densely hairy as Creeping
Lady's-tresses. Their flower structure is similar
but the *Spiranthes* have the tip of the lip broadly
frilled or crimped, rather than being a simple
unadorned wedge shape.

Autumn Lady's-tresses is very unlikely
to be found in the same pinewood habitat as
Creeping Lady's-tresses (although it did occur
until 1979 in a grassy woodland ride within
a few metres of Creeping Lady's-tresses at a
remarkable site at Holt in Norfolk). Once the
possibility of confusion is acknowledged, the
two species can be separated easily because

▶ 11 July, Norfolk. Typically grows under pines, sometimes mixed with birch or, as here in Norfolk, oak.

◀ 10 July, Norfolk. Creeping Lady's-tresses.

Autumn Lady's-tresses has its flowers arranged into a distinct row that is often spirally twisted.

Irish and Summer Lady's-tresses grow from a rosette of long, strap-shaped leaves which have parallel veins, and are rather taller than Creeping Lady's-tresses; their flowers are also arranged into a more definite pattern.

Habitat

Creeping Lady's-tresses is found in mature pinewoods with a damp, well-shaded forest floor, growing in the deep humus formed by the accumulation of dead pine needles. It can be found in areas with a relatively open understorey of grasses and small shrubs, such as Heather and Bilberry, or in places where there is merely a carpet of moss over the needles (sometimes even bog mosses, *Sphagnum*), indicating a suitably moist microclimate. The classic habitat is ancient 'Caledonian' woodland where Scots Pine is mixed with birches. It has also spread into pine plantations that are

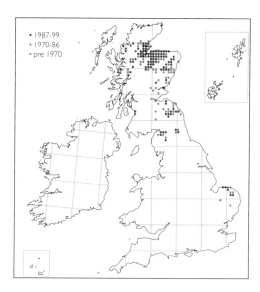

• 1987-99
• 1970-86
• pre 1970

sufficiently mature to have a shaded, moist open, forest floor. A balance of light conditions is required; too little light and the orchid will not flower, too much sun and a dense, overwhelming shrub layer develops. Rarely,

▲ 10 July, Norfolk. Growing in an old pine plantation on sand dunes.

Creeping Lady's-tresses is found on damp dunes or among Heather and Bell Heather on moorland, sometimes far from woodland (perhaps most often in coastal areas; for example on a 'peat moor' at Auckengill Loch in Caithness). Unlike most British orchids, Creeping Lady's-tresses is found on acid as well as neutral soils. Most sites are in the lowlands but it is found up to 335m above sea level (Morinsh, Banffshire).

Flowering period

Late June to late August but often at its best in mid-July. In dry weather the individual flowers are short-lived.

Range

Northern and eastern Scotland, with an isolated population in Ayrshire, also northern England in Cumbria, Northumberland and Co. Durham, with an outpost in Norfolk (see History and Conservation). **World range:** This species has a circumpolar distribution and occurs throughout Europe, northern Asia and northern North America. Found north to 70°N in Scandinavia and south to the Pyrenees, Corsica, Alps, northern Apennines in Italy, northern Greece, the Crimea and the Caucasus, although confined to the mountains in the south of the range. In Asia it ranges across Siberia to the Kamchatka Peninsula, Sakhalin and Japan and is also found in the mountains of southern Asia in Turkey, Central Asia, Afghanistan, the Himalayas and in a band from southwest China to Korea. In northern North America it occurs from Alaska east to Newfoundland and south in the Rocky Mountains to New Mexico and Arizona and in the Appalachians to North Carolina.

How to find it

Often abundant where it is found, any site in the 'Caledonian' pinewoods of Scotland could yield this species. In Norfolk the well-known population at Holt Country Park was largely destroyed by forestry operations in 2002 (but may recover in time), and the species is best looked for in the coastal pines at Wells-

Holkham, although the colonies there are scattered and hard to find.

DESCRIPTION

Height: 7-20cm, occasionally to 35cm.
Stem: Pale green and ridged, with dense glandular hairs towards the tip.
Leaves: The flower spikes grow from a rosette of three to nine dark-green (almost blue-green) leaves which have a network of faint paler veins (reticulations). The leaves are oval and taper to a pointed tip and the leaf-stalk is short but broad (winged). They are held more-or-less flat to the ground, although there may be one or

▲ 14 July, Norfolk. The stem, bracts and flowers have abundant glandular hairs.

two leaves at the base of the flower spike, and several very small, long and narrow sheathing leaves further up the stem. Sterile, non-flowering rosettes are also produced and the leaves are evergreen.

Spike: The 5-25 flowers are arranged spirally around the stem but mostly face in the same direction, and the spiral pattern is seldom obvious.

Bract: Green, with scattered glandular hairs towards the base. The bracts are lanceolate and slightly longer than the ovary, which they clasp.

Ovary: Green, narrowly pear-shaped, tapering towards the base, three-ribbed and with glandular hairs. The ovary is held upright but bends at the tip, so that the flowers lie either horizontally or are slightly drooped, and is either stalkless and slightly twisted or has a short stalk, in which case it is the stalk that is slightly twisted.

Flower: Small, creamy-white and densely hairy. The sepals are oval and concave, with the upper sepal a little narrower than the lateral sepals; they may have a faintly greener midrib and have many conspicuous long, glandular hairs on their outer surface. The petals are similar but slightly smaller and more spatulate. The upper sepal and petals form a tight hood and the lateral sepals are held drooped and slightly spreading with their tips bent outwards. The lip is white and is shorter than the sepals, oval in shape with a pointed tip; the basal hypochile is sometimes tinged pink and forms a deep, rounded, bag-shaped pouch that contains nectar. The epichile forms a narrow, blunt-tipped triangle, folded into a shallow groove and bent downwards towards the tip. The column is creamy and the rostellum is formed into short, curved horns which enclose the single, roughly circular viscidium. The anther cap is ochre with a reddish-brown margin and the two pollinia are yellowish. The flowers have a sweet scent.

Subspecies
None.

Variation and varieties
None.

BIOLOGY

Pollination and reproduction

The flowers are thought to be pollinated by bees which are attracted to the nectar at the base of the lip. Bumblebees of the genus *Bombus* are usually mentioned as pollinators and have certainly been seen carrying pollinia, but smaller bees of the genus *Lasioglossum* may be more important. The mechanism of pollination is thought to be very similar to that of Autumn Lady's-tresses and other orchids in the genus *Spiranthes*. The flower tube is initially only wide enough to allow an insect's proboscis to enter; this trips the mechanism and removes the pollinia. The lip then moves slowly downwards, allowing access to the stigma, which becomes sticky and receptive. Fragments of pollinia, picked up from other flowers and attached to a visiting insect's proboscis, can then effect pollination. The mechanism is effective and seed-set is good, with 77% of flowers setting seed in one Scottish study.

Vegetative reproduction may be more important than reproduction from seed. Buds are produced on the tip of the rhizome in the autumn, and these grow into slender runners which grow horizontally through the cushion of moss. At first these runners have merely a few short, sheathing scales, but eventually green leaves are produced from buds at or near their tip (a period of five years was given by Summerhayes (1968) for the production of green leaves but this seems excessively long). Once it has appeared above ground, the new rosette will live for between two and eight years before flowering and dying (and in Norfolk a period of at least six years has been recorded between the first appearance of rosettes and the production of flowers). Each runner can produce a separate plant; after flowering the central 'mother' plant dies off, leaving the surrounding rooted runners as separate entities. In this way large patches can form.

Development and growth

The aerial stem grows from a creeping rhizome which is often only shallowly buried and which

▲ 10 July, Norfolk. The flower structure is very similar to the Spiranthes *lady's-tresses*, but the lip forms a simple spout-shape rather than being crimped or frilled.

ground and assume an existence totally dependent on fungi.

Seeds probably germinate in spring, but the period between germination and the first appearance above ground is not known.

Hybrids
None.

Name and classification
The specific name *repens* derives from the Latin and means 'creeping'. The American name 'Lesser Rattlesnake Plantain' probably derives from it use, including a poultice of the chewed leaves, in the treatment of snakebites.

HISTORY AND CONSERVATION
The first published British record dates from 1777, when Rev. John Lightfoot (1735-1785), curate of Uxbridge, noted in his *Flora Scotica*: 'We found it … in an old shady hanging birch wood … about two miles from the head of Little Loch Broom … Ross-shire'. (The species had, however, been found a few years before by a Scotsman, James Robertson (*c*. 1745-1796), 'in a wood called Cregenon', but this was not published at the time.)

Nationally Scarce. It is common to locally abundant in northeast and north-central Scotland, especially in the relict 'Caledonian' pinewoods of the Strathspey and Cairngorm regions, but it is scarcer in the west of Scotland and northern England. Colonial, it may occur in large numbers, and we have counted 620 flower spikes in an area of only about 50m x 20m.

Although still locally common, there has been a significant reduction in the range, and it has now gone from 44% of its historical distribution. It is extinct in Dumfries-shire, West Lothian, Peebles-shire and Orkney (where recorded in the 1950s). There are also old records from southeast Yorkshire (1888, Houghton Hall Woods, near Market Weighton) and east Suffolk (1932-1935, Stuston Common, a site with no pine trees).

With its requirements for a certain minimum level of shade in order to thrive,

puts out a few short, thick, fleshy roots that have numerous hairs. Both rhizome and roots are heavily 'infected' with fungi, and the species is probably dependent on its fungal 'partner' to a significant extent throughout its life.

Creeping Lady's-tresses is the only British orchid which is evergreen (some other species, such as Autumn Lady's-tresses and Early Spider Orchid, bear leaves through the winter but are leafless and 'dormant' for at least part of the year). Unlike most other orchids, this species shows no tendency to disappear below

Past and present occurrence of Creeping Lady's-tresses in Britain and Ireland (based on presence or absence in 10km squares of the National Grid; data from the New Atlas*).*

	Britain	Ireland
total historical range, 1500-1999	186	0
current range	104 (3.6%*)	0
% lost, 1500-1969	29.5%	
% lost, 1970-1986	14.5%	
% lost, total	44%	

* current range as a % of the total number of 10km squares

Creeping Lady's-tresses is vulnerable to woodland management. Colonies can survive even if a wood is felled and replanted, but it takes many years for the number of flowering plants to recover in these circumstances and the woods must be replanted with pines; many sites have been lost when restocked with alien conifers such as spruce and fir. The extensive thinning of plantations can also have a very adverse effect, although perhaps not a permanent one.

The status of the species in Norfolk has been the subject of controversy since its discovery in 1885 at Westwick. Subsequent records came from Holt and adjacent localities from 1890, Beeston Regis from 1900, Sheringham from 1909, Cawston from 1910, Wells from 1952, Horsford from 1958, Holkham from 1962 and Cranwich from 1965.

Scots Pine is not native to Norfolk, but there are plantations of conifers dating from at least the 1830s. It has been widely assumed that Creeping Lady's-tresses was accidentally introduced with pine seedlings brought in from Scotland, but there is little evidence to support this. Investigations by W.H. Burrell in 1909 established that pines supplied by a selection of nurseries in Scotland came bare-rooted and thus free from 'weeds' and that Creeping Lady's-tresses was unknown as a 'weed' in these nurseries. The trees were, however, sometimes packed in dry Bracken, Heather and moss 'collected from the woods' and this packing could have been a source of seeds or plants.

An alternative theory is that Creeping Lady's-tresses was present in Norfolk before the advent of pine plantations and merely moved in when they became suitable. There is some support for this, in that it was found at Sheringham in 1909, concealed among Heather on open heathland, and similarly it was found on heathland at Beeston Regis in 1900. Alternatively, the Norfolk populations may originate from wind-blown seed, either from Scotland or the Continent. The timing of records is interesting, as Creeping Lady's-tresses were recorded for the first time from some of the plantations many years after they were established; pines were first planted at Wells and Holkham in the 1850s, largely with seedlings produced in a nursery at Holkham itself, but the lady's-tresses were not found until 1952.

At some sites there have been documented introductions by well-meaning naturalists, as at Horsford in Norfolk in 1955-58 (although there were probably already 'natural' populations there) and Warwick Moor Wood in Cumbria in 1931 (where the plantation was clear-felled in 1987). Other Cumbrian populations may well have been accidentally introduced with conifers when plantations were established.

Whatever their origin, the populations in Norfolk are extremely interesting from a scientific point of view, yet the controversy over their status has compromised their conservation. After showing keen and active concern in the 1950s and 1960s, the attitude of the Nature Conservancy and Nature Conservancy Council (predecessors of English Nature) to the largest and best-known population at Holt changed, and in 1986 its status as part of an SSSI was removed. As the *New Atlas* maps all the British populations as 'native', attitudes may now change.

GENUS *SPIRANTHES*
LADY'S-TRESSES (II)

These small orchids have distinctive small, tubular white flowers and swollen, tuber-like roots. Sadly, one member of the genus, Summer Lady's-tresses, is the only orchid that is extinct in Britain and Ireland.

Distribution

The genus contains 45-300 species (the taxonomy is very uncertain), found in Europe, Asia, Australia and South America, with the majority in North and Central America. Four species occur in Europe, with three in the British Isles.

Floral structures

The column is held horizontally within the tubular flower with the circular stigma on its underside, facing downwards. The rostellum is well-developed and deeply forked with the single torpedo-shaped viscidium held between the two prongs of the fork. There are two pollinia, each composed of two leaf-like plates, and both are attached to the viscidium. Once shed by the anther, the pollinia lie on top of the column with the viscidium below their tips, waiting to be removed by a visiting insect.

Growth pattern

The aerial stem grows from a very short rhizome which puts out two to six fleshy, tuberous roots. Unlike the tubers of *Orchis* and *Dactylorhiza*, the roots are heavily 'infected' with fungi. And, again unlike *Orchis* and *Dactylorhiza*, the plant does not spend a 'resting period' as a single tuber and the rhizome does not die off. New, swollen roots develop each year and these push the roots from the preceding season, which are shrunken and depleted, out towards a horizontal position; this may give the impression that there are two types of roots: vertical, fleshy roots and horizontal, fibrous roots.

The aerial stem dies off once seed has been set, but a bud develops on the side of the base of the stem and this will go on to form the new leaves and aerial stem.

Vegetative reproduction

Additional lateral buds may develop in the late summer or autumn at the base of the aerial stem. These can produce their own roots and leaves and may eventually become separate 'daughter' plants.

Name

The generic name *Spiranthes* means 'twisted flowers' and derives from the Greek *speira* meaning 'twisted' or 'coiled' and *anthos* meaning 'flower'. The English name probably refers to the flower spikes of Autumn Lady's-tresses, which look like plaited hair.

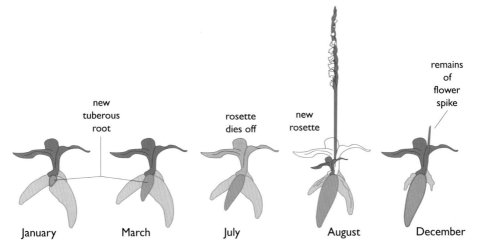

▲ Growth pattern of Autumn Lady's-tresses (after Wells 1981).

◀ 18 August, Norfolk. Autumn Lady's-tresses.

IRISH LADY'S-TRESSES
Spiranthes romanzoffiana

Other names: Hooded Ladies'-tresses (North America)
This delicate, white-flowered, late summer orchid has one of the most unusual distributions of any British plant, occurring in North America, Ireland, western Scotland and southwest England but nowhere else in Europe. It is also one of the hardest orchids to find, partly due to the remote location of the colonies and partly to the unpredictable nature of its flowering. The biology of this species is a mystery. It is fairly widespread, with many recorded sites, but very rarely sets seed in Britain and Ireland and has no obvious method of dispersal or of maintaining its numbers.

Identification
Distinctive, with long, grass-like leaves and a compact spike of small, white, tubular flowers, which are usually arranged into three spirally twisted rows. The upper stem, ovaries, bracts and sepals have numerous glandular hairs. These features, combined with its usual damp grassy habitat, restricted range and late flowering, are unique.

Similar species
Creeping Lady's-tresses is very occasionally found on moorland and also has glandular hairs on the flowers, but it is usually smaller, with a different flower structure and very different leaves.

Autumn Lady's-tresses also flowers in August and September but is much commoner, has a predominantly southerly distribution and is almost always found on short, dry, calcareous turf. Its flowers are arranged into an obvious single row.

Summer Lady's-tresses is now extinct in Britain. Like Irish Lady's-tresses, it has long, lanceolate leaves on the stem and is found in wet, acid grassland but the flowers, as well as being arranged into a single row, are significantly smaller; 6-8mm long rather than 10-14mm, with the bracts 6-9mm long rather than 10-20mm, sometimes even 30mm.

Other white-flowered orchids, such as Small White Orchid and some Heath and Common

◀ *7 August, Colonsay, Inner Hebrides* (Richard Gulliver).

Spotted Orchids, may be found in the same habitats and in the same geographical area but flower earlier in the season. They all lack glandular hairs on the upper stem and flowers and can also be excluded by looking at the details of the flower structure.

Habitat

Irish Lady's-tresses is frequently found in open grassy areas where the soil is low in nutrients and permanently damp or wet, either because it is flushed with ground water or, more usually, because it is close to a river, stream or lake and is flooded from time to time. It often grows close to the shore of a lough and has even been recorded flowering with the leaves submerged. At most sites the water and soil are mildly acidic to neutral but Irish Lady's-tresses is also sometimes recorded from more alkaline, base-rich flushes.

Suitable conditions are provided by damp meadows and rushy pastures, flushed grassy slopes, wet heathland, and bogs, where it may grow amongst *Sphagnum* on the disturbed ground around old peat workings. In the Hebrides it may particularly favour the band of marginal land (known locally as 'blackland') that is found at the transition between the lime-rich machair and the acid moorland inland. And, although often growing in damp habitats, it has also been found on heather moorland. 'Old lazy beds' is often given as a prime habitat for Irish Lady's-tresses (lazy beds are used to grow potatoes). Recent studies on Coll and Colonsay have, however, comparatively rarely found the species in this habitat.

Most of the sites in Britain and many in Ireland are subject to extensive grazing, which helps to keep the sward comparatively short and reduce competition from other vegetation. Disturbance by grazing animals may also stimulate dormant plants, and it can favour areas where cattle are fed in the winter or where the ground has been broken up by ditching or fencing. Generally found at low altitudes but recorded up to 240m above sea level in Ireland.

In North America the Irish Lady's-tresses is found in similarly damp habitats, such as bogs, marshes, wet meadows and stream-sides, but in California it is also found in coastal grasslands and pine forests that are baked dry in summer.

Flowering period

Early July to early September, depending on weather conditions and water levels, but mostly in late July and early August.

Range

In Ireland, it is very local in Eire but there are some good populations in the lakes area of western Co. Galway and Co. Mayo, especially around Loughs Corrib, Conn and Mask. Otherwise, it occurs at a few sites in the far southwest, in Co. Kerry and Co. Cork, and in the northwest, in Co. Donegal. In Northern Ireland the main concentration of populations lies in Co. Antrim, around Lough Neagh and the streams and rivers that flow into it. It is also present along the River Bann through Lough Beg and as far north as Coleraine in Co. Derry and around the southern shores of Lough Neagh in Co. Armagh. There are also some scattered sites elsewhere in Co. Antrim, including Gortnagory on the Garron Plateau, and it has recently been found at Aird on the north coast near the Giant's Causeway. There are also a very few sites in Co. Fermanagh, Co. Down and probably also still Co. Tyrone.

• 1987-99
• 1970-86
• pre 1970

▲ *3 August, Benbecula, Outer Hebrides (Richard Gulliver). The flowers are arranged into three rows, sometimes, as in this plant, very distinctly so.*

In Scotland the Irish Lady's-tresses is widespread but scattered on Coll and Colonsay in the Inner Hebrides and has been recorded from around 30 sites on each island. Other concentrations are found in the southern Outer Hebrides on Vatersay, Barra, South Uist and Benbecula. Otherwise it is rare but has been recorded from Islay, Mull and Tiree. On the mainland the species is found in three small areas of Inverness-shire close to its Hebridean strongholds: Moidart, Morvern and Ardnamurchan (where small numbers have been found around the western end of Loch Shiel). There are also old records from

Kintyre. In England it is known only from one site in Devon, to the east of Tavistock on the southwest fringe of Dartmoor. **World range:** Widespread in North America, where it extends from the Atlantic to the Aleutian Islands and south to California, New Mexico and Arizona in the west and to Illinois and Pennsylvania in the east.

Irish Lady's-tresses is found in North America and on the western fringe of Europe in the British Isles. This is an extreme example of a pattern of distribution known as 'amphi-Atlantic' and is shared by just a few other plants, including Blue-eyed Grass, Pipewort and American Pondweed. A variety of theories have been advanced to account for the distribution of Irish Lady's-tresses but the simplest and most likely is that it arrived in Britain and Ireland either via the long distance dispersal of wind-blown seed or by pieces of root and rhizome being carried across the Atlantic by birds.

How to find it

The grass-like leaves are very hard to see, making this species effectively invisible when not in flower, and many plants that would flower have their spikes grazed off. In addition, the number of plants flowering (or attempting to flower) varies from year to year and can be very low in dry summers. All in all, in any given year, only a minority of the known sites will actually contain plants in bloom. A visit to the Hebrides, Lough Corrib (Co. Galway) or Lough Mask and Lough Con (Co. Mayo) would, nevertheless, be worthwhile.

DESCRIPTION

Height: 10-35cm.

Stem: Yellowish-green with scattered glandular hairs towards the tip.

Leaves: There are three to five (sometimes up to eight) yellowish-green leaves. The lower are long, narrow and parallel-sided with a hooded tip and are held very erect. The upper leaves are short, pointed and loosely sheathe the stem. The margins of the leaves may be rolled inwards, making them even narrower and more grass-like, especially in Northern Ireland. The shoots appear in the autumn, around October, but the leaves may not expand until the spring; in North America this species is wintergreen.

Spike: Five to 40 flowers are arranged in three rows up the stem (rarely only two rows) and each row is variably twisted; this arrangement is most obvious on plants with numerous flowers.

Bract: Narrow and pointed, sheathing the ovary, with glandular hairs on its outer surface. The lower bracts are as long as the flowers, the upper bracts shorter.

Ovary: Cylindrical, three-ribbed, on a very short stalk and with a few glandular hairs. It is held vertically but bends at the tip so that the flowers lie horizontally.

Flower: White and tubular. The sepals and petals are creamy-white, washed green towards the base. The sepals are narrowly triangular and blunt-tipped, with glandular hairs on their outer surface and three greenish veins; the petals are narrower and more strap-shaped. The sepals and petals form a hood that encloses the column and the basal half of the lip, with the tips of the sepals distinctly turned outwards. The lip is creamy-white with fine green veining and is fiddle-shaped, with the 'waist' nearer the tip. The sides of the larger and broader basal portion are turned upwards to form a trough or gutter, with two small nectar-producing bosses at the extreme base. The smaller distal portion is tongue-shaped or square-ended, frilled and toothed along the edges and sharply bent downwards. The flowers have, at most, a faint scent (earlier reports of a strong vanilla-like scent are presumably errors).

Subspecies
None.

Variation and varieties
Plants in Northern Ireland are said to be on average taller and 'leggier' than those in southern Ireland. They have creamy rather than white flowers, a looser spike, narrower lip and leaves that are often in-rolled at the edges, giving them an especially grass-like appearance. Plants from Scotland and Devon

▲ 16 August, Colonsay, Inner Hebrides (Richard Gulliver). *The lip is frilled and spout-like as in all the* Spiranthes; *this plant has rather widely-spaced flowers.*

are intermediate. At one time Northern Irish plants were treated as the same species as in North America although separated as a distinct variety (*S. romanzoffiana* var. *stricta*) and the southern Irish plants were treated as a distinct, endemic, species (named 'S. gemmipara'). Examination of the variation across the entire range in North America showed, however, that in large populations plants resembling these extremes and a range of intermediates were present, and no subspecies or varieties are usefully recognised in the British Isles.

Recent genetic studies have shown that there is a split between a northern group

◀ 4 August, Benbecula, Outer Hebrides (Richard Gulliver). In a small minority of cases two plants grow together, presumably the product of vegetative reproduction. These are very few-flowered spikes.

of populations, from Coll and the Outer Hebrides, on the one hand, and a southern group, from Colonsay and Ireland, on the other. There has been little recent contact or gene flow between these two groups, but this division is not reflected in any known differences in appearance or ecology between the plants.

BIOLOGY

Pollination and reproduction

In North America, medium-sized, long-tongued bees pollinate Irish Lady's-tresses.

Similar bees have occasionally been seen visiting the flowers in Britain but plants have virtually never been found to set seed; there are no confirmed records of mature seed capsules from Scotland, despite careful searches, and just one or two observations from Ireland. However, recent studies have shown that the northern group of populations have a high level of genetic diversity, suggesting that they reproduce sexually and are cross-pollinated. If this is so, either seed is produced occasionally, perhaps in very favourable seasons, or cross-pollination has recently ceased, perhaps due to a decline in suitable pollinators.

The southern group of populations have very much lower levels of genetic diversity. There are four possible explanations for this: 1. Self-pollination (unlikely; as in many *Spiranthes* the flower structure functions to prevent this). 2. Apomixis, that is the production of seed without fertilisation taking place. This has been recorded in some of the other lady's-tresses in North America but, as noted, seed is very rarely found in the British Isles. 3. Reproduction is largely vegetative. 4. These populations went through a genetic bottleneck when they were reduced to a very small number of individuals. The most likely of these four explanations has yet to be determined but may have implications for the conservation of the species.

British and Irish populations can reproduce vegetatively through the development of an additional bud at the base of the stem (rarely two or very occasionally three extra buds). The presence of two buds allows two aerial stems to develop in the next growing season, and these may eventually separate to form two plants. Extra buds are produced by a small percentage of plants each year (less than 5% in the Hebrides), but it seems that many of these extra buds disappear for one reason or another and relatively few may develop into new aerial shoots; the incidence of 'twinned' orchids in a population, presumably the product of vegetative reproduction, varies from very low to over 25% of plants. Similarly, genetic studies do not indicate that groups of clones are at all common. It is also possible that new plants may develop from buds on the roots (as they do in some American *Spiranthes*), or that fragments of root, perhaps broken off by cattle or sheep, could develop into new plants, but these mechanisms have yet to be observed.

Irish Lady's-tresses is an enigma. Seed is apparently rarely produced. Vegetative reproduction is uncommon and does not account for long-distance dispersal. Yet, genetic evidence shows that at least some populations reproduce sexually, and there is an apparently high turnover of populations, with new colonies discovered as others disappear (but see below).

Development and growth

Poorly understood. The aerial stem grows from a cluster of two to six thick, fleshy, tuberous roots, more-or-less vertical in the soil and connected at the top by a very short rhizome. A lateral bud develops at the base of the aerial stem (or on the rhizome if the plant is 'dormant' underground) between July and October and overwinters, going on to form the leaves in the spring of the following year and, if the plant is to flower, the stem appears in early June. The species may become 'dormant' underground, with up to six year's absence recorded.

Little is known about the development from seed to flowering plant, but the species possibly spends five years growing underground before the first leaves appear.

Hybrids

None recorded in the British Isles.

Name and classification

The specific name *romanzoffiana* honours Nicholas Romanzof, a Russian minister of state. The species was discovered in Alaska around 1828 when it was still a Russian territory.

HISTORY AND CONSERVATION

Nationally Scarce in Britain and specially protected in Northern Ireland under Schedule 8 of the 1985 Wildlife Order (NI) and in Eire under the Flora (Protection) Order. It is the subject of a UK Biodiversity Action Plan and a priority for conservation because Britain and Ireland hold the only European populations.

The first Irish record was published in 1828 by Sir J.E. Smith in the *English Flora*: 'Near Castletown opposite to Bearhaven on the northern side of Bantry Bay, County of Cork, Mr Drummond…communicated to me in August, 1810'. Irish Lady's-tresses was first found in Northern Ireland in 1892, at Brackagh Bog near Lough Neagh, Co. Armagh, on an old dug-out peat bog.

Past and present occurrence of Irish Lady's-tresses in Britain and Ireland (based on presence or absence in 10km squares of the National Grid; data from the New Atlas).

	Britain	Ireland
total historical range, 1500-1999	21	44
current range	17 (0.6%*)	17 (1.7%*)
% lost, 1500-1969	5%	36%
% lost, 1970-1986	14%	25%
% lost, total	19%	61%

* current range as a % of the total number of 10km squares

The first positive identification for Scotland came from Colonsay in 1930 (a lady's-tresses had been found on Coll in August 1921 but was not certainly identified until 1939). The first record for the Scottish mainland was as recent as 1954.

Irish Lady's-tresses is known from just one site in England, on the southwestern edge of Dartmoor in Devon, where it was found in July 1957. There were seven plants on a heavily grazed lawn of Purple Moor-grass and on the adjacent 'bog'. It has not been seen there since around 1993, however, but the site is essentially unchanged; it is still heavily grazed, as it was when the plants were present, and Irish Lady's-tresses may still survive in a vegetative state.

Most populations of Irish Lady's-tresses are small and scattered but some of the largest produce between 100 and 200 spikes annually, with 400 spikes recorded recently from one area in Co. Mayo. The largest site in Scotland was recently estimated to hold 1,100 plants (flowering and vegetative combined).

Irish Lady's-tresses is a very hard species to survey, and the population trends are not clear. On the one hand, it is known from an increasing number of sites, both in Ireland and Scotland, largely due to particular efforts being made to find it; it was found for the first time on Mull in 1990 and on Tiree in 2002. On the other hand, it tends to 'vanish' unpredictably and often rapidly from known localities. Irish Lady's-tresses is, however, effectively impossible to find unless in flower. Therefore, the most likely explanation for its erratic appearances is that populations are relatively stable but grazing and, perhaps sometimes, the weather prevent many or most plants from flowering. Sheep, cattle or rabbits often graze-off the flower spikes and whole colonies can appear to vanish overnight if sheep are turned out in the vicinity (grazing pressure is intense in much of western Scotland). As with many orchids, slugs can also be a particular problem, grazing-off both the flower spikes and the leaves. Recent experiments, where sheep have been excluded from large populations, have produced a profusion of flowers, and careful long-term monitoring on Barra has indicated that the population there is comparatively stable and long-lived.

The impact of grazing on Irish Lady's-tresses is of conservation concern, but the situation is not clear-cut. Colonies, sometimes large, have been recorded on sites with a variety of grazing regimes, and indeed, it may be tolerant of heavy grazing. It is becoming clear that many orchids do best when grazing reduces competition and breaks up the sward, providing suitable sites for the establishment of seedlings, even if this means that many or most of the flowers are grazed-off before setting seed. This may apply to Irish Lady's-tresses. However, some well-established Irish sites are only lightly grazed or even ungrazed.

The species is certainly vulnerable to changes in the management of its sites, such as drainage, and colonies have even been damaged by spray drift when fertilisers or herbicides have been used nearby. Relatively few sites are protected as SSSIs or reserves.

AUTUMN LADY'S-TRESSES
Spiranthes spiralis

This delicate little orchid blooms in August and September and is the last species to flower in the orchid season. It is confined to short turf, often near the sea, and is one of the orchids that has taken happily to lawns. If conditions are right, hundreds or even thousands of flower spikes may appear, but it can exist undetected for many years if the grass is cut too often.

Identification

Distinctive. The delicate, slender spike is decorated with a row of small, tubular, white flowers that are usually arranged in a spiral pattern. A few tiny, bract-like leaves clasp the stem and there is a rosette of short, oval leaves lying flattened to the ground a little to one side.

Similar species

Irish Lady's-tresses is confined to Ireland and northwest Scotland with an outpost on Dartmoor. When in flower it has prominent, long, narrow leaves on the stem. Habitat is also a good distinction, as it is found in wet grassland and bogs.

Summer Lady's-tresses is extinct in Britain and, like Irish Lady's-tresses, has long, narrow leaves along the stem when in flower.

Creeping Lady's-tresses is found in coniferous woodland (rarely moorland or dunes), usually on acid soils. It is found in northern England and Scotland with a few populations in Norfolk. Soil conditions can change over a very short distance, however, and prior to 1979 Autumn and Creeping Lady's-tresses could be found growing within a few metres of each other at Holt in Norfolk. Creeping Lady's-tresses is easy to distinguish as it grows from horizontal rhizomes that form irregular patches of leaves with scattered flower spikes. Its little bell-like flowers are exceptionally hairy and its leaves are faintly net-veined.

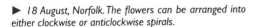

▶ 18 August, Norfolk. The flowers can be arranged into either clockwise or anticlockwise spirals.

▲ *18 August, Norfolk. The new rosette of leaves appears alongside the current flower spike but is hidden in the grass.*

◀ *18 August, Norfolk.*

Habitat

Found on short, dry, nutrient-poor turf in sunny situations, often near the sea. It usually grows on calcareous soils on chalk, limestone, dunes, shingle banks or in the grykes of limestone pavements. Ancient earthworks are favoured, as are lawns; some old lawns were made with turf from nearby pastures and the orchids may have come with the turves, but they can certainly also colonise lawns via wind-blown seed. It is also sometimes found on old tennis courts, road verges and reservoir embankments and has occasionally been recorded from grassy places on less-acid heaths. The critical factor is the lack of competition from taller and more vigorous herbs and grasses, and the correct conditions may be provided by grazing or mowing; grazing

animals may knock-over or bite off the flower spikes but ignore the leaf rosettes, and mowing also leaves the rosettes unharmed. Conversely, the lessening or abandonment of grazing or 'improvement' with fertilisers will promote more vigorous vegetation that will swamp the orchid. In the past, Autumn Lady's-tresses was also found in damp meadows in the drier climate of eastern England, but these are almost all now drained and 'improved' and the orchids have gone.

Flowering period

Early August to the end of September or even early October.

Range

Southern England from the Isles of Scilly to Kent, now mostly south of a line from Bristol to London and rare to the north of this, although there are some scattered sites as far north as Norfolk, southeast Lincolnshire, Yorkshire and in Cumbria around the northern shores of Morecambe Bay. Also found in Wales, especially the southeast and coastal regions, the Isle of Man and Ireland, where it is scattered in the west and on the south and east coasts, and absent from the northern third of the island. **World range:** Almost confined to Europe, with outposts in North Africa and around the Caucasus. Found north

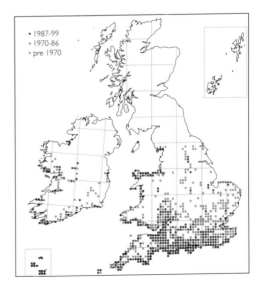

• 1987-99
• 1970-86
• pre 1970

▲ 22 August, Norfolk. The tiny flowers are arranged in a
spiral around the stem, resembling a lady's braided hair.

to Denmark and southernmost Sweden, east
to the Baltic States and western Ukraine
and south to the Mediterranean, including
most of the Mediterranean islands from the
Balearics to Cyprus. Also Algeria and Tunisia,
northern Turkey, Israel, Syria, the Caucasus and
northwestern Iran.

How to find it

The slender spikes of small greenish-white
flowers do not grab the attention and can easily
be missed from a walking height. They become
much more obvious from a low vantage point,
and squatting down to scan along the ground
is often the easiest way to see the plants. Non-
flowering lady's-tresses are almost impossible
to find, however, as the rosettes are only 2.5-
7cm in diameter, lie hidden in the grass and
are easily overlooked as plantains. But, from
nothing, flower spikes may appear and start to
bloom in just a week.

The number of flowering spikes may
fluctuate very widely from year to year, but
the total number of plants present, including
non-flowering rosettes or those 'dormant'
underground, is much more stable. The
proportion of plants producing flower spikes
is probably related to the weather, but the
optimum set of conditions is not known.
Some populations may not be able to flower
for several years but will then bloom en masse
when grazing or mowing ceases. In a dry
summer lawns may be left uncut, allowing
the orchids to flower, and until this happens
Autumn Lady's-tresses may grow unseen for
many years; suitable lawns may be picked out
later in the autumn as they often support a
good variety of fungi, including the colourful
waxcaps.

DESCRIPTION

Height: 3-15cm, sometimes to 20cm high, but
in the wet summer of 2004 a population in
Norfolk averaged 15cm high, with the tallest
28.5cm.

Stem: Pale green, densely covered towards
the spike with fine, white glandular hairs.
The flower spike grows from the centre of the

previous season's rosette, with or without the remains of the dead leaves at its base. The next season's rosette grows beside it.

Leaves: The flowering spike has three to seven small, narrow, lanceolate, bract-like leaves that tightly sheathe the stem. They are greenish with a narrow, whitish or translucent fringe. Just to one side of the base of the spike there is a tight rosette of up to ten leaves. These are around 3cm long, dark, shiny green with a faint blue tone, oval or elliptical in shape, taper to a point, have a thick keel and broadly sheathe the stem at their base. This rosette of leaves emerges in August or September and overwinters, dying off in late May or early June.

Spike: 3-21 flowers (the average is 9-11) are arranged in a row up the stem. In most plants this is twisted so that the flowers form a spiral pattern, but in some the twist is so slight that the flowers simply form a line along one side of the spike. The spiral can be either clockwise or anti-clockwise and is mostly twisted through less than 360°, although in some plants it may be through three full turns.

Bract: Pale green with scattered glandular hairs towards the base and a narrow transparent-whitish fringe. The bracts are lanceolate, taper abruptly to a fine point and are a little less than twice the length of the ovary, which they clasp.

Ovary: Green, three-ribbed, stalkless, with fine glandular hairs. The ovaries are held upright but bend at the tip so that the flowers are held more-or-less horizontally.

Flower: A small, white, trumpet-shaped tube. The sepals and petals are white, often washed green towards the base. The sepals are oblong but taper slightly to a blunt tip and have glandular hairs on the outer surface. The petals are slightly shorter, rather narrower and more strap-shaped. The upper sepal and the petals, together with the lip, form a long, narrow tube with the tip of the upper sepal curved upwards. The lateral sepals are held slightly drooped and spread horizontally away from the tube. The lip is pale green, becoming whiter towards the edges, with two small, globular nectaries at the base. It can be oval or even heart-shaped with a slightly squared-off tip, and the sides curve upwards to form a trough or gutter; for its entire length the lip also bends downwards to resemble the lip of a china teapot's spout, and the extreme tip is rolled downwards and crimped. The greenish column projects horizontally into the tube made by the petals and lip. The flowers are honey-scented.

Subspecies
None.

Variation and varieties
None.

BIOLOGY

Pollination and reproduction
The flowers are pollinated by bumblebees. When the flower opens the longboat-shaped rostellum lies close to the lip at the bottom of the tubular flower with the sticky viscidium facing downwards. In this position the rostellum blocks access to the stigma so that the flower cannot be self-pollinated. A bumblebee lands on the lip and inserts its proboscis in search of the nectar that is produced at its base. There is just enough room for the proboscis to

▲ *22 August, Norfolk. The lip has a spout-like tip with crimped edges, and there are abundant glandular hairs on the stem, ovaries and sepals.*

▲ 22 August, Norfolk. Despite their small size, the flowers are pollinated by bumblebees.

all flowers. The production of abundant seed is probably a factor is the lady's-tresses success in colonising new sites (although the capsules contain an average of only 850 seeds each, a relatively low figure).

The species also reproduces vegetatively from lateral buds at the base of the stem. This leads to the formation of clusters of two or three plants (clusters of up to 12 have been recorded). Vegetative reproduction is, however, thought to play only a minor role in the turnover of a population of Autumn Lady's-tresses.

Development and growth

The aerial stem arises from a very short rhizome that is almost concealed by two or three (rarely up to five) thick, fleshy, tuberous roots that are very much like miniature parsnips in shape and have a few short, transparent hairs. The roots that supported the current year's leaves and flower spike eventually shrivel when their store of food is exhausted and are replaced by new ones. The protocorm that is produced by the germinating seed is heavily infected with fungus, but by the time the roots appear the rhizome is free of 'infection'. However, the roots are each infected in turn as they develop.

Plants may spend one or possibly more years underground with no aerial leaves and still flower the following year. This indicates that the fungal 'partner' plays a significant part in the nutrition of the mature plant. In a study in Bedfordshire the 'half-life' averaged 6.9 years and varied from 4.6-9.2 years (the 'half-life' is a measure of the life expectancy of the orchid after its first appearance above ground. It marks the point at which 50% of the population that emerged in any given year have died).

Early researchers concluded that Autumn Lady's-tresses took many years to go from seed to flower. However, in the laboratory green leaves have been produced six months after germination, and flowering plants in five years.

reach the nectaries but in the process it pushes past the rostellum, and the pollinia are attached to the proboscis by the fast-drying glue of the viscidium. The bee then moves on, carrying the pollinia with it. Over the following 24 hours or so the column and lip move apart, creating enough space for a visiting bumblebee to insert its proboscis, with the pollinia attached, into the flower, where they rub against the stigma (which is now exposed and has become much stickier). The pollinia are brittle and break off in small pieces. A single bee can pollinate several flowers. Due to the 24-hour interval, older flowers are always pollinated with pollinia from a younger flower. The lowest flowers in a spike open first and, as bumblebees work upwards from the bottom of a spike (i.e. from older to younger flowers), they visit the older flowers first and cannot pollinate them with pollinia taken from the same spike. In this way cross-pollination is virtually guaranteed. The mechanism is efficient and seed is set by almost

Hybrids

None.

Name and classification

The specific name *spiralis* means 'twisted' or 'spiral' (as does the generic name).

HISTORY AND CONSERVATION

In 1548 William Turner wrote in his *Names of Herbes*: 'Satyrion is very commune in Germany, and a certeyne ryghte kynde of the same groweth besyde Syon [Sion, Middlesex], it bryngeth furth whyte floures in the end of harueste and it is called Lady traces'. With this statement the Autumn Lady's-tresses became the first species of wild orchid to be recorded in Britain, an honour it shares with Common Twayblade.

Past and present occurrence of Autumn Lady's-tresses in Britain and Ireland (based on presence or absence in 10km squares of the National Grid; data from the New Atlas).

	Britain	Ireland
total historical range, 1500-1999	668	117
current range	302 (11%*)	34 (3.4%*)
% lost, 1500-1969	50%	62%
% lost, 1970-1986	5%	9%
% lost, total	55%	71%

* current range as a % of the total number of 10km squares

▲ *September, Norfolk. Autumn Lady's-tresses can occur in large numbers and, although the number flowering each year is very variable, the total population is relatively stable.*

In the 450 years since William Turner's account, the species has not fared too well in the British Isles and has disappeared from 55% of its historical range in Britain and 71% in Ireland. On the edge of its range in Britain and Ireland, Autumn Lady's-tresses has retreated to its core habitats, and the losses are concentrated in the northern and eastern parts of its former range and at inland sites in general. Sadly, it has almost gone from northern England, the Midlands, East Anglia and Kent. It is extinct in Northamptonshire, Warwickshire, Staffordshire, Nottinghamshire, Derbyshire, Cheshire and, needlees to say, Middlesex.

With its requirement for short, nutrient-poor grassland the Autumn Lady's-tresses cannot tolerate any sort of 'improvement' by the addition of fertilisers. Ploughing of downland and pastures and their conversion to arable or reseeding with vigorous grasses are even more directly destructive processes. Conversely, the abandonment of grazing leads to the invasion of grassland by scrub. These practices have been taking their toll since the 19th century, but the losses are mitigated to a small extent by gains as the species is able to colonise new sites and has appeared in large numbers on the lawns of a few favoured housing estates.

SUMMER LADY'S-TRESSES
Spiranthes aestivalis

The delicate, pure white flower spikes of Summer Lady's-tresses once graced a few favoured bogs on the Channel Islands and in the New Forest. Sadly, it is the only orchid to have become extinct in the British Isles and was last recorded in about 1952. Changes to the habitat were important factors in its decline, but it may have been given the final death knell by collectors. It has also declined sharply throughout northwest Europe and the chances of it reappearing naturally in England appear to be slim.

Identification

The small, white, trumpet-shaped flowers, arranged on the stem in a spiral pattern, identify this species as one of the lady's-tresses. When in flower it has several long, narrow leaves at the base of the stem.

Similar species

Autumn Lady's-tresses is relatively common on short, dry grassland but has also been found, albeit rarely, in damp meadows and in grassy places on less acid heaths. When in flower it has a few small, bract-like leaves on the stem but the basal rosette has already died off; the new rosette appears a little to the side and the leaves are always much shorter and blunter than in Summer Lady's-tresses.

Irish Lady's-tresses is largely confined to Ireland and western Scotland but has been found on Dartmoor and could conceivably turn up elsewhere in southern England. It too favours wet, boggy habitats but it has larger flowers than Summer Lady's-tresses, usually arranged into three spiral rows. Each flower has a longer bract, 10-20mm long, rather than just 6-9mm.

Habitat

In the New Forest the species was confined to wet, peaty, valley bogs with bog mosses (*Sphagnum* spp.). It favoured areas that were slightly less acidic and where the vegetation

▶ *The flowers are very similar in shape to Autumn Lady's-tresses, but this species grows in acidic bogs, in this case with Cross-leaved Heath (Bob Gibbons/Natural Image).*

was relatively low and open. On the Channel Islands it was found in a *Sphagnum* bog on Guernsey and on wet sandy ground on the margin of St. Ouen's Pond on Jersey. In Europe it is also found on moist heathland, damp dune slacks and other damp, base-rich areas with short, open vegetation.

Flowering period
Mid-July to mid-August.

Range
Extinct in the wild in Britain. Formerly found in the New Forest in Hampshire and on Guernsey and Jersey in the Channel Islands.
World range: Central and southern Europe, north to Germany and northwest France, east to the Czech Republic and the former Yugoslavia, and south to the Mediterranean, including the Balearic Islands, Corsica and Sardinia. Also found in North Africa in Morocco and Algeria, and possibly also in Turkey. It is rare and declining in much of Europe due to habitat destruction, especially towards the northern edge of the range, and is extinct in Holland and Belgium.

How to find it
On the surface there seems little chance of finding this species. From time to time there are rumours that it has appeared again in the New Forest, but these have never come to fruition.

DESCRIPTION
Height: 10-20cm, sometimes to 40cm.
Stem: Yellowish-green, with fine glandular hairs towards the tip.
Leaves: Yellowish-green, glossy, narrow and strap-shaped; three to six leaves are held erect at the base of the stem and there are one to three smaller, bract-like sheathing leaves above these. The leaves emerge in spring and are retained all summer.
Spike: Five to 20 flowers are arranged into a single row which is twisted spirally around the stem, sometimes several times.
Bract: Lanceolate, finely hairy at the base. The bracts are rather longer than the ovary, which they tightly clasp.

Ovary: Yellowish-green, finely hairy, six-ribbed and slightly twisted. The ovaries are stalkless and held upright but bend at the tip so that the flowers lie horizontally.
Flower: White and trumpet-shaped. The sepals and petals are glandular-hairy on their outer surfaces and strap-shaped, with the petals a little shorter and narrower than the sepals. They form a tight tube around the column with their tips splayed outwards at the mouth of the tube. The lip is tongue-shaped with two small, nectar-secreting glands at the base. Towards the rear, the sides of the lip curve upwards to form a gutter shape and at the tip the lip turns sharply downwards and has a conspicuously frilled or crimped margin. The flowers are slightly scented.

Subspecies
None.

Variation and varieties
None.

BIOLOGY

Pollination and reproduction
The structure of the flower is very similar to Autumn Lady's-tresses, and the flowers are presumably pollinated in the same manner but there is no specific information on this species. The flowers are said to be fragrant in the evening, which may indicate that they are pollinated by night-flying moths. The species also reproduces vegetatively from additional lateral buds at the base of the stem.

Development and growth
The aerial stem grows from a cluster of two to six thick, fleshy roots. Little is known about the period between germination and first flowering. Development may be relatively rapid, however, because, following germination, protocorms appear by the spring, the first root forms in July and the first tiny leafy shoot appears above ground in the late summer.

Hybrids
None.

Name and classification

The specific name *aestivalis* means 'of the summer'.

HISTORY AND CONSERVATION

The first British record dates from 1840. At a meeting of the Linnean Society on 17 November of that year, 'Mr. Janson exhibited a specimen discovered in August last by himself and Mr. Branch near Lyndhurst, Hampshire' (*Proceedings of the Linnean Society*).

In England this species was always confined to the region southwest of Lyndhurst in the New Forest. In this area it occurred regularly, sometimes in large numbers, in at least five sites until the end of the 19th century. As with many species of orchid, the number of flowering plants varied tremendously from year to year. Thus, in 1901, E.D. Marquand noted that he 'once saw half an acre of bog perfectly white with these flowers, but the following year only a few spikes of bloom appeared'. At another site 200 flowering spikes were noted around 1900. There was, however, a marked decline in the 20th century, and the species had vanished from most sites by 1940. It persisted in the original 1840 location, a bog north of the A35, just north of New Forest Gate and east of Highland Water, until 1952 (with a possible sighting nearby in 1959).

The decline was partly due to habitat destruction, especially drainage and afforestation (thus a site west of Brick Kiln Inclosure was unwittingly destroyed when drained by the Forestry Commission). Some of the original sites are still very wet, however, and superficially unchanged, although shading by trees and scrub and subtle changes to the vegetation through a process of natural succession may have made them unsuitable. Summer Lady's-tresses may also be one of the few cases where collecting was a genuine cause

of decline and extinction; rare and on the edge of its range, it was perhaps especially vulnerable. In the 19th and 20th centuries all-too-numerous collections were made of flowering plants, often complete with roots, both for private and public herbaria.

Summer Lady's-tresses was also found on the Channel Islands. The first record was on 24 July 1837, from the banks of St. Ouen's Pond on Jersey. This was its only locality on the island and it was always scarce at this site. Due to overcollecting it quickly became even scarcer and was last recorded in 1926, when just a single plant was seen (and even this last plant was possibly later collected). On Guernsey it was found on boggy ground around the lake of Grande Mare in around 1841 and was fairly common to start with, but collecting and drainage led to its demise by 1914.

There are occasionally rumours that Summer Lady's-tresses has been refound in the New Forest or reports that it has been discretely reintroduced, without official sanction, to one or more of its former sites. Nothing has ever come of these stories, but the possibility of an undocumented reintroduction will cast a permanent shadow over any natural reappearance.

◀ *Extinct in Britain, Summer Lady's-tresses is also on the decline throughout northwest Europe (Bob Gibbons/ Natural Image).*

Distribution

Primarily Asian, with 30 species in total, but just one ranging west to Britain and Europe.

Name

The origin of the generic name *Herminium* is uncertain. It may derive from the Greek and means 'buttress' or 'foot of the bed'. This is supposedly an allusion to the 'pillar-like' tubers but these are spherical in Musk Orchid, the first species to be given the name. Alternatively, it may derive from *Hermes*, the messenger of the gods.

GENUS *HERMINIUM*
MUSK ORCHID

MUSK ORCHID
Herminium monorchis

Despite its name, this small orchid does not smell of musk. It is confined to a relatively few sites in southern England, where it is found in very short turf on chalk or limestone, occasionally in large numbers. Surprisingly, and despite its status as a Nationally Scarce orchid that has been lost from around 70% of its former range, it seems to have received remarkably little attention from scientists and conservationists.

Identification

This diminutive orchid is easily overlooked but when found is not hard to identify. The flower spike is crowded with tiny greenish-yellow flowers. Unless examined closely, the lip is hardly different in appearance to the petals and sepals, and the flower therefore appears to be made up of six almost identical narrow 'petals' that form a little bell.

Similar species

Bog Orchid is also very small and greenish-yellow in colour but is strictly confined to acid, boggy ground, and the structure of its flower is completely different.

Habitat

Musk Orchid is found exclusively on short, well-drained grassland on chalk or limestone soils. Its small stature means that it cannot compete if the vegetation is tall, so thin or compacted soils that restrict plant growth are favoured. It particularly likes the narrow 'terracettes' formed on steep downland slopes by soil creep, as well as ancient earthworks, abandoned quarries, chalk and lime pits, and spoil heaps. It has been recorded up to 215m above sea level.

Flowering period

Early June to early July, sometimes to early August. There can be large variations from

◄ *29 June, Hampshire. The colour of the flower varies a little, from slightly yellower to slightly greener. The smallest plants may be just 2cm high.*

▶ *29 June, Hampshire. The small, slender spikes of Musk Orchid are often hard to see from walking height.*

year to year in the number of flowering
spikes, with the temperature and amount of
rainfall over the previous summer being the
determining factors. A hot dry summer can
cause a big drop in the number of flowers the
following year.

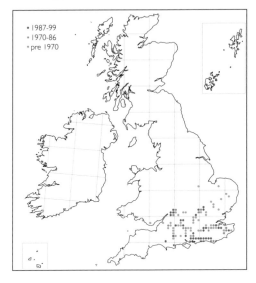

Range

Confined to the chalk of the North and
South Downs in Kent, Sussex and Surrey,
also Hampshire, Dorset (just two sites),
Wiltshire and Berkshire, the Cotswolds
in Gloucestershire and the Chilterns in
Buckinghamshire, Hertfordshire and
Bedfordshire. It is very local and is absent
from large areas of apparently suitable habitat.
World range: Widespread in Europe and
Asia. In Europe it is found north to *c.* 61°N
in Scandinavia, southern Finland and the
Baltic States, and it ranges south to southeast
France, Italy (the Apennines) and the Balkans,
with isolated populations in northwest Turkey
and the Caucasus. The species reaches its
western limit in northern and eastern France,
but there is an isolated population in central
Spain. It ranges in a narrow band across Siberia
to the Russian Far East, North Korea and
northeast China, and is also found in another
narrow band across northern China, with
scattered records from northern Japan and the
Himalayas.

How to find it

This small, greenish-yellow orchid is hard
to spot. This is especially so on anything but
the shortest turf or if the spikes are few and
scattered. In those situations, scanning carefully
from a low-level vantage point, sitting or
squatting, can help. Once one spike has been
seen, however, others will usually be found
nearby. It can be easier to tread on than to
see, so it is good practice to keep to whatever
paths are available. On the other hand, in
a few favoured sites Musk Orchid occurs
in large numbers and can form dense and
obvious stands. One of the best sites for this
species is Noar Hill (Hampshire), and others
include St Catherine's Hill (Hampshire) and
Malling Down (Sussex), with small numbers
at Tottenhoe Knolls (Bedfordshire), Park Gate
Down (Kent), Box Hill (Surrey) and Ham Hill
(Wiltshire).

▲ *29 June, Hampshire. In the tiny, bell-like flowers the
lip appears similar to the petals and sepals, with only its
narrow central lobe visible.*

◀ *28 June, Hampshire.*

▲ *29 June, Hampshire. The flowers are scented but smell of honey, not musk.*

DESCRIPTION

Height: 2-30cm but usually 3.5cm-15cm and rarely more than 20cm.

Stem: Yellowish-green to dark green, distinctly ridged towards the tip.

Leaves: There are two mid-green basal leaves (rarely three or four), strongly keeled and oblong to oval-oblong in shape, and one to three small, lanceolate, bract-like leaves further up the stem. The leaves emerge from early May onwards and persist until mid-September but, in a dry season, they may not appear until early June and will wither early.

Spike: The flowers appear densely packed on the spike due in part to the relatively large ovary. There are 20-30 flowers on most plants but over 70 on the very largest. The spike is often one-sided.

Bract: Green, lanceolate and roughly the length of the ovary.

Ovary: Relatively large and inflated, even when the flowers are fresh, greenish-yellow, prominently ribbed and slightly twisted. The ovary is upright but narrows at the top into a stalk-like base for the flower which is bent through more than 90°, thus holding the flower pendant.

Flower: The whole flower is greenish-yellow and very small, about 2.5mm wide x 3mm from front to back. It does not open widely and the sepals, petal and lip all point forward and are more-or-less parallel, giving the flower a spiky, tubular or bell-like shape. The sepals are oval, with the lateral sepals slightly smaller than the upper sepal. The petals are slightly paler and, rather unusually, longer than the sepals. They are spear-shaped, with variable small side-lobes towards the base and a narrower tip. The lip has a long and narrow central lobe and rather shorter side-lobes. To the rear the lip narrows into a short, blunt chamber (a rudimentary spur) which secretes nectar. There are two oval pollinia, each attached by a very short, elastic caudicle (stalk) to a saddle-shaped viscidium that is almost the same size as the pollinia. The viscidia each have a delicate skin but are not enclosed in a bursicle (pouch). The flowers have a sweet, honey-like scent.

Subspecies

None.

Variation and varieties

None.

BIOLOGY

Pollination and reproduction

The flowers are pollinated by a variety of tiny insects such as flies, parasitic wasps, gnats and beetles, typically just 1-1.5mm long. As it feeds on the nectar at the rear of the lip, the insect ruptures the skin of the relatively large viscidia, and these stick the pollinia to the insect's legs. Once the insect leaves the flower, the pollinia rotate forward to be in the correct position to make contact with the stigma of the next flower to be visited; this can be on the same plant. There are conflicting reports on the possibility of self-pollination. A study in Sweden found that it did not take place, but it has also been stated that the flowers can be self-pollinated, the anther withering and the pollinia dropping onto the stigma immediately below. Whatever the mechanism, 70-95% of flowers set seed.

The species also reproduces vegetatively and this may be the major means of recruitment to the population; two to five 'daughter' tubers are produced at the ends of slender rhizomes up to 20cm from the parent tuber. In this way extensive clones can develop.

Development and growth

The leaves and flower spike grow from a single spherical tuber which starts to wither away by flowering time, and there are a few short, thin roots. The tip of the tuber and usually also the roots are 'infected' with fungi. Two or more new tubers are formed each growing season, the larger of which provides for the next year's leaves and flower spike, the smaller ones are 'daughter' tubers. Musk Orchid is sometimes described as 'migratory' because the replacement tuber grows at the end of a short rhizome and therefore the aerial shoot appears in a slightly different place each season. After flowering once, plants may appear again merely as vegetative rosettes or even remain 'dormant' underground for one or two years before they flower again.

▲ 29 June, Hampshire. Musk Orchid can reproduce vegetatively to form extensive patches of clones.

Musk Orchid is reported to flower after a period of immaturity lasting several years, but in cultivation plants have flowered within two years of seed being sown. Individuals can be long-lived, with an age of 27 years being recorded.

Hybrids
None.

Name and classification

The specific name *monorchis* means 'one-testicle' (i.e. 'one-tuber'). When flowering this species *appears* to grow from a single tuber, unlike members of genera such as *Orchis* and *Dactylorhiza*, which have two obvious tubers at the base of the stem. In fact, Musk Orchid has several, but the replacement and 'daughter' tubers are formed at the end of thread-like rhizomes and easily missed. The specific name is therefore a misnomer.

HISTORY AND CONSERVATION

Musk Orchid was first recorded in Britain in 1663 by John Ray in his *Catalogus Plantarum circa Cantabrigiam nascentium* ('Catalogue of plants found around Cambridge'): 'Orchis pusilla odorata...In the chalk pit close at Cherry Hinton'.

Past and present occurrence of Musk Orchid in Britain and Ireland (based on presence or absence in 10km squares of the National Grid; data from the New Atlas).

	Britain	Ireland
total historical range, 1500-1999	104	0
current range	32 (1.1%*)	0
% lost, 1500-1969	52%	
% lost, 1970-1986	17%	
% lost, total	69%	

* current range as a % of the total number of 10km squares

Musk Orchid has been lost from 69% of its total historical range and is Nationally Scarce, having been recorded from just 32 10km squares in the *New Atlas* period of 1987-99.

The ploughing of chalk grasslands from the late 18th century onwards caused the first wave of losses, especially in East Anglia, and many sites had gone by 1930, including John Ray's in Cambridgeshire. Subsequently, the 'usual suspects' of agricultural intensification, the scrubbing-over of grassland (especially following the outbreak of myxomatosis) and overgrazing have taken their toll. It is now extinct in Somerset, Glamorganshire, Oxfordshire, Rutland, Cambridgeshire, Suffolk and west Norfolk, where three 18th or 19th century records included a site at Heacham, the northernmost locality for the species. However, it can, at least occasionally, colonise new areas. Many sites are now protected as SSSIs and reserves, and a few colonies hold hundreds or even thousands of plants.

Despite its predilection for dry chalk grassland, the species is vulnerable to summer drought, which can lead to the early withering of the leaves and thus a reduction in the amount of carbohydrates stored in the tubers for the following season. In some cases there may then be a big fall in the number of flowering spikes, the plants appearing merely as non-flowering rosettes, but the population can recover rapidly following a good growing season. Prolonged droughts can, however, devastate the species; the long, hot summer of 1976, the worst drought in southern England for 250 years, caused big losses in Sussex from which it has not yet recovered.

▶ *14 May, Kent, Lady Orchid.*

This genus contains some of the rarest and most spectacular orchids in the British Isles. Many species have flowers that recall tiny human figures, with lips that are divided into 'arms' and 'legs'. All grow from tubers and can spend part of the year underground in a safe 'resting' state. This allows the orchid to survive unfavourable periods, such as the summer drought in the Mediterranean or sub-zero winter temperatures.

Distribution

There are about 50 species, most of which are found in Europe and adjacent areas in North Africa and the Middle East. Just five species occur in the British Isles.

Floral structures

There are two pollinia, each narrowing to a caudicle (stalk) which is attached to one of the two viscidia. The viscidia are each in turn contained within a bursicle, a pouch-like cavity on the column.

Pollination

Members of this genus are pollinated by insects, but only a few species produce nectar to reward their pollinators. The majority rely instead on deceit; insects are attracted to the brightly coloured and scented flowers but receive no reward.

Growth pattern

At flowering time all *Orchis* species have two almost spherical tubers side by side at the base of the aerial stem. The 'tubers' are more accurately termed 'root-tubers' or 'root-stem tubers' and are essentially roots that have been modified to become specialist storage organs.

To follow the pattern of growth through the year it is best to start in the late summer when the orchid is 'resting' and consists only of a single tuber with one terminal bud; the leaves, rhizome and roots die off once the orchid has flowered.

In the autumn the bud on the tuber produces a short rhizome and from this a few roots develop. The roots serve two functions. First, their 'infection' with fungi provides the plant with nutrients. Second, they supply the plant with water and this becomes particularly important once the leaves have appeared. In some members of the genus the leaves develop in the autumn, in others they do not expand until the spring.

Once the roots have developed, they begin to produce nutrients. Some of these are stored in a new tuber that has started to form on the

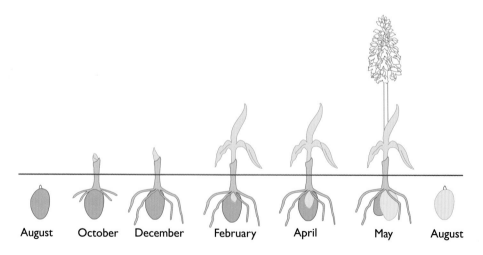

August   October   December   February   April   May   August

▲ *Annual cycle of growth and replacement of tubers in the genus* Orchis *(after Wells, 1981).*

rhizome, side by side with the old; due to its relationship with fungi, the orchid can produce nutrients even before its leaves appear. The rhizome goes on to form the aerial stem and when the flowers open in the spring this has two tubers at its base. The older of these has supplied the current season's growth, including the leaves, stem and flower spike. This tuber is starting to shrink and will have vanished by the late summer's 'resting period'. The newer tuber is plump and swollen and continues to grow until the leaves die down. It will go on to overwinter and form the flower spike in the following year.

Fungal partners

The tuber does not have a fungal 'infection' although fungi are found in its epidermis (and in hot, dry, climates the fungus may only be able to survive the summer drought in the skin of the orchid's tubers). Fungal activity is concentrated in the roots and sometimes also the rhizome. All *Orchis* species are able to spend one or more years underground, presumably sustained by fungi.

Development from seed

In all species the seed germinates in late summer or autumn and forms a protocorm. This rapidly forms the first root, which is 'infected' with fungi and supplies the protocorm with nutrients. The following summer, a small

rhizome develops and the first tuber develops on this rhizome, the root and protocorm dying away in the late summer to leave only the tuber. In the autumn, a new rhizome grows from this tuber and produces one or more roots and in the spring a leafy shoot is produced and a new tuber forms at its base during the summer; the pattern of growth is then similar to that of the adult plant. Some species spend several years as an underground seedling, producing a new tuber each year.

The pattern of development of the seedling apparently varies slightly between species and even between populations. Some may produce a tuber directly from the protocorm, without any roots developing beforehand, whereas others develop an aerial stem and root in the first season after germination and then go on to produce a tuber.

Vegetative reproduction

Additional tubers may be formed at the base of the aerial stem and these will go on to form separate plants as the connecting stem dies off in the autumn.

Name

The generic name *Orchis* derives from the Greek *orkhis* and means 'testicle'. The two rounded tubers have long been considered to resemble male genitalia.

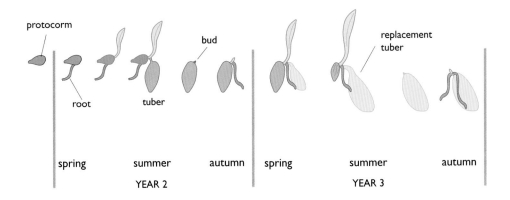

▲ *Development from seed in the genus* Orchis *(after Rasmussen 1995).*

MAN ORCHID
Orchis anthropophora

Formerly: *Aceras anthropophorum*

The narrow flower spikes of Man Orchid do not command attention from a distance but on closer acquaintance they reveal how apt the English name is. Just why do they look so much like tiny, hooded, human figures, and what benefit does the plant gain by having flowers of this particular size and shape? As with so many questions about orchids, we do not know the answer. Man Orchid is relatively widespread in southern England, occurring north to Lincolnshire and west to Gloucestershire, but away from Kent and Surrey it is extremely local and either uncommon or rare; in the long term the future of the few remaining isolated populations must be in doubt.

Identification

The long, narrow spike and very man-like flowers are distinctive. The sepals and petals form a 'hood' or 'cowl' and the tiny figure faces downwards, concealing its 'face'. The lip is deeply lobed to form the 'arms' and 'legs'. The flowers are yellowish to greenish, variably washed with red; plants in full sun may be on average the reddest and some may even have bright foxy-red lips.

Similar species

Frog Orchid may be similarly coloured but is usually rather smaller, and the lip is not divided into 'arms' and 'legs'.

Common Twayblade is also vaguely similar but the tiny green flowers are rather different in shape and it has only two large, rounded leaves.

Habitat

Typically found on well-drained grassland on chalk or limestone, often on or at the foot of a slope, with a predilection for abandoned quarries and pits. Roadside verges, churchyards, field margins and stabilised dunes or shingle can also provide suitable habitat. It frequently grows in relatively long, rank grass and among scrub and it will sometimes spread under the eaves of nearby woodland. It is vulnerable to competition, however, and dense scrub will crowd it out; conversely, populations can be eliminated by heavy grazing.

◄ 9 June, Northamptonshire. The spikes are often tall and very slender with little of the basal leaves visible.

Flowering period

Early May to late June, sometimes from late
April, but usually at its best in late May.
The flowers open in slow progression from
the bottom of the spike, so flowering can be
protracted.

Range

Southern and eastern England, with the bulk of
the population on the North Downs in Surrey
and Kent. It is rare and very local elsewhere
and confined to the region south and east of
a line from Bristol to the Humber. There are
four or five sites in Hampshire, around four in
Suffolk, mostly on protected roadside verges,
and between two and four sites in Essex. Two
each remain in Sussex, Northamptonshire
and Lincolnshire, with just one in Wiltshire,
Gloucestershire, Oxfordshire, Bedfordshire and
Norfolk; there is a single site in Warwickshire
but it was apparently introduced there, in 1968.
World range: Western and southern Europe,
North Africa and the Levant. It ranges north
to Holland, southern Germany, Switzerland,
the former Yugoslavia and Greece and south
to the Mediterranean, including most of the
Mediterranean islands from the Balearics to
Cyprus. In North Africa it is found in Tunisia,
Algeria and Morocco, and it also occurs in
southwest Turkey and Lebanon.

• 1987-99
• 1970-86
• pre 1970

▲ *9 May, Kent. Man Orchid sometimes grows in light
woodland.*

▲ *9 June, Northamptonshire. The flowers are truly man-like.*

How to find it

A very localised species, nowadays only likely to be found on reserves or protected road verges. It can be hard to spot if it is growing among long grass. Two of the best sites for this species are Barnack Hills and Holes (Peterborough) and Wye (Kent). Box Hill (Surrey) is another classic locality, although it has declined there in recent years.

DESCRIPTION

Height: 15-65cm but usually 20-30cm and rarely over 45cm.

Stem: Pale green with some membranous sheaths at the extreme base.

Leaves: Green, dull or slightly bluish, distinctly veined, keeled and narrowly oval-lanceolate to strap-shaped. There is a basal rosette of three or four leaves, some lying flat and some held at about 45°, and higher on the stem one or two smaller and more lanceolate sheathing leaves. In some areas the leaves appear in spring, in others in November or December, becoming fully formed by January or February. In all plants the tips of the lower leaves are often scorched by May and they all die off after flowering; this pattern of growth is probably an adaptation to the mild wet winters and hot dry summers in the core area of its distribution around the Mediterranean.

Spike: Tall, narrow, more-or-less cylindrical and dense, with up to 50 or even 90 flowers.

Bract: Green, lanceolate and half the length of the ovary.

Ovary: Pale green, long, cylindrical, boldly ribbed and twisted.

Flower: Green or yellow, variably tinged red, and very man-like. The sepals are oval and various shades of yellowish-green, often with a distinct maroon fringe and midrib. The petals are pale green, slightly shorter, much narrower and more strap-shaped. Both the sepals and petals form a hood over the column, with the petals fully concealed. The lip is variably green or yellow, often strongly washed red or

▲ *8 May, Kent. Many flowers have largely red 'arms' and 'legs'.*

reddish-brown, especially around the edges, but can be pure red or yellow. It hangs almost vertically downwards and has three lobes: two long, narrow side-lobes at the base (the 'arms') and a terminal lobe that is itself divided half way to the base into two lobes (the 'legs'). There is sometimes a tiny projecting tooth between the 'legs'. There is no spur, rather there are two shiny, whitish swellings on either side of the base of the lip which curve round to join the column and enclose a shallow pit with two small, nectar-secreting depressions. The flowers have a faint, unpleasant smell.

Subspecies
None.

Variation and varieties
Var. *flavescens* lacks red pigments (anthocyanins) and has a green hood and contrasting yellow lip. It is rare.

BIOLOGY

Pollination and reproduction
Little is known about the pollination of this species. However, the numerous hybrids with Lady, Monkey and Military Orchids found in Europe would suggest that it shares a suite of pollinating insects with those species; in England ants and hover flies have been seen with pollinia on their heads. Seed-set is moderate to good, but despite this it is thought that most reproduction is vegetative via the production of additional tubers.

Development and growth
Once they have appeared above ground for the first time, plants may live for up to 14 years although they may not flower every year or even appear above ground. Conversely, some may flower for five years in a row. Man Orchids only rarely die after flowering just once, and in a study in Bedfordshire the 'half-life' averaged 5.8 years and varied from 4.0-7.8 years (the 'half-life' is a measure of the life expectancy of the orchid after its first appearance above ground and marks the point at which 50% of the population that emerged in any given year have died). There

▲ *8 May, Kent. The flowers have just a rudimentary spur, unlike other members of the genus* Orchis.

is no information on the period between germination and flowering.

Hybrids
In Europe, hybrids with Monkey, Military and Lady Orchid are common but in England such hybrids have only been found twice.
O. x bergonii, the hybrid with Monkey Orchid, was found in Kent in 1985, although it has been suggested that this may be the result of inadvertent hand pollination.
O. x macra, the hybrid with Lady Orchid, was found in Kent in 1998, when two plants were seen.

Name and classification
The specific name *anthropophora* means 'man-bearing'.

Man Orchid was formerly placed in the genus *Aceras* as *Aceras anthropophorum*. Indeed, it was the only species in that genus, which was distinguished from the genus *Orchis* by the lack of a spur. Recent DNA studies have confirmed that this difference is purely superficial and that

▲ *9 June, Northamptonshire. The lip of the orchid flower acts as a landing platform for pollinating insects, but the function of the 'arms' and 'legs' is a mystery.*

Man Orchid is a perfectly good *Orchis*. The generic name *Aceras* derived from the Greek and meant 'without-a-horn', a reference to this absence of a spur.

HISTORY AND CONSERVATION

The first British record dates from 1690, when John Ray published his *Synopsis Methodica Stirpium Britannicarum* ('Methodical synopsis of British plants'): 'Found by Mr. Dale in an old Gravel-pit at Dalington (Ballingdon) near Sudbury'.

Nationally Scarce and still decreasing in numbers, Man Orchid has been lost from 56% of its historical range. It was formerly much commoner in East Anglia but vanished as pastures were ploughed from the late 19th century onwards. Sites were also destroyed when quarries and pits were used as 'landfill', field margins were sprayed or subject to drift from nearby operations and road verges cut or sprayed unsympathetically. Conversely, sites have also been lost to scrub

encroachment. Extinct in Somerset, the Isle of Wight, Hertfordshire, Buckinghamshire, Cambridgeshire, Leicestershire and also Derbyshire (where it was introduced at Ashover but not seen there recently).

Past and present occurrence of Man Orchid in Britain and Ireland (based on presence or absence in 10km squares of the National Grid; data from the New Atlas).

	Britain	Ireland
total historical range, 1500-1999	109 (1.7%*)	0
current range	48	0
% lost, 1500-1969	46%	
% lost, 1970-1986	10%	
% lost, total	56%	

* current range as a % of the total number of 10km squares

▲ *8 May, Kent. Some flowers are much yellower with little or no red.*

MONKEY ORCHID
Orchis simia

One of our rarest orchids, the exotic, monkey-like appearance of the flowers, combined with the inevitable secrecy that surrounded such a rarity, has excited botanists for generations. It is confined to three sites in the Chilterns and Kent, two of which welcome visitors.

Identification
To see a Monkey Orchid you will almost certainly have to visit one of its two 'public' sites, so identification is straightforward. The flowers are distinctive and definitely resemble a Spider Monkey, with the hood forming the 'head' and the lobes of the lip, the slender, curved 'arms' and 'legs'.

Similar species
Military Orchid is also very rare and the two species are not found together anymore in England. However, should a new colony of plants be discovered, identification would be an issue. In Military Orchid the 'legs' are straight, distinctly broader than in Monkey Orchid and widen towards the tip, and the hood forms a longer, neater 'helmet'. The shape of the flower spike is rather different, too, being taller and less crowded, with the flowers opening in sequence from the bottom of the spike upwards.

Habitat
Monkey Orchid prefers south-facing slopes on open, grazed chalk grassland. It probably favours the interface between grassland and woodland or scrub, benefiting from the shelter which scattered trees and shrubs provide from desiccating winds and grazing animals. The slightly moister conditions in light shade are also likely to be beneficial and the bare ground under scrub can provide suitable conditions for seedling establishment. Should the shade become too dense, however, it ceases to flower or even to appear above ground. Monkey Orchid may be badly affected by drought; for example at Faversham in Kent the population 'crashed' after the hot, dry summers of 1975 and 1976 and was slow to recover.

▶ *28 May, Kent. The rosette of shiny, green basal leaves is usually hidden in the grass.*

▲ *28 May, Kent. At Parkgate Down in Kent, Monkey Orchid grows on open downland, but it can also grow in light scrub.*

Flowering period

Late May to early June; flowering peaks around a week earlier in the Chilterns than in Kent. In most orchids the flowers open from the bottom of the spike upwards, but in Monkey Orchid the flowers often open rapidly from the top downwards, although they may open synchronously (or even from the base upwards in Kentish plants). Overall, it is the rapidity with which all the flowers open that is characteristic of Monkey Orchid, rather than the direction of opening. The spike is at its best for a rather brief period.

Range

Currently confined to Hartslock in Oxfordshire and two sites in Kent (a confidential site near Faversham and Park Gate Down, where it was introduced). **World range:** Southern Europe and the Mediterranean region, including the Balearics, the Aegean islands, Crete and Cyprus, north to Holland (very rare), southern Germany, Hungary and Romania. Ranges east to Syria, Turkey, the Crimea, Caucasus, Iran and Turkmenistan, and also found in North Africa in Algeria, Tunisia and Libya.

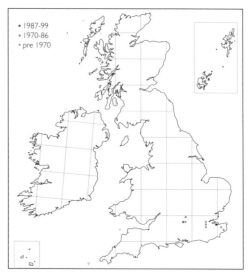

- 1987-99
- 1970-86
- pre 1970

How to find it

Park Gate Down and Hartslock reserves are the places to go, and Monkey Orchids are easy to find at both.

DESCRIPTION

Height: 10-30cm tall, occasionally to 45cm.
Stem: Green, usually washed brownish-purple towards the tip, angled and with two or three sheaths at the base.
Leaves: There are three or four shiny green basal leaves, oval-oblong, often keeled and blunt-tipped, and two or three sheathing leaves higher on the stem. The leaves may appear above ground as early as November but more usually do so in January or February.
Spike: Roughly globular in shape with the flowers crowded together, and the whole thing

looking a bit scruffy. Most spikes have ten to 20 flowers but there are up to 30 on well-developed plants and as many as 42 on the most robust.

Bract: Very small, around a third of the length of the ovary, triangular, chaffy and whitish.

Ovary: Green, heavily washed purple, boldly six-ribbed, twisted and curved.

Flower: Monkey-like, white or pink, with darker spots and variably redder extremities. The sepals are lanceolate, and the petals are slightly shorter, much narrower and more strap-shaped; together they form a hood that encloses the column with the sepals slightly splayed outwards at the tips. The sepals are whitish on their outer surface, variably washed pink and with irregular violet-purple dots, blotches and streaks. The inner surfaces are more heavily blotched and streaked, sometimes almost solidly so. The petals are similar but sometimes more solidly washed purplish-pink. The lip has two lobes forming the 'arms' and two lobes forming the 'legs', with an additional small projection between the 'legs' (more phallic than tail-like); the tips of the 'arms' and 'legs' are curved forwards and upwards. The lip is whitish in the centre, variably flushed violet-purple and spotted violet (the spots are formed by tufts of papillae), becoming violet-purple towards the extremities of the 'arms' and 'legs'. The spur is pale pink, about half to three-quarters the length of the ovary, slightly down-curved and blunt-tipped. The column is reddish. The flowers have a faint scent of vanilla.

Subspecies
None.

Variation and varieties
The Kentish Monkey Orchids are on average taller than those in the Chilterns, with stouter stems and, more significantly, more and bigger leaves; their largest leaf is up to twice as long. Their flowers have a more extensive area of purple spotting on a more purple-washed ground, and the spots are larger. The sepals have larger and darker markings on their inner

▲ 28 May, Kent. With long 'arms', 'legs' and a 'tail', it is not hard to see the 'monkey' in a Monkey Orchid.

surfaces, making the hood appear pale pink rather than white on the outer surface, and the spur is pale pink to purple (white to pale pink in the Chilterns). However, there is much overlap, and the differences do not warrant the recognition of distinct varieties. 'Var. *macra*', with a violet hood and purplish-red 'arms' and 'legs', was recorded many years ago and may have been more prevalent in large populations but probably falls within the normal range of variation and may not be worthy of recognition.

BIOLOGY
Pollination and reproduction
Some natural pollination does occur in England, with the flowers visited by flies, bees and butterflies. Although the spur is not thought to contain nectar, two swellings near its mouth may contain sugars which can be extracted by insects. Seed-set has been poor in England and some populations have been hand-pollinated. Pollination rates appear to improve significantly, however, once a population of Monkey Orchids is above a certain threshold;

◀ *28 May, Kent. Kentish Monkey Orchids are, on average, taller and more richly-coloured than those in the Chilterns.*

the spectacle of large numbers of flowers may be more attractive to potential pollinators. In a study in Holland, vegetative reproduction was found to be rare and only to occur following good growing seasons.

Development and growth

Much of the information about the life cycle of the Monkey Orchid comes from observation of a small population in the Netherlands. This originated with a single founder plant and may not be entirely typical. A period of three or four years elapses between germination and the appearance of the first aerial leaf and a further three to six years before flowers are produced, by which time the plants have at least four basal leaves. A similar time scale has been recorded for Kentish Monkeys. Young plants occasionally disappear underground after they have produced their first leaves and then reappear again after one or two years.

Individual plants can be long-lived, flowering for up to 19 consecutive seasons although this may be exceptional. Plants often 'rest' between bouts of flowering as vegetative rosettes and may even be 'dormant' underground for one or two years. If absent for three years, however, they are almost certainly dead. Severe winters will inhibit flowering and may result in many plants dying, as the tubers typically lie in shallow soil. Similarly, if the leaves are grazed off the plant will not flower the following season, presumably because without leaves it is unable to build up sufficient resources.

Hybrids

O. x. beyrichii, the hybrid with Military Orchid, occurred in the Thames Valley until the middle of the 19th century, after which the two parent species were not found together.
O. x. bergonii, the hybrid with Man Orchid, was recorded in 1985 at Faversham in Kent (but it has been suggested that this may have been the result of hand pollination 'gone wrong').

Name and classification

The specific name *simia* means 'of the ape' or 'of the monkey'.

HISTORY AND CONSERVATION

In 1666 Christopher Merrett noted both Monkey and Military Orchids in his *Pinax Rerum Naturalium Britannicarum* ('A picture of British natural history'): '...on several Chalkey hills neer the highway from Wallingford to Redding on Barkshire side the river...' This reference to the Berkshire Downs was apparently the first record of both species in England and originated with information supplied by a William Brown of Magdalen College, Oxford.

Old records of Monkey Orchid are often difficult to assess because for a long time the species was confused with Military or even Lady Orchid. Monkey Orchid went on to be recorded from Kent, Surrey, Berkshire,

Oxfordshire and East Yorkshire but there are now only three sites, one in Oxfordshire and two in Kent. A *Red Data Book* species, it is classified as Vulnerable and is specially protected under Schedule 8 of the Wildlife and Countryside Act 1981.

Monkey Orchid has apparently always been very local in England, but in the 18th and early 19th centuries it was frequent in south Oxfordshire, in the area between Wallingford, Reading and Henley. Most records came from the slopes overlooking the north bank of the Thames between Goring and Caversham (the latter now on the northern outskirts of Reading) where the river cuts through the southern outliers of the Chilterns. The species then declined dramatically from about 1840, due to the ploughing of downland and the collection of specimens for both herbaria and gardens. However, the main cause of its demise may well have been a big increase in the number of rabbits. By the mid-1920s there was only one substantial colony remaining in

▲ *28 May, Kent. The 'monkeys' often look as if they have been thrown into a heap.*

the Chilterns, at Hartslock, but such was the secrecy surrounding this site that the species was generally thought to have become extinct in Britain.

Past and present occurrence of Monkey Orchid in Britain and Ireland (based on presence or absence in 10km squares of the National Grid; data from the New Atlas).

	Britain	Ireland
total historical range, 1500-1999	10	0
current range	2 (0.07%*)	0
% lost, 1500-1969	60%	
% lost, 1970-1986	20%	
% lost, total	80%	

* current range as a % of the total number of 10km squares

The Hartslock colony was stable at over 100 flowering plants in the 1920s and increased to 200 spikes in the years leading up to World War Two; in 1933 over 30 were picked. But, following the war, the increasing mechanisation of agriculture allowed steeper and steeper slopes to be cultivated and in 1949 and 1950 the field at Hartslock that held the Monkey Orchids was ploughed. Fortunately, the upper part of the slope (the area where the orchids now grow) escaped as it was steeper, scrubbier and protected by a thick hedge. There may already have been a few Monkey Orchids growing in this refuge, and some tubers rescued from the lower part of the field were replanted there but with unknown results.

Just one Monkey Orchid flowered at Hartslock in 1950-52 and numbers remained painfully low for many years. It was not until 1968 that the population reached even the modest total of eight flower spikes, and even in 1977 there were just eight plants. In 1975 BBOWT bought Hartslock but, as on most downland sites, scrub encroachment was a problem. This led to a substantial programme of scrub removal, and the area is now grazed in the autumn and winter by sheep.

Despite the initial management efforts, the orchid population increased very slowly

to around 60 plants in the late 1980s, with roughly a third flowering each year. In the early 1990s the number of flower spikes actually dropped, to as few as five in 1990, although the total number of plants was more constant. Then, in 1994 the population at Hartslock started to expand rapidly. Three factors may have helped; first, a run of mild winters, which probably reduced mortality and encouraged plants to flower. Second, systematic hand pollination, which began in 1977; this has now ceased, as rates of natural pollination and seed production are high. Third, in 1992 the main colony was fenced against rabbits. Over the next three years the number of plants trebled and by 1995 there were 123, including 47 new individuals, of which 72 flowered. It is thought that prior to the erection of the fence rabbits ate most of the first orchids to emerge; they can appear above ground as early as January, well before the seasonal warden puts wire netting cages on the orchids in April.

By 1999 there were 200 plants with 100 of them flowering, and from 2000 Hartslock held around 300 plants, with one to two-thirds flowering each year. Despite this apparently healthy population, however, DNA studies have shown that the genetic variability at Hartslock is very low, as the population had gone through a genetic 'bottleneck' when it was reduced to a tiny handful of individuals. In the long term, it may be better to introduce more variability by hand pollinating again using pollen from other Chiltern plants, Kent or even France. In the last few decades Monkey Orchid has appeared sporadically and in very small numbers at other sites in the Chilterns. In 1966 it was found near Pangbourne and in 1965 and 1971-74 at Aston Rowant.

In Kent, Monkey Orchid was first recorded in 1777 from near Faversham and then again in the early 1800s but it was not seen again until 1920-23 when a few plants flowered at Bishopsbourne (near Canterbury). At the other end of the county, in west Kent, from 1952 onwards a single Monkey Orchid appeared on the rough grass of a disused tennis court at a vicarage at Otford. Every year, until 1955, the vicar took the seed capsules and scattered seed onto nearby downland. In 1956 there was a single robust spike and a further six non-flowering plants at the vicarage. However, on the retirement of the botanically minded vicar the new incumbent would not guarantee to safeguard the colony. All the orchids were moved to nearby private land, where the largest flowered once only, in 1957, and then the Monkeys vanished.

In 1955 a Monkey Orchid appeared near Faversham in Kent (at the current native site), but the single plant was eaten, perhaps by a horse. It may well have been able to bloom due to the outbreak of myxomatosis which resulted in the mass-flowering of orchids in Kent in that year. More were found in the following years, with up to 38 plants, ten of which flowered, in 1957-58, growing partly on open downland and partly in a nearby hazel copse. From 1958 until at least 1985 the plants in this colony were hand-pollinated to make sure that seed was produced. Numbers steadily increased, with 246 plants and 162 flowering spikes in 1964 and 205 flowering plants in 1965. The 1975-76 drought badly affected the colony, however, with none flowering but in 1977 plants reappeared and by the mid-1980s there were again 30-50 plants, with ten or so flowering. The population here is now stable at over 200 plants, although only a small proportion flower.

From 1958 onwards seed from the Faversham site was scattered at several other places in Kent, and a population became established at Park Gate Down. The first three plants flowered in 1965, seven years after seed was sown, but then not again until 1976 when two spikes appeared. This population stabilised at about 100 plants in the mid-1990s but has increased significantly since then.

A few plants appeared in dune grassland at Spurn Point in southeast Yorkshire in 1974, over 250km from the nearest known source of seed. This colony increased to a maximum of 25 plants, with nine flowering, but only persisted

▲ *28 May, Kent. The colour of the flowers is very variable. Some appear pale pink at a distance, others are darker and redder.*

until 1983, after which the site was washed away in a storm.

The Sainsbury Orchid Project organised by the Royal Horticultural Society has become involved in the conservation effort. Each year a few seedpods are sent to Kew from Hartslock. Progress with propagating Monkey Orchid has been slow because cultivation has been restricted to sterile, asymbiotic techniques, and germination and growth rates are low. By 1996, ten plants had been raised to a size where they could be planted out, and in September 1996 the tubers were placed in two clumps on the edge of the existing colony. In 1997 two of these came up, but since then only one has appeared.

MILITARY ORCHID
Orchis militaris

The Military Orchid combines two of the qualities which make orchids so alluring; great rarity and great beauty. It is one of Britain's most attractive species and is found regularly at just three sites (two of which are, happily, open to the public). Thought to be extinct in Britain by the early part of the 20th century, it was dramatically rediscovered in 1947, although for a long time the site was kept a closely guarded secret. Like its cousin, the equally rare Monkey Orchid, it has been monitored, managed and mollycoddled since its rediscovery, but we are still far from unlocking all its secrets.

Identification

One of the so-called 'manikin' orchids in which the flower resembles a tiny human figure, Military Orchid brings to mind a soldier. The sepals and petals form a 'helmet', purple-striped on the interior, and the lip has four lobes, two for the 'arms' and two for the 'legs'. The rows of purple spots down the centre of the lip are reminiscent of buttons on a soldier's tunic. The allusion to the military was coined before soldiers habitually wore red uniforms and may refer to the resemblance of the hood to an ancient 'coal-scuttle' helmet.

Similar species

Monkey Orchid resembles this species in the general structure of the flower, but its 'legs' are kinked, narrower and do not broaden towards the tip, and the hood formed by the sepals and petals is more open. Also, its flower spike is not only shorter and more crowded but also more jumbled and disarrayed, lacking 'military precision', and all the flowers open at roughly the same time.

Habitat

Military Orchid is found in grassland, scrub, woodland glades, on woodland edges and, formerly, rough fields. It always grows on chalk. The species does best in light scrub on old pastures and in the shelter of woodland edges. It favours some shade and needs bare ground for seedling establishment (rather than a closed grass sward), but it does not do well if there is too much shade. Recorded up to 183m above sea level in the Chilterns.

▲ *31 May, Suffolk. The colony at Mildenhall has thrived since the overshadowing trees were removed.*

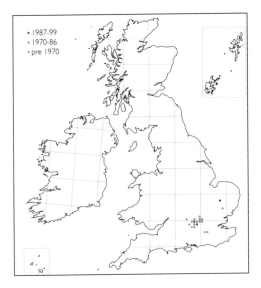

• 1987-99
• 1970-86
• pre 1970

Flowering period

Mid-May to mid-June, the flowers are at their best in late May and early June. Once a flower has been pollinated it usually shrivels within a day.

Range

Currently confined to two sites in the Chilterns, in Buckinghamshire and Oxfordshire, and one in Suffolk. Plants have been introduced into industrial waste-ground at Bolton in Lancashire (apparently from outside the United Kingdom) and to sites in Cambridgeshire and Kent. **World Range:** Europe and Siberia. In Europe occurs north to Holland, northern Germany, southeast Sweden and Estonia and south to northern Spain, central Italy, the former Yugoslavia, Bulgaria, Romania and European Turkey. Confined to the mountains in the southern parts of the range. In Siberia it extends east to the Altai Mountains and Lake Baikal.

How to find it

Homefield Wood in Buckinghamshire and the Rex Graham Reserve at Mildenhall in Suffolk are the two public sites for the species.

DESCRIPTION

Height: 5-60cm but usually 20-45cm.
Stem: Green, variably tinged purple towards the tip.

Leaves: Bright shiny green, prominently keeled, strap-shaped or, on more robust plants, broader and more oval, and slightly hooded at the tip. Two to five leaves are carried in a basal rosette at around 45° above the horizontal, and there are two or three sheathing leaves higher on the stem, although the upper part of the stem is bare. In Suffolk the tip of the shoot appears above ground in late December or more usually early January and the leaves start to unfurl by early March.

Spike: Oval or conical, becoming cylindrical as all the flowers open. There are two to 25 flowers but up to 57 have been recorded on a particularly robust spike.

Bract: Triangular to oval, very short (much shorter than the ovary) and green, strongly washed purple or rose.

Ovary: Green, washed purple, boldly ribbed and strongly twisted.

Flower: Man-like, whitish, with purple spots and purple extremities. The sepals are oval with pointed tips, and the petals are narrower and more strap-shaped; they form a hood with the tips of the sepals swept upwards and the mouth of the hood very open. The sepals are pale dove grey, their outer surfaces lightly washed with lilac, becoming more purplish at the base; the unopened buds are therefore pale pinkish-grey. The inner surfaces have bold, longitudinal purplish lines and an irregular purplish wash. The petals are more uniformly pale purplish. The lip has two narrow, strap-shaped lobes forming the 'arms' and two shorter and broader lobes forming the 'legs', with an additional small pointed projection between the 'legs'. It is whitish, flushed pink, with the 'arms' and 'legs' more-or-less solidly purple. There are two rows of purple spots down the centre of the lip (the spots are formed by tiny papillae) and solid dark purple lines along the centre of the 'arms'. The spur is purple, short (about half the length of the ovary), cylindrical and slightly down-curved. The flowers are faintly vanilla-scented.

Subspecies

None.

▲ *31 May, Suffolk.*

Variation and varieties

Var. *militaris* is on average taller, with seven to 42 flowers. It has a relatively lax, open spike and paler flowers. The Suffolk colony has been assigned to this variety which is widespread in Europe.

Var. *tenuifrons* is on average shorter, with two to 26 flowers, a denser spike, darker flowers and narrower leaves. Endemic to England, the Chilterns plants belong to this variety

BIOLOGY

Pollination and reproduction

Military Orchid is pollinated by hover flies and bumblebees. It produces no nectar but insects may be attracted to the sugary sap in the wall of the spur. It has always been thought that few flowers are pollinated in Britain; rates of 3-11% are given for plants in the Suffolk colony and 2-28% of flowers were recorded as setting seed by Summerhayes (1968). At Homefield Wood, however, 40% and 24% of flowers were naturally pollinated in 1999 and 2000 respectively. Vegetative reproduction is probably important for the British populations, maintaining numbers when recruitment from seed is low.

Development and growth

This is a relatively long-lived orchid. Many plants will live for ten years after their first appearance above ground and a significant proportion live for at least 17 years. In a study in Suffolk the 'half-life' varied from 2.2-7.8 years (the 'half-life' is a measure of the life expectancy of the orchid after its first appearance above ground and marks the point at which 50% of the population that emerged in any given year has died).

The period between germination and the appearance of the first aerial shoot is three to five years and between 30% and 50% of plants flower in their first year above ground. Once they have appeared, most plants flower at least once and many do so every year, but intervals of 11 years between flowering have been noted. Perhaps a third of plants retreat underground during their life, usually spending only one year 'dormant', but in some cases up to three years and absences of up to eight years have been recorded in Suffolk. In any given year, 5-15% of the adult population can be underground. However, 'dormancy' is not a good option for the plants as underground plants have the highest probability of dying.

Hybrids

O. x. beyrichii, the hybrid with Monkey Orchid, occurred in Oxfordshire until the middle of the 19th century, after which the two parent species were not found together.

Name and classification

The specific name *militaris* means 'military'.

HISTORY AND CONSERVATION

A *Red Data Book* species that is classified as Vulnerable and specially protected under Schedule 8 of the Wildlife & Countryside Act 1981.

Gerard's *Historie of Plants*, first published in 1597, contains a description of 'Souldier's Satyrion' or 'Soldier's Cullions' (literally 'testicles') which presumably pertains to the Military Orchid: 'Souldiers Satyrion bringeth forth many broad large and ribbed leaves, spread upon the ground like unto those of the great Plantaine: among the which riseth up a fat stalke full of sap or juice, clothed or wrapped in the like leaves even to the tuft of flowers, whereupon doe grow little flowers resembling a little man, having a helmet upon his head, his hands, and legs cut off; white upon the inside, spotted with many purple spots, and the backe part of the flower of a deeper colour tending to redness. The rootes be greater stones than any of the kinds of Satyrions.' Gerard gives, however, no localities for his Souldier's Satyrion and may have copied his description from a European herbal.

The earliest localised record for the British Isles was in 1666 when Christopher Merrett noted both Military and Monkey Orchids in his *Pinax Rerum Naturalium Britannicarum*

▲ *31 May, Suffolk. A few-flowered spike with very lightly marked flowers.*

('A picture of British natural history'): '...on several Chalkey hills neer the highway from Wallingford to Redding on Barkshire side the river...' This reference to the Berkshire Downs was apparently the first record of both species in England and originated from information supplied by a William Brown of Magdalen College, Oxford.

Military Orchid was often confused with Monkey and Lady Orchids, and many older records, unless supported by identifiable specimens, are open to doubt. It was recorded reliably from Belchamp Walter near Sudbury in Essex in 1729, and there are also old records for the North Downs of Surrey, including Box Hill in the 1830s, and Kent (a herbarium specimen dated 1836 from Cobham near Rochester).

Like Monkey Orchid, the stronghold of the species was always the Chilterns, where it ranged from 'just west of the Thames in the region of Streatley and Basildon, along the Chiltern Hills through Oxfordshire and

Buckinghamshire, to the neighbourhood of Tring in Hertfordshire and to Harefield in Middlesex. It seems to have been particularly abundant around High Wycombe and between this town and Great Marlow on the Thames' (Summerhayes, 1968). Once fairly common within this limited area, it declined dramatically from around 1850 and was thought to be extinct after 1929 when the last specimen was collected from Hertfordshire. Several factors contributed to the decline, including the ploughing-up of downland and the collection of specimens for both herbaria and gardens, but the main cause may well have been a big increase in the number of rabbits. There have been no subsequent records from Berkshire, Hertfordshire or Middlesex.

The Military Orchid became something of a Holy Grail for British botanists. Indeed, it was the title and main subject of Jocelyn Brooke's semi-autobiographical *The Military Orchid*, published in 1948. In May 1947 it was dramatically rediscovered by J. E. Lousley at Homefield Wood in Buckinghamshire, an area from which it had not previously been recorded. 'The excursion was intended as a picnic, so I had left my usual apparatus at home and took only my note-book. But I selected our stopping places on the chalk with some care, and naturally wandered off to see what I could find. To my delight I stumbled on the orchid just coming into flower' (Lousley 1969). There were 39 plants, with 18 flower spikes, although five had been bitten off, probably by rabbits. Lousley noted that the orchids growing in shade were either flowerless or had small spikes and thought that the increase in available light after trees were felled during World War Two had probably prompted the appearance of the plants.

Lousley kept his discovery a closely guarded secret, fearing that the colony would be wiped out by collectors, and many others tried to track down this hidden treasure but to no avail. At last, in 1956, after a long and systematic search

◀ *31 May, Suffolk.*

▲ *31 May, Suffolk. A richly-coloured spike.*

of all likely sites, the colony at Homefield Wood was found by Richard Fitter and Frances Rose. They dispatched a postcard to Lousley with the simple but cryptic message 'The soldiers are at home in their fields'. The discovery was not made public even then, but Homefield Wood came to be managed by BBOWT in 1969 and they eventually announced to the press in 1975 that the Military Orchid had returned. This resulted in headlines like 'The Beauty that must blossom in secret'. It was not until the end of the 1980s that the location was made truly public, and visitors are now welcomed.

Homefield Wood was originally largely composed of Beeches with some areas of chalk grassland on a south-facing slope. The wood was largely clear-felled in the winter of 1947, and the Military Orchid was found in the spring of that year on chalk grassland with scattered trees and scrub. The Forestry

Commission has owned the wood since 1955, and most of the felled areas were replanted with conifers in the 1950s. The area around the colony was planted with Beech in 1960-61, and other trees regenerated naturally to form a mixed woodland; trees also invaded the grassland.

When first found, there were two distinct colonies at Homefield Wood. Colony 'A' held 31 plants in 1947 and peaked at 35 in 1949, but the numbers fell steadily until the last few were seen in 1958, with a single plant reappearing in 1961. Myxomatosis had decimated rabbit populations in 1955, and this probably caused a dramatic increase in scrub which, combined with disturbance during tree-planting and the spread of Rosebay Willowherb, led to the extinction of this colony. Colony 'B' presumably held just eight plants when found, but this is the area where the orchid survives to the present day. This colony was fenced off in 1968, brambles invaded and a thick understorey developed. The population of Military Orchids slowly fell to a low point of 28 plants in 1984, with just five flowering.

Active habitat management started in 1981 with the removal of scrub and later on large, overshadowing Yews. This may have led to a recovery in numbers in this area to over 50 plants (with over 30 flowering) by 1989. In 1985 a small adjacent area was clear-felled and the orchids eventually spread into this, flowering for the first time in 1995; this clearing held half the flowering plants by 2003. Military Orchids also appeared over 100m away through the wood in a third open area in 1983. Overall, the number of plants at Homefield Wood steadily increased to about 80 in 1995, with 45 in flower.

Since 1995 there has been a dramatic upturn, with over 200 plants, at least half of which flowered, in 2003. In recent years management has included fencing the colonies to exclude rabbits and deer during the growing season. These enclosures are grazed by sheep in the autumn and winter, before the orchids appear above ground. They are also mown and

raked, and scrub is controlled. In addition, up to 20% of the plants at Holmfield Wood were hand-pollinated from 1986-98. Hand-pollination can result in almost 100% seed set and does not 'weaken' the plants (as had been suggested); hand-pollinated individuals have flowered every year for a decade.

Military Orchid was found at a second site in the Oxfordshire Chilterns in 1970. The number of flowering plants did not exceed five until 1999 and there were none in 1984-87. Since 1999, however, there has been a rapid increase, with 25 flowering plants in 2003, together with a further 25 vegetative rosettes. This population was also hand-pollinated for at least 10 years from 1988.

As part of the conservation programme, plants propagated asymbiotically at the Royal Botanic Gardens were planted out at Homefield Wood and the nearby Warburg reserve in 1996 (a total of 231 tubers, both one and two years old). Survival was poor but those that remained first flowered in 2000 and 2002 respectively. In addition, 25 wild plants were transplanted from Homefield Wood in 2000 to a site around 25km away. Survival of these mature plants has been better than young seedlings, with some flowering and setting seed.

On 2 June 1955 the Military Orchid was found at Mildenhall in Suffolk, a region from which there were no previous records. The colony was in an old chalk pit where there were at least 500 plants, mostly on a heap of pure chalk among birch and Wild Privet. There were over 100 flowering spikes, but within a short time the majority had been nibbled off, perhaps by deer, and only 16 fruiting spikes remained by mid-August. The colony was within a Forestry Commission plantation and at the time of its discovery the surrounding pines were only 1.5m tall, thus the site was open and sunny.

By 1958 the number of plants in the Suffolk colony had risen to 2,854 and remained at this level until the late 1960s, although only about 10% flowered. However, the population then

▲ 7 June, Suffolk. A large spike, well-out.

declined rapidly to 252 plants in 1971, with perhaps only 100 in the following years. To protect the orchids the Forestry Commission had erected a tall wire fence around the pit in the 1960s. This excluded both deer and people and within a few years Sycamore and Wild Privet had taken over. These were cleared in autumn 1972 and the colony increased slightly and stabilised at 300-400 plants, with about 100 flowering. Scrub clearance continued and the overshadowing Corsican Pines were finally removed in 1985-86, allowing in much more light, and from 1987 there was a dramatic increase in the population. In 1990 there were 279 flowering spikes and 1,115 plants and in 2000 there were 748 flowering plants and too many non-flowering plants to count.

The story of the two Military Orchid colonies highlights the need for the appropriate management of rare orchids. For example, in both cases the colonies were fenced in the 1960s, and although this excluded deer and rabbits it came close to destroying them because scrub took over. The recent increases in Military Orchid are likely to be directly attributable to better management rather than a more favourable climate. This species seems well-adapted to hard winters and is therefore unlikely to have benefited from recent mild years, unlike Monkey Orchid.

Genetic fingerprinting has shown that the three English colonies are distinct and may represent independent colonisations from Europe. Each colony is thus valuable and worthy of conservation in its own right.

Past and present occurrence of Military Orchid in Britain and Ireland (based on presence or absence in 10km squares of the National Grid; data from the New Atlas).

	Britain	Ireland
total historical range, 1500-1999	19	0
current range	3 (0.1%*)	0
% lost, 1500-1969	79%	
% lost, 1970-1986	5%	
% lost, total	84%	

* current range as a % of the total number of 10km squares

LADY ORCHID
Orchis purpurea

The sight of a group of Lady Orchids in a woodland glade in May is always a delight. Even those lucky enough to see them regularly cannot fail to be impressed by the spectacular show put on by this stately orchid. It is largely confined to Kent where it is relatively common in chalky woodlands on the North Downs.

Identification
Straightforward. It is usually rather large and statuesque, and the unopened buds are dark reddish-purple. Lady Orchid is one of the 'manikin' orchids, and the flowers form a miniature human figure. The sepals and petals form a dark 'bonnet' which, with the unopened buds, contrasts strongly with the whitish, dark-spotted lip. The lip itself is divided into several lobes to form the 'arms' and the 'skirt' of the lady.

Similar species
Burnt Orchid is superficially similar, with dark buds, a dark hood and a white, purple-spotted lip but it is very much smaller, seldom more than 15cm tall.

Habitat
Lady Orchid is found in woodland, both ancient woodland and secondary woods, but almost always on thin, well-drained chalky soils (rarely also on limestone or other calcareous substrates). It favours beechwoods and often grows on south-facing slopes, frequently on banks or on the 'terraces' formed by the root plates of the trees, either among a carpet of Dog's Mercury or on bare leaf-litter. However, its preferred habitat may be scrub or coppice, and it does not flower so freely in shade, being happier in open, well-lit situations, such as along paths and rides, in clearings and along the lower edges of woods. Indeed, it may cease to flower and 'disappear' if the shade becomes too dense, only spectacularly to reappear after coppicing, tree falls or felling opens up the canopy. Conversely, although it is often found

▶ 14 May, Kent. The leaves are shiny green and rather flaccid.

just outside a wood, it rarely occurs in the full sun of open downland. Lady Orchid also likes shelter from the wind, and in exposed situations the leaves and flowers may be scorched in a cold spring, the leaves often turning yellow. It occurs up to 200m above sea level.

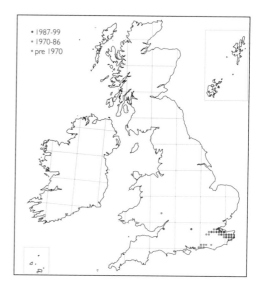

- 1987-99
- 1970-86
- pre 1970

Flowering period

Early May to early June, exceptionally from mid to late April, varying from season to season, but plants are generally at their best in mid to late May.

Range

Lady Orchid is locally frequent on the North Downs in Kent with more than 100 sites in two areas. First, the downs on either side of the Medway Valley and sporadically eastwards towards the Stour Valley. Second, the downs between the eastern slope of the Stour Valley and Dover. Elsewhere, there are two current sites in Oxfordshire (see History and Conservation). **World range:** Essentially Europe, with outlying populations in North Africa, Asia Minor, the Crimea and the Caucasus (the last sometimes treated as a distinct species). In Europe it occurs north to Holland and Denmark, east to western and southern Poland and Ukraine and south to central Spain, Italy, northern Greece and

▲ 14 May, Kent. There are around 100 sites in Kent, some with over 1,000 flowering plants.

▲ *14 May, Kent. Although Lady Orchid is associated with woodland, it does best where there is some sun.*

Bulgaria, also found on Corsica and Sardinia and, in North Africa, in Algeria and Tunisia. In the south of the range Lady Orchid is confined to the mountains.

How to find it

This large and conspicuous species is easy to spot when in flower, but as with all orchids, non-flowering plants can be hard to find and the proportion of a population in flower varies from year to year. Especially good sites in Kent include Yocklett's Bank and it also occurs at Wye.

DESCRIPTION

Height: 20-50cm, exceptionally to 100cm.
Stem: Green, becoming purplish-brown towards the tip.
Leaves: Green and shiny or almost 'greasy'. There are three to five, sometimes seven, broad, oval to oval-oblong leaves. The lower leaves are blunter and form a basal rosette, the upper leaves becoming successively more pointed, keeled and clasping. They appear above ground between mid-January and mid-February.
Spike: Oval to oblong in shape and lax or densely flowered. Robust plants have up to 50 flowers.
Bract: Greenish to purple, tiny, elongated and scale-like.
Ovary: Bright green, sometimes washed purple along the six ribs, and distinctly twisted.
Flower: Whitish, finely spotted with reddish-purple and with a contrastingly dark hood. The sepals are oval, and the petals are shorter, much narrower and more strap-shaped but broaden to a spear-shaped tip; together they form a hood (the 'bonnet'). They are pale green, irregularly blotched on both surfaces with dark purple or purplish-brown, the blotches becoming more numerous and coalescing towards the tip, base and sides; the unopened buds are therefore very dark. The lip is pale pink to white, washed violet or rose around the edges, variably spotted pink to reddish-purple (the spots are formed by tufts of tiny papillae). It is deeply lobed with two long, narrow 'arms' and two broad terminal lobes, often with frilled

▲ 14 May, Kent. The spots on the lip are composed of tufts of tiny papillae.

edges, which form the lady's 'skirt' (the latter usually have a tiny tooth between them). The spur is cylindrical, from a quarter to a half of the length of the ovary, curved and pale green blotched with purple. The column is pale green washed pinkish or purplish, and the pollinia are blotched purple. The flowers are variably reported to smell of vanilla or bitter almonds or to be unscented.

Subspecies
None.

Variation and varieties
Relatively variable. Plants growing in the open tend to be shorter and darker-flowered than those in woods with a tendency towards brown rather than purple markings. There is also much variation in the shape, colour and markings of the lip; this may be white and even unspotted in some plants and heavily washed pink with dark purple spots in others. The hood may also vary from paler to darker shades of purple.

Plants in west Kent differ slightly from those in east Kent (from the eastern side of the Stour Valley to Dover). They are, on average, shorter (20-38cm tall rather than 30-76cm) with a shorter, denser flower spike, shorter ovaries (13-19mm rather than 19-25mm) and lips that are more heavily spotted and washed rose to purple (rather than salmon to brownish-red); their lips are also blunter and less deeply lobed. These two groups of populations have not, however, been given names.

Var. *albida* lacks anthocyanin pigments and thus has a pure white lip and a distinctive white or straw-coloured hood with green veins. It is scarce.

Var. *pseudomilitaris* has narrower and more reddish lobes on the lip, resembling the 'arms' and 'legs' of a Military Orchid. The hood is, however, the normal reddish-purple. It is rare.

BIOLOGY

Pollination and reproduction
The flowers are pollinated by small flies and bees, including small digger wasps. Seed-set is variable, sometimes very low, with only 3-10% of flowers producing ripe capsules. However, in some years and at some sites it can be good. Most reproduction is by seed although vegetative reproduction also takes places, and clumps of plants can be formed in this way.

Development and growth
From germination to first flowering takes eight to ten years and the pattern of development is typical of the genus *Orchis*. Plants may live for at least another ten years, flowering at least three times in that period but seldom every year; the remains of the previous year's dried, dead spike is not often seen next to the current flowers. There are therefore usually large numbers of non-flowering plants in any population.

Hybrids
O. x *wilmsii*, the hybrid with Early Purple Orchid, has been reported very rarely in Kent. *O.* x *macra*, the hybrid with Man Orchid, was found in east Kent in 1998.

◀ 14 May, Kent. A flower with a relatively pale hood and fine markings.

Hybrids with Military Orchid have also been reported (Summerhayes, 1968).

Name and classification

The specific name *purpurea* means simply 'purple'.

HISTORY AND CONSERVATION

First recorded by Christopher Merrett in 1666 in his *Pinax Rerum Naturalium Britannicum* ('A picture of British natural history'), 'On Gadshill in Kent'.

Since its first discovery, the Lady Orchid has been largely restricted to Kent, where there are many sites. Currently, there are also two sites in south Oxfordshire. In the Thames Valley area a single plant was discovered growing under Beeches in mixed woodland in 1961. It flowered again in 1962 and 1964 but then vanished. Seven plants were found at the same site in 1986 (the Beeches and nearby Yews having been felled in the late 1970s) and this colony has subsequently flourished, with at least

46 plants and 29 flower spikes in 1997. Also in south Oxfordshire, there have been up to three plants (mostly non-flowering) at Hartslock since at least 2000.

Past and present occurrence of Lady Orchid in Britain and Ireland (based on presence or absence in 10km squares of the National Grid; data from the New Atlas).

	Britain	Ireland
total historical range, 1500-1999	37	0
current range	16 (0.6%*)	0
% lost, 1500-1969	46%	
% lost, 1970-1986	11%	
% lost, total	57%	

* current range as a % of the total number of 10km squares

Lady Orchid is Nationally Scarce and has been lost from 57% of the historic range. It was formerly found in Surrey, mostly prior to 1930, but the last site was at Coulsdon, where it was present until 1959. Also extirpated in West Sussex, where there were at least five sites, the most recent record being in 1976; there is an old, unconfirmed record for East Sussex. Elsewhere, recorded from Herefordshire in a disused quarry in 1967, at Leigh Woods in the Avon Gorge, Somerset, in 1990 (although this plant quite possibly originated from Lady Orchids in cultivation at the University of Bristol Botanic Gardens a short distance away), and formerly occurred in the Channel Islands. A widely quoted 1738 record from Essex has been shown to have involved Military Orchid.

Past declines were due to the loss of woodlands and the cessation of coppicing. The population in Kent is now stable and some colonies are large (over 3,000 plants were counted at one site in recent years) although others are declining, and it does not easily colonise new areas. It has long been noted that Lady Orchids are subject to the depredations of rabbits and deer which nip off the flowers and attack the leaves. Slugs are also attracted to the species. Deer are now commoner in England than at any time for a thousand years, making this more of an issue. Feral wild boars are also a potential problem as they can root out and eat the tubers.

▲ 14 May, Kent. The spike is pyramidal at first but becomes cylindrical as more flowers open.

EARLY PURPLE ORCHID
Orchis mascula

As its name suggests, this is the first orchid to appear in the spring in most of Britain and Ireland. It heralds the coming season and gladdens the heart on an early spring day, whether as splashes of purple among a carpet of Bluebells or scattered among Cowslips and violets on a roadside bank. One of the commonest and most widespread orchids, Early Purple Orchid is nevertheless very local in many areas and has largely vanished from farmland habitats in the lowlands where it is now confined to woods, roadsides, churchyards and nature reserves.

▲ 22 May, Co. Clare. In most places this is the first orchid to bloom, with rich purple flowers; well-named indeed.

Identification

Early-flowering, purple flowers and spotted leaves are a distinctive combination. Unspotted leaves are not uncommon, however, and there is a scarce white-flowered variant; these could be more problematic but a look at the structure of the flower should prevent any confusion.

Similar species

Green-winged Orchid is easily separated by the parallel green stripes on its sepals. The hood of its flower is formed by all the sepals and petals, so that it lacks the erect 'wings' of Early Purple Orchid. In addition, Green-winged Orchid always has unspotted leaves and usually also a smaller, fewer-flowered spike, and it does not grow in woodland.

Marsh orchids have flowers of various shades of purple and some have spotted leaves, but the flowers are usually more extensively and more heavily marked with black dots, lines and squiggles. Their spur is short and often sack-like and is either straight or curves downwards, whereas it curves slightly upwards in Early Purple Orchid. The spots on the leaves tend to be regular and often elongated sideways rather than irregular and often elongated lengthwise as in Early Purple Orchid.

Habitat

Very variable. It can occur in both grassland and woodland and on a variety of soils, although it does have a definite preference for calcareous soils on chalk, limestone or boulder clay and avoids acid conditions. It is found in a wide variety of old grasslands, both dry chalk downland and damp hill pastures, as well as meadows, rocky mountain ledges, railway embankments and cuttings, road verges, grass-covered dry-stone walls and limestone pavements. It also grows in deciduous woodland, usually in the better-lit areas along rides, tracks and woodland edges. Early Purple Orchid is particularly associated with coppice woodland, where there is usually a great increase in the number of flowering plants in the second or third year after coppicing but a decline thereafter as the canopy closes again. The species does not colonise new sites easily and is usually found in ancient woodland rather than relatively recently established plantations or secondary woodland (unless, of course, woodland and scrub have invaded old orchid-rich grassland). Conversely, many colonies on road verges and banks may be relicts of long-gone woods. Recorded up to 880m above sea level (Caenlochan, Angus).

Flowering period

Early April to early June in the south, exceptionally from mid-March, although most are in flower from late April to late May. Flowering is on average a little later in upland areas and in Scotland, the season occasionally lasts until early July. Plants in sunny, sheltered spots flower earliest, whereas those in cool, shaded, wet areas will be last. Once it has set seed, the tall spikes with numerous dark purplish-brown capsules are conspicuous well into the summer.

Range

Found throughout the British Isles, including the Channel Islands, Isle of Man, Hebrides, Orkney and Shetland. Although generally fairly common or even abundant, it may be very local in areas of acid soils and is largely absent from some regions, such as the Fens, south Lancashire and mid-west Wales. It is also very scattered in the Borders, northeast Scotland, Orkney, Shetland, the Outer Hebrides and southeast Ireland. **World range:** Western Europe, extending to North Africa and Asia Minor. Occurs north to the Faeroe Islands, *c.* 70°N in Norway, central Sweden and the Baltic States. The southern and eastern limits are

▲ 24 May, Co. Clare. Early Purple Orchid is very conspicuous in The Burren and sometimes forms beautiful 'rock gardens' with Primroses and other flowers.

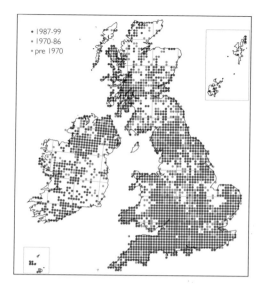

Spike: Oval or cylindrical but often rather irregular in shape and rather open, especially in the lower half, with ten to 50 flowers, occasionally more.

Bract: Green, usually strongly washed purple. The bracts are lanceolate and about as long as the ovary, which they clasp.

Ovary: Green, variably washed purple and clearly ribbed.

Flower: Various shades of purple, occasionally pale rose-pink or white. The sepals are lanceolate, the lateral sepals asymmetrical, and the petals are smaller and more arrow-shaped. The upper sepal and petals form a hood over the column and the two lateral sepals are held erect and pushed backwards, resembling 'angel's wings' (they may almost touch at the rear). The lip points downwards and outwards and is three-lobed with the central lobe usually the

poorly known due to confusion with closely-related species, but it is found south and east to Italy, Greece, Turkey and Bulgaria and is probably absent from much of Central Europe. Also present in the Canary Islands, Balearics, Corsica, Sicily and Malta, and Tunisia in North Africa.

How to find it

Generally common and easy to find. In some areas, such as the Peak District, Yorkshire Dales and The Burren in western Ireland, Early Purple Orchid occurs in large, extensive colonies but it is more usually found in small and often scattered groups.

DESCRIPTION

Height: 10-45cm, occasionally to 60cm.
Stem: Stout, pale green, angled and usually flushed purple towards the tip.
Leaves: The three to eight basal leaves are variably oblong-lanceolate in shape and often blunt-tipped. They are glossy green, usually marked with large, irregular, rounded or elongated blackish-purple spots on the upper surfaces and rarely also on the undersides. They are held close to the ground, either spreading upwards and outwards or in a flatter rosette. There are two or three rather smaller and more pointed sheathing leaves higher on the stem and these may have a few spots or a purple wash.

▲ 10 May, Norfolk. The flowers are usually purple but can be a delicate rose-pink.

◀ 22 May, Co. Clare.

largest. The side-lobes are folded downwards, and the entire lip is sometimes folded or creased along its centre line. The terminal lobe is shallowly notched and the edges of all three lobes are crinkled (crenate). The base of the lip and mouth of the spur are much paler and whiter, sometimes with some yellow tones, and usually spotted with purple, the spots composed of dense tufts of short papillae. The spur is long and narrow, at least as long as the ovary, broadens a little towards a blunt tip and curves upwards. The column is variably greenish or purple, and the pollinia are dark green. The flowers are initially sweet-smelling, recalling honey or Lily-of-the-valley, but this quickly changes to a rank smell, usually said to be like tomcat's urine and to be especially pungent at night.

Subspecies
None recognised. In the Outer Hebrides, far north of mainland Scotland, Shetland and a few places in western Ireland plants are just 5-10cm tall and flower from early June to early July. These populations are sometimes named *O. m. ebudium.*

Variation and varieties
As in many orchids, plants growing in the open are often shorter and stockier than those in woodland. These are sometimes referred to as

▲ 25 May, Co. Clare. The white flowered variety alba has an unmarked lip and yellow pollinia. It is scarce.

the 'grassland' and 'woodland' forms.

Var. *alba* lacks anthocyanin pigments and has white, unmarked flowers with yellow pollinia, an entirely green stem and bracts, and no leaf spots. It is rather scarce. An even scarcer variant has white flowers which retain purple spots at the base of the lip and sometimes has spotted leaves too. A 'broken-coloured' variant has also been recorded very rarely and this has a pale pink lip, copiously flecked with tiny purplish markings.

BIOLOGY

Pollination and reproduction
The flowers are pollinated by bumblebees and to a lesser extent cuckoobees and a variety of solitary bees. A visiting insect touches the

▲ 12 May, Norfolk. The long spur contains no nectar; the bright colours of the flower are therefore a 'deceit' to lure potential pollinators.

column and the pollinia are stuck to its head
by the sticky viscidia. Once the bee has left
the flower, the pollinia on the insect rotate
forward in about 30 seconds so that they will
make contact with the stigma in the next flower
visited. Early Purple Orchid is self-compatible
and is sometimes self-pollinated.

The flowers of Early Purple Orchid have
no nectar and offer no reward to a pollinator,
although it has been suggested that a sugary sap
is produced inside the wall of the spur. Rather,
it is thought that the orchid takes advantage of
the naivety of the bees which, newly emerged
from hibernation in the spring, have yet to learn
which flowers are genuine sources of nectar.
These naive bees are attracted, at least for a
while, by the bright colours and scent of the
flowers. The various species of bee emerge from
hibernation at different times, and therefore
the orchid can take advantage of a succession of
pollinators as the season progresses. Seed-set
is variable, with the lowest, earliest-opening
flowers most likely to be pollinated. Vegetative
reproduction may occur occasionally via the
production of additional tubers.

Development and growth

The first aerial leaves are usually produced in
the fourth year after germination, and more
and bigger leaves appear in successive seasons
until enough reserves have been accumulated
to produce a flower spike; up to eight years
may elapse between the first appearance above
ground and the first flowers. Around 60%
of plants will flower in successive years; the
remainder either appear as a rosette of leaves
or, in about 17% of cases, spend a year 'dormant'
underground before appearing again. Up to
12 years dormancy has been noted in Europe.
A maximum lifespan of 13 years after the first
appearance of leaves has been recorded.

Hybrids

O. x wilmsii, the hybrid with Lady Orchid, has
been reported very rarely in Kent.

▶ *22 May, Co. Clare. The influence of the different flower
colours on potential pollinators is unknown.*

▲ *24 April, Norfolk. Hazel coppice is the classic habitat.*

Name and classification

The specific name *mascula* means 'male' and may be a reference to its vigour, early flowering or is perhaps another allusion to the masculinity of the tubers.

HISTORY AND CONSERVATION

The first British record dates from as long ago as 1562 when William Turner noted in his *Herball*, 'There are divers kindes of orchis … one kinde … hath many spottes in the leafe and is called adder grasse in Northumberland'.

Locally common in many areas, Early Purple Orchid is the third most widespread species of orchid in the British Isles (after Common Spotted and Heath Spotted Orchids). However, it has vanished from 28% of its historical range in Britain and 21% in Ireland, and the decline appears to be ongoing in Britain. Losses are due to the destruction or 'coniferisation' of woodland and, perhaps more importantly in recent years, the loss of permanent grasslands as pastures and meadows have been ploughed and reseeded. In most of lowland Britain, away from reserves, the species is now largely confined to ancient woodland and to marginal sites, such as road verges and churchyards, which have escaped agricultural improvement. In the north and west overgrazing may be a problem as the species is tolerant of light grazing only.

Past and present occurrence of Early Purple Orchid in Britain and Ireland (based on presence or absence in 10km squares of the National Grid; data from the New Atlas).

	Britain	Ireland
total historical range, 1500-1999	1,971	475
current range	1,416 (50%*)	377 (37%)
% lost, 1500-1969	17%	17%
% lost, 1970-1986	11%	4%
% lost, total	28%	21%

* current range as a % of the total number of 10km squares

Intergeneric hybrids

'*O. x morioides*', the hybrid with Green-winged Orchid, has been recorded rarely and sporadically in England and Wales. As Green-winged Orchid is no longer in the genus *Orchis*, a new name is needed for this hybrid.

The single species in this genus is found in Europe and Greenland, with just a toe-hold in North America, in eastern Canada.

Taxonomy
Sometimes *Pseudorchis* is united with the fragrant orchids in the genus *Gymnadenia*. It differs in having a shorter spur, all three sepals arranged with the petals to form the hood of the flower (not just the upper sepal) and a tuber that is so deeply divided that it may appear to be several cylindrical tubers.

Name
The generic name *Pseudorchis* derives from the Greek '*pseud*' meaning false and is a reference to its relationship to the genus *Orchis*.

GENUS *PSEUDORCHIS*
SMALL WHITE ORCHID

SMALL WHITE ORCHID
Pseudorchis albida

Other names: *Leucorchis albida, Gymnadenia albida*; in North America *Pseudorchis straminea* Newfoundland Orchid

This delicate and unassuming orchid is a boreal species whose generally northern distribution worldwide is reflected in Britain and Ireland. In this respect it is similar to Lesser Twayblade and Creeping Lady's-tresses. Like many other northern plants, it has declined drastically in the southern parts of its range and disappeared from much of England, Wales and Ireland.

▲ 6 June, Cumbria. Despite its white flowers, this petite orchid can be hard to see in long grass.

◄ 6 June, Cumbria.

Identification

The combination of its small stature, dense spike of creamy-white flowers and deeply three-lobed lip is distinctive. The individual flowers are bell-shaped and very small, just 2-4mm across (smaller even than the ovary). The spike is carried on a long stem with a cluster of shiny green leaves at the base.

Similar species

Creeping Lady's-tresses is superficially similar but flowers later in the year, on short, dry turf (although occasionally on moorland). Its flowers also have glandular hairs but its lip is rather different, being spout-shaped rather than three-lobed.

Irish Lady's-tresses flowers even later in the summer than Creeping Lady's-tresses and barely overlaps with Small White Orchid. It has bigger flowers arranged in three columns around the spike. The lip is also formed into a spout.

Dense-flowered Orchid is superficially similar to Small White Orchid, and the flowering periods may just overlap, but the lip is very different and the hood is tightly closed.

White-flowered varieties of Pyramidal, spotted and fragrant orchids have been mistaken for Small White Orchid, but their flowers are larger and differ in many other details.

Habitat

Small White Orchid grows in rough grassland on poor, well-drained soils, both mildly acidic and base-rich. It is found on hill pastures, hay meadows, road verges, banks, streamsides and grassy ledges. It will grow in the partial shade of shrubs and bushes and is sometimes found on recently burnt moorland among short Heather (disappearing again once the Heather regenerates to form a closed community). Very rarely, the species has been found in oak woodland on acid soils and on stabilised coastal dunes. Generally it occurs in the uplands at over 165m above sea level and has been recorded as high as 500m at Alston Moor in Cumbria and 550m at Ben Chaisteil in Argyll, but it is also found near sea level in western Scotland.

Flowering period

Late May to mid-July, depending on altitude and latitude. It is latest at higher altitudes in the north and earliest in Ireland but is generally at its best around mid-June. The flowers tend to wither quickly.

Range

Small White Orchid is commonest and most widespread in northern and western Scotland, including the Inner Hebrides and Orkney. It is now almost absent from the central lowlands and southern uplands of Scotland, merely clinging on at a few isolated sites in Dumfriesshire, Ayrshire and Roxburghshire. The species is similarly much reduced in northern England and is now found rather rarely in

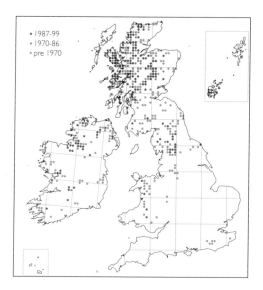

* 1987-99
* 1970-86
* pre 1970

▲ 6 June, Cumbria. The sepals are whiter than the petals and lip, which tend to be distinctly yellowish (or greenish).

▲ *6 June, Cumbria. The three-lobed lip can only be seen on close inspection.*

over the Urals into northwest Siberia). In the south it is found in the Pyrenees, Massif Central, Corsica, Alps, Apennines, Balkans, Carpathians and Transylvanian Alps east to Ukraine. Between and around these two centres of distribution there are scattered records, e.g. in Bulgaria, northern Greece and recently from Crete. But, as in the British Isles, the species has vanished from many lowland areas and is extinct in Belgium, Luxemburg and Holland. It is also found in southern Greenland and in North America, where it is restricted to a small area in northwest Newfoundland and western Quebec.

How to find it

Small and inconspicuous, this orchid can be hard to spot, especially as it is often found singly or in small numbers. Sites in Scotland include Keltneyburn (Perth & Kinross), Glen Cova (Angus) and Feoch Meadows (Ayrshire).

DESCRIPTION

Height: 8-40cm but usually less than 20cm and only very exceptionally to 40cm.

Stem: Greenish, slightly angled towards the tip, with two or three whitish or brownish sheaths at the base.

Leaves: There are four to six shiny, green, oval to oval-lanceolate, keeled sheathing leaves at the base of the stem and one or two narrower and more bract-like leaves above them.

Spike: Dense, cylindrical and often rather one-sided, with 20-40 flowers (exceptionally as few as ten or as many as 70).

Bract: Green, lanceolate with a pointed tip, and as long as or just longer than the ovary, which it clasps.

Ovary: Green, slightly twisted, with three obvious ridges. The ovary is strongly curled over towards the tip so that the flower faces more-or-less downwards.

Flower: The flowers are small (rather smaller than the ovary and bracts) and very pale, with the sepals whitish or creamy and the petals, lip and spur washed more greenish or yellowish. The sepals are elliptical and blunt-tipped and

Cumbria, Northumberland, Co. Durham and mid-west and northwest Yorkshire. In Wales it is found at a few scattered sites in Breconshire, Merionethshire, Denbighshire and Caernarvonshire. In Ireland it is similarly very scattered, with odd sites in Co. Kerry, Co. Limerick, Co. Clare, Co. Cavan and Co. Donegal. There are small clusters of sites in northern Co. Tipperary and central Galway but the main concentration lies in the northwest, in Co. Sligo, Co. Leitrim and Co. Fermanagh. Elsewhere there is another cluster of sites in Co. Tyrone, Co. Derry and Co. Antrim in Northern Ireland. **World range:** Small White Orchid has an 'amphi-Atlantic' distribution and is found in Europe and northeast North America. In Europe it occurs in two discrete areas. To the north it is found in Iceland (where it is abundant), the Faeroe Islands, Denmark, Scandinavia (north to northernmost Norway) and northern Russia (just creeping form a loose hood that encloses the similarly shaped petals and the column. The lip is short, broader than long and deeply three-lobed. The central lobe is triangular, usually longer, wider and blunter than the side-lobes, which are narrower and more lanceolate in shape. The spur is short (2-3mm), tubular or sack-shaped, blunt-tipped and down-curved and contains abundant nectar. The flowers have a delicate scent of vanilla.

Subspecies

Small White Orchid is divided into two subspecies. The nominate subspecies *P. a. albida* is found in the British Isles, central Europe and lowland Scandinavia. Subspecies *straminea*, with larger and yellower flowers, is found in the mountains of central Europe and Scandinavia, Faeroe Islands, Iceland, Greenland and North America. The latter is often treated as a distinct species, *Pseudorchis straminea*.

Variation and varieties

British plants belong to the nominate subspecies, *P. a. albida*, which in turn is divided into two varieties.

Var. *albida* is found on more acid soils and has the lateral lobes of the lip clearly shorter than the central lobe.

Var. *tricuspis* favours calcareous soils and has the lateral lobes almost as long as the central lobe. The distribution and abundance of the two varieties in the British Isles has not been studied.

BIOLOGY

Pollination and reproduction

The flowers produce nectar and are visited by butterflies, day-flying moths and solitary bees. The specific pollinator has not been identified, but the narrow entrance to the spur suggests that it may be butterflies. Some self-pollination also occurs, as the pollinia eventually fall onto the stigma if an insect has not removed them. Seed may be set by over 90% of flowers.

Development and growth

The aerial stem grows from paired tubers that

taper gradually to a long, pointed tip and are often deeply divided into several long 'fingers' that diverge widely. There are also long, fleshy roots that lie horizontally close to the surface of the soil. The roots and the slender tips of the tubers have a heavy fungal 'infection'. The first aerial stem is reported to appear four years after germination.

▲ *6 June, Cumbria. The flowers are small – smaller than the ovary. The specific pollinatior is unknown but seed-set is good.*

Intergeneric hybrids

X *Pseudadenia schweinfurthii*, the hybrid with fragrant orchid (presumably Heath Fragrant Orchid), has been recorded from several places in Yorkshire and Scotland, where it is fairly frequent in the northwest.

X *Pseudorhiza bruniana*, the hybrid with Heath Spotted Orchid, was recorded from Orkney in 1977.

Name and classification

The specific name *albida* means 'white'.

HISTORY AND CONSERVATION

The first British record was in 1670 when it was discovered by John Ray on Mount Snowdon in North Wales: 'This we found on the back of Snowdon-hill by the way leading from Llanberis to Carnarvan' (*Catalogus Plantarum Anglicum et Insularum adjecentium*).

Specially protected in Northern Ireland under Schedule 8 of the 1985 Wildlife Order (NI) and in Eire under the Flora (Protection) Order.

Past and present occurrence of Small-white Orchid in Britain and Ireland (based on presence or absence in 10km squares of the National Grid; data from the New Atlas).

	Britain	Ireland
total historical range, 1500-1999	385	110
current range	132 (4.6%*)	33 (3.3%*)
% lost, 1500-1969	52%	63.5%
% lost, 1970-1986	13.5%	6.5%
% lost, total	65.5%	70%

* current range as a % of the total number of 10km squares

Small White Orchid is commonest in northern and western Scotland and becomes rarer further south; in the remainder of Scotland it has almost vanished from the area south of a line from the Clyde to Aberdeen and has not been recorded recently from Kirkcudbrightshire, Lanarkshire, Selkirkshire, Berwickshire, the Lothians, Fife and Stirlingshire. It is extinct in Shetland, where there has only been one record, from Bressay prior to 1845.

In England, Small White Orchid is now rare even in Cumbria, a former stronghold that still holds the bulk of the English populations, although most colonies comprise just a handful of plants. It is now extinct in Kent (with just one old record, from near Lyminge), East and West Sussex (where present until at least 1913, with three localities in West Sussex and ten in East Sussex, notably Ashdown Forest), Gloucestershire (last recorded 1899), Herefordshire, Staffordshire, Shropshire (last recorded 1856), Derbyshire, Cheshire, Lancashire, southwest and northeast Yorkshire (where it has recently gone from the North York Moors National Park). The situation in Wales is probably even worse, as numbers there have collapsed in recent years, with no records from Monmouthshire, Glamorganshire, Carmarthenshire, Cardiganshire, Montgomery-shire and Flintshire. In total, Small White Orchid has been lost from 66% of the historical range in Britain. In Ireland there has also been a very sharp drop in numbers. It has been lost from 70% of the historical range and is extinct in Co. Cork, Co. Waterford, Laois, Co. Wicklow, Co. Dublin, Co. Mayo, Co. Monaghan and Co. Down.

Populations tend to be small and scattered and even in Scotland many vice-counties have just one or two sites for the species. Colonies were lost throughout the 20th century due to habitat destruction, forestry, agricultural improvement and overgrazing. As with many grassland orchids it requires both a short sward and areas of bare soil so that seedlings can become established. It therefore needs a certain level of grazing to thrive; too little and it is swamped by coarse grasses and scrub, too much and it can never flower and is eventually eliminated.

▶ *14 June, Kent. Greater Butterfly Orchid.*

GENUS
PLATANTHERA
BUTTERFLY
ORCHIDS

Distribution

There are 80-200 species in this genus. They are scattered almost worldwide, although most are found in the temperate regions of the Northern Hemisphere, with eight in Europe and two in the British Isles.

Floral structures

The column is short and there are two pollinia. They taper into slender caudicles (stalks), each attached to one of the two viscidia, which are naked (there is no pouch-like bursicle). There is a single flat stigmatic zone.

Growth pattern

The aerial stem grows from a pair of spindle-shaped tubers which taper to a long, narrow point, and there are also a few slender roots that spread into the surface layers of the soil. As with the genus *Orchis*, one of the tubers forms the summer before and has supplied the current year's growth, while a new tuber, complete with a bud ready for next year's flower spike, develops beside it.

Fungal partners

All the roots are 'infected' with fungi.

Development from seed

Seed probably germinates in the spring, usually not far below the surface of the soil. The protocorm produces a large bud in the first autumn and this develops into a leafy shoot the following spring. Following the emergence of this shoot, a root is produced. These die off, presumably in the late summer, and the seedling overwinters as a short, two-segmented rhizome. Similarly, a leafy shoot and one or two roots are produced the following summer, and it is not until the third year that the first tuber is produced and the protocorm finally vanishes. A full-sized tuber appears after the fourth summer. (This chronology is based on work in the 1920s and, as with many other orchids, development may be rather faster.)

Vegetative reproduction

Additional tubers may be formed at the base of the aerial stem. These will go on to form separate plants as the connecting stem dies off in the autumn.

Name

The generic name *Platanthera* derives from the Greek *plat* meaning 'broad', 'wide' or 'flat' and *antherus* meaning 'flowery' or 'anther'. It is usually taken to mean 'flat-anthers', a reference to the shape of the anther, which has a hollow at its base to hold the pollinia.

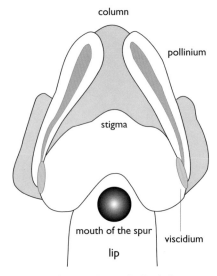

Greater Butterfly Orchid

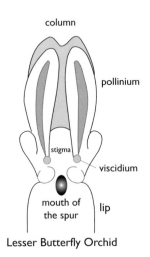

Lesser Butterfly Orchid

▲ *Columns of butterfly orchids showing position of pollinia (sepals and petals removed).*

LESSER BUTTERFLY ORCHID
Platanthera bifolia

The more delicate and daintier of the two butterfly orchids, this species has a northerly and westerly bias to its distribution and has vanished from much of central and eastern England. It is found on rough pastures, damp heathland, bogs and, rather less frequently, in woodland. The delicate flowers are highly scented at night in order to attract hawkmoths; as the moth sips nectar from the orchid's long spur the pollinia are glued to its proboscis and it becomes the unwitting servant of the orchid.

Identification
The two butterfly orchids are distinctive. They have two oval, shiny leaves, placed at the base of the stem and often hidden away in the grass, and exquisite white flowers. The lip of the flower is long, narrow and undivided, and the spur is extremely long and slender and projects prominently to the rear. There are two subtly different forms of Lesser Butterfly Orchid, 'heathland' and 'woodland' (see Variation and varieties).

Similar species
Greater Butterfly Orchid can easily be separated by the size and shape of the pollinia. In Lesser Butterfly Orchid the two pollinia are placed close together and parallel, while in Greater Butterfly Orchid the bases of the pollinia are well separated and they lean inwards towards the tip. Other differences between the two species are subtler and less consistent. Lesser Butterfly Orchid is generally smaller and daintier, with fewer, smaller flowers in a narrower spike; the mouth of the spur is smaller and the spur tends to be straighter.

Habitat
The 'heathland' form of Lesser Butterfly Orchid is by far the commoner and grows on heathland in the south and east and on moorland and damp pastures in the north and west. On both heathland and moorland it usually occurs in the damper areas, and these are frequently marked out by the dusty grey foliage of

▶ 19 June, Norfolk. A robust plant with numerous flowers in a compact spike.

▲ *20 June, Norfolk. A rather small, few-flowered plant in the early morning dew.*

▶ *19 June, Norfolk.*

beechwoods, on calcareous soils, especially 'clay-with-flints'. It can also occur on open chalk downland and among Bracken on the less acid areas of dry grassy heaths. Lesser Butterfly Orchid occurs up to 365m above sea level (Glenfeshie, Inverness-shire).

Flowering period

Late May and June in woodland populations, June to July for heathland forms. On average it flowers latest in the north of Scotland.

Range

Lesser Butterfly Orchid occurs throughout Britain and Ireland, including the Isle of Man, Inner and Outer Hebrides and Orkney. There is, however, a distinct western and northern bias to the distribution, and the species was always scattered and local in much of England, eastern Scotland and in southern and southeast Ireland. It is now extinct in most of East Anglia, the Midlands and northern England, although it is still widespread in Cumbria. **World range:** Widespread in Europe and Asia and also found in North Africa. In Europe it occurs north to the Faeroe Islands and *c*.70°N in northern Scandinavia. It ranges south to Spain, Italy, northern Greece, the Crimea and Caucasus. It is found on the Balearic Islands, Corsica, Sardinia, Sicily and the Aegean islands. In North Africa it is found in Algeria and Tunisia.

Cross-leaved Heath. It can often be found around the margins of valley bogs or growing on drier tussocks and other raised areas amidst sodden, boggy ground. It grows on neutral or mildly acidic soils; on moorland and around bogs it favours the areas where springs and flushes buffer the general acidity to some extent. The 'woodland' form is much scarcer and largely restricted to southern England. It is found in open deciduous woodland and scrub, often

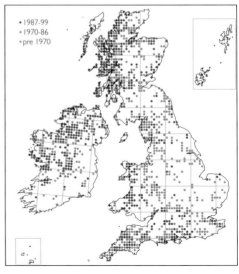

• 1987-99
• 1970-86
• pre 1970

In Asia it occurs in northwest and northeast Turkey and northern Iran. The range extends across southern Siberia to at least Lake Baikal.

How to find it

Often rather small and slender, this can be a hard plant to find wherever the vegetation is tall. However, in other areas it can be very obvious, especially when found in large numbers.

DESCRIPTION

Height: 15-30cm, occasionally to 45cm.
Stem: Pale green, more-or-less triangular and ribbed towards the tip, with two or three whitish or brownish sheaths at the extreme base.
Leaves: The two pale green, slightly shiny or 'greasy' looking leaves are held opposite each other, one just above the other, at the base of the stem. They are variable in shape, from oval to narrower and more strap-shaped, and taper at the base to a whitish, winged stalk. There are also one to five small, lanceolate, bract-like leaves higher on the stem.
Spike: Variable, the five to 25 flowers (occasionally more) form a compact cylindrical spike in moorland plants but are more widely spaced in woodland plants.

▲ *20 June, Norfolk. The pollinia lie parallel to each other, above the mouth of the spur.*

Bract: Green, narrow, pointed and slightly shorter than the ovary.
Ovary: Pale green, long, narrow, clearly ribbed and twisted and also curled into a C-shape to hold the flowers pointing outwards and slightly downwards.
Flower: Whitish, with a long, strap-shaped lip and extremely long spur. The sepals are white, washed greenish towards the tip and bluntly lanceolate in shape. The upper sepal is slightly broader and more triangular and may be bent upwards at the tip. The petals are creamy and variably washed greenish. They are smaller, narrower and more strap-shaped than the sepals. The upper sepal and petals form a loose hood over the column. The lateral sepals are held spreading and slightly drooped. The lip is creamy, sometimes greener towards the tip, narrow, strap-shaped and 6-12mm long. It projects forwards and downwards. The spur is long and slender (1mm wide x 13-23mm long, occasionally to 27mm), sometimes slightly curved and it may be washed with green. The pollinia are whitish, about 2mm tall and lie parallel, 1mm apart, at the front of the column. The flowers emit a heavy, sweet scent, sometimes likened to carnations, especially at night.

Subspecies

None.

Variation and varieties

In both Greater and Lesser Butterfly Orchids plants growing in the open tend to be shorter and more compact than those in shaded woodland localities. In Lesser Butterfly Orchid the 'heathland' form has leaves that are egg-shaped and a relatively dense flower spike whereas the 'woodland' form has narrower and less pointed, more tongue-shaped leaves. The heathland form is found on acid soils throughout Britain and Ireland whereas the woodland form is most frequent in southern England, often growing on calcareous soils, and becomes rare to the north, although it has been found in southern Scotland. Intermediates occur and the differences between the two forms may be caused solely by the different environments in which the plants are growing. **Var. *trifolia*** has three main leaves rather than two. It is not rare.

Var. *quadrifolia* has four leaves.

BIOLOGY

Pollination and reproduction

The flowers are pollinated by insects attracted by the copious nectar in the spur (nectar can be seen filling the tip of the spur, which is translucent). However, the nectar can only be reached by an insect with a suitably long proboscis and Lesser Butterfly Orchid is pollinated by night-flying moths, especially hawkmoths such as Elephant, Small Elephant and Pine Hawkmoths. The flowers' scent, which is particularly pungent around dusk, and white coloration (they almost 'glow in the dark') help the moths to find them. Hawkmoths hover in front of the flower to feed, resting their forelegs on the lateral sepals, whereas other moths land on the flower itself. The two pollinia, which are relatively small, extremely short-stalked and placed parallel to each other at the mouth of the spur, have small sticky pads, the viscidia, at their base. As the moth inserts its proboscis into the spur, the viscidia glue the pollinia to it. The moth continues on its way, visiting other flowers, and after a short while the pollinia rotate forwards and in this new position will make contact with the stigma in the next flower visited. The mechanism is fairly effective and seed-set is moderate to good.

Development and growth

Grows from a pair of underground tubers. There is no information on the period between germination and flowering in the wild but in cultivation plants may flower in three or four years.

Hybrids

P. x *hybrida*, the hybrid with Greater Butterfly Orchid, has been reported from scattered localities but never confirmed, and the plants concerned were most likely to be aberrant forms of one or other species. The differences

▲ 19 June, Norfolk. The flowers are pollinated by moths, especially hawkmoths, and a long proboscis is required to access the nectar in the spur, visible here.

in habitat, flowering time and flower structure make hybridisation less likely than it seems; in Lesser Butterfly Orchid the pollinia are attached to the proboscis of a visiting moth, whereas in Greater Butterfly Orchid they are typically attached to the eyes. In these different positions the chances of the pollinia making contact with the stigma of the 'wrong' species are greatly reduced. Hybrids have been recorded in Europe and these have the pollinia in an intermediate position, reducing the effectiveness of the pollination mechanism and making such hybrids less likely to reproduce successfully.

▲ 13 July, Norfolk. The parallel pollinia are clearly visible.

Past and present occurrence of Lesser Butterfly Orchid in Britain and Ireland (based on presence or absence in 10km squares of the National Grid; data from the New Atlas).

	Britain	Ireland
total historical range, 1500-1999	950	308
current range	342 (12%*)	159 (16%*)
% lost, 1500-1969	48%	36%
% lost, 1970-1986	16%	12.5%
% lost, total	64%	48.5%

* current range as a % of the total number of 10km squares

Name and classification

The specific name *bifolia* means 'two leaves'. The two butterfly orchids, although easily separated in the field, are extremely close genetically. This suggests that they have only very recently separated into two species.

HISTORY AND CONSERVATION

The first reference to the Lesser Butterfly Orchid was in the second edition of John Ray's *Synopsis Methodica Stirpium Britannicarum* ('A methodical synopsis of British plants'), published in 1696, which simply noted its presence in 'pastures'.

Lesser Butterfly Orchid has declined greatly, with a loss of 64% of the historical range in Britain and 48.5% in Ireland. The species has vanished from much of southern and eastern England and is now extinct in Essex, Suffolk, Hertfordshire, Middlesex, Berkshire, Northamptonshire, Worcestershire, Lincolnshire, Nottinghamshire, Derbyshire, Cheshire, Denbighshire, Roxburghshire and the Lothians. It is also seriously reduced in many other areas. For example, in Norfolk it was 'locally common' on wet heaths in 1914 but only 'fairly frequent on bog and wet heath, always on acid soils' in 1968, when 12 localities were listed, and by 1999 Lesser Butterfly Orchid was present at only three sites with just a handful of plants at each. It has now gone altogether from some classic heathland area in southern England such as Woolmer Forest in Hampshire and Ashdown Forest in Sussex.

Some losses are due to the outright destruction of heathland, with both agriculture and urban development being responsible. Even where heathland remains, the losses continue, probably due to the lack of grazing and resulting transformation of heathland into scrub and woodland. Notably, Lesser Butterfly Orchid is still common in the New Forest, which continues to support large numbers of grazing animals. Away from heathland sites the 'improvement' of pastures and hay meadows and the clearance or 'coniferisation' of woodland are responsible for the decline. Paradoxically, overgrazing is a problem in the uplands of western and northern Britain.

GREATER BUTTERFLY ORCHID
Platanthera chlorantha

Found locally throughout mainland Britain and Ireland but with a distinctly southern bias, this species favours both grassland and woodland. The exquisite white flowers, often held on a tall, stately spike, have evolved to 'glow in the dark' as the pollinators are night-flying moths.

Identification

The two butterfly orchids are distinctive, with a pair of oval, shiny green leaves at the base of the stem and an open spike of beautiful 'waxy' white or greenish-white flowers. The lip is long, narrow and undivided, and the extremely long slender spur projects backwards from the rear of the flower across the width of the flower spike.

Similar species

Lesser Butterfly Orchid is distinguished by the shape and position of its pollinia, which lie close together and are parallel for their entire length. In Greater Butterfly Orchid the pollinia are well-separated at the base but lean inwards so that their tips almost touch. There are other, subtler differences between the two species but none of these can be taken as diagnostic. Greater Butterfly Orchid is on average taller and sturdier, with a broader flower spike (the ovaries are longer, holding the flowers further away from the stem). It has greener flowers with a larger and more obvious mouth to the spur, and the spur itself is usually slightly expanded at the tip.

Habitat

Rather variable but it almost always grows on calcareous soils: chalk, limestone and base-rich clays. It is found in deciduous woodland (where it is strongly associated with ancient woodland) and has a preference for hazel coppice. It grows in light, dappled shade and is usually found in the more open areas around the edge of a wood and in clearings and

▶ 14 June, Kent. In woodland the spike is often very attenuated.

▲ 15 June, Kent. Greater Butterfly Orchid will grow on open grassland as well as in woodland. This plant has three leaves rather than the usual two.

along rides. It is tolerant of both dry and wet conditions but in woodland on chalk may have some preference for the heavier and wetter soils found at the foot of slopes. Greater Butterfly Orchid has occasionally been found growing in rides through conifer plantations but such

populations may be relicts of deciduous woodland previously on the site.

In the north and west of Britain and Ireland Greater Butterfly Orchid is most frequently found in grassland such as old pastures and hay meadows, again usually on calcareous soils; it has been found on rare occasions on mildly acidic soils on moorland, wet heath and pastures but is clearly less tolerant of acid conditions than Lesser Butterfly Orchid. It was probably frequent in pastures and meadows in southern England prior to their 'improvement' but in the south, away from woodland sites, is now only likely to be found on chalk grassland, often in long grass with variable amounts of scrub. It is sometimes also found in calcium-rich dune slacks and on railway embankments. Occurs up to 460m above sea level (Harwood Dale, Northumberland).

Flowering period

Late May to late July, being earliest in the south, where it is sometimes in flower from mid, or even early, May. Usually it is at its best in early June in much of England but it may not be in full flower in parts of Scotland until July. Typically it flowers one or two weeks earlier than Lesser Butterfly Orchid.

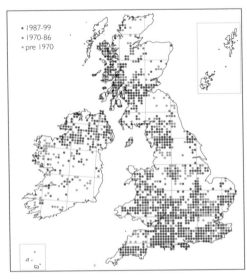

• 1987-99
• 1970-86
• pre 1970

Range

Found throughout Britain and Ireland except Orkney and Shetland, although rather scattered in the southern half of Ireland and absent from large areas of the Midlands, northern England, southern and eastern Scotland and the Outer Hebrides. The centre of gravity of the distribution lies in southern England and Wales, in contrast to the northern and western bias shown by Lesser Butterfly Orchid. **World range:** Almost confined to Europe, occurring north to *c.* 63°N in Scandinavia, southern Finland and the Baltic States. It ranges south to the Mediterranean, Crimea and Caucasus, including Corsica, Sicily, the Aegean Islands, Cyprus and possibly Sardinia. Occurs eastwards to central European Russia. It is also found in North Africa in Tunisia and possibly Morocco and in Turkey, northeast Syria and northwest Iran.

How to find it

Woodland plants are often easy to spot, being rather tall, but those in the open among grass and scrub can be well hidden. A large proportion of most populations are non-flowering, and when heavily shaded in overgrown coppice or very dark woods plants can remain in a vegetative state for decades. They 'reappear' and flower again following coppicing, tree-falls or other changes that let more light in. In woods with a regular coppice-cycle, flowering is most prolific two or three years after coppicing.

DESCRIPTION

Height: 20-40cm, sometimes to 65cm.
Stem: Pale green, more-or-less triangular and ribbed towards the tip, with one to three brownish sheaths at the extreme base.
Leaves: Two, oval to elliptical, keeled, pale green (often slightly bluish) and rather shiny. They lie opposite each other at the base of the stem, one just above the other, and are held variably erect. There are also one to six small, lanceolate, bract-like leaves higher on the stem.
Spike: Variable. The ten to 30 flowers (occasionally up to 40) form a loose, open spike in woodland plants, but in full sun the spike tends to be more compact.

Bract: Green, narrow, pointed and as long as the ovary.
Ovary: Pale green, long, narrow, clearly six-ribbed and twisted. It is also curved to hold the flowers pointing outwards and a little downwards.
Flower: White, washed green, with a long strap-shaped lip and extremely long curved spur. The sepals are white, washed greenish towards the tip; the lateral sepals are oval-triangular, asymmetrical and even sickle-shaped whereas the upper sepal is rather shorter, broader and more triangular or heart-shaped. The petals are white, variably washed greenish

▲ 14 June, Kent. The flower spike is extraordinarily graceful.

▲ 14 June, Kent. The extraordinarily long spur contains nectar that can only be reached by insects with an equally long proboscis.

and are shorter, narrower and more strap-shaped than the sepals. The upper sepal and petals form a loose hood over the column, and the lateral sepals are spread horizontally and are often a little twisted or wavy-edged. The lip is creamy but becomes greener towards the tip and is narrow and strap-shaped, 10-16mm long and projects forwards and downwards. The spur is long and slender, 19-35mm long x 1mm wide, broadens towards the tip and is often strongly curved; it is washed green. The pollinia are conspicuously yellow and relatively large, 3-4mm tall including the long caudicle (stalk). The viscidia at the base of the pollinia lie about 4mm apart on either side of the foot of the column, and the pollinia lean inwards towards each other. The flowers emit a heavy scent, especially at night, and it is said that people with a sensitive nose can smell them from several hundred metres on a still summer's evening.

Subspecies
None.

Variation and varieties
As in Lesser Butterfly Orchid, plants growing

in the open tend to be shorter and more compact and to have shorter leaves than those in shaded woodland localities. It seems likely that these differences are produced by the local environment rather than by any genetic difference. Plants may occasionally have just one leaf or sometimes three or four.

BIOLOGY
Pollination and reproduction
The pollination mechanism is very similar to that of Lesser Butterfly Orchid, and night-flying moths are the primary pollinators. But although hawkmoths are involved, members of the large family of Noctuid moths are more important as pollinators. In the Greater Butterfly Orchid the sticky viscidia at the base of the pollinia face inwards on either side of, and just above, the entrance to the spur. Due to this more widely spread position, the pollinia usually become attached to the large compound eyes of the visiting moth rather than its proboscis. The mechanism is effective and seed is set in 70-90% of flowers.

▲ 14 June, Kent. The pollinia are wide apart at the base but lean inwards towards their tips, the most reliable distinction from Lesser Butterfly Orchid.

Vegetative reproduction can occur via the formation of additional tubers but is of little importance in the dynamics of a population.

Development and growth

The process of development from seed to flowering plant is very similar to Lesser Butterfly Orchid. The adult plant is reported to be entirely independent of fungi, but this seems highly unlikely given that it can become 'dormant' in heavy shade for long periods.

Hybrids

None (see Lesser Butterfly Orchid).

Name and classification

The specific name *chlorantha* means 'green flowers'. The two butterfly orchids, although readily separated by the shape of the pollinia, are genetically almost indistinguishable, suggesting that they have only very recently separated into two species.

HISTORY AND CONSERVATION

The first British record dates from 1597 when John Gerard noted this species in his *Herball*: '...in the wood belonging to a worshipfull gentleman of Kent named Master Sedley of Southfleete.'

Past and present occurrence of Greater Butterfly Orchid in Britain and Ireland (based on presence or absence in 10km squares of the National Grid; data from the New Atlas).

	Britain	Ireland
total historical range, 1500-1999	1,163	251
current range	626 (22%*)	117 (11.6%*)
% lost, 1500-1969	32%	41.5%
% lost, 1970-1986	14%	12%
% lost, total	46%	53.5%

* current range as a % of the total number of 10km squares

It has been lost from 46% of the historical range in England and 53.5% in Ireland. The destruction and the replanting of woodlands with conifers, as well as agricultural improvements to pastures and hay meadows, have been responsible for the decline. The species will also 'vanish' from woodland if it becomes too intensely shaded but may reappear if the canopy is opened again.

▲ *28 May, Norfolk. The spike may be relatively few-flowered and can be inconspicuous.*

GENUS *GYMNADENIA*
FRAGRANT ORCHIDS

Distribution

Europe and Asia, with about 14 species, five of which occur in Europe and three in Britain. Until recently all three were treated as subspecies of a single species, the 'Fragrant Orchid'.

Floral structures

The column is short and erect with a long rostellum that projects forward between the two viscidia. The two club-shaped pollinia each narrow into a caudicle (stalk) that is attached to one of the two long, narrow viscidia, but there is no bursicle (the flap or pouch-like structure found in many orchids which covers and protects the viscidia). The two stigmas lie on the side-lobes of the column.

Growth pattern

The aerial shoot grows from a pair of flattened, deeply divided tapering tubers. Roots develop in the autumn and penetrate the upper layers of the soil. The roots and the root-like tips of the tubers are 'infected' with fungi. The annual cycle of growth and the replacement of tubers are similar to those of the genus *Orchis* (see p.200).

Development from seed

Early observations suggested that seeds probably germinate in the spring. The resulting protocorm produces roots in the second autumn, the first leaves in the third spring (i.e. when it is two years old) and the first tuber the following season. Given the dry habitats, however, in which fragrant orchids often grow, it seems unlikely that protocorms could survive for over two years, and the period prior to the development of the first tuber may be very much shorter. The sequence protocorm-root-aerial stem-tuber is shared with other genera, including some of the *Orchis* and *Dactylorhiza* orchids.

Vegetative reproduction

Additional tubers may be formed at the base of the aerial stem. These will go on to form separate plants as the connecting stem dies off in the autumn.

Name

The generic name *Gymnadenia* originates from the Greek *gymnos* 'naked' and *aden* 'gland' and means quite literally 'naked-gland', a reference to the lack of a bursicle (see Floral structures).

COMMON FRAGRANT ORCHID
Gymnadenia conopsea

Other names: Chalk Fragrant Orchid
This attractive orchid is found in species-rich grassland on chalk and limestone soils throughout England and Wales but is rather rare in Scotland and Ireland. It sometimes occurs in large numbers, and the fragrance emitted by a big colony can be quite overpowering, especially in the evening.

Identification
The fragrant orchids are easy to separate from other orchids. The pink flowers are held in a tall, narrow, spire-like spike. Each flower has two 'wings' (the lateral sepals) that are held roughly horizontally, a flat, three-lobed lip and a long, slender, down-curved spur.

Similar species
Pyramidal Orchid has flowers that are a similar colour, size and shape to those of Common Fragrant Orchid and also have a long slender spur. Pyramidal Orchid has, however, an obviously shorter, more conical and more closely-packed flower spike. Its flowers are a deeper pink with a more markedly three-lobed lip that has two diagnostic parallel raised ridges at the base. Pyramidal Orchid also flowers later in the summer, and there is usually relatively little overlap between the two species.

Fragrant orchids are difficult to separate from each other, although they are usually found in distinct habitats. Common Fragrant Orchid favours old, species-rich grassland on chalk or limestone and is just occasionally found in fens. Its scent is sickly-sweet but has a slightly acid, rancid, or musty background. Its main flowering period is June and early July. However, even in its preferred dry grassland habitat, Marsh Fragrant Orchid or Heath Fragrant Orchid could also occur, and a careful examination of the flower is necessary to be reasonably certain of the identification.

◀ 14 June, Kent. At some sites Common Fragrant Orchid occurs by the thousand.

▶ 14 June, Kent.

Intermediates also occur, and it is best to examine several plants in a population to gain an overall impression. The criteria used to separate the three fragrant orchids are still being developed, and some plants or even whole populations may not yet be identifiable.

In Common Fragrant Orchid the flowers are medium sized, the lip is about as wide as long, lacks 'shoulders' and is distinctly three-lobed. The central lobe is the longest. The 'wings' are angled downwards and are pointed, narrow and parallel-sided (with the lateral sepals rolled into a tube to produce this linear shape). See also p.258.

Habitat
Found in dry, species-rich grassland on calcareous soils, mostly chalk downland in the south and limestone pastures in northern England but sometimes also on stabilised dunes, road verges, railway banks and in old quarries on suitable calcium-rich soils. It occasionally occurs in base-rich fens (together with Marsh Fragrant Orchid) or on alkaline Leblanc waste in Lancashire. Recorded up to 365m above sea level (near Whitely Shield, Northumberland).

Flowering period
Late May (sometimes mid-May) to late July, but most are in flower during June.

Range
Widespread in England, although confined to areas with suitable habitat, such as the North and South Downs, the chalk districts of Hampshire, the Berkshire Downs and Chilterns, Dorset, and the

Separation of Common, Marsh and Heath Fragrant Orchids.

	Common Fragrant Orchid	Marsh Fragrant Orchid	Heath Fragrant Orchid
Width of florets*	10-11mm (7-13mm)	11-13mm (10-14.5mm)	8-10mm (7-12mm)
Lip: width	5.5-6.5cm (4.5-7mm)	6.5-7mm (5.5-8mm)	3.5-4mm (3-5mm)
Lip: length	5-6mm (4-6.5mm)	3.5-4mm (3-4.5mm)	4-4.5mm (3.5-5mm)
Lip: shape	fractionally broader than long	much broader than long	longer than broad
Lip: lobes	distinctly 3-lobed, central lobe longest	distinctly 3-lobed, side-lobes largest	obscurely lobed, longer than wide
Lip: shoulders**	absent	distinct	narrow
Lateral sepals: width	c. 1mm	c. 1mm	c. 2mm
Lateral sepals: length	c. 5-6mm	c. 6-7mm	c. 4-5mm
Lateral sepals: shape	linear, pointed at tip	linear, blunt at tip	oval-lanceolate, pointed at tip
Lateral sepals: position	deflexed at c. 30°	horizontal	deflexed
Length of spur	12-14mm (11-17mm)	14-16mm (13-17mm)	11-14mm (8-15mm)
Height	20-40cm, sometimes more	30-60cm, less in dry habitats	15-25cm, rarely more
Fragrance	sickly-sweet with 'acid' or 'rancid' overtones	spicy sweet, clove-like; no acid overtones	spicy sweet, recalling cloves
Flowering period	early June-mid July	early July-mid August	June-August
Habitat	chalk & limestone grassland	fens; rarely chalk grassland on north-facing slopes	mildly acidic to base-rich grassland; base-rich heathland flushes; very rarely chalk grassland

Largely after Francis Rose in Rich & Jermy (1998).
* The width of the floret is measured from tip to tip of the lateral sepals
** The 'shoulders' are formed by the abrupt angle at the base of the lip where it narrows towards the mouth of the spur.

limestone areas of the Cotswolds, Mendip Hills, Northamptonshire, Lincolnshire, the Derbyshire and Yorkshire Dales, Cumbria and Co. Durham. Widespread in Wales, but in Scotland it is rare and local and information about its distribution is incomplete; it may have been recorded from Dumfries-shire, Roxburghshire, Banffshire and a few areas in the far north, in Sutherland, Caithness and the Outer Hebrides. Its status in Ireland is also obscure due to confusion with the other fragrant orchids and with hybrids between them. It may be most frequent in the central counties, but it is probably scarce or rare.
World range: The 'Fragrant Orchid', i.e. an aggregate of all three species, is found in Europe

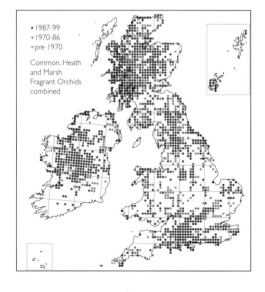

• 1987-99
• 1970-86
• pre 1970

Common, Heath and Marsh Fragrant Orchids combined

and Asia east to Japan and Korea. In Europe it ranges north to northernmost Scandinavia and south to the Mediterranean (although it avoids the Mediterranean lowlands), Turkey and the Caucasus. Further east it occurs in the Himalayas and in central China. Records seldom distinguish the three species of fragrant orchid, and their exact ranges have yet to be defined. 'Fragrant Orchid' has been found once in North America, in Connecticut in 1887.

How to find it

This is usually an easy species to find at suitable sites, now often reserves or SSSIs. It sometimes appears in large numbers but the number of flowering spikes can vary widely from year to year.

DESCRIPTION

Height: 10-60cm but usually 15-30cm and seldom over 40cm.

Stem: Green, becoming more purplish towards the flower spike.

Leaves: Mid-green. The three to five narrow, strap-shaped basal leaves, keeled and with pointed tips, are held loosely erect. These grade into two or three narrow, lanceolate, bract-like leaves higher on the stem.

Spike: More-or-less cylindrical and moderately densely packed with 20-50 flowers, rarely more. The spike becomes looser as more flowers open.

Bract: Green, sometimes tinged purple, strap-shaped, narrowing around the mid-point into a finer pointed tip and roughly as long as the ovary.

Ovary: Green, variably washed purple, long, narrow, prominently three-ribbed and twisted.

Flower: Pink with a hint of purple, varying in the exact shade. The sepals are elongated-oval in shape, the lateral sepals being slightly irregular but with their upper and lower margins rolled backwards so that face-on they appear as parallel-sided oblongs with a short pointed tip. The petals are a little shorter, more oval-triangular in shape and asymmetrical, with one side squared off. The upper sepal and petals form a hood over the column, whereas

▲ *9 June, Northamptonshire. A full, densely-flowered spike.*

the lateral sepals are held to the side, about 30° below the horizontal and pressed backwards. The lip is flat and about as wide as long, with three well-developed, rounded terminal lobes; the central lobe is longer than the lateral lobes and often broader. The spur is a darker, more purplish-pink, very slender, down-curved and rather long, around twice the length of the ovary. It is filled with nectar and this can sometimes be seen through its semi-translucent walls. The flowers have a strong sickly-sweet scent.

Subspecies
None.

Variation and varieties
Var. *albiflora* has white flowers and is fairly frequent.

Var. *crenulata* has broad lateral lobes to the lip which are narrowly serrated at the edges. It is rare.

BIOLOGY

Pollination and reproduction
Nectar is produced in the bottom of the long spur, and only insects with a sufficiently long proboscis can reach this. Pollinators include butterflies and both day- and night-flying moths, including Large Skipper, Six-spot Burnet and hawkmoths. Night-flying moths may, however, be the most important pollinators; the scent becomes more pungent towards dusk, and, with its white flowers, var. *albiflora* may only be attractive to nocturnal moths. As the visiting insect advances to sip nectar from the spur, the pollinia are fixed by their sticky viscidia (which lie just above the mouth of the spur) to the insect's proboscis. The pollinia are then carried to another flower or another plant, having in the meantime swung forward into a position ready to make contact with the stigma. Pollination is very efficient and seed is set in large quantities.

Vegetative reproduction may also occur via the production of additional tubers.

Development and growth
The interval between germination and flowering is usually around five years but may be as short as three.

Hybrids
Opposite is a list of all the hybrids listed officially for 'Fragrant Orchid' by Stace (2004), which does not separate the three fragrant orchids into distinct species. The names of these hybrids may well need to be revised to reflect the new status of the fragrant orchid parent:

◀ 14 June, Kent. The white-flowered variety albiflora is fairly frequent.

▶ 9 June, Northampton-shire. The lip is distinctly three-lobed and about as long as it is wide, while the 'wings' formed by the lateral sepals are narrow, parallel-sided and held slightly drooped.

X *Gymnanacamptis anacamptis*, the hybrid with Pyramidal Orchid, has been recorded rarely (presumably x Common Fragrant Orchid).

X *Pseudadenia schweinfurthii*, the hybrid with Small White Orchid, has been recorded from Yorkshire and Scotland, where it is fairly frequent in the northwest (presumably x Heath Fragrant Orchid).

X *Dactylodenia jacksonii*, the hybrid with Frog Orchid, has been noted rarely but widely.

X *Dactylodenia st-quintinii*, the hybrid with Common Spotted Orchid, is uncommon but has been found widely through Britain and Ireland; all three species of fragrant orchid may be involved.

X *Dactylodenia legrandiana*, the hybrid with Heath Spotted Orchid, has been found widely scattered through Britain and Ireland (presumably x Heath Fragrant Orchid).

X *Dactylodenia vollmannii*, the hybrid with Early Marsh Orchid, has been recorded from Cornwall and Cumbria.

X *Dactylodenia wintonii*, the hybrid with Southern Marsh Orchid, has been found in Devon and Hampshire.

X *Dactylodenia varia*, the hybrid with Northern Marsh Orchid, has been found in northern England, Scotland and Co. Down in Ireland.

Common Fragrant Orchid can also hybridise with Marsh Fragrant Orchid and Heath Fragrant Orchid, but these hybrids do not yet have names.

Name and classification

The specific epithet *conopsea* means 'gnat-like' or 'cloudy' but the reason for this reference is obscure.

Since 1997 the 'Fragrant Orchid' has been separated into three distinct species, Common, Marsh and Heath Fragrant Orchids. Long treated as separated varieties or subspecies, new molecular and genetic evidence has shown that they merit specific status, even though they can be hard to identify with certainty.

HISTORY AND CONSERVATION

The first British record of 'Fragrant Orchid' dates from 1634 when Thomas Johnson published the *Mercurius Botanicus* ('Botanical Mercury') and recorded the 'Orchis palmata minor calcaribus oblongis…. In montosis' ('lesser palmate *Orchis* with oblong spurs… In mountains'). In 1660 John Ray stated that the 'Fragrant Orchid' could be found 'in meadows everywhere' in Cambridgeshire.

Although the species is still common or even abundant at suitable sites, it declined significantly in the 19th and 20th centuries due to the conversion of downs and pastures into arable land and the 'improvement' of grazing land. Even where the habitat still remains, like all grassland orchids this species requires a specific level of grazing; too little and scrub invades, too much and the diversity of species is lost.

The identification and recording of the three fragrant orchids is still in its infancy, and it is hard to identify trends for the individual species. But, taken together, the 'Fragrant Orchid' has vanished from 39.5% of the total historical range in Britain and 30.5% in Ireland.

Past and present occurrence of the fragrant orchids (all three species combined) in Britain and Ireland (based on presence or absence in 10km squares of the National Grid; data from the New Atlas).

	Britain	Ireland
total historical range, 1500-1999	1,341	365
current range	810 (28%*)	253 (25%*)
% lost, 1500-1969	26.5%	24.5%
% lost, 1970-1986	13%	6%
% lost, total	39.5%	30.5%

* current range as a % of the total number of 10km squares

▲ *29 June, Hampshire. A rather open, few-flowered spike.*

HEATH FRAGRANT ORCHID
Gymnadenia borealis

Formerly: *Gymnadenia borealis* subspecies *densiflora*
Until very recently this species was, like Marsh Fragrant Orchid, considered to be merely a subspecies of the composite 'Fragrant Orchid'. It favours a variety of heathy and grassy habitats and is the commonest fragrant orchid in northern and western Britain with scattered outposts in southern England. It may yet be discovered elsewhere.

Identification
This is a relatively small, delicate, few-flowered cousin of Common Fragrant Orchid. The conical spikes of pink flowers, each with a vaguely tri-lobed lip and long slender spur, should nevertheless identify it as one of the three fragrant orchids. These can be difficult to separate from each other and, although they are usually found in distinct habitats, can occur together. Unlike Common and Marsh Fragrant Orchids, Heath Fragrant Orchid does not require alkaline soils and can be found in neutral grassland in the uplands of northern and western Britain and also very locally in boggy hollows on grassy heaths in southern England. Its status in Ireland is not certain due to confusion with the other two fragrant orchids. The scent is very sweet and carnation- or clove-like and its main flowering period is from mid-June to late July.

Similar species
Marsh and Common Fragrant Orchids are similar, and where there is a possibility that these could also occur a closer look is required to be certain of the species. In Heath Fragrant Orchid the flowers are relatively small, around 8-10mm across. The lip is longer than wide and often rather obscurely lobed, with small side-lobes and a longer central lobe. The 'wings' (lateral sepals) are oval, taper to a pointed tip and are held angled downwards to about four and eight o-clock. Intermediates occur, however, and it is best to examine several plants in a population and take an average. See table on p.258.

▲ 15 June, New Forest. Genetic evidence has recently confirmed that Heath Fragrant Orchid is distinct.

Habitat

In the north and west it is found on unimproved hill pastures, roadside verges and grassy moorland, often in areas flushed with ground water. In such places it grows on tussocks of grass and heathers, sometimes with Lesser Butterfly Orchid and Heath Spotted Orchid. It is also found on machair, dunes and in old quarries. It is tolerant of a wider range of pH than Common and Marsh Fragrant Orchids and will grow on soils that are both mildly acidic and alkaline, on sands, limestones and clays. In the New Forest and Ashdown Forest it is found in 'marl bogs' (flushes and hollows on grassy heaths on base-rich clays). Very rarely it has been recorded from chalk grassland, as near Lewes in Sussex. Occurs up to 610m above sea level (Ben Lawers, Perthshire).

Flowering period

June to August in Scotland and Ireland and early June to early July in the New Forest (around the same time as Common Fragrant Orchid or just a little later); anomalously, the population on chalk grassland in Sussex flowers from late July to early August.

Range

Poorly understood as it has only recently been separated from the other fragrant orchids. So far it is known to occur in southern England in Cornwall (including the Lizard Peninsula and Bodmin Moor), Devon, Dorset, the New Forest in Hampshire (about 12 relatively small populations of 50-100 flowering plants), East and West Sussex (Ashdown Forest and three sites on the South Downs), and in Shropshire

◄ 15 June, New Forest. Growing with Heath Spotted Orchid on a large tussock.

(one site), Derbyshire, Northumberland and Cumbria (just two sites). In Wales it is known only from Breconshire and Cardiganshire. Scattered through much of Scotland, including the Inner and Outer Hebrides, Orkney and Shetland (although very rare there and now found only on Unst). Occurs in western and northern Ireland but there is very little information on the distribution of Heath Fragrant Orchid in Ireland. **World Range:** Apparently more widespread in Europe than Common Fragrant Orchid and found in France as far south as the Dordogne. See Common Fragrant Orchid.

How to find it
Widespread and locally common in Scotland but very local in England and Wales. The

▲ 15 June, New Forest. The lip is longer than wide and often only obscurely lobed, and the 'wings' are oval, pointed and held more or less drooped.

New Forest, where it is locally frequent, is undoubtedly the best area to look for this species in southern England. It can be surprisingly elusive among tussocks of long grass, and the number of flowering spikes can vary widely from year to year.

DESCRIPTION
Height: 10-25cm, rarely to 30cm.
Stem: Green, becoming more purplish-brown towards the tip.
Leaves: Mid-green, the three to five narrow, strap-shaped basal leaves are keeled and have pointed tips. They are held loosely erect, often in two ranks, and grade into two or three narrower and more lanceolate bract-like leaves higher on the stem.
Spike: More-or-less cylindrical, although often slightly irregular in shape, with 20-30 or more flowers in a fairly lax spike.
Bract: Green, tinged purple (especially on the edges), strap-shaped, narrowing abruptly around the mid-point into a finer pointed tip, and about one-and-a-half times the length of the ovary.
Ovary: Green, variably washed purple, long, narrow, three-ribbed and twisted.

▲ 15 June, New Forest. The spike can be relatively squat.

Flower: Dark pink to lilac. The sepals are oval or drop-shaped with the margins of the lateral sepals rolled back to give them an oval-lanceolate shape with a pointed tip. The petals are shorter, more oval-triangular but less regular in shape. The upper sepal and petals form a hood over the column, whereas the lateral sepals are held to the side, a little below the horizontal and pressed backwards. The lip is flat and longer than wide, lobed at the tip with the side-lobes shorter than the central lobe; the lobes are usually poorly developed with the incisions between them reduced or absent. The spur is a darker, more purplish-pink, very slender, down-curved and rather long, around twice the length of the ovary; it is filled with nectar. The flowers have a powerful, sweet scent, recalling cloves, which is strongest when they are newly opened and lacks the rancid overtones of Common Fragrant Orchid. See also table on p.258.

▲ 15 June, New Forest. The spikes are variable in shape and in the density of flowers.

Subspecies
None.

Variation and varieties
Var. *albiflora* has white flowers and is fairly frequent.

BIOLOGY
Pollination and reproduction
No specific information, although the differences in the size and shape of the flower suggest that a different suite of pollinators is involved for each of the three fragrant orchids. See Common Fragrant Orchid.

Development and growth
No specific information.

Hybrids
Hybrids have been recorded with both Common Fragrant and Heath Fragrant Orchids. See also Common Fragrant Orchid (p.260).

Name and classification
The specific name *borealis* means 'northern', a reference to the generally northerly distribution.

This species was originally described as a variety of 'Fragrant Orchid' by the British botanist G.C. Druce in 1918. It was raised to the status of a subspecies in 1991 before finally achieving specific status (yet to be universally recognised) a few years later. Despite the difficulties in identification, DNA evidence strongly supports the separation of Heath Fragrant Orchid from Marsh and Common Fragrant Orchids.

HISTORY AND CONSERVATION
This species is the most poorly known of the three fragrant orchids and has only really been brought to the attention of botanists since 1988 (when it was treated in the Botanical Society of the British Isles' *Plant Crib*). Its history and conservation is obscure, but there has undoubtedly been a considerable decline, with overgrazing of upland grasslands being a particular problem.

MARSH FRAGRANT ORCHID
Gymnadenia densiflora

Formerly: *Gymnadenia conopsea* subspecies *densiflora*

Until recently this orchid was treated as a subspecies of 'Fragrant Orchid', a composite that encompassed Common, Marsh and Heath Fragrant Orchids, but genetic evidence has recently confirmed that all three are 'good' species. It has been recorded from scattered localities throughout the British Isles and is rather scarce, being mostly confined to alkaline fens, a habitat that has suffered badly from drainage and water abstraction. Although coverage was undoubtedly incomplete due to confusion with its cousins, the *New Atlas* mapped it from just 58 10km squares in Britain during the period 1987-99, and it probably qualifies for the status of Nationally Scarce.

Identification

With spire-like spikes of pink flowers, each with a distinctly three-lobed lip and a long, slender, curved spur, this species is easy to identify as one of the three fragrant orchids.

Similar species

The fragrant orchids can be hard to separate from each other, although they usually grow in different habitats. Marsh Fragrant Orchid is found in meadows and fens where the ground water is distinctly alkaline and sometimes occurs in large numbers, often together with Marsh Helleborine. It is occasionally recorded from chalk downland and can sometimes occur together with either Common or Heath Fragrant Orchids. Marsh Fragrant Orchid is nevertheless relatively distinctive, being a tall, robust plant with numerous broad basal leaves that are usually held noticeably erect and a good-sized spike of relatively large, dark pink flowers. To clinch the identification, a careful examination, preferably of several plants, is necessary. In Marsh Fragrant Orchid the flowers are around 11-13mm across and the lip is broader than long, prominently lobed (with the side-lobes larger than the central lobe) and has distinct 'shoulders'. The 'wings' (lateral sepals) are long and narrow with parallel sides and a blunt tip and are held roughly horizontal.

▶ *11 July, Norfolk. The robust fragrant orchids of fenland habitats have long been recognised as distinct.*

See table on p.258. Intermediates and hybrids do occur, however, and some populations do not 'fit' any of the three species (see photograph on p.270).

Habitat

Usually found in fens and meadows flushed with calcareous, base-rich water, also dune slacks and, on the Isle of Wight, slumped clay cliffs. Occasionally occurs on chalk grassland on north-facing slopes, as at Ditchling Beacon

▲ 17 July, Co. Durham. Growing on the floor of a dry limestone quarry, the broad lips and late flowering indicate that this is Marsh Fragrant Orchid.

▶ 11 July, Norfolk. A typical tall, spire-like spike.

and Heyshott Down in Sussex. Recorded up to 310m above sea level (Tomintoul, Banffshire).

Flowering period

Late June to mid-August.

Range

Rather poorly known because until recently many records were given merely as 'Fragrant Orchid'. In England found in a belt of counties along the south coast from Cornwall to Kent (including the Isle of Wight), at a handful of sites in Berkshire and Hertfordshire, in Norfolk and adjacent parts of Suffolk, and then through the Midlands and northern England north of a line from Cambridgeshire to Herefordshire, although very scattered. In Scotland the species is similarly local and has been recorded from Peebles, Midlothian, Banffshire, Coll in the Inner Hebrides, Ross & Cromarty, Sutherland and Orkney. Similarly scattered in western and northern Wales. Apparently the commonest of the three fragrant orchids in Ireland but there are few specific records. **World range:** Widespread in Europe and especially common in the southeast, particularly the Balkans.

How to find it

The tall plants in fens and calcareous meadows are easy to find, although this habitat is very local. Chalk grassland populations can very easily be overlooked, however, and any population of fragrant orchids is worth careful examination.

DESCRIPTION

Height: 30-60cm, exceptionally to 90cm; plants in chalk grassland are the smallest.
Stem: Green, washed purple towards the tip.
Leaves: There is a rosette of several erect, lanceolate and relatively broad leaves at the base of the stem and several smaller, narrow and more bract-like leaves higher up.
Spike: Up to 100 flowers form a rather tall, narrow spike.
Bract: Green, washed purple (especially towards the edges) and narrowly oval, tapering

to a point; the bracts are roughly the length of the ovary.

Ovary: Green, variably and sometimes heavily washed purple; the ovary is long, narrow, curved, prominently three-ribbed and twisted.

Flower: Deep pink, variably tinged purple and often whiter around the base of the lip. The sepals are elongated-oval in shape with the upper and lower margins of the lateral sepals rolled back so that they appear to be parallel-sided with a blunt tip. The petals are a little shorter and more oval-triangular in shape. The upper sepal and petals form a hood over the column whereas the lateral sepals are held horizontally to the side. The lip is flat, broader than long and has distinct 'shoulders' (abrupt angles on each side at the base where it narrows towards the mouth of the spur). It has three well-developed rounded lobes,

▲ 11 July, Norfolk. The lip is wider than long, with large side lobes and distinct 'shoulders', and the 'wings' are long, narrow, blunt and usually carried horizontally.

with the side-lobes larger than the central lobe. The spur is relatively dark, very slender, down-curved and long. The scent is spicy sweet, recalling cloves, and lacking the rancid overtones of Common Fragrant Orchid. See also table on p.258.

Subspecies
None.

Variation and varieties
None.

BIOLOGY

Pollination and reproduction
No specific information but the differences in the size and shape of the flower, notably the long spur and distinct scent in Marsh Fragrant Orchid, suggest that a different suite of pollinators is involved for each of the three fragrant orchids. See also Common Fragrant Orchid.

Development and growth
No specific information.

Hybrids
Hybridises with Heath Fragrant Orchid in Ireland and sometimes with Common Fragrant Orchid. See also Common Fragrant Orchid.

▲ 9 July, Norfolk. The shape of the flowers is variable.

Name and classification

The specific name *densiflora* refers to the densely packed flower spike, although the spike is not necessarily more crowded than Common Fragrant Orchid.

Originally described as a distinct species in 1806, *Orchis densiflora* was quickly reduced to being merely a variety of 'Fragrant Orchid' (although it did appear as a distinct species in Francis Rose's excellent *Wild Flower Key* as long ago as 1981). Recently, DNA evidence has shown that it, together with Heath Fragrant Orchid, merits full specific status.

HISTORY AND CONSERVATION

Confusion with Common Fragrant Orchid means that its past history in Britain is obscure. Although 'var. *densiflora*' warranted some attention, the identification criteria used were sometimes dubious, notably the width of the lower leaves and the length of the flower spike, and many records merit re-examination.

Marsh Fragrant Orchid has undoubtedly undergone a serious decline in much of Britain. The direct drainage and destruction of fens and marshes has caused some losses. However, subtler effects, including eutrophication and the lowering of water tables, have also caused declines which reserve or SSSI status could not protect against. The few chalk grassland populations are also subject to losses due to 'improvement' or abandonment. The species is now much reduced in Norfolk, one of its strongholds, and has withdrawn to just five sites in Suffolk. There are no recent records from Somerset, Wiltshire, Gloucestershire, Bedfordshire, Lincolnshire, Co. Durham, Lanarkshire, Berwickshire, Perthshire or Angus.

▶ *27 July, Norfolk. The lip is narrow and longer than broad and the 'wings' are oval, pointed and downward-pointing, all suggesting Heath Fragrant Orchid, but it is growing in a calcareous fen and flowering relatively late. It could be a hybrid, but Heath Fragrant Orchid is unknown in East Anglia.*

GENUS *DACTYLORHIZA*
MARSH ORCHIDS AND
SPOTTED ORCHIDS

This genus, which includes the marsh and spotted orchids, presents the toughest identification challenge among British and Irish orchids. The species are closely related and individually quite variable. Indeed, there is disagreement as to how the various populations should be classified into species, subspecies and varieties. Hybridisation is also relatively common, making identification even more difficult. The situation can be particularly complex in Ireland, west Wales and western Scotland due to the number of possibilities that have to be considered. If in doubt it may be necessary to take a 'statistical' approach and carefully measure a selection of plants in order to reach a satisfactory identification. On the other hand, a field full of Southern Marsh Orchids or the scatter of Heath Spotted Orchids across a heather moor are straightforward to identify and, indeed, spectacular.

Distribution

Approximately 75 species are found in Europe and temperate Asia. The range of one species extends into Alaska via the Aleutian Islands, and Frog Orchid has a circumpolar distribution.

Classification

Dactylorhiza is one of several closely related genera that all have well-developed tubers. It is probably most closely related to the fragrant orchids *Gymnadenia* and butterfly orchids *Platanthera* and only more distantly to the 'typical' orchids in the genus *Orchis*. This is despite the fact that until the 1930s and 1940s the marsh and spotted orchids were placed in the genus *Orchis*.

The *Dactylorhiza* orchids can be divided into two groups depending on the number of chromosomes they possess. The diploid group has a chromosome count of $2n = 40$. This includes Early Marsh Orchid and Common Spotted Orchid. The tetraploid marsh orchids have a chromosome count of $2n = 80$. This group includes Southern, Pugsley's, Northern, Irish and Hebridean Marsh Orchids. The chromosome count is significant for two reasons. The first is hybridisation as it has some influence on the fertility of hybrids. Second, the tetraploid marsh orchids are thought to have evolved from a cross between the ancestors of two members of the diploid group, Early Marsh Orchid and Common Spotted Orchid, followed by a doubling of the chromosomes (in which $2n = 40$ became $2n = 80$). This allowed the hybrid to become reproductively isolated from its parents. This hybridisation event occurred several times and with slightly differing parents, producing the closely similar species we see today.

On genetic evidence the Frog Orchid has recently been moved into *Dactylorhiza*. It is thought to be a 'primitive' member of the genus and differs from the other British species not only in its general appearance but also in having a rudimentary spur and bursicle, by producing nectar, and by having the 'hood' of the flower made up from all of the sepals and petals (in the other species the lateral sepals are held away from the hood).

Identification

The most useful tools in the identification of marsh and spotted orchids are a small ruler, a notebook and pencil. The ruler is useful because for many species the width of the flower's lip is a critical measurement, as well as its length. Sometimes the width of the widest leaf and the total height of the plant are important too. The notebook and pencil are useful because it is almost always necessary to take the details of several plants. The following are worth noting:
1. Lip size: the width across the widest point of the flattened lip and also the length (from the mouth of the spur to the tip of the central lobe).
2. Lip shape: the lip is often folded or has the sides turned down. To judge its shape it is necessary to flatten it. This can easily be done by sliding the ruler or a finger below the lip and gently pushing upwards. The degree to which the side-lobes are turned downwards in its

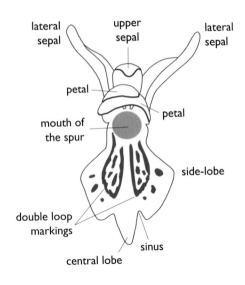

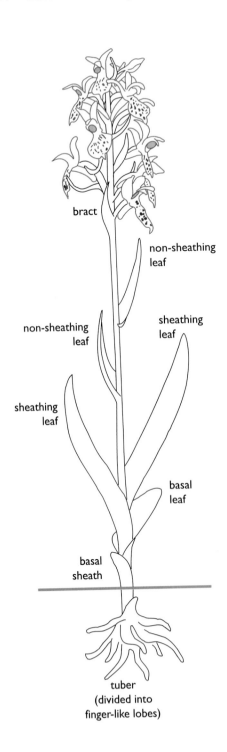

bract

non-sheathing leaf

non-sheathing leaf

sheathing leaf

sheathing leaf

basal leaf

basal sheath

tuber (divided into finger-like lobes)

▲ *A typical* Dactylorhiza *orchid.*

◀ *15 June, New Forest. Heath Spotted Orchid; the coloration in some regions is very variable.*

natural position may also be important. The lip is almost always lobed but it may also have small cuts or incisions (sinuses) separating the lobes; see figure above.

3. Lip markings.

4. Flower colour: only useful in some cases, as the tetraploid marsh orchids (Southern, Northern, Pugsley's, Irish and Hebridean) are all similar shades of purplish-pink.

5. Position of lateral sepals: these may be held horizontally at the side of the flower, vertically over the flower or at any angle in between.

6. Lateral sepal markings.

7. The shape of the spur.

8. The number of flowers: surprisingly hard to count and only really useful in the identification of Pugsley's Marsh Orchid. If there are too many to count, it cannot be that species.

9. The number of leaves: the leaves are divided into sheathing and non-sheathing. Sheathing leaves are found on the lower part of the stem and at their base they completely encircle the stem with a short, unbroken, tubular sheath. Non-sheathing leaves are found higher on the stem, are narrower and more bract-like. They have a clearly defined base that may encircle the stem but never have an unbroken sheath.

Importantly, the basal leaf is not included in any counts. This can range from a very short sheath at ground level with a green tip to a fully-formed leaf up to half the length of the sheathing leaf immediately above it (see figure opposite).

10. Leaf markings.

11. Leaf hooding: the tips of the leaves in some species are described as hooded but this is a subtle and very variable character and is of limited use (see figure below).

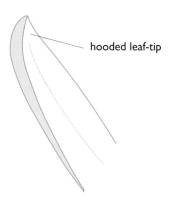

hooded leaf-tip

Floral structures

There are two pollinia, each narrowing into a caudicle (stalk) and attached by a basal disc to one of the viscidia. A two-lobed bursicle is present and encloses the two viscidia. The stigma is more-or-less two-lobed and situated at the roof of the entrance to the spur.

Pollination

Dactylorhiza are cross-pollinated by bees but most members of the genus produce no nectar. The insects receive no reward and are perhaps just attracted to the mass of brightly coloured flowers which are often found in large numbers. The attraction is therefore a deceit. The exception is Frog Orchid, which does produce nectar.

Growth pattern

The aerial stem grows from a pair of tubers. These are flattened and each divided into two to five finger-like lobes which taper to a fine point. They may be long in dry habitats, extending well down into the soil, but in wet areas may bend upwards towards the surface of the soil, perhaps to avoid becoming waterlogged. There are also several long, fleshy roots growing near the surface of the soil.

As in the genus *Orchis*, the next season's tuber develops alongside the current one and the system of annual replacement is similar (see p.200).

Fungal partners

In the adult plant only the roots and sometimes the tips of the tubers are 'infected' with fungi. Members of this genus have well-developed foliage, and fungi may play a relatively minor role in their nutritional budget.

Development from seed

Seed probably germinates in the autumn to produce a tiny, conical or turnip-shaped protocorm about 2mm long. The first root and leafy shoot are produced the following spring, and the first tuber develops from a bud at the base of this leafy shoot. This tuber is rod-shaped with just one finger-like extension and in the late summer the protocorm, root and leafy shoot disappear, leaving just the tuber. In the autumn a short rhizome grows from a bud at the tip of the tuber. This produces roots and, in the spring, elongates to produce the next leafy shoot. The sequence of events is very similar to that of the genera *Orchis*, *Gymnadenia* and *Platanthera* (see p.201). A regular annual cycle now begins. The tuber that produced the current year's growth gradually shrivels away, and a new tuber forms beside it from a bud on the short rhizome. This swells over the summer as it stores up nutrients produced by photosynthesis. The period between germination and flowering is four or five years in most species of *Dactylorhiza*.

Vegetative reproduction

Additional tubers may develop at the end of short shoots growing from the base of the stem, and these become separate plants when the central stem dies away in the autumn.

Name

The generic name *Dactylorhiza* originates from the Greek *daktulos* 'finger' and *rhiza* 'root' and means 'finger-like root', a reference to the distinctive shape of the tubers.

EARLY MARSH ORCHID
Dactylorhiza incarnata

Formerly: *Orchis latifolia, Dactylorchis latifolia*
This is the most widespread of the marsh orchids, occurring throughout Britain and Ireland in a wide variety of habitats. However, it is always rather local, often uncommon and indeed has disappeared from many areas. It is also the most variable marsh orchid with five named subspecies and flowers that range in colour from deep red to creamy. Because the subspecies are so different and occur in different habitats, they are discussed separately in the text.

▲ 6 July, Lancashire. Subspecies incarnata. A very stout plant.

◀ 13 June, Norfolk. Subspecies incarnata. A slender, petite plant with few flowers.

Identification

The five subspecies in brief:

1. ***D. i. incarnata*** has flowers that are usually very pale pink but sometimes purplish-pink. It is found in alkaline fens and marshy meadows throughout the British Isles.

2. ***D. i. coccinea*** has flowers that are deep red and often looks like a fat little hyacinth. It occurs scattered on both the east and west coasts in coastal dune slacks. There are also some inland sites, especially in Ireland.

3. ***D. i. pulchella*** has flowers that are purplish-pink. It is largely confined to bogs on acid heathland in southern England.

4. ***D. i. cruenta*** Flecked Marsh Orchid has flowers that are mid to dark pink. It also frequently has bold spots on the leaves and bracts. It is confined to alkaline fens in western Ireland and northwest Scotland.

5. ***D. i. ochroleuca*** has unmarked creamy flowers and is found in alkaline fens in East Anglia but is now very rare.

Early Marsh Orchid is probably the most variable species of orchid in the British Isles, both in flower colour and in stature. It may be very petite and just 5cm tall or a robust giant at 60cm. Nevertheless, it is relatively distinctive because the individual flowers have a characteristic size and shape: They are always small, indeed disproportionately so on robust plants compared to the stem, bracts and ovaries. The lip is no more than 9mm wide and usually rather less (push a finger gently upwards from below to flatten the lip before measuring it). Furthermore, the flowers appear even narrower

▲ *29 June, Norfolk. Subspecies* coccinea. *This subspecies appears in many different shades of red, from orange-red to purplish-red.*

◄ *29 June, Norfolk. Subspecies* coccinea. *Grows in dune slacks and also on slumped clay cliffs.*

because the sides of the lip are often folded downwards, sometimes sharply so, especially as the spike matures. This narrow appearance is further accentuated by the lateral sepals, which are held vertically above the flower as if it is holding its 'arms' up in surrender. And, whatever their coloration, the flowers have the same basic pattern of markings (with the exception of the unmarked creamy flowers of subspecies *ochroleuca*). The centre of the lip has a scatter of wriggly lines of varying length and these are all bounded by a solid dark line that forms a double loop, with few, if any, dark markings outside this loop.

Similar species

The pink-flowered subspecies *D. i. incarnata* is distinctive as no other British marsh orchid shows this coloration. Similarly the deep red

D. i. coccinea is characteristic, but the various purple-flowered forms can be more confusing.

Southern Marsh Orchid always has larger flowers with a broader lip. The sides of the lip are quite frequently folded downwards but never as sharply as in some Early Marsh Orchids, and the lip is often held flat or even dished. It typically lacks prominent double loop markings and although Leopard Marsh Orchid (var. *junialis* of Southern Marsh Orchid) does have loop markings it also has ring-shaped spots on its leaves.

Northern Marsh Orchid is quite similar to purple-flowered Early Marsh Orchids but its flowers are on average slightly larger with a broader, distinctively diamond-shaped lip which is usually held flat. It is often an intense reddish-pink, lacks the double loop markings,

▲ 15 June, New Forest. Subspecies pulchella. *Grows in acid bogs with bog-mosses Sphagnum.*

and its lateral sepals are not usually held as near to the vertical. Subspecies *cambrensis* of Northern Marsh Orchid has boldly spotted leaves and a slightly more three-lobed lip than typical plants, but the lip is still broader than in Early Marsh Orchid.

Pugsley's Marsh Orchid has narrower leaves than Early Marsh Orchid, a rather few-flowered spike and relatively large flowers. The lip is usually over 9.5mm wide and distinctly three-lobed, often with a prominent projecting central lobe. The dark markings are variable but usually

extend to the edge of the lip and it often lacks the double loop of Early Marsh Orchid. In Scotland, 'Lapland Marsh Orchid' (subspecies *lapponica* of Pugsley's Marsh Orchid) has been found in the same localities as *D. i. cruenta*, the spotted-leaved subspecies of Early Marsh Orchid, but although they share spotted leaves and bracts and heavily marked lips, they can be separated as above.

Irish Marsh Orchid is usually stouter than Early Marsh Orchid with the leaves neither as rigidly upright nor hooded. It has a proportionally larger flower spike and a flatter, broader lip that has more evenly rounded lobes.

Flowering period
Late May to late June, occasionally from mid-May or to late July. There is considerable variation both within individual colonies and between sites but late May and early June is probably the peak for many. Beyond a tendency for plants in the south and west to flower earlier and plants in wetter sites and at higher altitudes to flower later, there seems to be no real difference between the flowering times of the various subspecies.

Habitat
Subspecies **incarnata** is found on calcareous or neutral soils on damp to wet grassland. It is especially characteristic of unimproved wet meadows on floodplains. It is also found in spring-fed fens and flushes, even in the mountains of Scotland. Paradoxically, although it is usually found in wet areas, the species cannot survive a prolonged submergence. Other habitats include dune slacks (where it may be found with the red-flowered subspecies *coccinea*), old fly-ash tips, occasionally old chalk quarries where soil compaction may cause seasonal water-logging and, very rarely, chalk grassland. Recorded up to 440m above sea level (Ben Lawers, Perthshire; plants not referred to any subspecies have been found at 610m in the Atholl District in Perthshire and also at 610m at Caenlochan in Angus). Subspecies **coccinea** is found in damp dune slacks, the machair grasslands of the Hebrides, the flushed slopes

▲ 15 June, New Forest. Subspecies pulchella. The flower is purplish-pink.

vegetated areas. Suitable sites were created when peat was cut for fuel and the workings subsequently flooded. Such 'turf ponds' slowly fill with vegetation which eventually forms a floating mat or 'hover' but in the long run the continued build-up of material dries them out and they become unsuitable.

Range

Subspecies *incarnata* is locally frequent in England and Wales but is very scattered in Scotland and Ireland. Subspecies *coccinea* is very locally common on the west coast from Devon north to the Inner and Outer Hebrides and Shetland (South Mainland only; it is absent from Orkney). On the east coast it is scattered in southeast Scotland, northeast England and north Norfolk. It has been recorded inland in Hertfordshire and Derbyshire, and in Ireland is very scattered but occurs both inland and on the coast. Subspecies *coccinea* is often found in very large numbers. Subspecies *pulchella* occurs in Cornwall, Dorset, the New Forest, the heaths around the Surrey/Hampshire border, Ashdown Forest in Sussex and perhaps also Dartmoor in Devon. Similar plants, perhaps subspecies *pulchella* (rather than subspecies *incarnata* with pinkish-purple flowers), may be found in acid habitats elsewhere in Britain, especially Ireland, but the exact status of these populations is

of slumped clay cliffs in east Norfolk and damp lake shores inland in Ireland. It is also recorded from alkaline Leblanc waste in Lancashire and pulverised fly-ash waste. Subspecies *pulchella* is found in valley bogs and acid marshes on heathland, often growing among *Sphagnum* and sundews. Subspecies *cruenta* Flecked Marsh Orchid is found in the limestone districts of Ireland in calcium-rich fens around loughs and turloughs, frequently with Black Bog-rush; indeed, it often grows in the hollows amongst slabs of limestone. Its only three Scottish sites are on roughly neutral flushes and mires up to 450m above sea level. Subspecies *ochroleuca* is found in calcareous spring-fed fens where it grows on a mossy carpet in the more sparsely

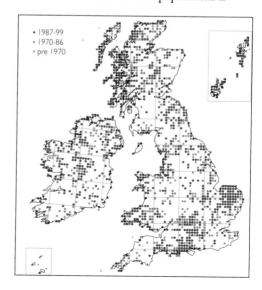

• 1987-99
• 1970-86
• pre 1970

▲ *23 May, Co. Clare. Subspecies cruenta. Grows in calcareous fens. Not all plants have spotted leaves.*

through the mountains of Central Asia to the Himalayas. Subspecies *coccinea* and subspecies *pulchella* are endemic to Britain. Subspecies *cruenta* is widespread in Scandinavia and the Alps and is also found in Poland, the Baltic States and through central and northern Russia to eastern Siberia. Subspecies *ochroleuca* is local and rare but occurs widely in central Europe from Haute-Savoie in southeast France, Switzerland, Austria, Hungary and Romania north to Denmark, southern Scandinavia, Poland, the Baltic States and perhaps northwest Russia; it has also been recorded from Spain. But as in Britain, confusion with pale-flowered variants of the other subspecies has obscured its precise distribution.

How to find it

With the exception of dune populations, Early Marsh Orchid tends to occur in small numbers, unlike the massed ranks of Southern, Northern or Irish Marsh Orchids, and is easily overlooked. A search of any rough-looking riverside meadows, with a good growth of rushes, is recommended. In the London area, the Lee Valley Park is an excellent site for this species. The red-flowered form can be found in good numbers at most of the larger protected dune systems, and the purple-flowered subspecies *pulchella* is common in many of the New Forest bogs and also at Thursley Common in Surrey. A visit to western Ireland is necessary to see Flecked Marsh Orchid, subspecies *cruenta*.

unclear. Subspecies **cruenta** occurs in western Ireland in Co. Galway, Co. Mayo and the southeastern portion of The Burren in Co. Clare. In Scotland there are a couple of tiny populations near Ullapool in Ross & Cromarty and one in Assynt in Sutherland. Subspecies *ochroleuca* is confined to East Anglia. **World range:** Europe and Asia. Subspecies *incarnata* is found throughout Europe away from the Mediterranean lowlands, north to northern Scandinavia and south to Spain, Italy, Greece, the Crimea and Caucasus. In Asia it occurs from northern Turkey to northern Iran and in Siberia east to Lake Baikal and south

DESCRIPTION *(incarnata)*

Height: 7-65cm but typically 20-40cm and rarely more than 20cm in Scotland.

Stem: Bright yellowish-green or apple green and usually hollow; in larger plants the thick, hollow stem is conspicuous.

Leaves: Bright yellowish-green or apple green. There are three to five sheathing leaves, often crowded towards the base of the stem and rather broad (the largest more than 2cm wide, sometimes as much as 3.5cm), with up to two non-sheathing leaves higher on the stem. The leaves are typically held rather erect at *c.* 45°, are strongly keeled and often hooded at the tip.

Spike: Crowded, with ten to 70 flowers.

Bract: Apple green, sometimes flushed rose-pink or purplish, lanceolate and fairly long, up to twice as long as the **ovary** and projecting well beyond the flowers in the lower part of the spike.

Ovary: Green, six-ribbed and twisted, also bent through approximately 45°.

Flower: The flowers are usually pale pink but at some sites there may also be plants with flowers of various shades of purplish-pink. The sepals and petals are off-white, variably washed rose-pink. The lateral sepals are oval to strap-shaped, rather like donkey's ears, and slightly asymmetric; they are held erect and often have dark pink spots or sometimes ring-shaped markings. The upper sepal and petals are more oval in shape (the petals a little smaller) and form a tight hood. The lip is off-white washed rose-pink, especially towards the edges, with irregular dark pink dots and lines in a central zone enclosed within two complete or near-complete loops. It is usually less than 8.5mm wide and 7mm long and is slightly to moderately lobed, with the sides usually strongly turned downward; indeed, this deflexing may be so marked that the lip is almost folded in two. The spur is pale pink, stout, slightly tapering and slightly to moderately decurved (rarely straight); it ranges from half as long to nearly as long as the ovary (but less than 7.5mm long).

Subspecies

Each of the five subspecies is sometimes treated as a distinct species by European authors, but recent genetic analyses show that they are very similar indeed, with the exception of subspecies *cruenta*, which does show some genetic differences. The dividing lines between the various subspecies are not hard and fast and intermediates occur. See also Habitat and Range.

D. i. incarnata is the 'typical' subspecies and is described above.

In southern England the vast majority of plants have pale pink flowers but at a few sites both pale pink and purplish-pink Early

Marsh Orchids can be found growing together. This variation in flower colour appears to be commoner in Wales, Cumbria, Scotland and Ireland, but even in these areas 'mixed' colonies are still mostly or always found in neutral or base-rich habitats.

(Note that 'D. i. gemmana' has been recorded from east Norfolk and east Galway with similar plants found elsewhere in England, Wales and Ireland. Ignored or forgotten for many years it has recently been 'resurrected' but it may be best to treat it as a large, late-flowering variant of subspecies *incarnata*. It is robust, growing to 50cm (sometimes 80cm), has six or more leaves and is large flowered, with the lip more than 8.5mm wide x 7mm long and the spur usually longer than 7.5mm. The flowers are either pink or purple and the lip is marked with fine dots rather than a double loop, suggesting perhaps a hybrid origin.)

D. i. coccinea is often relatively small at 5-20cm but may grow to 30cm; it can appear stout, squat and apparently stemless. The flower is a

▲ *23 May, Co. Clare. Subspecies* cruenta. *The flower is mid to dark pink. This is a heavily marked plant.*

distinctive deep red with even darker markings although these are less obvious than in other subspecies due to the reduced contrast with the dark red ground colour; the markings on the lip are rather narrow and appear quite faint. The bracts are rather long and are washed and edged purple, and the upper stem and ovaries are also strongly washed purple. The spur is stout and bag-like or conical. The leaves are broad-based but sharply tapering, dark green and unspotted. In most dune colonies there are also plants with flowers which are paler and pinker, intermediate with subspecies *incarnata*, and often some typical pale pink *incarnata* too.

D. i. pulchella has purplish-pink flowers that fade to white around the mouth of the spur; they are rather similar in colour to Southern Marsh Orchid although slightly more purple. The upper stem, bracts and ovaries are variably washed purple, and as in subspecies *incarnata* the lateral sepals may have ring-shaped markings. Apart from the colour of the flower

it differs from subspecies *incarnata* in having thicker, bolder and more complete double loop markings on the lip, which is less obviously lobed. The sides of the lip either do not fold downwards at all or do so only as the flower gets older, and the lip may therefore be flat or even slightly dished. On average the leaves are narrower and a darker and deeper green. The bracts are shorter and less prominent. There is some variation in flower colour and in some colonies very pale yellowish flowers are relatively common; these are subspecies *pulchella*, var. *ochrantha*.

The subspecific name *pulchella* is often used willy-nilly for any purple-flowered Early Marsh Orchid wherever it grows. We prefer to reserve the name *pulchella* for the heavily marked, purple-flowered populations growing in acid bogs and to treat the purple Early Marsh Orchids that grow with pale pink-flowered plants in alkaline habitats as colour variants of subspecies *incarnata*.

▲ *6 July, Lancashire. Subspecies* incarnata *among Creeping Willow. On the edges of dune slacks subspecies* incarnata *and subspecies* coccinea *can be found growing together.*

◀ *4 July, Norfolk. Subspecies* incarnata.

▲ *1. 19 June, Norfolk. Subspecies* incarnata. *2. 19 June, Norfolk. Subspecies* incarnata. *3. 17 June, Norfolk. Subspecies* coccinea. *4. 15 June, New Forest. Subspecies* pulchella. *5. 23 May, Co. Clare. Subspecies* cruenta. *6. 14 June, Suffolk. Subspecies* ochroleuca.

D. i. *cruenta* 'Flecked Marsh Orchid' has mid to dark pink flowers that lack the purple tones of subspecies *pulchella*. Around 30-65% of plants have dark purplish-brown spots on one or both surfaces of the leaves, the spots becoming denser towards the tips of the leaves and sometimes merging. If present, the spots on the underside of the leaves are paler, smaller and sparser. The stem, bracts and ovaries are more strongly washed purple than in subspecies *pulchella* and are sometimes spotted or flecked darker. There are sometimes ring markings on the bracts, too (almost never spotted in *pulchella*), and the lateral sepals more often have ring markings. The lip is more distinctly three-lobed, about 4.5-7.5mm long x 4.5-9mm wide, the side-lobes are moderately reflexed and the margins of the lip are often slightly wrinkled (crene). The lip has broader, bolder loop markings but few dashes within the loops and these markings often spread over most of the lip (extending over no more than two-thirds of the lip in *pulchella*). The stem is slender, the leaves are held stiffly erect, and the spike is looser and less crowded than in subspecies *incarnata*, especially in Scottish plants.

Controversy surrounds this subspecies and doubts are sometimes expressed as to whether British and Irish plants are 'true' *cruenta* as found in Europe. Bizarrely, it is sometimes suggested that while Scottish plants are the 'real thing', Irish plants are not, being merely spotted-leaved variants of subspecies *pulchella*. **D. i. ochroleuca** is often relatively large, sometimes as much as 70cm tall, with a broad stem and large leaves that are usually held very erect. The bracts are large, the lowest usually larger than 30mm x 20mm. The flowers are creamy to pale yellow with a relatively large lip, around 9mm wide x 7mm long, that is deeply three-lobed with notches on the side-lobes. This subspecies has often been confused with pale-flowered variants of other subspecies, i.e. with var. *ochrantha*, but it has larger and more distinctly lobed flowers.

Variation and varieties

As well as the various subspecies, several varieties have been named. In principle, each different subspecies could be found as each different variety, giving around 15 different combinations.

Var. *punctata* is usually rather small with a few small dots on the leaves towards the tip. It is rare but has been recorded from Yorkshire, the New Forest and the Isle of Coll, among subspecies *incarnata* and *pulchella*.

Var. *leucantha* has unmarked pure white flowers but is very rare.

Var. *ochrantha* has unmarked pale creamy-yellow flowers with the lip pale yellow or rarely green at the base (it is similar to subspecies *ochroleuca* but has smaller and less distinctly three-lobed flowers). It is scarce and usually found among subspecies *pulchella*, although

▲ 13 June, Norfolk. Subspecies incarnata. *Early Marsh Orchid can be robust, with many proportionally small flowers.*

it has also been recorded among *incarnata*, *coccinea* and *cruenta*.

A hyperchromic variant with an excess of pigmentation and a solidly dark lip has also been recorded, albeit rather rarely.

BIOLOGY

Pollination and reproduction

There is no nectar, and pollination is by bumblebees that are 'duped' into visiting the flowers. The process is efficient and seed-set is good.

▲ *14 June, Suffolk. Subspecies* ochroleuca. *Grows in calcareous, spring-fed fens.*

Development and growth

Seed probably germinates in the spring, and the first leaves appear a year later. Early estimates of the period between germination and first flowering were as long as 16 years, but these were made by counting growth marks in tubers and other structures that were thought to represent a year's development. This technique is probably unreliable, and in cultivation plants flower aged four or five years. Individual plants have been recorded living for up to 25 years after their first appearance above ground.

Hybrids

Most or all of these hybrids are sterile and only found as isolated individuals or in small groups.

D. x kernerorum, the hybrid with Common Spotted Orchid, has been found scattered throughout Britain and Ireland. It is sterile.

D. x carnea, the hybrid with Heath Spotted Orchid, has been recorded scattered in Britain and Ireland but is rare. It is probably sterile.

D. x wintoni, the hybrid with Southern Marsh Orchid, has been found scattered throughout the range of the latter but is rare. It is sterile.

D. x latirella, the hybrid with Northern Marsh Orchid, has been recorded throughout the range of the latter but is scarce.

D. x dufftii, the hybrid with Pugsley's Marsh Orchid, has been found in northwest Wales, Yorkshire and Co. Wicklow. It is rare.

D. x aschersoniana, the hybrid with Irish Marsh Orchid and Hebridean Marsh Orchid, has been recorded in Co. Limerick and the Outer Hebrides respectively. This name is no longer valid for both species due to changes in the classification.

Intergeneric hybrids

X **Dactylodenia vollmannii**, the hybrid with fragrant orchid (in the broad sense), has been recorded twice from Cornwall.

Name and classification

The specific name *incarnata* means 'flesh-coloured'. Most of the subspecific names also refer to the flower colour; *pulchella* is Latin for 'beautiful', *coccinea* means 'crimson' or 'scarlet' (as in the dye produced from galls on the Kermes Oak), *cruenta* is Latin for 'blood-coloured' and *ochroleuca* comes from the Greek for 'yellowish-white'.

The Early Marsh Orchid and its relatives are often known as the 'diploid marsh orchids'. This is because their chromosome count is 2n = 40 compared with a count of 2n = 80 in the 'tetraploid marsh orchids', a group that includes all the other British and Irish marsh orchids. Although of little use to the orchid-lover in the field, it represents a fundamental division.

HISTORY AND CONSERVATION

For a long time this species was amalgamated with the other marsh orchids. The first British record that distinguished the Early Marsh Orchid was in the *Flora of Shropshire* published in 1841.

Early Marsh Orchid is frequently found in small numbers and is often the first of the marsh orchids to vanish if its habitat dries out due to drainage or other changes. Overall, the species has gone from 43.5% of its historical range in Britain and 39% in Ireland. In lowland areas the species declined significantly as riverside meadows were ploughed, drained or otherwise 'improved', the water table fell due to abstractions, or indeed meadows were abandoned to scrub.

Past and present occurrence of Early Marsh Orchid (all subspecies) in Britain and Ireland (based on presence or absence in 10km squares of the National Grid; data from the New Atlas).

	Britain	Ireland
total historical range, 1500-1999	1,192	331
current range	671 (23.5%*)	202 (20%*)
% lost, 1500-1969	29.5%	30.5%
% lost, 1970-1986	14%	8.5%
% lost, total	43.5%	39%

* current range as a % of the total number of 10km squares

Similar factors have led to the near-extinction of the creamy-flowered subspecies *ochroleuca*, which is treated in the *British Red Data Book* and classed as Critically Endangered. It was first recorded from Roydon Fen (near Diss) in Norfolk in 1936 and was subsequently found at several fens in the Waveney Valley on the Norfolk-Suffolk border and at Chippenham Fen in Cambridgeshire. It is now extinct at all sites with the exception of Chippenham Fen, where it has declined from around 30 plants in 1990 to a single clump, and one of the Waveney Valley fens in Suffolk, where it was rediscovered in the late 1990s, and there are currently around a dozen flowering plants.

The red-flowered dune subspecies *D. i. coccinea* has suffered declines due to the scrubbing-over of sand dunes and also coastal development but still occurs in very large numbers at some favoured sites. The spotted-leaved Flecked Marsh Orchid *D. i. cruenta* is also treated in the *British Red Data Book* and is classified as Endangered. It is only found at three sites in Scotland which, although remote, may suffer from overgrazing. It is rather commoner in Ireland but with the rapid changes occurring there, including The Burren region, it could be vulnerable to development and 'improvement'.

▲ 14 June, Suffolk. Subspecies ochroleuca. *A well as being a pale cream colour, the lip is very distinctly three-lobed.*

FROG ORCHID
Dactylorhiza viridis

Formerly: *Coeloglossum viride*; Other names: Bracted Green Orchis (North America)
The English names of many orchids make sense, and it is easy to see the 'man' in a Man
Orchid or the 'monkey' in a Monkey Orchid. Not so this species, for although the name has
been in use since the 17th century it is hard to see the 'frog' in a Frog Orchid; the two-lobed
lip could resemble hind legs, and the hood may look like a frog's body, but to anyone except
the most imaginative any real resemblance to a frog is fanciful. Frog Orchid grows in short
grassland, frequently on chalk or limestone, but is inconspicuous and often hard to find. It
has undergone a serious decline and is now missing from much of its former range.

Identification
The small size, generally greenish or reddish-
purple flowers, tight hood and rather plain,
strap-shaped lip are distinctive.

Similar species
Of the vaguely similar species, Man Orchid has
long and narrow 'arms' and 'legs' on its lip and
Common Twayblade has a smaller flower, again
with 'arms' and 'legs'.

Habitat
In southern Britain this species is confined
to well-drained short grassland on chalk or
limestone, especially the slopes of ancient
earthworks, abandoned quarries, old chalk
and lime pits and spoil heaps. It is tolerant of
grazing and trampling but cannot compete
with rank vegetation. In the past it was also
found in damp or wet permanent pastures and
meadows in southern England, but this habitat
has almost entirely vanished, taking the Frog
Orchid with it. In the north and west it is found
in a wider range of short-grass habitats, often
damp, and on both calcareous and neutral soils,
including limestone pavements, rocky ledges,
road verges, railway embankments, upland
flushes, mountain pastures, coastal grassland,
machair and dune slacks. It occurs from sea
level to 915m (Glen Doll, Angus).

◀ *29 June, Hampshire. Frog Orchid is 'shy' and the flowers typically face downwards without showing their 'face'.*

Flowering period

Early June to early August, sometimes from late May or even until early September, but usually peaking in late June and early July. Once pollinated, the flowers persist for a long time, although the lip will have withered.

Range

Frog Orchid is widely distributed in Britain and Ireland, including the Inner and Outer Hebrides, Orkney and Shetland, but has declined severely in much of lowland Britain. In southern England it is now almost confined to the chalk districts of Hampshire, northeast Dorset and Wiltshire, extending very locally into the Berkshire Downs, Chilterns and the South Downs in Sussex. In the Midlands it is more-or-less restricted to the Peak District. It is very local in Wales, lowland Scotland and the southern half of Ireland (and absent from southernmost Ireland from Co. Cork to Co. Wicklow) but more widespread in northern England, upland Scotland and the northern half of Ireland. **World range:** Frog Orchid has a circumpolar distribution and is found in Europe, Asia and North America. It is mostly confined to the temperate regions but extends north to Iceland, the Faeroes, northernmost Scandinavia and Alaska. It ranges furthest south in the mountains, to Spain, Italy, Greece, the Crimea and Caucasus (and adjacent

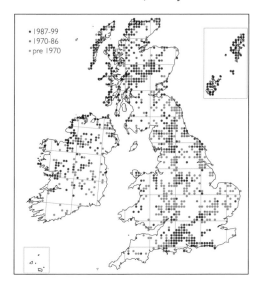

▲ 13 July, Dorset. Frog Orchid varies from overall green to generally very reddish.

northeast Turkey); in Asia to Central Asia and the eastern Himalayas; in North America to Washington, New Mexico, Iowa and North Carolina.

How to find it

Although variable, this species is often small, green, rather inconspicuous and easy to tread on. It can easily be overlooked; the first record in Cornwall for over 50 years was when over 4,000 flower spikes were found near Colliford Reservoir in 1986. It is also rather local in

occurrence, and the number of flowering plants can vary greatly from year to year. As with Musk Orchid, another short-turf specialist, it can be easiest to spot when scanning from a low-level vantage point. In southern England small numbers are found at several chalk grassland reserves from Dorset east to Sussex. Notable sites in Scotland include North Berwick and Crail golf courses which hold populations of many thousands.

DESCRIPTION

Height: 4-45cm but mostly 5-15cm and only very exceptionally over 25cm.

Stem: Green, on some plants washed reddish-purple towards the flower spike. There are one or two brown, leafless sheaths at the extreme base.

Leaves: There are three to five dark green, strap-shaped sheathing leaves, sometimes rather broad, with the two lowest leaves being the largest and bluntest. They are held at around 30°-45° above the horizontal. Higher on the stem there are also several narrower and more lanceolate non-sheathing leaves. The rosette appears in the autumn and overwinters, and there may be a relatively large number of non-flowering plants; these have fewer leaves.

Spike: Rather loose and often irregular in shape, with the ovaries variably twisted and the flowers therefore pointing in different directions. Mostly there are 5-25 flowers but sometimes only two, and particularly large plants may have up to 50.

Bract: Green, variably washed reddish-purple and lanceolate in shape; the lower bracts may be rather longer than the flowers (up to a maximum of twice the flower's length), but towards the tip of the spike the bracts become shorter.

Ovary: Green, variably washed reddish-purple, spindle-shaped, six-ribbed and twisted.

Flower: Green or yellowish-green, variably washed brown or reddish-purple, in some the whole flower may be reddish-purple. The sepals are dark green variably washed reddish-purple, roughly oval to oval-triangular in shape. The upper sepal is a little smaller than the lateral sepals. The petals are pale green, washed reddish-purple around the edges and strap-shaped, much smaller and narrower than the sepals. The sepals and petals form a tight hood over the column, with the petals often showing as much paler slots between the sepals. The lip is usually paler and greener than the rest of the flower and is even paler and yellower towards the base, with reddish tones usually confined to the tip and edges. It is tongue-shaped and may broaden slightly towards the tip, with two small terminal lobes that have a notch between them and a third smaller lobe within this notch. There is also a thickened ridge down the centre of the lip, and nectar is secreted from two hollows formed by the raised and curved margins of the lip at its base. The lip may hang downwards or be folded backwards below the ovary. The spur is very short (1-2mm), almost

◀ *29 June, Hampshire.*

▶ *29 June, Hampshire. It is not easy to see the 'frog' in a Frog Orchid.*

hemispherical in shape and rather colourless. The anthers are washed purple, and the pollinia are club-shaped and pale yellowish with a very lobed surface. The flowers are faintly honey-scented.

Subspecies
None.

Variation and varieties
On average shorter, stouter and more reddish-brown in the dry grassland habitats of southern England and taller and greener in the north. Some plants, including the flower spike, may be entirely yellowish-green.

Var. *longibracteatum* has unusually long bracts and is rather taller and more robust. It has been found in northern England.

BIOLOGY

Pollination and reproduction
Unlike the other *Dactylorhiza* orchids, the flowers produce nectar, and this is secreted into the short spur. A variety of insects visit the flowers, including small beetles and wasps, especially ichneumons. These alight on the lip and are directed by its central ridge to either side; as they approach the spur, the pollinia are stuck to their head by the viscidia which lie on either side of the spur. Once on the insect's head it takes about 20 minutes for the pollinia to rotate forward. They are then in position to make contact with the stigma of the next plant to be visited. Self-pollination is also reported to occur. Seed-set is variable, with the capsules maturing rapidly and containing around 1,250-5,000 seeds. This species only occasionally reproduces vegetatively.

Development and growth
The aerial stem grows from a pair of tubers that are forked into three or four finger-like lobes. They are typical of the genus *Dactylorhiza* although rather small.

The period between germination and flowering is short. The first green leaves appear one to three years after seed has germinated and a flower spike is usually produced in that first year above ground. Frog Orchid is short-lived with a rapid turnover of the population. Many plants are monocarpic and die after just one year above ground, although some may live and flower for at least seven years. In a study in Holland the 'half-life' of a population averaged 1.5 years and varied from 1.0 to 2.4 years (the 'half-life' is a measure of the life expectancy of an orchid after its first appearance above ground and marks the point at which 50% of the population which emerged in any given year have died). Occasionally, plants may be 'dormant' underground but not for more than one year.

Hybrids
D. x *mixtum*, the hybrid with Common Spotted Orchid, is rare but has been found at widely scattered localities.

D. x *conigerum*, the hybrid with Heath Spotted Orchid, has been found rarely (the two parent species do not occur together as frequently).

D. x *viridella*, the hybrid with Northern Marsh Orchid, has been recorded from Co. Durham and the Inner and Outer Hebrides.

Intergeneric hybrids
X *Dactylodenia jacksonii*, the hybrid with fragrant orchid (in the broad sense) has been noted sporadically but widely in England.

Name and classification
The specific name *viridis* means 'fresh-green' or 'youthful'.

Until recently the Frog Orchid was named *Coeloglossum viride*, and indeed the genus *Coeloglossum* contained just this one species. However, genetic and biochemical techniques have shown that *Coeloglossum* is sufficiently similar to the genus *Dactylorhiza* for the Frog Orchid to be transferred to it. This explains why the Frog Orchid has such a propensity to form hybrids with the other members of the genus *Dactylorhiza*, the spotted orchids and marsh orchids. The chromosome number is 2n=40, and Frog Orchid is one of the more primitive *Dactylorhiza*. (The old name *Coeloglossum* means 'hollow-tongue', a reference to the short conical spur at the base of the lip.)

▲ 13 July, Dorset. Frog Orchid has recently joined the spotted and marsh orchids in the genus Dactylorhiza but any similarity is not obvious.

HISTORY AND CONSERVATION

Despite its inconspicuous nature, the Frog Orchid was known to early naturalists and was first recorded in Hertfordshire in 1650 by William How in his *Phytologia Britannica natales exhibens Indigenarum Stirpium sponte emergentium* ('A British botany presenting the origins of native wild plants'): 'Orchis Batrachites…By Barkway, Dr. Johnson's MS.' The species was then listed in John Ray's flora of Cambridgeshire in 1660 and noted by Christopher Merrett growing near Lewes in Sussex and, 'in many places about Oxford' in his *Pinax* of 1666.

Generally commoner in the north, especially in Scotland, Frog Orchid is abundant at a few favoured localities with hundreds or even thousands of flower spikes. It is rather local, however, even in Scotland and very much so in the rest of Britain.

Past and present occurrence of Frog Orchid in Britain and Ireland (based on presence or absence in 10km squares of the National Grid; data from the New Atlas*).*

	Britain	Ireland
total historical range, 1500-1999	964	214
current range	381 (13%*)	99 (9.8%*)
% lost, 1500-1969	49%	47%
% lost, 1970-1986	11.5%	6.5%
% lost, total	60.5%	53.5%

* current range as a % of the total number of 10km squares

This species has declined throughout almost the entire range in the British Isles and in much of Europe too. The biggest losses have been in England, especially the Midlands and East Anglia, where the ploughing-up of old pastures on neutral or chalky boulder-clay soils appears to have been a major factor as well as the development of scrub and rank vegetation on what had been short grassland. Frog Orchid is extinct in Essex, Norfolk, Middlesex, Huntingdonshire, Worcestershire, Warwickshire, Lancashire, Monmouthshire, Breconshire, Radnorshire, Pembrokeshire, Montgomeryshire, the Isle of Man, Dumfries-shire, Wigtownshire, Berwickshire, Kincardineshire and Dunbartonshire. It was last seen in Kent in 1988, and just one site each remains in Suffolk, Cambridgeshire, Lincolnshire and Herefordshire.

COMMON SPOTTED ORCHID
Dactylorhiza fuchsii

Formerly: *Orchis fuschii, Dactylorchis fuschii*

Aptly named, this species is both common and has boldly spotted leaves. Indeed, it is the commonest and most widespread orchid in the British Isles and is found in a very wide variety of habitats from open grassland to woodland and fen. An opportunist, it can colonise new areas relatively easily and quickly and can sometimes appear in very large numbers; the massed ranks of thousands of Common Spotted Orchids on a road verge or in an abandoned quarry or chalk pit has to be one of the most spectacular sights of the summer. Common Spotted Orchid is the county flower of West Lothian and Linlithgowshire and the 'Hebridean Spotted Orchid' (subspecies *hebridensis*) is the county flower of the Western Isles.

▲ 6 July, Norfolk. The leaves are typically well-spotted.

Identification

Identification is usually straightforward. The leaves are marked all over with solid dark spots or bars, the flowers are various shades of pink or lilac (and are often very pale or almost white), and the lip is divided into three roughly equal lobes and decorated with bold dark lines and loops. It is, however, very variable: the leaves may be heavily or lightly marked; plants with unspotted leaves are not uncommon; and the flowers vary from white to rather dark pinkish-purple. It tends to be tall, attenuated and pale-flowered in shady woodland sites but shorter and more compact in the open. It thrives best in damp or wet habitats; plants on dry chalk grassland can be very petite while those in exposed, windswept sites may be short and squat.

Similar species

Early Purple Orchid has spotted leaves, but the lip is a very different shape and does not have bold darker lines and loops. It also flowers rather earlier in the spring.

Heath Spotted Orchid can be very similar to Common Spotted Orchid but is separated by its fewer, rather narrower, more obviously keeled and more pointed leaves, with the lowest leaf *not* significantly shorter or blunter than the remainder. The spots on its leaves are often small and rounded, compared to the larger and bolder marking of Common Spotted Orchid, and plants with unspotted leaves are more frequent. The lip of Heath Spotted Orchid is broader and the lobes are very unequal in size. The central lobe is rather small and barely longer than the side-lobes, and the incisions (sinuses) between the lobes cut much less than halfway to the base of the lip. The lip is often more faintly marked, with dots and fine dashes rather than bold loops and lines, and the spur is longer and rather finer.

Marsh orchids mostly have darker and more purple flowers, although there is some overlap, and often have unspotted leaves. Both Common and Heath Spotted Orchids can be distinguished from the marsh orchids by having a spur that is slender and parallel-sided rather than short, fat and bag-like (but beware hybrids). The stem of the spotted orchids is usually solid and 'unsquashable', whereas that of some of the marsh orchids is obviously hollow. However, Common Spotted Orchids growing in wet habitats may have hollow stems, so this is not always a safe distinction. The number of non-sheathing leaves on the upper part of the stem may also be helpful; often two to six in Common Spotted (but sometimes just one) and one or two in most marsh orchids.

Hybrids are common, particularly with Southern and Northern Marsh Orchids. Identification of hybrids requires a good knowledge of the range of variation of both species and even then is not always certain. First generation hybrids usually show 'hybrid vigour' and may be obviously large, sometimes ridiculously so. Hybrids with marsh orchids often have the fat, conical spur of the marsh orchid parent rather than the thin spur of the spotted orchid but in subsequent generations back-crossed with the parent species, or in hybrid swarms, these distinctions will break down.

Habitat

Common Spotted Orchid favours a very wide range of habitats. It occurs on dry grassland, from heavily grazed downland swards to ranker and scrubbier sites, and also thrives in damper

▲ 22 June, Norfolk. A petite, few-flowered plant.

conditions in wet meadows, the machair of northwest Scotland, marshes, fens and dune slacks, including alkaline flushes in otherwise unsuitable moorland. The species is also found in woodland, usually in the better-lit areas along rides, clearings and edges, although it can tolerate quite deep shade where it may persist in a non-flowering state. Common Spotted Orchid is usually found on alkaline or neutral soils but it can grow in slightly acidic conditions, such as among grass and Heather on less acid areas of heathland. An opportunist, it is capable of colonising new sites, including

man-made habitats such as abandoned gravel
and chalk pits and industrial waste sites (e.g.
fly ash tips and alkaline Leblanc waste). It is
often found on roadside verges and cuttings,
including motorways, on railway embankments
and sometimes on lawns, and can quickly build
up in numbers to form substantial populations.
Recorded up to 530m above sea level in
Cumbria (Garrigill) and 600m in Perthshire
(Loch na Lairige).

Flowering period

Mid-May to early August, being earliest in
open, sheltered localities in the south (where
generally best around mid-June) and later in
woodland sites and in the north.

Range

Found throughout Britain and Ireland,
including the Isle of Man, Inner and Outer
Hebrides and Shetland, and also the Channel
Islands. However, it is absent from most of
Cornwall, much of north Devon and from
large areas of northern and northeast Scotland.
Formerly recorded from Orkney and the Isles
of Scilly. **World range:** Widespread in Europe
away from the Mediterranean lowlands, south
to Spain, northern Italy and Greece, north to
Scandinavia and Finland and east to Russia
and Siberia. The precise boundaries of the
distribution are obscure due to confusion with
Heath Spotted Orchid.

▲ *20 June, Norfolk. 'Typical' coloration.*

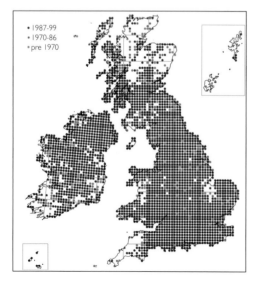

• 1987-99
• 1970-86
• pre 1970

How to find it

In much of Britain and Ireland this is the
commonest orchid, and it is often found in large
numbers. Nevertheless, there are large tracts of
countryside that are not graced by its presence.

DESCRIPTION

Height: 7-70cm but usually 15-50cm.
Stem: Pale green, sometimes lightly washed
with purple towards the tip, grooved and
usually solid (but can be hollow, especially in
larger plants in wetland habitats).
Leaves: Green, usually marked all over with
elongated solid dark spots and blotches but
sometimes unmarked. There is a relatively
small, oval, blunt-tipped leaf at the base of the

▲ *6 July, Norfolk. A relatively pale spike.*

stem and the three to six (sometimes two to seven) sheathing leaves are crowded together above this; they are broad, up to 4cm or even 5.5cm wide, and lanceolate. The two to six (sometimes one to nine) non-sheathing leaves higher on the stem become narrower and more bract-like towards the spike.

Spike: Variable in shape but often pyramidal or conical as the flowers begin to open, becoming longer and more cylindrical later on, with 20-70 flowers, exceptionally 150.

Bract: Green, sometimes washed purple, lanceolate and finely pointed; the lowest are longer than the ovaries but higher on the spike they are about equal in length.

Ovary: Cylindrical, six-ribbed, twisted and green, often with a violet tinge.

Flower: Various shades of pale lilac, pink or purplish-pink or sometimes almost white. The sepals are oval-lanceolate with the lateral sepals asymmetrical, marked with lines and spots and usually held spreading horizontally (but they may be closer to 45°). The upper sepal and the petals, which are a little shorter, form a hood over the column. The lip is a flattened oval in shape, 8-12mm wide, divided into three lobes by deep wedge-shaped incisions (*sinuses*) that extend about halfway to the base. The side-lobes have broad rounded tips that are sometimes toothed with roughly parallel sides. The central lobe is slightly narrower and more triangular in shape but as long or longer than the side-lobes. The lip is held flat or with the side-lobes lightly depressed. It is usually paler and whiter towards the centre and is marked with bold dashes and broken dark pink or dark reddish-purple lines which often form a pattern of concentric double loops (occasionally just dots and dashes). The spur is about half as long as the ovary to roughly the same length, narrow, cylindrical, slightly tapering and either straight or very slightly curved. The pollinia are pale brownish-pink to purple, or sometimes yellowish. The flowers are faintly scented.

Subspecies

D. f. fuchsii is the commonest and by far the most widespread subspecies.

D. f. hebridensis 'Hebridean Spotted Orchid' is characterised by dark flowers and a broad lip. It is found on the machair and similar coastal habitats in the Outer Hebrides, northwest Scotland, Shetland and western Ireland (Co. Donegal, Co. Galway and Co. Kerry). It tends to flower relatively late and often occurs in large numbers. In some areas overlaps and mixes with subspecies *fuchsii*.

Hebridean Spotted Orchid is small and stocky, 8-20cm tall (range 6-40cm), with the upper stem usually washed purple and the leaves heavily spotted. The spike is often pyramidal or conical and densely packed, the lip is usually over 9.5mm wide (8-15mm), and

the flowers are often deep rose-pink or reddish-purple (rarely white) with the spur relatively long at 7-8.5mm. It is sometimes treated as a separate species by European authors but its distinctiveness has been exaggerated and, conversely, it is also sometimes treated as merely 'var. *hebridensis*'.

Variation and varieties

Woodland and grassland plants are sometimes separated as distinct varieties but the differences between the tall leafy plants found in the shade of woodland and scrub and the shorter plants of sunny grassland (the so-called var. 'trilobata') seem to be purely a product of their different growing conditions.

Var. *alpina* is a dark-flowered variant of subspecies *fuchsii*. The dark flowers recall those of subspecies *hebridensis* but they are smaller, with the lip usually less than 9.5mm wide and with narrower side-lobes. It is found in Scotland, both at inland sites and on the machair on the Hebrides and northwest coast (including some populations in the Inner Hebrides traditionally called 'hebridensis'). It is also present at inland sites in northern England and possibly also Wales and western Ireland.

Var. *cornubiensis* is very similar to subspecies *hebridensis* and essentially differs only statistically. It is a little bigger and more robust, with a larger and looser flower spike, longer bracts (often over 8mm long) and a narrower lip. The lateral sepals are rarely held horizontally, and the spur is stouter. Confined to Cornwall, where it is found on the north coast on stabilised dunes at Lelant golf course and cliffs near St Ives and at Tintagel.

Var. *albiflora* has unmarked white flowers (rarely washed cream or pink) and unspotted leaves. It is widespread but rather uncommon.

Var. *okellyi* has narrow leaves and flowers which are sometimes a little smaller or broader than typical plants and often almost white or creamy with very faint pink or lilac markings, although in some areas a substantial proportion (often the majority) have darker and heavier markings; the leaves are spotted or unspotted.

▲ *10 June, Norfolk. A particularly richly-coloured spike.*

◀ *11 July, Norfolk.*

It is found along the western seaboard of Ireland, on the Isle of Man and in northern Britain; individual white-flowered plants within these populations are well-nigh identical to var. *albiflora* (and vice-versa).

A lot of controversy surrounds *okellyi* with some European authors treating it as a distinct species and other botanists treating it merely as a poorly defined variety. The classic *okellyi* of the literature always has white, almost unmarked flowers and is said to be confined to western Ireland (especially The Burren region of Co. Clare and Co. Galway), the Isle of Man and the west coast of Kintyre in western Scotland (with single records for Tiree and Sutherland). However, in The Burren and elsewhere these classic white-flowered *okellyi* are just part of a population of plants with a variable flower colour. **Var. *rhodochila*** is an attractive hyperchromic variant with an excess of pigmentation. The lip is solidly reddish or purple, usually with a narrow paler pink or white border. The leaves may be more heavily spotted or in extreme cases entirely washed purple. It is widespread but rare.

▲ *6 July, Norfolk. A few-flowered spike.*

BIOLOGY

Pollination and reproduction

A wide variety of insects has been recorded carrying off pollinia from this species, but studies in Austria and Poland have identified beetles, especially longhorn beetles, as the major pollinators. In common with other members of the genus *Dactylorhiza*, Common Spotted Orchid does not produce 'nectar'. Insects may therefore be deceived into visiting the flowers, although Charles Darwin suggested that visiting insects feed on sap sucked from inside the wall of the spur. This hypothesis has since been disputed, and it has been suggested that they feed instead on tiny sugar-rich papillae that are present in a zone from the middle of the lip down into the spur. A third option is that bumblebees receive no reward and are deceived into pollinating the flowers but that honeybees are able to access a sugary liquid produced on the surface of the stigma.

Whatever the mechanism, pollination is efficient and around 50-90% of flowers produce seed. Notably, twice as many of the lower flowers, which open first, produce ripe capsules, compared with the upper flowers, which open later on. This suggests that as the season progresses insect pollinators become scarcer or lose interest as there is little or no reward. Vegetative reproduction is also possible.

Development and growth

The length of the period between germination and flowering in the wild is unknown but in cultivation it can be as little as two years although it is more often four or five years. It is thought that the plant can flower for several years in a row or remain as a dormant non-flowering rosette if conditions become unsuitable.

Hybrids

Sterile hybrids are likely to be found either singly or in very small numbers, whereas even partial fertility can result in large numbers of hybrids which in turn can show a great deal of individual variation.

D. **x** *transiens*, the hybrid with Heath Spotted
Orchid, is widespread but scarce and can be
hard to identify with certainty. It is sterile. See
also Name and classification.

D. **x** *kernerorum*, the hybrid with Early Marsh
Orchid, has been found scattered throughout
Britain and Ireland. It is sterile.

D. **x** *mixtum,* the hybrid with Frog Orchid, is
rare but there are widely scattered records.

D. **x** *venusta*, the hybrid with Northern Marsh
Orchid, occurs throughout the range of the
latter and can be common. It is partially fertile
and can back-cross with either parent species
to produce a range of characters in a hybrid
swarm.

D. **x** *grandis*, the hybrid with Southern Marsh
Orchid, can be found not only where both
species occur together but also in the absence
of one or even both parents. The pollen is
highly sterile and seed production is very low.
Nevertheless this partial fertility allows back-
crossing with both parents, creating hybrid
swarms which may be very persistent. It is
probably the commonest orchid hybrid in
southern Britain.

D. **x** *silvae-gabretae*, the hybrid with Pugsley's
Marsh Orchid, has been recorded from
northwest Wales, Yorkshire and Ireland. The
pollen is highly sterile.

'*D.* **x** *braunii*', the hybrid with Irish Marsh
Orchid, has been recorded in Co. Clare.
(The name may be changed following the
elevation of Irish Marsh Orchid to the status
of a full species.)

Intergeneric hybrids

X *Dactylodenia st-quintinii*, the hybrid with
fragrant orchid, is uncommon and scarce but
has been found widely through Britain and
Ireland. All three species of fragrant orchid may
be involved.

Name and classification

The specific name *fuchsii* commemorates
Leonard Fuchs (1501-66), a German botanist
who is also celebrated in the name 'Fuchsia'.

Common Spotted Orchid is closely related
to Heath Spotted Orchid and although they

▲ 10 June, Norfolk. Presumably Common Spotted Orchid
x Southern Marsh Orchid. Such hybrids can sometimes
occur where one of the parents is absent.

▲ *30 June, Norfolk. A densely-flowered spike; as all the flowers open the spike typically becomes more cylindrical.*

between the two are not absolute. Common Spotted Orchid is generally found on calcareous or neutral soils and Heath Spotted Orchid on acid soils. However, there is some evidence that spotted orchids growing on intermediate, neutral or slightly acidic soils do tend to be intermediate in appearance.

HISTORY AND CONSERVATION

Although spotted orchids had been known from the time of Turner's *Herball* of 1562, this species was not distinguished from the Heath Spotted Orchid until 1915 when it was described by the English botanist George Claridge Druce.

This is the most widespread species of orchid in the British Isles and is currently present in 67% of the total available 10km squares in both Britain and Ireland. There has been some decline but Common Spotted Orchid is so versatile that it can usually 'hang-on' somewhere within any particular 10km square. The *New Atlas* figures are thus likely to conceal a significantly greater fall in the number of actual populations. Notably, much of the decline in Britain appears to be recent and it could be that a fall in the number of populations is increasingly expressing itself as a decline in the overall range. At least some of the losses are compensated for, however, by the colonisation of new areas, especially in recent man-made habitats.

are clearly distinct in Britain, France and Scandinavia they are rather similar in central Europe and are considered to be the same species by many European authors. They are usually quoted as differing in the number of chromosomes, with Common Spotted Orchid having 2n=40 and Heath Spotted Orchid 2n=80, but various studies have given chromosome counts of 2n=40, 2n=60 and 2n=80 for both species (i.e. diploid, triploid and tetraploid). Even in Britain the differences

Past and present occurrence of Common Spotted Orchid in Britain and Ireland (based on presence or absence in 10km squares of the National Grid; data from the **New Atlas***).*

	Britain	Ireland
total historical range, 1500-1999	2,219	774
current range	1,913 (67%*)	673 (67%*)
% lost, 1500-1969	7%	12%
% lost, 1970-1986	7%	1%
% lost, total	14%	13%

* current range as a % of the total number of 10km squares

HEATH SPOTTED ORCHID
Dactylorhiza maculata

Formerly: *Orchis ericetorum, Dactylorchis ericetorum*

Closely related to Common Spotted Orchid, this species replaces it in more acid, heathy habitats. It is similarly very widespread but has a northern and western bias to its range and is now absent from much of the Midlands and southeast England. The flowers are usually rather pale pink with delicate markings, and the lip is broad, resembling a frilled skirt. It can occur in large numbers and gives a real splash of colour to otherwise sombre tracts of moor or bog.

Identification

A dainty and very attractive orchid, variable in stature but often just 10-20cm high, especially in exposed or relatively dry sites. The flowers are very variable but are often a pale shade of pink or pinkish-lilac and marked with fine dots and dashes, the ground colour frequently fading to whitish as they age. The broad lip resembles a voluminous petticoat and its side-lobes are much larger than the small, tooth-like central lobe and often have serrated or frilly edges. The leaves are usually marked with numerous dark spots.

Similar species

Common Spotted Orchid is rather similar but can be separated by its broader and flatter leaves with the lowest leaf usually *significantly shorter* than the rest with a broad, rounded tip. In both species the leaves are usually spotted but in Common Spotted the spots are often larger, bolder and usually elongated into short bars rather than being rounded. In Common Spotted the lip is more deeply lobed with the incisions (sinuses) between the lobes cutting around halfway to the base of the lip and the three lobes more equal in size; the central lobe is at least half the width of the side-lobes and usually a little longer too. Finally, in Common Spotted Orchid the lip is marked with loops and lines rather than dots and the spur is shorter, thicker and tapers slightly towards the tip.

▶ *5 July, Norfolk.*

Marsh orchids are usually easily separated as most have darker and more boldly marked flowers than is typical in Heath Spotted Orchids. Sometimes, however, Heath Spotted may have darker and more purplish flowers and, especially if the leaves are unspotted, may superficially resemble a marsh orchid. In case of doubt check the spur: long, slender and roughly parallel-sided in Heath Spotted and squat and sack-like in marsh orchids. Also check the number of non-sheathing leaves: often two to five in Heath Spotted (but sometimes just one) and one or two in most marsh orchids. Finally, the stem of the spotted orchids is usually solid and 'unsquashable' and that of at least some of the marsh orchids is obviously hollow.

Hybrids are common, particularly with Northern and Irish Marsh Orchids. First generation hybrids usually show hybrid vigour and may be obviously large. Hybrids with marsh orchids often have the fat, conical spur of the marsh orchid parent rather than the thin spur of the spotted orchid. Later generations of hybrids, if back-crossed with one or other of the parent species, become harder and harder to determine.

Habitat

Heath Spotted Orchid is found in a wide variety of habitats. It favours heathland and moorland, especially the damper, more peaty areas on the margins of valley bogs, flushes and mires and the raised and slightly drier areas within *Sphagnum* bogs; suitable areas are often picked out by the greyish foliage and dusty-pink flowers of Cross-leaved Heath. It is also found on acid grassland (for example rhos pastures in Wales and culm grassland in southwest England), damp unimproved meadows and hill pastures. It usually grows on mildly acidic soils and in areas of chalk or limestone bedrock; suitably acidic conditions may be provided by pockets or blankets of peat or areas of drift (superficial deposits of sands and gravels). It may sometimes grow in neutral or even slightly alkaline marshes and fens and in such habitats can be very robust. Heath Spotted

▲ 15 June, New Forest. A petite but richly marked plant.

Orchid is not as tolerant of shade as Common Spotted and is much less commonly found in light woodland and even then usually on the edge or along rides rather than in dense shade. Recorded from sea level up to 915m (Ben Lawers, Perthshire).

Flowering period

Mid-May to July, sometimes from the second week of May or rarely to early August. Typically it flowers earliest in drier situations and later in wetter habitats. The flowering time relative to Common Spotted Orchid varies in different

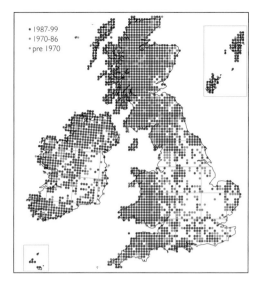

parts of the country and can be later or earlier, perhaps depending on their respective habitat in the area.

Range

Found throughout Britain and Ireland, including the Scottish Islands, Isle of Man and the Channel Islands, but with a predominantly northern and western bias to the distribution.
World range: Western Europe, north to Iceland, the Faeroes, Scandinavia, Finland and the Baltic States, east to Russia and south to northern Portugal and Spain, Italy, the former Yugoslavia and Bulgaria. As with Common Spotted Orchid, dispute over the exact definition of the species makes it hard to be precise about the boundaries of the range.

How to find it

Usually common in suitable habitats, the delicate pale pink blooms stand out among the grasses and heathers that typically surround it.

DESCRIPTION

Height: 4-50cm but usually 10-25cm. Plants have been noted up to 75cm tall but such robust individuals are probably hybrids.
Stem: Pale green, washed purple towards the tip and slightly ridged.
Leaves: There are one or no basal leaves (or sheaths) and two to four (one to five) sheathing

leaves crowded towards the base of the stem. These are long, narrow, keeled and pointed, the largest up to 20mm wide (more rarely to 25mm) with the tips sometimes hooded. There are also two to five (one to seven) non-sheathing leaves and these become more bract-like towards the flower spike. All the leaves are green, variably marked with solid dark spots which are rounded or only slightly elongated; the leaves are fairly frequently unspotted.
Spike: Usually rounded or pyramidal, even when all the flowers are open, with 5-20 flowers, sometimes up to 60 on robust plants.
Bract: Green, often washed purple around the edges and towards the tip, lanceolate, tapering to a fine point, one-and-a half to two times longer than the ovary on the lower flowers but around equal in length higher up.
Ovary: Green, cylindrical, six-ribbed and twisted.

▲ 21 July, Norfolk. A relatively few-flowered spike, with sparse but bold markings.

▲ *21 July, Norfolk. The flower often has a 'blousy' look and the central lobe of the lip is much smaller than the side lobes.*

Flower: Usually whitish to pale pink or pale lilac, sometimes purplish-pink, with dark reddish markings. The lateral sepals are lanceolate, asymmetrical, marked with darker spots and lines and held horizontally or drooping. The upper sepal and petals are slightly shorter and form a hood over the column. The lip is shorter than wide (around 5-9.5mm long x 6.5-13mm wide), roughly circular or circular-diamond shaped. It is divided into three lobes by relatively shallow, triangular notches (sinuses). The side-lobes are much larger than the central lobe and their edges may be wavy or toothed. The central lobe is small, triangular, rather tooth-like and does not usually project beyond the side-lobes (if it does, it rarely projects by more than 1mm). The lip is held flat, slightly dished or with the side-lobes slightly deflexed. It is whitish to pink, sometimes deep lilac-pink, variably marked all over with darker dots and dashes

that are usually rather fine and form a pattern of concentric loops or circles but are sometimes bolder and form the clear double loops more typical of Common Spotted Orchid. The spur is slender, cylindrical or slightly tapering, about half as long as the ovary to roughly the same length and straight or slightly decurved. The flowers are faintly scented.

Subspecies

British and Irish plants are conventionally treated as belonging to subspecies *ericetorum* which also occurs along the Atlantic seaboard of Europe from northern Portugal to northern Scandinavia and Finland. The typical subspecies, *D. m. maculata*, is found in the remainder of continental Europe.

Within the British Isles there is much variation but it does not show any consistent pattern, and no other subspecies can usefully be recognised, even though some European authors state that subspecies *maculata* and/or subspecies *elodes* occur here (and some split the spotted orchids into many different species and treat subspecies *maculata* and *ericetorum* as different species, stating that both occur in Britain).

Plants from Rhum in the Inner Hebrides with dark flowers intermediate in shape

▲ *21 July, Norfolk. A boldly marked plant.*

between Heath and Common Spotted Orchids were described as subspecies *rhoumensis*. But the population on Rhum is very variable and such dark, three-lobed flowers occur elsewhere. It is not worthy of recognition.

Variation and varieties

Var. *concolor* has an excess of pigmentation. It has a solidly dark reddish-purple lip and the leaves may also be washed purple. It is extremely rare, with just one or two records. **Var.** *leucantha* has pure white flowers. It is widespread but rare.

BIOLOGY

Pollination and reproduction

A variety of insects have been observed carrying pollinia, especially bees and flies, and seed production is good (45% of flowers set seed in one Scottish study). The mechanism is probably similar to Common Spotted Orchid, although the pollinia are relatively small, possibly an adaptation to smaller and less robust pollinating insects.

Development and growth

The pattern of development is probably similar to Common Spotted Orchid, with seedlings appearing above ground less than two years after germination and the first flower spike three years later.

Hybrids

Sterile hybrids are likely to be found either singly or in very small numbers, whereas even partial fertility can result in large populations of hybrids displaying a great deal of individual variation.
D. x transiens, the hybrid with Common Spotted Orchid, is widespread but scarce. It is highly sterile.
D. x carnea, the hybrid with Early Marsh Orchid, has been recorded scattered in Britain and Ireland but is rare. It is probably sterile.
D. x conigerum, the hybrid with Frog Orchid, has been found rarely but widely.
D. x hallii, the hybrid with Southern Marsh Orchid, occurs infrequently as the parent species favour different habitats. It is fertile and

▲ *20 June, Norfolk. The white flowered var.* leucantha *is widespread but rare.*

can therefore create hybrid swarms.
D. x formosa, the hybrid with Northern Marsh Orchid, occurs throughout the range of Northern Marsh Orchid. It is fertile and frequently back-crosses with the parents to form hybrid swarms. This is probably the commonest hybrid orchid in northern Britain and Ireland.
D. x jenensis, the hybrid with Pugsley's Marsh Orchid, has been recorded from northwest Wales, Yorkshire and Ireland. It appears to be sterile.
D. x dinglensis, the highly fertile hybrid with Irish Marsh Orchid, has been found widely.

▲ 20 June, Norfolk. Hybrid Heath Spotted Orchid x Common Spotted Orchid. Surprisingly infrequent, such hybrids are typically very robust.

Intergeneric hybrids

X *Pseudorhiza bruniana*, the hybrid with Small White Orchid, was recorded from Orkney in 1977.

X *Dactylodenia legrandiana*, the hybrid with fragrant orchid (presumably x Heath Fragrant Orchid), has been found widely scattered through Britain and Ireland.

Name and classification

The specific name *maculata* means 'spotted' or 'blotched'.

Heath and Common Spotted Orchids are members of a complex group of *Dactylorhiza* orchids which have generated a great deal

of disagreement over the number of species involved. Some European authors treat them both as the same species, and there is some support for this argument as the differences between the two are not as clear cut in parts of Europe as they are in the British Isles. Even in Britain the differences are not as absolute as some field guides suggest (see also discussion under Common Spotted Orchid).

HISTORY AND CONSERVATION

The first British record of a spotted orchid dates from 1562 when the second part of William Turner's *Herball* noted: 'There are divers kindes of orchis…one kinde…hath many spottes in the leaf and is called adder grasse in Northumberland'.

One of the commonest and most widespread orchids in the British Isles. There has been some decline, however, especially in lowland areas in England, and the species now occupies only around three-quarters of its historic range (and many of the losses in Britain are relatively recent). Agricultural changes, leading to the ploughing and 'improvement' of meadows and pastures and the destruction of heaths have caused some losses, as has the abandonment of heathland causing it to scrub-over and turn into woodland; extensive heath fires can also be damaging. The species tolerates, and even benefits from, some grazing but in northern Britain it has, like much native vegetation, suffered from overgrazing.

Past and present occurrence of Heath Spotted Orchid in Britain and Ireland (based on presence or absence in 10km squares of the National Grid; data from the New Atlas).

	Britain	Ireland
total historical range, 1500-1999	2,025	687
current range	1,587 (56%*)	531 (53%*)
% lost, 1500-1969	12.5%	20.5%
% lost, 1970-1986	9%	2%
% lost, total	21.5%	22.5%

* current range as a % of the total number of 10km squares

SOUTHERN MARSH ORCHID
Dactylorhiza praetermissa

Formerly: *Orchis praetermissa, Dactylorchis praetermissa*

This species often occurs in large numbers and can produce a spectacular show in riverside meadows and pastures. Locally common and widespread in much of England (south and east of a line from the Ribble to the Humber) and in south and southwest Wales, it can tolerate a wide variety of conditions, not always 'marshy', and is even found on certain favoured brownfield sites where a variety of chemical wastes have been dumped. In size and flower colour it is rather variable, and it also hybridises readily with the spotted orchids, making identification difficult at times.

Identification

In its typical form Southern Marsh Orchid is distinctive. It is usually a robust orchid with a stout stem, numerous rather broad, unmarked green leaves and a spike of purplish-pink flowers. The lip is broad and rounded with a tooth-like central lobe; to judge the shape of the lip it needs to be flattened out from below, using a finger or a ruler. In its natural pose the lip may be held flat, slightly dished or with the sides turned downwards, and it is marked in a central zone with fine dots and short dashes.

Southern Marsh Orchid is, however, rather variable. Most plants have flowers that appear a little 'dusty' or washed-out, but they may be a darker and more intense colour or have bolder and darker markings on the lip. In addition, two varieties of Southern Marsh Orchid are markedly different: var. *junialis*, the so-called Leopard Marsh Orchid has large ring-shaped spots on the leaves and a boldly marked flower and var. *bowmanii* has a very prominently three-lobed lip in various shades of pink with bold, dark dashes and loops (recalling Common Spotted Orchid in lip shape and pattern).

Similar species

Early Marsh Orchid is usually easily distinguished by flower colour alone (very pale pink, deep red or creamy). The various purple-flowered forms of Early Marsh Orchids can be very similar in colour to Southern Marsh but always have smaller flowers with a narrower

▲ *22 June, Norfolk. Southern Marsh Orchid can be tall, slender and stately.*

lip that usually has the side-lobes clearly folded downwards and prominent double-loop markings.

Northern Marsh Orchid usually has darker and redder flowers (deep magenta), a smaller, more angular, diamond-shaped lip with heavier, more blotched or looped dark markings and often fewer non-sheathing leaves.

Pugsley's Marsh Orchid has a more slender stem, fewer, narrower leaves, and a rather loose, one-sided spike composed of a few, relatively large flowers.

Hybrids are a major identification headache. Southern Marsh Orchid frequently hybridises with Common Spotted Orchid, and the hybrids are usually tall and robust with the sheathing leaves shorter and blunter than Southern Marsh Orchid and the non-sheathing leaves narrower and more pointed. Importantly, the leaves are usually faintly spotted, and the flowers are intermediate between the two parents. These hybrids can be harder to distinguish from Leopard Marsh Orchid as

this, too, has spotted leaves (see below for more details). Southern Marsh Orchid also freely hybridises with Pugsley's Marsh Orchid, and as these hybrids are fully fertile, back-crossing can lead to a range of plants intermediate between the two parent species.

Habitat

Found in a variety of habitats on calcareous to neutral or even acidic soils that are usually (but not always) moist or wet. Typical habitats include damp meadows, fens, marshes, the less acid parts of bogs and wet heathland, dune slacks, marshy gravel pits, road verges and also old industrial sites, especially in northwest England and the West Midlands (waste alkali, colliery and fly-ash tips). It is also found in old chalk quarries where compacted ground may lead to water-logging, and it occasionally grows, often in a dwarf form, on dry chalk grassland and downs. Perhaps, surprisingly, Southern Marsh Orchid cannot tolerate being submerged for long periods, and winter floods lasting more

▲ 21 June, Suffolk. *Often occurs in large numbers.*

▶ 6 June, Norfolk.

◀ 17 June, Norfolk. Southern Marsh Orchid can be short and squat.

than a month may cause a severe decline or even kill all the plants.

Flowering period
Late May to early July, occasionally from mid-May to mid-July or even to early August.

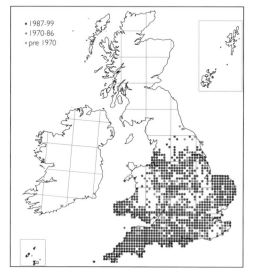

• 1987-99
• 1970-86
• pre 1970

Range
Widespread in England roughly south of a line from the Ribble to the Humber with a few scattered colonies a little to the north of this. It is also found in south and southwest Wales, the Isles of Scilly and the Channel Islands. **World range:** A European endemic found along the Atlantic fringe of the continent from northern France through Belgium, Holland, Germany and Denmark to southwest Norway (and possibly also Sweden and Finland); reported recently from northern Italy. Introduced to

North America, where it has been present for many years at Tilt Cove, Newfoundland. It was probably accidentally imported with mining equipment from Europe in the early 1900s.

How to find it
Southern Marsh Orchid is fairly common and sometimes occurs in large numbers, although in the modern agricultural landscape it is necessarily local. Big colonies stand out but odd plants in marshy meadows may be easy to miss; the presence of quantities of rushes is a good clue.

DESCRIPTION
Height: 20-50cm, occasionally to 70cm or even 95cm (the largest plants possibly show some hybrid influence). Dwarfed plants, just 10cm high, may occur in marginal habitats such as chalk grassland.

Stem: Stout (usually over 5mm in diameter), hollow and green.

Leaves: Mid-green, sometimes slightly tinged greyish-green. There are three to nine sheathing leaves (typically four to six), held erect at 45° or more and often slightly more crowded towards the base of the stem. Oblong-lanceolate, the leaves are more-or-less flat, lack a marked keel and may be slightly hooded at the tips. The largest are usually 2-3.5cm wide but they can be as narrow as 1.5cm. There are one to three narrower and more pointed non-sheathing leaves higher on the stem.

Spike: Rather crowded and occupies around 20% of the stem with 20-60 flowers, although

▲ 22 June, Norfolk. The markings on the lip are very variable but tend to be relatively fine, short dashes and dots concentrated in the central zone.

large plants may have over 100. Conical as the first flowers open, becoming cylindrical later on.
Bract: Green, often washed purple. The bracts are around twice the length of the ovary and project beyond the flowers (although usually not as prominently as in Early Marsh Orchid and less obviously so once the spike is fully open).
Ovary: Green, variably washed purple, cylindrical, six-ribbed and twisted.
Flower: Purplish-pink but variable in its exact shade; sometimes a deep, intense colour but usually a little 'washed-out'. The lateral sepals are lanceolate, asymmetrical and occasionally blotched darker. They are variably positioned, from nearly vertical over the flower to nearly horizontal but usually held at around 45°. The upper sepal and petals are lanceolate, the petals slightly shorter than the sepals, and together they form a loose hood over the column. The lip is 9-12mm long x 8.5-14mm wide (but mostly more than 10mm wide). Overall it is roughly circular in shape (if slightly 'squashed') and subtly three-lobed, with broad, rounded side-lobes and a small, often tooth-like central

lobe which usually projects slightly; there are shallow incisions (sinuses) between the lobes. The side-lobes turn downwards at the base but are often level or turn upwards towards the tip of the lip, which therefore appears drop-shaped or like a well-rounded triangle in its natural position. It is purplish-pink, becoming paler towards the base and then white around the mouth of the spur, and is marked with fine dark spots and short dashes, usually concentrated in the centre. The spur is two-thirds to four-fifths the length of the ovary, stout, tapering slightly to a blunt tip and may be slightly down-curved.

Subspecies
None.

Variation and varieties
Var. *junialis* 'Leopard Marsh Orchid'
has leaves marked with large oval spots or sometimes bars which are hollow, and its lip is marked with unbroken dark loops or horseshoe-shaped marks rather than just dots and dashes. It is found most often in the south and southeast but is uncommon.

▲ 22 June, Norfolk. A 'Leopard Marsh Orchid' with bold loop markings on the lip and ring-spotted leaves; it is easy to confuse this variety with hybrid Southern Marsh Orchid x Common Spotted Orchid.

At one time, Leopard Marsh Orchid was thought to be a variation of the hybrid between Southern Marsh Orchid and Common Spotted Orchid which is commonly found whenever the two species grow together. The occurrence of relatively uniform populations of Leopard Marsh Orchid, lacking hybrid vigour and often without Common Spotted Orchids growing nearby, suggests, however, that *junialis* is a variety of Southern Marsh, and this has been supported by genetic evidence.

Both Leopard Marsh Orchid and hybrids can have hollow, ring-shaped spots on the leaves, and the presence of such annular spots is not diagnostic of Leopard Marsh Orchid, although hybrids are more likely to have solid dark spots. The following characters are useful in distinguishing Leopard Marsh Orchid from ring-spotted hybrids:

Size: Relatively small and slender, with fewer leaves (averaging smaller and more slender than normal Southern Marsh Orchids). Hybrids are often robust, with many leaves, especially many non-sheathing leaves.

Lip size: On average narrower, up to 10mm wide. Hybrids have broader lips, 10mm or more – sometimes much more.

Lip shape: Often more obviously three-lobed than typical Southern Marsh Orchids but not as distinctly three-lobed as the hybrid.

Lip markings: Confined to the central zone, within the heavy double loop, with just one or two faint markings outside this area. In hybrids heavy markings extend over most of the lip.

Var. *bowmanii* is relatively slender, with slightly fewer, narrower leaves than typical Southern Marsh Orchid (three or four sheathing leaves and one to three non-sheathing leaves). The flowers have a prominently three-lobed lip with a very long central lobe and heavy line and loop markings. Recorded from marshy areas or dry grassland on acid soils in Devon, Dorset and Hampshire. Initially described as a variety of Pugsley's Marsh Orchid but clearly outside the range of that species and genetic evidence places it with Southern Marsh Orchid.

Var. *macrantha* has a lax flower spike and large flowers (the lip usually much more than 7.5mm long x 9.5mm wide) with an obvious central lobe that exceeds the lateral lobes by more than 1mm. It is rare and found mostly at sites where Southern Marsh and Pugsley's Marsh Orchids occur together; it may be an intermediate between the two.

Var. *albiflora* has white flowers but is very rare.

BIOLOGY

Pollination and reproduction

Pollination is efficient and large quantities of seed are produced. Vegetative reproduction, although far less important, may sometimes produce groups of plants.

Development and growth

The period between germination and flowering is two or three years.

Hybrids

D. x grandis, the hybrid with Common Spotted Orchid, is rather frequent and can usually be found where both species occur together (even on dry chalk grassland and in the absence of one or both parents). It is probably the commonest hybrid orchid in southern Britain. The pollen is highly sterile, and seed production very low but even such partial fertility allows back-crossing and the creation of long-lived hybrid swarms.

D. x hallii, the hybrid with Heath Spotted Orchid, occurs much less frequently than *D. x grandis* as the two parent species favour different habitats. It is fertile and can form hybrid swarms.

D. x wintoni, the hybrid with Early Marsh Orchid, has been recorded north to Lancashire but is rare. It is sterile.

D. x insignis, the hybrid with Northern Marsh Orchid, is rare and has only been recorded from Wales. Despite their superficial similarity and 'complementary' distributions in northern and southern Britain, Northern and Southern Marsh Orchids may not be very closely related.

x Pugsley's Marsh Orchid has been recorded from Norfolk, Suffolk and Cambridgeshire. Importantly this hybrid is fully fertile and through a process of back-crossing with its parents can form a full range of intermediates (see also var. *macrantha* opposite).

Intergeneric hybrids

X Dactylodenia wintoni, the hybrid with fragrant orchid (in the broad sense), has been found in southern England.

Name and classification

The specific name *praetermissa* means 'overlooked' and refers to the fact that the Southern Marsh Orchid was not recognised until 1914.

This species is one of the tetraploid marsh orchids and the chromosome number is $2n = 80$.

HISTORY AND CONSERVATION

This species was overlooked (due to confusion with Early Marsh Orchid) until 1914 when it was described by the eminent English botanist, George Claridge Druce.

Past and present occurrence of Southern Marsh Orchid in Britain and Ireland (based on presence or absence in 10km squares of the National Grid; data from the New Atlas).

	Britain	Ireland
total historical range, 1500-1999	1,014	0
current range	812 (28.5%*)	0
% lost, 1500-1969	12%	
% lost, 1970-1986	8%	
% lost, total	20%	

* current range as a % of the total number of 10km squares

Southern Marsh Orchid has inevitably suffered quite significant declines as agricultural changes and development, especially the draining and ploughing of flood-plain meadows and pastures, have destroyed its habitats. It has vanished from 20% of the former range with much of the loss relatively recent. This statistic is likely to conceal a much greater decline, however, as the number of populations *within* each 10km square can fall significantly without it registering as a 'loss'. This problem applies to all orchids but is perhaps most acute with those species found in meadows and unimproved pastures, habitats that were once so much a part of the British landscape. The colonisation of derelict industrial sites is small compensation for such losses in the wider countryside.

PUGSLEY'S MARSH ORCHID
Dactylorhiza traunsteinerioides

Formerly: Narrow-leaved Marsh Orchid *Dactylorhiza traunsteineri*; also *Dactylorhiza majalis* subspecies *traunsteineri*

The scarcest, most enigmatic and most localised of the marsh orchids (with the exception of Hebridean Marsh Orchid), this species is endemic to Britain and Ireland. It occurs at scattered localities throughout the British Isles, almost always in wet fens that are formed by the upwelling of lime-rich but nutrient-poor springs. It hybridises freely, especially with Southern Marsh Orchid, making certain identification difficult at times. 'Lapland Marsh Orchid', a heavily marked plant found at a few localities in Scotland, has recently been shown to be a variant of Pugsley's Marsh Orchid.

Identification

This delicate marsh orchid can be identified by a combination of features which taken together give it a subtle but distinctive appearance. It is typically slender with a thin, weak stem, and some plants even appear to need to be supported by the surrounding vegetation. It has a few narrow leaves that are often held erect. The spike is made up of a few relatively large flowers and is usually rather open and one-sided, with all the flowers facing roughly the same way. The upper stem and especially the bracts are washed purple. The flowers themselves are variable in colour but often purplish-pink. The lip is usually obviously three-lobed with the side-lobes turned downwards and the central lobe projecting as a prominent 'tooth' (itself also sometimes turned downwards). It is well-marked with dark dots, loops and squiggles, the markings often extending right to the edge of the lip. Habitat is also a good clue, as the species is almost always found in alkaline fens, often in relatively low or sparse vegetation.

In order to confirm the identification it is necessary to look carefully and in detail at the orchids. It is best to examine a selection of plants to get a feel for the range of variation and work out some average measurements. It is

▲ 25 May, Norfolk. Typically slender, with narrow leaves and a few, relatively large flowers (in this plant there are 11).

unlikely that a Pugsley's Marsh Orchid would occur as a single isolated individual among a colony of commoner species such as Southern or Northern Marsh Orchid, and there should always be a few candidates to look at. To be Pugsley's Marsh Orchids, plants must have the following characteristics:

1. Number of flowers: Relatively few, usually just five to 14, but sometimes as many as 18, particularly on the robust plants found in some parts of Ireland.

2. Width of lip: At least 7mm wide and usually wider, up to a maximum of around 13mm (the average of several plants should be at least 9mm). The individual flowers are relatively large.

3. Lip shape: Distinctly three-lobed, usually with prominent incisions (sinuses) between the lobes and with the central lobe longer and rather narrower than the rounded side-lobes; flatten the lip from below with a finger in order to measure the width and accurately judge the shape. In a natural position the lip often has a characteristic triangular or deltoid shape, narrower at the base and broadest at the tip; a shape accentuated by the side-lobes being more strongly reflexed at the base and flatter towards the tip.

4. Total number of leaves: Three to five, including up to one, rarely two, bract-like non-sheathing leaves; do not count the short basal leaf hidden at the bottom of the stem. The leaves are more-or-less evenly spaced, rather than being gathered into a rosette.

5. Width of leaves: Relatively narrow, with the second leaf from the bottom, which is usually the widest, 6-15mm across (rarely to 18mm and usually averaging no more than 12mm wide).

6. Leaf spotting: Mostly unmarked but at a few sites in Yorkshire and Ireland the plants have a scatter of fine dark spots, and in Scotland the subspecies *lapponica* ('Lapland Marsh Orchid') has very boldly marked leaves and bracts

Similar species

Early Marsh Orchid is usually easy to separate from Pugsley's Marsh Orchid because most

▲ *28 May, Norfolk. The lip is usually marked with dots, loops and squiggles, the markings often extending right to the edge, and is typically three-lobed with the central lobe projecting as a little 'tooth'. This plant has 12 flowers.*

Early Marsh Orchids in similar habitats will have pale pink flowers. The purple-flowered forms of Early Marsh Orchid are, however, much more similar in colour and sometimes have few flowers on a spike. Also, in Scotland the rare spotted-leaved subspecies *cruenta* of Early Marsh Orchid has been found in the same localities as the similarly spotted 'Lapland Marsh Orchid'. But, whatever the colour of the flower, Early Marsh Orchid always has a more 'crowded' flower spike and the individual flowers have a rather smaller lip, less than 9mm wide. The markings are also different on Early Marsh Orchid, with dots and dashes in a central zone enclosed by bold double loops and few if any markings outside this area. Their leaves are broader and their spur is slightly tapering and slightly to moderately decurved.

Southern Marsh Orchid is typically taller and more robust than Pugsley's Marsh Orchid. It has a rather thicker stem and more leaves which are broader and frequently more crowded towards the base of the stem; there are often two or more non-sheathing leaves. The spike is larger and usually has many more flowers, and these have a less obviously three-lobed lip which is often held flat or slightly dished. Small, petite Southern Marsh Orchids are more similar to Pugsley's Marsh Orchid but still have relatively unmarked flowers with less prominent lobes.

Northern Marsh Orchid is rather closer in size and stature to Pugsley's Marsh Orchid but again has more leaves which are broader

▲ *30 June, Norfolk. Tends to flower early, from mid-May to mid-June, but as with all orchids, this can vary (12 flowers).*

and more crowded at the base of the stem. The spike usually has more than 20 flowers and the flowers themselves often have a slightly smaller lip (sometimes less than 8mm wide and averaging less than 9mm), which is usually roughly diamond-shaped and held flat or slightly dished. The flowers are also usually a dark, 'velvety' reddish-pink, a rather different colour to those of Pugsley's Marsh Orchid.

Irish Marsh Orchid can be of a similar size to Pugsley's Marsh Orchid and has a three-lobed lip (although not so deeply lobed), often with similar markings. It has, however, more leaves which are often broader and more crowded at the base of the stem and a denser spike with more flowers.

Hybrids with Common and Heath Spotted Orchids and Early Marsh Orchid should show clearly intermediate characters. Much more problematical is the hybrid Pugsley's Marsh Orchid x Southern Marsh Orchid which is apparently fully fertile. Through a process of back-crossing this can form a complete range of intermediates between the two species, and at some localities in southern England there are hybrid swarms and it is difficult to find any plants that are completely 'pure' Pugsley's Marsh Orchid.

Habitat

This species has very specific habitat requirements and is only found where these are met. It needs wet fens and flushes where the ground water is 'base-rich' due to the influence of chalk or limestone. It grows in the wettest areas among a relatively open community of sedges, rushes and scattered reeds, rooting into the mossy layer at the base of the taller vegetation. It is almost always associated with Black Bog-rush. Some of the sites are fairly extensive but at others the correct conditions are restricted to small patches within a larger area of marshland. In Ireland it has been recorded rarely from dune slacks. Pugsley's Marsh Orchid is only exceptionally found in very slightly acid conditions and in Scotland 'Lapland Marsh Orchid' may spread from its base-rich flushes into nearby wet heathland, which is slightly more acid. It is found from sea level to 370m (Carperby, Wensleydale, northwest Yorkshire), with subspecies *lapponica* recorded up to 310m (Knapdale, Kintyre).

Flowering period

Plants come into flower in late May in the south and west, exceptionally in early May, and some may still be in flower in late June. The onset of flowering can be a little later, towards early June in the north, with 'Lapland Marsh Orchid' sometimes in flower until July.

Range

Found across the British Isles but the colonies are very scattered and it is absent from most areas. The strongholds are in Norfolk (and formerly adjacent parts of north Suffolk), northern Yorkshire, Anglesey and the Llyn Peninsula in Caernarvonshire. Elsewhere there are a few sites (often just one) in north Somerset, north Hampshire, Berkshire, Cambridgeshire, Co. Durham, Cardiganshire and Pembrokeshire. Pugsley's Marsh Orchid is similarly scarce and local in Ireland: in Co. Carlow, Co. Wicklow and Co. Kildare in the east and from Co. Limerick north to Co. Mayo in the west, with just three sites in Northern Ireland, all in Co. Antrim. In Scotland it is rare, and both the typical form and 'Lapland Marsh Orchid' have a broadly similar distribution in the west, in Kintyre, west Inverness-shire,

▲ *28 May, Norfolk. Although it had 16 flowers and a total of 5 leaves, this well-marked plant was part of a larger population of classic Pugsley's Marsh Orchids.*

Ross & Cromarty, west Sutherland, the Inner Hebrides (Rum, Raasay, Tiree) and Outer Hebrides (Harris). **World Range:** Endemic to Britain and Ireland.

How to find it

Pugsley's Marsh Orchid is easily overlooked. This species is small, slender and often partially concealed among relatively long grasses and sedges. At some localities it can be abundant but it may also be scarce and 'hidden' amongst hybrids. At many sites, especially in Scotland, there may only be small numbers of flower spikes. Two good clues for locating the species are flowering period and habitat. Pugsley's Marsh Orchid is one of the first marsh orchids to come into flower and is almost always found with Black Bog-rush. This is a rather large,

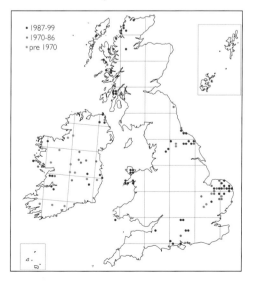

• 1987-99
• 1970-86
• pre 1970

tussock-forming member of the sedge family
that through the winter and into the spring
forms stands of distinctively grey vegetation.

Many of the sites for this species are rather
small and vulnerable to excessive disturbance
or, as at Beeston Common in Norfolk, have become dominated by hybrids. The best areas to
see it include Buxton Heath in Norfolk and
the Anglesey fens. In Ireland sites include
Slyne Head (Co. Galway) and Blacksod Bay
(Co. Mayo).

DESCRIPTION

Height: 6-40cm but usually 10-30cm with the
most robust plants in Ireland.

Stem: Green, usually washed purple towards
the flower spike, slightly hollow and rather
slender. The stem is often rather floppy or
bendy, averaging only 2.3-3.5mm in diameter
and is rarely more than 5mm across.

Leaves: Green, unspotted or occasionally with a
few, well-scattered, faint, purplish-brown spots
or transverse bars about 1mm in diameter;
spotting is only common in Yorkshire and
Ireland (see also Subspecies). The uppermost
non-sheathing leaf may be washed purple.
There is one short basal leaf and two to four
(rarely five) sheathing leaves. These are narrow,
strap-shaped, moderately keeled, sometimes
slightly hooded at the tip, well spaced along
the stem and often held erect at around 45°.
The longest leaf is rarely more than 12cm long
(17cm in robust Irish populations) and the
broadest leaf is usually 6-15mm wide (rarely
to 18mm). There are also up to one (rarely
two) bract-like non-sheathing leaves on the
upper part of the stem, and the total number of
sheathing and non-sheathing leaves is three to
five (this count excludes the short basal leaf).

Spike: Short and distinctly loose or 'lax' with
rather few flowers, usually just six to 14,
occasionally as few as two or as many as 18 on
the largest plants. The spike is rather irregular
in shape but roughly cylindrical or tapering and
the flowers all face in more-or-less the same
direction (the spike is thus described as secund
or subsecund).

▲ *28 May, Norfolk. The spike is often very one-sided (11
flowers).*

Bract: Lanceolate and long (the lower bracts
longer than the flowers), the bracts are green,
variably but often strongly washed reddish-
purple.

Ovary: Green, strongly washed purple,
cylindrical and six-ribbed.

Flower: Often purplish-pink, similar in colour
to Southern and Irish Marsh Orchids, but
variable in intensity from rather pale to dark
and deep. The sepals are oval-lanceolate and
the petals slightly smaller and more oval.
The lateral sepals are asymmetrical, very
occasionally have darker markings and are
held at an angle that varies between 45° and
vertical but is usually closer to the latter. The
upper sepal and petals form a hood over the
column. The lip is relatively large, 6.5-9.5mm
long x 7-13mm wide (usually at least 7.5mm
long x 9.5mm wide). It is very variable in
shape but is usually a flattened oval divided

into three obvious lobes with the central lobe rather narrower and variably longer than the side-lobes. The lobes are separated by incisions (sinuses) of various depths but sometimes there are no obvious sinuses, just a prominent central projection. The side-lobes are folded downwards to a variable extent (and the tip of the central lobe may also turn downwards), giving the lip a rather drop-shaped outline, narrowest at the base. The lip is a variable shade of purplish-pink, becoming whitish at the mouth of the spur, with dark lines, dots and blotches in an irregular pattern that extends more-or-less to the edges (sometimes forming a 'double loop' as in Early Marsh Orchid). There is no correlation between the ground colour of the lip and the extent and colour of the markings; dark plants in Yorkshire may have relatively small dot and dash markings whereas paler flowers on Anglesey may have long, heavy and contrastingly dark lines and blotches. Conversely, pale flowers in southern England may have relatively light markings. The spur is long, straight and thick but tapers slightly to a blunt tip.

Subspecies

D. t. lapponica 'Lapland Marsh Orchid' has bold, dark purplish-brown spots, blotches, bars and rings on the upperside of the leaves and bracts, which may also be edged with purple (and the bracts are often spotted below). There are up to two non-sheathing leaves which may also have a few small marks on the underside. The lip has intense dark purple or crimson lines, rings and spots on the lip, sometimes merging to form a dark patch in the centre, and the lateral sepals are marked with dark rings, elongated spots and dots. It averages slightly shorter than the typical form at 6-18cm tall, sometimes to 24cm, but Scottish populations of typical plants are also small.

Occurs very locally in western Scotland, in west Sutherland, Ross & Cromarty, west Inverness-shire (including Ardnamurchan and Morvern), Kintyre and, in the Inner Hebrides, on Skye, Rum and Raasay and on the Outer

Hebrides on Harris. It has also been identified in Northern Ireland, on the Garron Plateau in Co. Antrim. In at least one site 'Lapland Marsh Orchid' is found with typical Pugsley's Marsh Orchids, and intermediates have been recorded.

'Lapland Marsh Orchid' was first discovered at Knapdale (Kintyre) in 1967 and initially identified as Pugsley's Marsh Orchid. This identification was then revised and it became 'Western Marsh Orchid' (the form *cambrensis*, now itself a subspecies of Northern Marsh Orchid). Later still, in 1988, the plants were identified as 'Lapland Marsh Orchid *D. lapponica*' a species found in the Alps, Scandinavia and northern Russia which was new to the British Isles. Ironically, the wheel has now turned full circle and Scottish 'Lapland Marsh Orchids' have become a subspecies of Pugsley's Marsh Orchid, confirming in a roundabout way the initial identification.

'Lapland Marsh Orchid' may, in fact, be best treated as a variety of Pugsley's Marsh Orchid,

▲ 11 June, Ardnamurchan (Craig Robson). 'Lapland Marsh Orchid'. Relatively lightly marked but nevertheless a classic flower with a very tooth-like central lobe to the lip.

◀ 11 June, Ardnamur-chan (Craig Robson). 'Lapland Marsh Orchid'. The prominently three-lobed lips are very heavily marked and the bracts are also spotted purple.

rather than a subspecies; the Lapland Marsh Orchid of Scandinavia remains, however, a distinct species, *D. lapponica*.

Variation and varieties

Pugsley's Marsh Orchid is rather variable. The size and shape of the leaves, presence or absence of leaf spotting, number of flowers and their colour and markings all vary, both between colonies and within them. Yorkshire plants with spotted leaves are sometimes named var. *eborensis*. However, as there is disagreement about the other characteristics of this variety and as spotted leaves are also found in Irish populations it does not seem worthwhile to use this name. Rather small Scottish plants from near Loch Maree (Ross & Cromarty) with very pale flowers and contrasting dark markings have been named var. *francis-drucei* but may represent just one small aberrant population. (Note that var. *bowmanii*, originally described as a variety of Pugsley's Marsh Orchid, is treated under Southern Marsh Orchid.)

Var. *albiflora* has white flowers. It is very rare.

BIOLOGY

Pollination and reproduction

There is little specific information. Pollination is probably undertaken by bees and although other insects such as flies may remove the pollinia they do not go on to pollinate other orchids successfully. In studies of Pugsley's and 'Lapland' Marsh Orchids in western Scotland, only 17-35% of flowers set seed, reflecting low levels of pollination, probably due to a lack of suitable pollinators and the poor weather. Each ripe capsule that was produced contained about 3,000 viable seeds. Vegetative reproduction may also be possible.

Development and growth

No specific information.

Hybrids

D. x silvae-gabretae, the hybrid with Common Spotted Orchid, has been recorded from Ireland, Anglesey and Yorkshire. The pollen is highly sterile.

D. x jenensis, the hybrid with Heath Spotted Orchid, has been recorded from northwest Wales, Yorkshire and Ireland. It is probably sterile.

D. x dufftii, the hybrid with Early Marsh Orchid, has been found in northwest Wales, Yorkshire and Co. Wicklow but is rare.

x **Southern Marsh Orchid** has been recorded from Norfolk, Suffolk and Cambridgeshire. Fully fertile, it can be common where the two species occur together.

Name and classification

The specific name *traunsteinerioides* is derived from *traunsteineri*, the scientific name of Narrow-leaved Marsh Orchid, a European species that is, in turn, named in honour of Traunsteiner, a pharmacist who lived in Austria from 1798-1850.

This species is a tetraploid marsh orchid with the chromosome number 2n = 80. All of the tetraploid marsh orchids are thought to have originated from ancient hybridisation events involving the ancestors of Early Marsh Orchid and Common or Heath Spotted Orchids. Pugsley's Marsh Orchid is intriguing in that the same parent species have crossed on several occasions, in the British Isles, the Alps, Scandinavia and perhaps elsewhere, and each hybridisation event has given rise to a similar plant. After much debate, it was generally accepted that British and Irish plants were the same species as those in Europe and should be known as Narrow-leaved Marsh Orchid *D. traunsteineri*. However, recent genetic research has shown that, although very similar, they each have a distinct ancestry and represent separate lineages and are best treated as separate species. British and Irish plants therefore become an endemic species, *D. traunsteinerioides*, and should generate greater interest among scientists and conservationists. Note that Delforge (2005) gives the range of this species as Britain, Ireland and northern France but his concept of Pugsley's Marsh Orchid appears to be rather different; for example, he gives the number of flowers as 10-25, with extremes of 5-30.

HISTORY AND CONSERVATION

This species was first found in Ireland by H.W. Pugsley, who realised that it was something different from herbarium specimens and plants sent to him from Co. Wicklow. But, from the start, the exact status of Pugsley's Marsh Orchid was the subject of much debate. In 1936, Pugsley described his plants as a new subspecies of a widespread European marsh orchid and called it *D. majalis* subspecies *traunsteinerioides*. In 1940, however, Pugsley changed his mind and declared it to be an entirely new species, *D. traunsteinerioides*. Then, in 1953, the controversial British botanist J. Heslop-Harrison demonstrated that it belonged with another European species, *D. traunsteineri*. This determination generated a large and sometimes controversial literature, but the consensus eventually emerged that it was indeed the same as the European plant. Just as the question seemed to have been settled, however, genetic evidence showed that Pugsley had been right all along and that it should be treated as a separate, endemic species, *D. traunsteinerioides*. For more details of 'Lapland Marsh Orchid' see Subspecies.

Pugsley's Marsh Orchid is Nationally Scarce in Britain and is specially protected in Northern Ireland under Schedule 8 of the 1985 Wildlife Order (NI). In addition, 'Lapland Marsh Orchid' (until recently treated as a distinct species) is in the *Red Data Book* and is considered Near-threatened in Great Britain and fully protected under Schedule 8 of the Wildlife and Countryside Act 1981.

Past and present occurrence of Pugsley's Marsh Orchid (including 'Lapland Marsh Orchid') in Britain and Ireland (based on presence or absence in 10km squares of the National Grid; data from the New Atlas).

	Britain	Ireland
total historical range, 1500-1999	85	40
current range	63 (2.2%*)	13 (1.3%*)
% lost, 1500-1969	8.5%	37.5%
% lost, 1970-1986	17.5%	30%
% lost, total	26%	67.5%

* current range as a % of the total number of 10km squares

'Lapland Marsh Orchid' is mapped in the *New Atlas* for 18 10km squares (seven of which it shares with typical Pugsley's Marsh Orchid).

Pugsley's Marsh Orchid has declined by 26% in Britain, with most of the decline relatively recent and concentrated in East Anglia. It is probably extinct in Huntingdonshire and Northumberland. Losses have been even greater in Ireland, at 67.5%, and its numbers appear to have fallen there more than almost any other orchid. There are no recent records from Co. Cork, Co. Kerry, Co. Tipperaray, Co. Offaly, Westmeath, Meath, Co. Leitrim, Co. Cavan, Co. Louth and Co. Fermanagh.

In the lowlands, Pugsley's Marsh Orchid has disappeared due to the destruction and drainage of its habitat. Even where wetlands remain, often protected as SSSIs and reserves, a general lowering of the water table (due to drainage and abstraction) can cause a degradation of the habitat. This has been especially noticeable in East Anglia where the species has declined sharply in the Waveney-Ouse fens along the Norfolk-Suffolk border. A more insidious threat is posed by hybridisation. The hybrid with Southern Marsh Orchid is fully fertile and at some sites hybrids have come to dominate the population and Pugsley's Marsh Orchid has been 'hybridised out' (e.g. at Beeston Common in Norfolk there were several hundred Pugsley's Marsh Orchids in the late 1980s but by 2000 it was difficult or impossible to find a single 'pure' plant). At other sites, hybrids apparently involving this species are found where Pugsley's Marsh Orchid has never been recorded, indicating a more extensive distribution in the past. Similar threats face the species throughout Europe as its highly specialised habitat is degraded or destroyed.

In the uplands, sheep or deer graze most sites. This can keep the vegetation open and prevent a succession to scrub but it limits the number of flowers produced, sometimes severely so. When sites are not grazed the number of flowering plants has increased, although this may not reflect the number of seeds that are able successfully to germinate. More direct threats include forestry and drainage, and only a few of the 30 or so populations of 'Lapland Marsh Orchid' are protected in any way at all.

Any changes in the overall status of Pugsley's Marsh Orchid are hard to assess. It is a difficult species to identify with certainty and also easy to overlook and is therefore still being found and identified at new sites. These new records do not indicate, however, an expansion or increase as the species has presumably always been present at these sites. This applies particularly to Lapland Marsh Orchid, which has been actively searched for since its discovery. Conversely, Pugsley's Marsh Orchid is probably recorded from some sites by mistake (i.e. it is 'overrecorded').

HEBRIDEAN MARSH ORCHID
Dactylorhiza ebudensis

Formerly: *Dactylorhiza majalis* subspecies *occidentalis*
This is one of four species of orchid endemic to the British Isles (the others being Lindisfarne Helleborine and Pugsley's and Irish Marsh Orchids). It is known only from the north coast of North Uist in the Outer Hebrides where it is prominent in the spring on the flower-rich machair.

Identification
The highly restricted distribution makes identification straightforward, and the plant itself is distinctive. It is short and squat with a few very heavily marked leaves and deep purple-magenta flowers that have a markedly three-lobed lip.

Similar species
Northern Marsh Orchid occurs in the same habitat but flowers a little later in the spring. It has leaves that are unspotted or have a few small spots and its flowers, though a rather similar deep 'velvety' magenta, have a lip that is distinctly diamond-shaped with more-or-less straight, rather than curved, sides.

The subspecies *cambrensis* of Northern Marsh Orchid has been recorded from the Outer Hebrides and has heavily spotted leaves, but the spots tend to be smaller, more even in size and more evenly distributed over the leaf surface than in Hebridean Marsh Orchid. It is also usually taller, with more leaves, a relatively smaller flower spike and a less distinctly three-lobed lip. The distinction between the two may nevertheless be subtle at times; until recently Hebridean Marsh Orchid was not distinguished from some of the Scottish populations of subspecies *cambrensis*.

Habitat
Found on the machair, which is a unique, species-rich, coastal grassland habitat which

▲ 6 June, North Uist (Richard Bateman). The leaves are extensively and heavily blotched.

develops on low calcareous dunes in the wet and windy environment of western Scotland and Ireland. Hebridean Marsh Orchid grows in the damper areas of machair and also the marshy areas a little further inland. (Early Marsh Orchid of the red-flowered subspecies *coccinea* is found in the wetter hollows with Northern Marsh Orchids on the drier and higher areas.)

Flowering period
Late May to late June.

Range
Confined to the north coast of North Uist in the Outer Hebrides. **World range:** Endemic to Scotland.

How to find it
Only found on North Uist, where it occurs in scattered, well-separated groups on the machair of the north coast, including Lingay Strand. A visit to these remote but flower-rich islands is recommended.

DESCRIPTION

Height: 5-15cm, sometimes 18cm.

Stem: Green, heavily washed with dark purple towards the tip and hollow.

Leaves: There are two or three, sometimes four, keeled, lanceolate sheathing leaves that are relatively broad (10-14mm wide) and are crowded towards the base of the stem with the lower leaves tending to be held nearer the horizontal than the vertical; the lowest leaf is often rather shorter than the rest. They are green, almost always with large, round, brownish-purple spots and blotches which are concentrated towards the tips where they begin to coalesce; indeed, the spots may join together to cover much of the leaves with brownish-purple. They often also have a narrow purple margin and spotting is occasionally present on the underside of the leaves too. The single non-sheathing leaf is lanceolate and sometimes entirely purple.

Spike: Short, compact and cylindrical, with 5-20 flowers.

◀ *6 June, North Uist (Richard Bateman). The purplish-red flowers have a distinctly three-lobed lip.*

Bract: Lanceolate, the lower slightly longer than the flowers but becoming shorter towards the top of the spike. They are green, heavily washed purple or sometimes entirely purple and often spotted darker.

Ovary: Ribbed, twisted and very heavily washed purple.

Flower: Deep purple-magenta with darker markings. The sepals are elliptical and the petals similar but a little narrower. The lateral sepals are slightly asymmetric and held at 45° above the horizontal, or even higher, whereas the upper sepal and petals form a hood over the column. The lip is broader than long (6-8.5mm long x 8-11.5mm wide) and distinctly three-lobed with the central lobe longer than the side-lobes. It is flat or dished when the flower first opens but the side-lobes become slightly deflexed with age. The lip is rich purple-magenta, whiter towards the throat of the spur, and heavily marked with dark purple spots and dashes which are bounded within one or two concentric dark loops; the base colour is so dark, however, that these markings do not contrast very strongly. The spur is a little longer than the ovary, thick, cylindrical and slightly tapering.

Subspecies
None.

Variation and varieties
A hyperchromic variant has occasionally been found. This has an excess of pigmentation producing a solidly dark lip with a paler border.

BIOLOGY
Pollination and reproduction
No specific information.

Development and growth
No information.

Hybrids
x Northern Marsh Orchid? Plants apparently showing characters intermediate between these two species have been found but may be merely variant Northern Marsh Orchids; they are fertile.

Name and classification
The specific name *ebudensis* is from the Latin *ebudes*, 'Hebridean Islands'.

The taxonomy of this species is confusing. Until recently Hebridean Marsh Orchid was grouped together with Irish Marsh Orchid and the *majaliformis* form of Northern Marsh Orchid into one species named 'Western Marsh Orchid *D. majalis*'. Thus, in many recent books, the populations on North Uist will be found under the heading 'Western Marsh Orchid *Dactylorhiza occidentalis*' and either listed as subspecies 'scotica' or combined with Irish plants as subspecies 'occidentalis'.

Unexpectedly, genetic studies have shown that Hebridean and Irish Marsh Orchids should be treated as distinct species (and thus Western Marsh Orchid *D. occidentalis* does not occur anywhere in Britain or Ireland). Hebridean Marsh Orchid is one of the tetraploid marsh orchids and has a chromosome number of $2n = 80$. Genetic evidence suggests that it originated in a cross between Early Marsh Orchid of the subspecies *coccinea* and Common Spotted Orchid of the subspecies *hebridensis*.

HISTORY AND CONSERVATION
The distinctive orchids on North Uist first attracted attention in the 1930s, but it was not until 1976 that they were given a name. The first name to be used was 'scotica' but this was not published in the correct manner according to the *International Code of Botanical Nomenclature* and was eventually replaced by *ebudensis* as the scientific name.

Much of the machair of northern North Uist is subject to international conservation designations and is protected in SSSIs, including the machair at Rabach and Newton. There seems to be no immediate threat to the species, but the range encompasses just one or two 10km squares and such a limited distribution means that Hebridean Marsh Orchid will inevitably always be vulnerable.

NORTHERN MARSH ORCHID
Dactylorhiza purpurella

Formerly: *Orchis purpurella, Dactylorchis purpurella*
This is the most commonly encountered magenta-flowered orchid of damp, marshy ground in northern Britain and can sometimes be found in large numbers, giving a 'wow' factor to the landscape, even sometimes to derelict industrial sites. As its name suggests, this species has a northerly distribution and occurs widely in northern England, northern Ireland and Scotland, as well as in Wales. Although the intense reddish-pink flowers are usually distinctive, the presence of hybrids with the spotted orchids can be a complication.

▲ 6 June, Cumbria. As with all the marsh orchids, Northern Marsh Orchid is variable in size and structure and can look quite stocky.

Identification

Northern Marsh Orchid is relatively easy to identify. The spike is often flat-topped and the flowers are a distinctive deep 'velvety' magenta (reddish-pink with just a hint of purple). The lip is typically diamond-shaped and hardly lobed at all but with straight sides, especially to the base of the 'diamond', and its heavy dark markings may form a pattern of indistinct concentric rings. The leaves are either unspotted or have a few small spots, except in parts of west Wales and northwest Scotland where the subspecies *cambrensis* has dark spots all over the leaves.

Similar species

Early Marsh Orchids with deep pink or purple flowers are quite similar to Northern Marsh Orchid, but their flowers are on average slightly smaller with a narrower, usually three-lobed lip (which may be unlobed but is never the distinctive diamond shape of Northern Marsh). Also, the lip of Early Marsh Orchid is usually marked with a heavy, complete or almost complete double loop, the side-lobes are often sharply turned downwards and the lateral sepals are usually held vertically over the flower.

Southern Marsh Orchid has more purplish-pink flowers that are usually a little 'washed out', but they can be an intense, deep colour (albeit more purple and less red than Northern Marsh Orchid). Its lip is usually roughly circular, however, with rather broad rounded side-lobes and a small tooth-like central lobe. The dark markings are often small, fine and confined to the centre of the lip. Leopard Marsh Orchid (var. *junialis* of Southern Marsh) has bolder, more looped markings on the lip but also has heavily spotted leaves, with the spots usually in the form of hollow rings.

Irish Marsh Orchid has a distinctly rounded, three-lobed lip that is on average a little broader than Northern Marsh. It is more purplish-pink and often also paler and less intensely coloured. Up to 50% of Irish Marsh Orchids have spotted leaves.

Hybrids with both Heath Spotted and Common Spotted Orchids are relatively common and can be abundant where the two parent species grow together. Both hybrids are very variable. They can have either spotted or unspotted leaves and flowers intermediate between the two parent species.

Habitat

Northern Marsh Orchid is found in damp or wet sites on calcareous, neutral or slightly acid soils, such as marshy fields, roadside verges, lake margins, fens, marshes, flushes, seepages along coastal cliffs, dune slacks, machair and

▲ 6 June, Cumbria. The leaves may have some fine dark spots.

▼ 7 June, Northumberland. Northern Marsh Orchid can be common in dune slacks.

sometimes in less acidic peat bogs or in open, damp woodland. It is an opportunist and has colonised old quarries and urban 'brownfield' sites, including derelict industrial areas and old waste tips, such as alkaline Leblanc waste in Lancashire. Northern Marsh Orchid is sometimes found on drier substrates such as rubble and has been found in gardens. Recorded up to 610m above sea level (Creag Dhuba, Loch Ericht, west Inverness-shire).

Flowering period
Late May to late July (exceptionally from mid-May) but mostly early June to mid-July.

Range
Widespread in north and west Wales, northern England and Scotland, including the Isle of Man, Inner and Outer Hebrides, Orkney and Shetland. Occurs north of a line from Swansea to Hull, but the population is sparser and more scattered towards this southern boundary. Also found in Northern Ireland, especially in Co. Fermanagh, Co. Tyrone, Co. Derry and Co. Antrim, and in adjacent Co. Donegal, but otherwise rare and local in Eire, with almost all the current sites on the east coast or on the coasts of Co. Waterford, Co. Cork, Co. Galway and Co. Mayo. There are a few isolated records from southern England. In Oxfordshire a single specimen was found near Wychwood in 1981

▲ 6 June, Cumbria. The lip is usually a distinctive diamond shape.

and in Hampshire it was discovered in 1955 at Moorgreen near Southampton where two small colonies held up to 100 flowering plants at times. It was thought that a cutting for the M27 in 1986 had destroyed these colonies but plants were found again in the area in 1999. (It has been suggested, however, that this species was introduced to Hampshire.) **World range:** A European endemic found along the northwest fringe of the continent in western Norway (north to around Trondheim), Sweden, Denmark and the Faeroe Islands.

How to find it
Quite common and sometimes found in large numbers.

DESCRIPTION
Height: 5-45cm but usually 10-30cm.
Stem: Green, washed purple towards the tip, ribbed, often stout and slightly hollow.
Leaves: The four to eight lanceolate sheathing leaves are slightly crowded towards the base of the stem, broad (the largest 1.5-2.5cm wide), hooded at the tip and held at up to 45° above the horizontal. There are also one or two non-sheathing leaves higher on the stem (sometimes none, rarely up to four) and a small basal leaf.

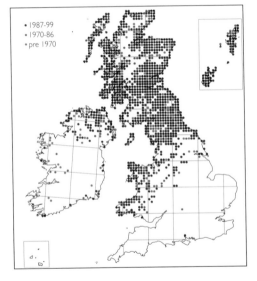

• 1987-99
• 1970-86
• pre 1970

◀ 6 June, Cumbria. Despite their names, Northern and Southern Marsh Orchids are not each other's closest relatives and are not analogous. Perhaps as a consequence, hybrids between these two species are surprisingly scarce.

The leaves are mid-green to dark green, unspotted or sometimes with a few very small spots near the tip.

Spike: Dense, with ten to 40 flowers (sometimes as many as 80), oval to cylindrical in shape and often flat-topped when fully open.

Bract: Green, often flushed purple, especially towards the edges. The bracts are narrow and lanceolate, the lower longer than their flowers, the upper shorter.

Ovary: Green, washed purple (and sometimes spotted on the ribs), cylindrical, six-ribbed and twisted.

Flower: Deep 'velvety' magenta, whiter around the mouth of the spur. The sepals are roughly oval and marked with irregular dark reddish-purple rings and lines. The petals are a little shorter and unmarked. The lateral sepals are held at around 45° and the upper sepal and petals form a loose hood over the column. The lip is relatively small, 5-8mm long x 6-10mm wide, and held flat or dished. Broadly diamond-shaped or triangular (with the point of the triangle forming the tip of the lip), the sides are more-or-less straight and the lip is either unlobed or only subtly three-lobed. There is some variation in lip shape and in some colonies, at least in west Wales, a significant number of plants have a larger, more rounded, shallowly three-lobed lip. Heavy dark reddish-purple lines, dots and swirls cover most of the lip in a concentric pattern. The spur is thick,

▲ 6 June, Cumbria. The lip markings are variable but there tend to be heavy lines, dots and swirls more or less all over the lip, often in a concentric pattern.

conical, slightly downward pointing and shorter than the ovary.

Subspecies

D. p. cambrensis (formerly 'majaliformis') has leaves that are boldly spotted dull purple, and bracts that are also spotted or washed purple. The spots are distributed over the whole surface of the leaf and can be sparse or occasionally so numerous that they coalesce into a solid dark patch; spotting is absent in a small minority of plants. The flowers average slightly paler and pinker than normal and therefore the dark markings are more contrasting. The lip is a little larger at 6-8.5mm long x 9-11mm wide and is rather distinctly three-lobed, often with incisions (sinuses) between the lobes and with the side-lobes slightly reflexed. It tends to be taller than typical Northern Marsh Orchids with longer and narrower leaves but with the spike smaller in proportion to the whole plant.

This subspecies grows near to the sea in western Scotland, often on damp grassy slopes, in the Outer Hebrides, Kintyre, Ross and Cromarty, Sutherland, Caithness and Orkney. In west Wales it has been found rather rarely in dune slacks and flood plain meadows on the coast from Cardiganshire to Anglesey. It has also been recorded from southeast Yorkshire but is otherwise only known from Denmark. It has a chequered history and both Scottish and Welsh plants started life as forms of 'Western Marsh Orchid' (a conglomerate of *cambrensis* with Irish and Hebridean Marsh Orchids).

Variation and varieties

Var. *albiflora* has white flowers.

Var. *atrata* is a hyperchromic variant with an excess of pigmentation. The lip is solidly dark magenta, lacking spots or lines but sometimes with a well-defined paler margin. The leaves are heavily spotted (rarely there is an overall purple wash) with a few small spots on their lower surfaces too. It is known only from damp fields near an industrial area at Hartlepool which may be contaminated with heavy metals.

Var. *crassifolia* has broad, fleshy leaves and a large lip. It is rare.

Var. *maculosa* has many small dots all over the leaves and sometimes a paler lip. Rare, it has been recorded in southeast Scotland.

Var. *pulchella* has the lip marked with spots and dashes rather than bold loops. It has been recorded from Scotland.

BIOLOGY

Pollination and reproduction

No specific information, but it is probably pollinated by bees, as bumblebees, especially queens of *Bombus terrestris*, have been recorded as frequent visitors. Pollination is efficient and seed-set is good (52% of flowers setting seed in one Scottish study).

Development and growth

No specific information.

Hybrids

Hybrids are frequently found, especially with Common and Heath Spotted Orchids.

D. x formosa, the hybrid with Heath Spotted Orchid, occurs throughout the range and is probably the commonest orchid hybrid in northern Britain and Ireland.

D. x venusta, the hybrid with Common Spotted Orchid, occurs throughout the range and can be common. It is variously noted that the pollen is highly sterile and little seed is produced or that this hybrid is sometimes partially fertile. Whatever the case, it is certainly capable of backcrossing with either parent species or crossing with itself to produce a range of intermediate characters in a hybrid swarm.

D. x latirella, the hybrid with Early Marsh Orchid, has been recorded throughout the range but is rare.

D. x insignis, the hybrid with Southern Marsh Orchid, has only been recorded in Cardiganshire and Merionethshire. Despite the relatively extensive area of overlap between the two species in Wales and northern England they tend to maintain a separate identity, even in mixed colonies.

D. x viridella, the hybrid with Frog Orchid, has been recorded from Co. Durham and the Inner and Outer Hebrides.

x Hebridean Marsh Orchid? Plants showing characters apparently intermediate between the two species have been recorded but these may be variant Northern Marsh Orchids; they are fertile.

Intergeneric hybrids

X Dactylodenia 'varia', the hybrid with one of the fragrant orchids, has been found in northern England, Scotland and Ireland.

Name and classification

The specific name *purpurella* means simply 'purple'. This species is a tetraploid marsh orchid (2n = 80).

HISTORY AND CONSERVATION

Northern Marsh Orchid was not distinguished from the other marsh orchids until 1920 when it was described from plants found near Aberystwyth by T. and T.A. Stephenson.

Inevitably there have been losses due to habitat destruction (drainage, ploughing-up of pastures, etc.) but the overall boundaries of the range have remained stable. It has declined by 21% in Britain, with many of the losses comparatively recent, and by 46% in Ireland.

Past and present occurrence of Northern Marsh Orchid in Britain and Ireland (based on presence or absence in 10km squares of the National Grid; data from the New Atlas).

	Britain	Ireland
total historical range, 1500-1999	1,202	151
current range	946 (33%*)	81 (8%*)
% lost, 1500-1969	11%	33%
% lost, 1970-1986	10%	13%
% lost, total	21%	46%

* current range as a % of the total number of 10km squares

▲ 6 June, Cumbria. The lip shape can vary. This plant has a projecting central lobe.

IRISH MARSH ORCHID
Dactylorhiza occidentalis

Formerly: *Dactylorhiza majalis* subspecies *occidentalis*; *Dactylorhiza comosa* subspecies *occidentalis*; *Orchis occidentalis*; *Dactylorchis occidentalis*

An Irish endemic, this species is fairly widespread and locally common in marshy or grassy habitats although it has suffered some decline, especially more recently. As with all the marsh orchids, it can be tricky to identify with certainty but its relatively early flowering season is a great help.

▲ 22 May, Co. Clare. Some have relatively paler and pinker flowers and at least 50% of plants have unmarked leaves.

Identification

The compact spike of purplish-pink, well-marked flowers identifies this species as one of the marsh orchids. It is rather variable, and the dwarf plants of coastal grasslands can look rather different to the robust populations in damper and more sheltered spots. The leaves may be spotted or unspotted. The lip has three rounded lobes and is usually heavily marked, often with double loops.

Similar species

Separation of the marsh orchids can be difficult at times, and in Ireland three species need to be eliminated: Early, Northern and Pugsley's Marsh Orchids.

Early Marsh Orchid is very variable and includes the purple and pink-flowered subspecies *pulchella* and *cruenta*, the latter often showing bold spots on the leaves. But, whether their leaves are spotted or unspotted, all Early Marsh Orchids have rather smaller flowers with a narrower lip that is usually less than 9mm wide and narrower leaves that are held stiffly erect.

Northern Marsh Orchid tends to flower a little later, has unspotted leaves or only a few small spots, and flowers that are a darker and deeper reddish-pink. Characteristically it has an unlobed, straight-sided, diamond-shaped lip that, on average, is a little narrower, no more than 10mm wide.

Pugsley's Marsh Orchid is reasonably distinctive, with a slender stem, a few relatively large flowers held in an open, one-sided spike and a lip that appears longer than wide.

Early Purple Orchid flowers at the same time as Irish Marsh Orchid, sometimes in the same grassy habitats, and also has heavily spotted leaves. It is generally tall and slender, however, with the leaves arranged in a floppy rosette at the base of the stem. Its flowers are much less heavily marked, with just a few dark spots in the centre of the lip.

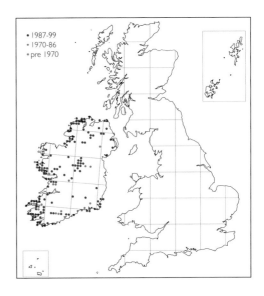

Habitat
Varied but mostly on neutral or slightly alkaline soils and including wet meadows and pastures, road verges, lough shores, the edges of acid bogs, dune slacks, damp hollows on short, closely grazed grassland and dry grassy slopes near the sea.

Flowering period
Mid-May to mid-June, sometimes to July.

Range
In Eire there are concentrations in Co. Donegal in the northwest, from Co. Galway south to Co. Cork in the west and in Co. Wexford. Otherwise, it is absent from much of Eire, especially the east, apart from a cluster of records from Co. Longford. Although mapped for Northern Ireland, its occurrence there is disputed. **World range:** Endemic to Ireland.

How to find it
Generally fairly common and sometimes found in large numbers.

DESCRIPTION
Height: 10-30cm, rarely to 40cm.
Stem: Green, variably washed purple, ridged towards the tip and slightly hollow.
Leaves: The four or five (sometimes only three) lanceolate sheathing leaves are fairly broad,

▲ 25 May, Co. Clare. Irish Marsh Orchid can still be found in large numbers, even on roadside verges.

▲ 21 May, Co. Clare. Some plants (perhaps especially in coastal grassland) are short and squat.

◄ 24 May, Co. Clare.

usually 15-25mm wide (extremes 12-30mm). They are grouped towards the base of the stem and are usually held rather spreading, closer to the horizontal than the vertical. There are also two, sometimes three, non-sheathing leaves higher on the stem. The leaves are green and in about 50% of plants spotted with brownish-purple. The spots are generally concentrated onto the outer half of the leaf and are variable in shape; they may be rings or elongated into transverse bars. Rarely, there are spots on the lower surface of the leaf, too, or it has a purple rim.

Spike: Crowded, with about 20 flowers occupying 25-50% of the stem length.

Bract: Fairly long, green, variably washed purple (sometimes strongly so) but only occasionally spotted.

Ovary: Slender, twisted and ridged, green, often heavily washed purple.

Flower: Purplish-pink with a well-marked three-lobed lip. The lateral sepals are oval, asymmetrical, variably marked darker with dots, squiggles, or rings (sometimes unmarked) and usually held closer to the horizontal than the vertical. The upper sepal is oval, and the petals are slightly shorter, narrower and more pointed. Together they form a hood over the column.

The lip is purplish-pink, often rather deep but becoming paler towards the centre and white around the mouth of the spur (near to Southern Marsh Orchid in colour but slightly deeper, more intense and closer to purple). It is usually wider than long, 7-11mm long x 9-14mm wide and broadest around the middle. It has three distinct rounded lobes with noticeable incisions (sinuses) between them. The side-lobes are variably reflexed, especially as the flower gets older, and sometimes notched or with wavy edges. The central lobe is smaller and sometimes tooth-like and often projects a little beyond the side-lobes. The lip is marked with heavy dots and dashes, often enclosed within double loops (sometimes concentric double loops), and there may also be markings outside the loops. The spur is roughly conical and straight.

Subspecies
None.

Variation and varieties
Var. *kerryensis* is found in southwest and western Ireland, sometimes in 'pure' colonies,

▲ 24 May, Co. Clare. The lip has three well-defined rounded lobes marked with heavy dots and dashes, often both within and without double loop markings.

▲ *24 May, Co. Clare. The coloration varies from a deep magenta to paler purple or deep pink.*

but is scarce. It always has unspotted leaves and bracts. Its flowers are, on average, paler and less intense and the lip is often flat and marked with dots and dashes that do not form a pattern of loops. It also tends to be slightly shorter and stockier and is said to flower a little later, into July.

This form is sometimes treated as a distinct species, 'D. kerryensis', due to its floral characters and later flowering, and allied with Southern

Marsh Orchid, which it resembles in flower colour and pattern although the dark spots on the lip are more numerous and more extensive.

A hyperchromic variant with an excess of pigmentation and a solidly dark lip has, rarely, been recorded.

BIOLOGY

Pollination and reproduction
No specific information.

Development and growth
No specific information.

Hybrids
'D. x aschersoniana', the hybrid with Early Marsh Orchid, has been recorded in Co. Limerick. This name may be changed following taxonomic changes.
D. x dinglensis, the highly fertile hybrid with Heath Spotted Orchid, has been found widely.
D. x braunii, the hybrid with Common Spotted Orchid, has been found in Co. Clare.

Name and classification
The specific name *occidentalis* derives from 'occidental', i.e. 'western', while the older name *majalis* means 'in May'.

Until recently this species was part of a conglomerate of marsh orchids that took the name 'Western Marsh Orchid *Dactylorhiza majalis*'. The conglomerate included *D. majalis* from mainland Europe as well as Irish Marsh Orchid, Hebridean Marsh Orchid and the *cambrensis* subspecies of Northern Marsh Orchid. Recent research, including the analysis of DNA, has suggested that Irish and Hebridean Marsh Orchids are unique endemic species and that *cambrensis* from west Wales belongs with Northern Marsh Orchid. This means that *D. majalis* of Europe does not occur anywhere in the British Isles.

This species is a tetraploid marsh orchid and the chromosome number is $2n = 80$.

HISTORY AND CONSERVATION
Irish plants were recognised as being distinctive

◀ *25 May, Co. Clare. The sides of the lip can be sharply folded downwards, and the markings are very variable.*

in the 1930s and were first given the name *occidentalis* in 1935 by the British botanist H.W. Pugsley.

Irish Marsh Orchid is vulnerable to agricultural changes, especially with European Union money funding agricultural 'improvement' in Eire, but so far losses appear to be modest. The difficulties of marsh orchid identification and the relatively low level of botanical recording in Ireland may be obscuring any changes in its status.

Past and present occurrence of Irish Marsh Orchid in Britain and Ireland (based on presence or absence in 10km squares of the National Grid; data from the New Atlas).

	Britain	Ireland
total historical range, 1500-1999	0	159
current range	0	130 (13%*)
% lost, 1500-1969		9%
% lost, 1970-1986		9%
% lost, total		18%

* current range as a % of the total number of 10km squares

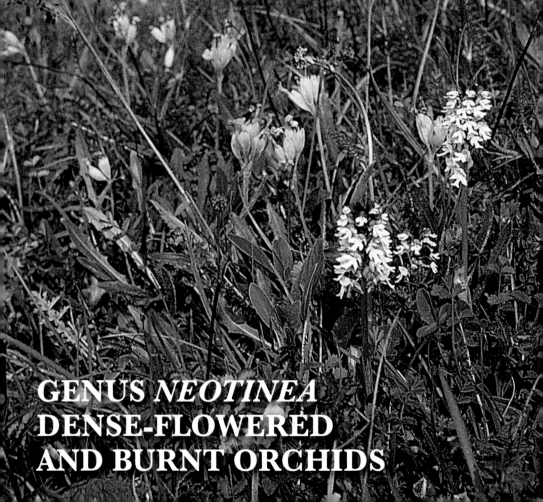

Distribution
Six species, found in central and southern Europe, North Africa and the Middle East.

Classification
Until recently Dense-flowered Orchid was the only species in this genus, but recent genetic studies have seen *Neotinea* enlarged to embrace five more from the genus *Orchis*, including Burnt Orchid. Paradoxically, *Neotinea* is probably as close to the bee orchids *Ophrys*, tongue orchids *Serapias* and Lizard Orchid as it is to the genus *Orchis*.

Floral structures
There are two pollinia, each narrowing to a short stalk which attaches it to one of the viscidia, which in turn are enclosed in a bursicle. There are two stigmas, placed on each side of the mouth of the spur but joined at the base.

Growth pattern
The aerial stem grows from a pair of tubers and the annual cycle of the replacement of tubers is similar to that of the genus *Orchis* (see p.200).

Vegetative reproduction
Additional tubers may be formed at the base of the stem and these will form separate plants when the connecting stem dies off in the autumn.

Name
The genus is named *neo* (= new) plus *tinea*, after Vicenzo Tineo, a Sicilian botanist (1791-1856). An alternative origin has been suggested, 'New-*Tinnea*', due to its supposed similarity to *Tinnea*, a genus of shrubby herbs from Africa named after Dutch explorers Henrietta Tinne and her daughters.

GENUS *NEOTINEA*
DENSE-FLOWERED
AND BURNT ORCHIDS

DENSE-FLOWERED ORCHID
Neotinea maculata

This small and rather inconspicuous orchid is confined to western Ireland, although for a while it also occurred on the Isle of Man. It has a very peculiar world range, being essentially a Mediterranean species adapted to the mild wet winters and hot dry summers of that region and seemingly ill-fitted to the damp, windy, oceanic climate of western Ireland. It is not unique, however, as several other Mediterranean species, such as Strawberry-tree, occur in Ireland. Various theories have been advanced to explain this distribution, including land-bridges between Ireland and the Continent or glacial refuges off western Ireland, and the subject has generated a good deal of controversy. Colonisation of Ireland via wind-blown seed seems, nevertheless, the simplest and most likely explanation.

Identification
The tiny off-white flowers are distinctive.

Similar species
Superficially similar to Small White Orchid, but the lip is a very different shape.

Habitat
Typically found on short turf on pastures, road verges, limestone pavements and around loughs and turloughs. It has occasionally been recorded on dunes or from ash and hazel woods in the hills. Although mostly confined to calcareous soils on limestone it has been found growing on gravels and also on light, peaty soils overlying more acidic rocks. Occurs up to 300m above sea level but most are found below 100m.

Flowering period
Late April to early June, usually peaking in mid-May. The flowers go over very quickly.

Range
Confined to Ireland, where most populations are in The Burren region of Co. Clare and adjacent Co. Galway, including the Arran Islands. Otherwise there are a few very scattered sites in eastern Co. Cork, Co. Limerick and

◀ *29 May, East Sussex. Burnt Orchids.*

▶ *21 May, Co. Clare. Var.* alba *is commonest in Ireland and has unspotted leaves and unmarked creamy flowers.*

• 1987-99
• 1970-86
• pre 1970

Co. Donegal and in Northern Ireland in Co. Fermanagh. Extinct in the Isle of Man.

World Range: The Mediterranean basin from Portugal and Spain east to Cyprus, Turkey, Syria and Israel; ranges north to southwest and southern France, the former Yugoslavia, Greece, Romania and the Ukraine, and south to Morocco, Algeria and Tunisia in North Africa. Also found on most of the Mediterranean islands, the Canary Islands and Madeira.

How to find it

Small and inconspicuous, this is a hard orchid to spot, especially from walking height. It is usually found in small scattered colonies, less commonly as single isolated plants. Locally frequent in The Burren, a mid-May excursion to this beautiful area is well worthwhile.

DESCRIPTION (var. *alba*)

Height: 4-40cm but mostly 6-15cm and very rarely over 30cm.

Stem: Green, with one or two brown membranous sheaths at the extreme base.

Leaves: There are three to six rather dark green leaves, of which two or three (sometimes four) are broadly oblong-elliptical in shape and held rather spreading at the base of the stem; the remainder are narrower and more pointed and loosely sheathe the stem with the uppermost even smaller and more bract-like. The leaves appear in October and are wintergreen.

Spike: Cylindrical and dense, composed of 15-20 tiny flowers (occasionally as many as 35), all facing more-or-less in the same direction.

Bract: Green, becoming whitish towards the tip. The bracts are lanceolate with a pointed tip and sometimes a tooth at the side and are a little shorter than the ovary, which they clasp.

▲ 21 May, Co. Clare. With Bird's-foot Trefoil in the rocky landscape of The Burren.

▲ 21 May, Co. Clare. The tiny flowers have a distinctly three-lobed lip and vaguely resemble human figures.

Ovary: Pale green, fat, cigar-shaped and twisted, with three diffuse ribs. The ovary is rather larger than the flower and stands upright. It narrows and bends at the tip, however, to hold the flower facing outwards.

Flower: Small and whitish, resembling a tiny man with a rather oversized helmet. The sepals are white, washed greenish and with green veins. They are oval-lanceolate to lanceolate, pointed at the tip and fused at the base to form a tight elongated hood. The petals are greenish-white with green veins, very narrow, strap-shaped and pointed; they are enclosed within the hood. The lip is small in relation to the hood and is held at an angle forwards and downwards. It is three-lobed with the central lobe strap-shaped and notched or shallowly forked at the tip (sometimes with a small tooth in the notch). The side-lobes are positioned near the base of the lip and are rather shorter and narrower. The spur is very short and conical. The flowers are reported to smell faintly of vanilla.

Subspecies
None.

Variation and varieties
Var. *alba* has unspotted leaves and whitish or creamy flowers (rarely more greenish). This is the common variety in Ireland.

Var. *maculata* has spotted leaves with the

▲ 21 May, Co. Clare. Like most 'Mediterranean' orchids, the leaves appear in October and are wintergreen, dying off after flowering.

▲ *24 May, Co. Clare. The 'typical' variety, which is scarce in Ireland, has spotted leaves, purple-veined flowers and often spotted ovaries, too.*

reddish or purple spots arranged in parallel longitudinal lines. The lip is pale pink or marked with a longitudinal pink stripe and, the sepals and petals have pink or brown veins. Occasionally the stem is spotted and sometimes also the bracts, ovaries and even sepals and petals. This is the 'typical' variety (in that it takes its name from the species) but it is relatively scarce in Ireland.

Var. *luteola* has primrose-yellow flowers. It is very rare and perhaps extinct in Ireland.

BIOLOGY

Pollination and reproduction

The spur contains abundant nectar, suggesting that the flowers are attractive to small insects. However, it seems that most or all plants are self-pollinated, sometimes before the buds have opened. The pollinia easily break up and become detached, perhaps by the wind, and there is no obstacle to them falling on the stigmas below. Seed is produced in good quantities.

Development and growth

No specific information.

Hybrids

None known.

Name and classification

The specific name *maculata* means 'spotted' or 'blotched'.

HISTORY AND CONSERVATION

First found in Ireland in May 1864 by Miss Frances More at Castle Taylor in Co. Galway. It was discovered on the Isle of Man in 1966 in an area of dunes on the north coast at The Ayres, Ballaghhennie. This colony persisted until 1986 but Dense-flowered Orchid is now extinct there.

In Ireland the species is scarce and local and has been lost from 46% of the historical range. Many of the losses are comparatively recent, although some of the decline has been offset by the discovery of new sites. It is extinct in Co. Offaly, Co. Roscommon and perhaps Co. Mayo (where noted from Lough Mask by Summerhayes, 1968). The 'improvement' of pastures and overgrazing are likely causes for the losses. With the current rapid pace of development in Eire there is cause for concern about the future of such a localised orchid.

Past and present occurrence of Dense-flowered Orchid in Britain and Ireland (based on presence or absence in 10km squares of the National Grid; data from the New Atlas).

	Britain	Ireland
total historical range, 1500-1999	1	24
current range	0	13 (1.3%*)
% lost, 1500-1969	0%	21%
% lost, 1970-1986	100%	25%
% lost, total	100%	46%

* current range as a % of the total number of 10km squares

BURNT ORCHID
Neotinea ustulata

Formerly: *Orchis ustulata*; Other names: Burnt-tip Orchid

This delicate species is one of our most attractive and delightful orchids but, sadly, is also probably the orchid that has suffered the greatest decline in the last 50 years or so. It is now confined to around 75 sites in England and just one in Wales, mostly on well-managed chalk grassland reserves in southern England but with a few colonies still surviving on the limestone of northern England. The unopened buds are deep purple, giving the top of the spike a scorched or burnt appearance, hence the name. Burnt Orchid is the county flower of Wiltshire.

Identification

Burnt Orchid is one of the group of orchids in which the flower resembles a tiny human figure, with the lip divided into 'arms' and short, stumpy 'legs'. It is easy to identify, with a distinctive combination of small size, dark reddish-purple buds and a white lip marked with fine reddish-purple spots. The contrast between the dark buds at the top of the spike and the white lips of the lower flowers is very striking. There are two forms of Burnt Orchid, early and late flowering, but they do not differ significantly in appearance.

Similar species

Lady Orchid resembles Burnt Orchid in general flower structure and colour but is very much larger, and its lip differs in the details of shape and coloration.

Habitat

Burnt Orchid is found on ancient short grassland on chalk and limestone soils, often on south- or west-facing slopes, although the late-flowering populations are not so fussy about the aspect. In southern England the species favours the narrow 'terracettes' that follow the contours of the slope on the chalk downs and also Bronze and Iron Age earthworks where the ground has been undisturbed for centuries. Only on rare occasions will it colonise new sites. For example, at Martin Down in Hampshire

▶ 13 July, Hampshire. In the late flowering var. aestivalis the hood does not fade after the flower has opened.

it appeared in the 1980s on grassland that had been under the plough until 1957. Burnt Orchid is also sometimes found in alluvial water meadows where the silt is derived from chalk, e.g. in Lincolnshire and formerly at sites in Hampshire and Oxfordshire. This habitat was always uncommon in southern England but in the past Burnt Orchid was found relatively frequently in riverside pastures in the north. It is predominantly a lowland species but has been recorded up to 275m above sea level.

Flowering period

There are two varieties that differ in their flowering period. The early-flowering form appears from the second or third week of May to mid-June in southern England and may, on average, be just a few days later in the north; it is usually at its best in the last ten days of May. The late flowering form flowers from the end of June through July to early August.

Range

Once found throughout the chalk and limestone areas of England, the species has undergone a major decline and is now extinct in many areas. In southern England, Burnt Orchid can still be found in Dorset, the Isle of Wight and West Sussex but the strongholds are the downs of Wiltshire, Hampshire and East Sussex. Outlying relict populations cling on in Gloucestershire, Berkshire, Hertfordshire, Bedfordshire and Kent. The decline has been even more marked in the Midlands and northern England, and the species is now only found in Derbyshire, Lincolnshire, northern Yorkshire and at a single site on the coast of Co. Durham (the most northerly in Britain). In 1993, bucking the trend of range contraction and decline, Burnt Orchid was recorded for the first time in Wales, on limestone grassland at Llanmadog, Glamorganshire.

The late-flowering variety *aestivalis* (see Variation and varieties) is only found in southern England. It has been recorded from

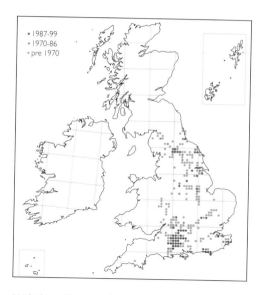

Wiltshire (four sites), Hampshire (five sites, plus one now destroyed) and East Sussex (14 sites, mostly between Lewes and Eastbourne, one holding nearly 1,000 spikes in 2002).

World range: Confined to Europe, although it extends just slightly into western Siberia (to *c.* 70°E). It occurs north to Denmark, southern Sweden, Estonia and the St Petersburg region of Russia and south to northern Spain, Italy, northern Greece, Bulgaria and the Ukraine. It is also found in the Caucasus. In the south of the range it is mostly found in the mountains and is absent from the Mediterranean lowlands. Extinct in Holland.

How to find it

Sadly, the chances of coming across this lovely little orchid unexpectedly have become slim but it is nevertheless still worthwhile looking for in suitable undisturbed short swards. Otherwise, a visit to a good chalk grassland reserve is necessary to see it but even then it can be hard to find. The colonies can be very localised, with hundreds of plants in one area and few or none elsewhere, even on seemingly suitable ground. Being so small, it can be surprisingly hard to spot among the various short downland herbs such as thyme and milkwort. As with many orchids, the number of flowering spikes varies greatly from year to year and in extremely dry seasons there may be none at all. One of the

◀ *29 May, East Sussex. In the early flowering form the hood fades once the flower has opened.*

▲ 13 July, Hampshire. The flowers look like tiny human figures; this is the late flowering var. aestivalis.

best sites is Mount Caburn (East Sussex). Others include Seven Sisters (also East Sussex), Martin Down (Hampshire) and Pewsey Downs, Parsonage Downs and Clearbury Rings (Wiltshire).

DESCRIPTION

Height: 2.5-15cm, very exceptionally to 30cm. In southern England it is usually around 4-10cm, with the very shortest plants found at heavily grazed sites. In northern England it is a little taller, usually around 9-12cm, even to 15-25cm when growing among taller vegetation.

Stem: Yellowish-green, slender and ridged towards the tip, with two or three membranous white sheaths at the very base.

Leaves: Green with a faint blue tone, fading to pale green by flowering time. There is a rosette of two to five elliptical-oblong keeled leaves at the base of the stem and one or two bract-like leaves higher up. The leaves appear in the autumn, are wintergreen and start to wither as the plant comes into flower (by which time non-flowering plants have already vanished).

Spike: The 15-50 flowers are densely packed

to form a spike that is initially conical but lengthens and becomes cylindrical when all the flowers have opened.

Bract: Reddish-purple, lanceolate and rather short, at around two-thirds the length of the ovary.

Ovary: Green, twisted and obscurely six-ribbed.

Flower: The sepals are oval, the lateral sepals asymmetrical with their outer surfaces dark reddish-purple (thus the unopened buds are very dark) and their inner surfaces greenish. The petals are paler and more strap-shaped. The sepals and petals form a compact hood that embraces the column; this is reddish-purple when the flower is fresh although it quickly fades (and see var. *aestivalis* below). The lip is white with a few scattered reddish-purple spots (formed by minute papillae) and is deeply lobed to form two broad chubby 'arms' and two short stumpy 'legs', sometimes with a tiny tooth between them. There is a groove in the centre of the lip towards the base that leads into the short, conical, down-curved spur. The column is short and whitish and the pollinia are yellow. The flowers of the early-flowering variety have a strong, sweet, honey-like scent said to be similar to Heliotrope, and var. *aestivalis* has a weak, citron-like scent that is vaguely unpleasant.

Subspecies
None.

Variation and varieties
Var. *ustulata* and **var. *aestivalis*** Very unusually there are two varieties of the Burnt Orchid which differ in their flowering time. The early-flowering var. *ustulata* is much the commoner and blooms in late May and early June. The late-flowering var. *aestivalis* is only found in southern England and flowers around July. The two varieties are rarely if ever found together, but at a site in East Sussex a colony of 200 late-flowering plants merges with a much smaller group of early-flowering plants on a north-facing chalk slope.

The two varieties differ slightly in appearance. In the late-flowering *aestivalis* the reddish-purple of the hood is on average darker and the colour does not fade once the flower has opened. There is also a distinct rose-purple wash to the edges of the lip and this wash may spread across the lip. The early-flowering variety never shows the persistent dark hood or the coloured fringe to the lip. Other differences are rather subtler. On average, var. *aestivalis* is taller, although this may simply be a product of the plants having to compete with the taller vegetation found later in the season. It has a more open spike of slightly smaller flowers and the lip is also shorter, with a slightly narrower 'waist' and shorter 'legs' which have a deeper cleft between them. Also, the spots on the lip are larger.

Similar late-flowering populations in Europe have been described as a distinct subspecies, *N. u. aestivalis*, and it has even been suggested that they should be treated as a different species. Genetic analysis shows that there is far too small a difference between the early- and late-flowering varieties to justify this. **Var. *albiflora*** has unmarked white flowers. It is very rare but has been recorded in Derbyshire, Kent, Berkshire, Hampshire and Wiltshire.

BIOLOGY

Pollination and reproduction

Poorly known. Early-flowering plants are pollinated by flies that feed on nectar and sugary plant juices. Presumably the flies are initially attracted by the combination of colour and scent, but this species does not produce nectar to reward them and they must be satisfied in some other way. Once on the flower, the flies work from the uppermost, unopened buds downwards and insert their proboscis in a head-down position. They 'taste' with their feet beforehand and there may be some sugary secretion from the flower to guide them into the 'correct' position; the groove at the base of the lip may in addition act as a 'leading line'. The mouth of the spur is narrow and rather like a keyhole; this shape and the design of the column may be related to the unconventional 'upside-down' position of the pollinating fly. Butterflies also visit the

▲ 13 July, Hampshire. The late flowering var. aestivalis differs slightly in appearance from typical plants as well as in its flowering period, but genetic research shows no appreciable difference between the two.

flowers but have not been recorded carrying pollinia. With its different scent and later flowering, var. *aestivalis* may attract a different suite of species and, in Europe, beetles have been recorded as pollinators. Whatever its mechanism, pollination is not very efficient in England and seed-set is relatively poor, with around 20% of flowers producing ripe capsules. Nevertheless, most new plants are recruited to the population from seed.

Vegetative reproduction takes place but is thought to be relatively unimportant. Groups of four to six spikes are not uncommon, however, and we have seen a compact cluster of 12 (see photo); such groups may well be the product of vegetative reproduction.

Development and growth

The aerial stem grows from a pair of tubers. The degree of fungal 'infection' is unclear, with both high and low rates being reported. 'Dormancy' is common, however, and Burnt Orchids are able to spend up to three years (sometimes even four) underground without producing aerial parts. During this period the fungal 'partner' must play a major role. Most plants flower for one to four seasons in succession (rarely for up to seven successive years) and then either die or retreat into a period of dormancy underground or as non-flowering rosettes.

Seed germinates to produce a protocorm which grows to a length of 20-30mm before the first root is produced (the longest protocorm known among orchids with a similar pattern of development). Both in cultivation and in the wild Burnt Orchids can flower within about three years of germination, but older estimates of up to 16 years are still quoted. This figure is based on the pioneering work of Fuchs and Ziegenspeck in the 1920s. They estimated the length of time the protocorm spent developing underground by examining it for 'constrictions', each of which was thought to represent a year's growth, like annual rings on a tree. This technique is now known to be unreliable.

Hybrids

None are known.

Name and classification

The specific name *ustulata* means 'scorched-looking'. Until recently Burnt Orchid was placed in the genus *Orchis*, but genetic studies have resulted in its transfer to the genus *Neotinea*. There it joins the superficially rather different Dense-flowered Orchid.

▲ 13 July, Hampshire. This group of 12 plants (var. aestivalis). is probably the product of vegetative reproduction.

HISTORY AND CONSERVATION

The first British record was in 1634 in Thomas Johnson's *Mercurius Botanicus* ('Botanical Mercury'): '...in montosis pratis' (mountain pastures). The first specific locality was given in 1650 in William How's *Phytologia Britannica natales exhibens Indigenarum Stirpium sponte emergentium* ('A British botany presenting the origins of native wild plants'): 'On Scosbylease, Mr Stonehouse'. Therefore the first localised record was from near Doncaster in northern England rather than the chalk downs of the south where it was presumably much commoner.

Formerly locally frequent over much of England, the Burnt Orchid has suffered one of the most catastrophic declines of our wild orchids and is now greatly reduced, both in terms of numbers and distribution. Out of a total historical range covering 265 10km squares, the *New Atlas* records a post-1987 presence in just 55, representing a 79% decline. It is now Nationally Scarce.

▲ *29 May, East Sussex. The reddish-purple buds and hood give the flowers a 'scorched' or 'burnt' appearance.*

Past and present occurrence of Burnt Orchid in Britain and Ireland (based on presence or absence in 10km squares of the National Grid; data from the New Atlas*).*

	Britain	Ireland
total historical range, 1500-1999	265	0
current range	55 (1.9%*)	0
% lost, 1500-1969	72%	
% lost, 1970-1986	7%	
% lost, total	79%	

* current range as a % of the total number of 10km squares

It is possible that subtle changes in climate in the 19th and 20th centuries may have caused some decline, but most losses can be directly attributed to agricultural changes. The species vanished from some counties at the edge of the range long ago (e.g. last recorded in Norfolk at the end of the 18th century), mainly due to the ploughing of grasslands following the Enclosures. The decline continued through the 19th and 20th centuries due to the continued loss of downland and pastures (perhaps especially during World War Two), while in the latter half of the 20th century the 'improvement' of grasslands with artificial fertilisers and pesticides continued to take a toll. The remaining grassland sites are vulnerable to scrub invasion due to a lack of grazing, especially in southern England, where first rabbits were decimated by myxomatosis and latterly livestock has become less economically viable. Paradoxically, overgrazing is also a problem, especially in northern England, where losses due to building and other development have also occurred. Sites were even wilfully destroyed, as at Cottondale in southeast Yorkshire, ploughed out in 1965 'to counter the attention shown it by botanists'.

There were around 350 historical localities in southern England but only around 75 colonies survived into the 1990s. Most sites have fewer than 50 flowering plants and, indeed, at some just one or two spikes make sporadic appearances; fewer than ten regularly hold more than 200 plants. The strongholds are now in Wiltshire, Hampshire and East Sussex, and notable concentrations include Parsonage Down in Wiltshire where there may be 30,000 flower spikes spread over 95ha in one continuous 'mega-colony', probably the largest surviving population in northwest Europe. In other counties where Burnt Orchid still survives, many or most of the sites have been lost. Thus in Dorset only two out of 12 known sites remain and the equivalent figures for the Isle of Wight are one of 12, for West Sussex one of six, for Kent seven of 18, for Berkshire one of 17, for Hertfordshire one of 11, for Bedfordshire one of ten and for east Gloucestershire one of 21.

Of over 120 sites recorded from northern England around 30 survive. There are a few in Derbyshire and northern Yorkshire; it reappeared in mid-west Yorkshire in 1988 but the single plant was promptly dug up. In the north and west of Lincolnshire there are three small colonies and just one remains in Co. Durham. Only two of the sites in the north, in Derbyshire and northwest Yorkshire, hold more than 200 spikes, and the total population in northern England is probably fewer than 1,000 flowering plants.

Fortunately many sites are now protected as SSSIs, nature reserves or are on Ministry of Defence land and managed for the benefit of their chalk flora and fauna. As the chalk landscape was created and maintained by hundreds or thousands of years of grazing, it is important to continue this practice. For Burnt Orchid the ideal regime is light spring grazing until late April with the return of sheep from late July until late September (when the new leaves start to appear); cattle are unsuitable as they can trample and destroy the plants and also damage the turf.

EXTINCT

The Burnt Orchid is extinct in the following vice-counties (the number of recorded sites, followed by the date of the last record, is given in parentheses). Source: Foley (1987, 1990, 1992).

South Devon (four sites, last seen in 1932)
North Somerset (seven, 1961)
West Kent (three, late 19th century)
Surrey (twelve, 1966)
North Essex (two, 19th century)
Middlesex (one, pre 1737)
Oxfordshire (two, 1982)
Buckinghamshire (five, 1961)
East Suffolk (but this 19th century site might have been in Norfolk)
West Suffolk (three, 1939)
West Norfolk (one, 18th century)
Cambridgeshire (twelve, 1955)
Huntingdonshire (one, 1890)
Northamptonshire (four, 1956)
West Gloucestershire (eight sites)
Herefordshire (two, 19th century)
Worcestershire (five, early 20th century)
Staffordshire (two, early 20th century)
Shropshire (six, 19th century)
Leicestershire (two doubtful old records)
Rutland (three, around 1915)
Nottinghamshire (three sites)
West Lancashire (two, 1940s)
Southeast Yorkshire (eleven, 1973)
Southwest Yorkshire (four, prior to 1888)
South Northumberland (one, prior to 1868)
Westmorland (seven, 1970s)
Cumberland (ten, early 1970s)

GENUS *HIMANTOGLOSSUM* LIZARD ORCHID

Distribution
There are five closely related species in Europe, North Africa and in the Middle East from Turkey and Lebanon to Iran. Perhaps surprisingly, their closest relatives include the bee and spider orchids *Ophrys*, tongue orchids *Serapias* and pyramidal orchids *Anacamptis*.

Name
The generic name *Himantoglossum* derives from the Greek *himas* 'leather strap' or 'thong' and *glossa* 'tongue', thus 'strap-tongued', a reference to the long, narrow lip.

LIZARD ORCHID
Himantoglossum hircinum

The bizarre flowers of this robust orchid bear a fanciful resemblance to a lizard and smell strongly of billy goat. It has always been rare in Britain but its range and numbers have ebbed and flowed, probably due to subtle changes in climate; it once occurred north to Yorkshire but retreated southwards and is now confined to a few sites in southern England, although it is currently on the increase again and could turn up almost anywhere in the south and east.

▲ *30 June, East Sussex. By flowering time the lower leaves, which appear in the autumn, have withered.*

◀ *25 June, Cambridgeshire. Smelling of billy goat and with such extravagant flowers, this is a truly bizarre orchid.*

▶ *27 June, Kent.*

Identification

Very distinctive. The tall spikes of large greyish-green flowers have an untidy, straggly, ragged appearance and on close inspection their structure is unique. The long central lobe of the lip resembles a lizard's tail, and the shorter side-lobes form the back legs. The hood of the flower is said to recall the head and body of the lizard, but it seems much more reasonable to say that the fore-quarters of the lizard have been swallowed and vanished into the throat of the flower.

Similar species
None.

Habitat

The Lizard Orchid usually grows in open sunny situations among fairly rank grass, although sometimes it also occurs on shorter and more closely-cropped swards. It can appear among scrub or on the edge of woodland but would eventually be shaded out if the canopy developed too much. It is always found on well-drained soils, usually on chalk but sometimes also on limestone and occasionally on boulder clays, sands or gravels; it has even been recorded growing through broken tarmac. Whatever the soil, it will probably be calcium-rich, although some recent records have been on neutral soils. Suitable sites include road verges, railway embankments, ancient earthworks, field margins, old chalk pits and dunes, and it even grows on lawns on one favoured housing estate. At least six of the 19 recent populations are on golf courses, and it has been suggested that golfers may have carried the seeds from one course to the next on

their shoes or equipment. Found from sea level to about 200m in Gloucestershire and on the North and South Downs.

Flowering period

Early June to late July, sometimes from late May. Traditionally peaking in the first week of July it has, like many other orchids, tended to flower earlier in the last few years, in mid-June.

Range

The distribution has ebbed and flowed, but all the records have been southeast of a line from the Severn to the Humber apart from one old site further north in Yorkshire and a doubtful record from Lancashire. In recent years there has been a very large established colony at Sandwich Bay in Kent and a smaller permanent colony at Newmarket in Suffolk, as well as small colonies in East Sussex, Dorset and Suffolk. Other recent records, either of sporadic appearances or tiny populations, come from north Somerset, north Hampshire, West Sussex, Surrey, Oxfordshire and west Gloucestershire. It has also been recorded from Jersey in the Channel Islands. **World range:** Southwest and southern Europe, north to Holland, Germany, Austria and the Czech Republic, south to northern Spain (and very scattered in central and southern Spain), Italy and Sicily and east to Greece, also North Africa in Morocco, Algeria and Tunisia. (The lizard orchids further to the east and in the Balkans

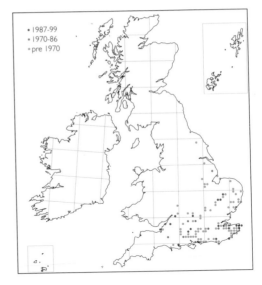

are often treated as separate species.) The species is commonest in France, where it is a roadside weed in the wine-growing regions.

How to find it

Despite their size, the greyish-green spikes can be hard to see among long grass. Undoubtedly the best site is at Sandwich Bay in Kent where there have been up to 3,000 flower spikes in recent years, with 5,000 in 2000 (when the total population was estimated at 27,500 plants over an area of 0.5 square km). Another well-known colony is on the Devil's Dyke that runs across Newmarket's July racecourse, with around 200-250 flowering plants.

▲ *27 June, Kent. Lizard Orchid is an adaptable species and a prestigious colonist on a lawn.*

▲ 28 June, Cambridgeshire. As wih many orchids, the function of the elaborate lip is obscure.

DESCRIPTION

Height: 25-90cm but usually below 60cm and commonly around 30cm.

Stem: Pale green with faint purple blotches, ridged towards the tip and with two or three scale leaves at the extreme base.

Leaves: Numerous, greyish-green and sometimes blotched with purple. There are four to ten large, oval-oblong, keeled basal leaves forming an untidy rosette and three to five smaller, narrower and more pointed leaves which loosely clasp the stem up to the flower spike. The leaves are wintergreen, and the basal leaves have yellowed and often withered by flowering time, especially in dry years.

Spike: Tall, occupying almost 50% of the stem, cylindrical and rather dense, with 15-80 flowers.

Bract: Pale green to off-white, variably but often strongly washed reddish, narrow and pointed, and up to twice the length of the ovary.

Ovary: Pale green, cylindrical, tapering both towards the flower and at the base into a short stalk, twisted and with three ridges.

Flower: Overall greyish-green. The sepals are oval and are fused at the base to form a loose hood. They are pale greyish-green, variably flushed or rimmed purple with a paler interior that has lines of reddish-purple spots and dashes along the veins (which may show through to the exterior). The petals are very narrow, strap-shaped and spotted reddish-purple. The lip is divided into three lobes. The central lobe is 2.5-6cm long, narrow, parallel-sided and ribbon-like, with a deeply notched tip. It is twisted through two or three turns and is whitish at the base, becoming pale lilac-brown for the outer 80%. The side-lobes are very much shorter and a little narrower, pointed and pale lilac-brown. The sides of the lip at the base are boldly folded or corrugated, and this corrugation continues on to the outer edges of the side-lobes. The centre of the base of the lip is trough-like with a dense 'fur' of tiny white papillae and with variable bright purplish-red tufted spots and blotches. The lip is coiled like a spring in bud and slowly unrolls to project outwards and downwards at about 45° (sometimes nearer the horizontal on few-flowered spikes). The spur is short, curved downwards and bluntly conical. The anther is greenish-white, and the two greenish pollinia are fixed to a single viscidium that is concealed in the purple bursicle. The stigmatic zone is purple. The strong scent recalls a billy goat and is most pungent in the evening.

Subspecies
None.

Variation and varieties
None.

BIOLOGY

Pollination and reproduction

The flowers are visited by a variety of insects, including hover flies, various bees, wasps, ants, beetles, butterflies and moths. Of these, bees are probably the main pollinators. There is no nectar (although glucose has been detected in the spur), and the flower seems to offer its pollinator no reward; despite this the pungent scent may serve to attract flies and night-flying moths. Self-pollination is physically possible but is thought not to occur. The species is self-compatible, however, and solitary isolated plants do set seed; for this to happen either self-pollination (autogamy) or cross-pollination from other flowers on the same spike (geitonogamy) must occur. Whatever the mechanism, it does not seem to be very efficient and only around 30% of flowers are pollinated, although each capsule contains up to 1,200 seeds, perhaps more. It is possible for the species to reproduce vegetatively by forming extra tubers, but this seems to be a rare event.

Development and growth

The Lizard Orchid spends the summer 'resting period' underground as a tuber. The aerial shoot appears from late August onwards, with the lower leaves unfolding and some short and rather thick roots growing from the base of the stem. These leaves will overwinter and by early spring may start to blacken at the tips. By then a new tuber has started to form from a bud at the base of the stem and by May the roots and older tuber, as well as the leaves, are often withering. At flowering time, therefore, the plant has two large, egg-shaped oval tubers (one old and withering, one new). After flowering and setting seed the plant will disappear, leaving only the new underground tuber to survive the summer.

Individual plants can be long-lived, surviving for up to at least 19 years after first emergence, but they may not flower every year and can remain 'dormant' as underground tubers for a year or appear merely as a rosette of leaves, sometimes for many years. An individual plant in Sussex flowered in 1984 and then not again until 1995, and a colony in Suffolk of between 16 and 40 plants did not produce any flowers over a ten-year period.

Seed germinates in the autumn up to two years after the seeds have ripened and dispersed. Although some of the seed may blow away, it is common for mature flowering plants to have large numbers of seedlings close by, and many seeds stay in the pods until the dead spike falls over. With the aid of fungi, the seedling initially develops into a protocorm the size of a small pea. In the spring following germination, the protocorm produces the first tuber and then withers away, leaving just the tuber to oversummer. In the autumn, a short rhizome grows from this tuber and develops a root and a second tuber which is fully developed by the following spring. This establishes the annual cycle of replacement tubers. When the seedling is more than two years old the first leafy shoot appears above ground. The seedling usually remains in the one-leaf stage for two or more years and then moves on to two leaves, again for several years, and then three leaves. Although in very favourable conditions a plant with two or three leaves can flower, it is only when it has grown four leaves that it can be considered mature. Even then it may not flower every year. The period between germination and first flowering may therefore be a minimum of six years.

Hybrids
None.

▶ *28 June, Cambridge-shire. The long central lobe of the lip uncoils like a spring.*

Name and classification

The specific name *hircinum* means 'of goats', a reference to the scent.

HISTORY AND CONSERVATION

The first British record dates from 1641 when Thomas Johnson published the second part of his *Mercurius Botanicus* ('Botanical Mercury') and recorded it 'Nigh the highway betweene Crayford and Dartford in Kent'.

The Lizard Orchid is a *Red Data Book*

species that is classed as Vulnerable and fully protected under Schedule 8 of the Wildlife and Countryside Act 1981. Despite this it has been targeted by collectors, and plants have been dug up at Sandwich Bay in Kent (where a 24-hour guard was maintained in the 1970s and 1980s) and as recently as 2003 from a road verge in Dorset.

The Lizard Orchid has an intriguing history in England. From its discovery until about 1850 the species was restricted to the Dartford area of Kent, although the original 1641 colony

Past and present occurrence of Lizard Orchid in Britain and Ireland (based on presence or absence in 10km squares of the National Grid; data from the New Atlas).

	Britain	Ireland
total historical range, 1500-1999	115	0
current range	20 (0.7%*)	0
% lost, 1500-1969	76.5%	
% lost, 1970-1986	6%	
% lost, total	82.5%	

* current range as a % of the total number of 10km squares

had been destroyed due to road-widening. There was then a decline in that area and just odd, isolated records in southeast England, mostly in Kent; by 1900 just four sites were known in England and it was thought that the Lizard Orchid was almost extinct. Then, during World War I and the 1920s there was a marked expansion northwards with the species turning up unpredictably, often just a single plant but sometimes in larger numbers, north to Yorkshire and west to Devon. A remarkably large proportion of the new sites were found by schoolgirls. This expansion peaked around 1927 with 36 populations, but the record is slightly clouded as Lizard Orchids had been dug up and transplanted to gardens (sometimes from as far away as France) and at least two sites in this period are thought to have originated with 'garden escapes'. Adding a further complication, plants were sometimes transplanted by well-meaning naturalists, often for 'safe-keeping', to new sites or even new counties. Whatever their origin, in addition to the counties detailed in 'Range' there are older records from north Devon, Wiltshire, Isle of Wight, north Essex, Hertfordshire, Berkshire, Buckinghamshire, Norfolk, Bedfordshire, Worcestershire, Lincolnshire and northeast Yorkshire.

In another change of fortunes, there was a sudden drop in the number of colonies after 1934, although the geographical spread was maintained. From the mid-1940s to 1993 the total number of populations remained stable at nine to 11, although some sites were lost and others were gained. During this period all the colonies were small and even the most thriving lasted only about 20 years. A further increase started around 1994 with plants appearing west to Somerset and Gloucestershire. There were 16 sites in 1996 and 19 by 2000. As usual some of the new sites are ephemeral with the orchid flowering once and vanishing, e.g. by 2000 four of the 1996 sites had disappeared but there were seven new ones (thus a net increase of three). With protection, some colonies, such as the very large population at Sandwich Bay, have expanded.

Lizard Orchid is on the edge of its range in England, and it seems that subtle shifts in climate have a big impact on its distribution. The species is wintergreen, and the amount of rainfall during the growing period of September-April has a marked influence on the flowering success, with a dry autumn and winter limiting flowering. Furthermore, flower buds are initialised and formed over two seasons so the rainfall over a two-year period is important in determining flowering success. Conversely, severe drought may kill many plants and wipe out small populations.

Lizard Orchid favours areas of long but sparse grass that is cut once or twice a year. None of the English sites are grazed but the species is tolerant of grazing, at least by cattle, although rabbits have caused severe damage at times, especially during hard winters, as have slugs. Some sites are managed to open up the vegetation and prevent scrub invasion (with the Newmarket site, for example, being burnt every fifth year during the winter), but those on dune grassland do not need much management.

GENUS *ANACAMPTIS*
LOOSE-FLOWERED,
PYRAMIDAL AND
GREEN-WINGED ORCHIDS

This genus formerly included just the Pyramidal Orchid. It is now a rather heterogeneous combination of superficially different species, three of which occur in Britain.

Distribution

The genus contains about 20 species, in northern, central and southern Europe, North Africa and southwest Asia, east to Afghanistan and south to Yemen in the Arabian Peninsula.

Classification

From 1817, when it was described and named, until 1997, this genus contained just one species, Pyramidal Orchid. However, genetic studies then led to the transfer into *Anacamptis* of 19 species from the genus *Orchis*, including Green-winged and Loose-flowered Orchids. Surprisingly, the genus *Anacamptis* is closer to the tongue orchids *Serapias*, bee orchids *Ophrys* and lizard orchids *Himantoglossum* than to the genus *Orchis* from which those additional 19 species came.

Floral structures

In Loose-flowered and Green-winged Orchids the two pollinia narrow to a caudicle (stalk) and each is attached to their own viscidium which, in turn, is enclosed in a bursicle. The two-lobed stigma lies on the roof of the mouth of the spur. In Pyramidal Orchid the two pollinia are attached to a single strap-shaped viscidium.

Pollination

The flowers do not produce nectar and may rely on deceit to attract bees as pollinators. Pyramidal Orchid, and perhaps also Green-winged Orchid, do, however, produce a sugary sap in the walls of the spur and this may function as a reward for insect visitors.

Growth pattern

The aerial stem grows from a pair of spherical tubers, as in the genus *Orchis* (see p.200).

Vegetative reproduction

Additional tubers may be formed at the base of the aerial stem and these will go on to form separate plants when the connecting stem dies off in the autumn.

Name

The generic name *Anacamptis* derives from the Greek *anakampto* 'to bend back'. It is a reference to the structure of the flower of Pyramidal Orchid but there is disagreement as to which particular bit of the flower is being referred to. It may be the long spur of the flower, the 'guide-plates' at the base of the lip or the position of the pollinia.

◀ *10 May, Norfolk. Sadly, although relatively common not so long ago, Green-winged Orchid has been banished from around half its range.*

LOOSE-FLOWERED ORCHID

Anacamptis laxiflora

Formerly: *Orchis laxiflora*; Other names: Jersey Orchid
This stately orchid provides a real splash of colour to wet meadows in the spring. In Britain it is confined to the Channel Islands, but it is widespread in the Mediterranean region, although everywhere it is threatened by drainage and agricultural 'improvement'.

Identification
A 'typical' orchid with a tall, loose spike of purple flowers. The leaves are narrow and held erect. The lip is purple with a long white central zone that is unspotted or has some darker purple markings. The central lobe is shorter than the side-lobes and the sides of the lip are very sharply folded downwards; the lateral sepals are held vertically upwards. This gives the lip a tall but 'flattened' profile.

Similar species
Early Purple Orchid is superficially similar but has broader leaves that are usually spotted and held in a rosette flat on the ground. Its flower spike is more compact, and the centre of the lip is spotted. The lip itself is distinctly three-lobed with the central lobe larger and longer than the side-lobes.

Habitat
Damp meadows and marshy fields flushed with base-rich water.

Flowering period
Early May to mid-June but mostly in late May.

Range
Confined to Guernsey and Jersey in the Channel Islands. There are old records from Co. Durham, including one dating from 1872 when it was found growing north of Hartlepool. These plants may have originated as casual imports with wool 'shoddy'. **World range:** Essentially Mediterranean, found from Portugal east to Greece, Cyprus and Turkey, and including most of the Mediterranean islands. Occurs north to north-central France

▶ *27 May, Sussex (Wakehurst Place).*

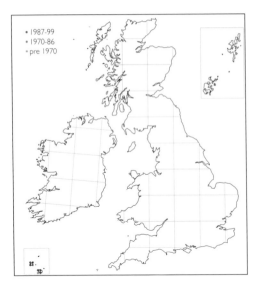

(Seine-Maritime and Marne), Switzerland and the former Yugoslavia. It was discovered for the first time in Holland relatively recently but is extinct in Belgium.

How to find it

The tall purple flower spikes are conspicuous. The best site on Jersey is Le Noir Pré and on Guernsey the Orchid Fields at Les Vicheries.

DESCRIPTION

Height: 15-60cm.

Stem: Green, usually strongly washed reddish-purple towards the tip, with two to four loose, brownish scales at the base.

Leaves: Three to eight, keeled, pointed and strap-shaped, well-spaced along the stem and held rather erect, with the upper leaves small and bract-like. The leaves appear in autumn and are wintergreen.

Spike: The six to 20 flowers are held in a very loose spike.

Bract: Green, washed reddish-purple or sometimes entirely reddish-purple. The bracts are strap-shaped, narrow, pointed and roughly the length of the ovary (which they clasp) or longer.

Ovary: Green, washed reddish-purple or sometimes entirely reddish-purple. The ovaries are long, slender, cylindrical and twisted.

Flower: Dark purple to reddish-purple with a broad white stripe down the centre of the lip. The sepals are oval to oblong and blunt-tipped; the lateral sepals are asymmetrical and held erect above the rest of the flower (sometimes touching), and the upper sepal is held over the petals, which are slightly smaller and form a loose hood over the column. The lip is broader than long with two large, rounded side-lobes and a rather shorter blunt central lobe (the central lobe is sometimes absent altogether). The sides of the lip are so sharply folded downwards that the side-lobes may touch at their tips. The spur is long and slender but broadens towards the tip, which is usually notched, and either straight or slightly up-curved. The centre of the lip may have small, dark, vertical streaks within the white central zone, extending into the purple borders.

Subspecies
None.

Variation and varieties
Var. *rosea* has pale rose-pink flowers but is rare.
Var. *albiflora* has white flowers but is rare.

▲ 27 May, Sussex (Wakehurst Place). The more or less two-lobed, unspotted lip is sharply folded, and the spur is often upturned.

► 27 May, Sussex (Wakehurst Place). The lateral sepals are held upwards, and the upper sepal and petals form an untidy hood.

BIOLOGY

Pollination and reproduction
No specific information.

Development and growth
No specific information, but in cultivation the period between germination and the production of the first green leaves is short.

Hybrids
A. x *alata*, the hybrid with Green-winged Orchid, has been recorded occasionally on Jersey and once on Guernsey.

Name and classification
The specific name *laxiflora* derives from the Latin *laxus* 'wide' or 'loose' and *flos* 'flower' and means 'loose-flowered'.

Until very recently this species was considered to be a member of the genus *Orchis*, and its overall similarity to some of the other members of that genus, such as Early Purple Orchid, certainly supported this. Recent genetic studies have shown, however, that Loose-flowered and Green-winged Orchids should join the Pyramidal Orchid in the genus *Anacamptis*, although this change is not universally accepted.

HISTORY AND CONSERVATION
Loose-flowered Orchid was first found on Guernsey around 1788 by Joshua Gosselin, a local naturalist, and discovered on Jersey in 1837 by C.C. Babington.

There have been declines due to habitat loss, but the species is still locally common or even sometimes abundant on Jersey and especially Guernsey. Most of the populations are in reserves, although water abstractions for agriculture and golf courses can affect even protected areas. Loose-flowered Orchid is naturalised at Wakehurst Place in Sussex (the Royal Botanic Gardens' country annexe). In 1987, 350 plants grown from seed collected in Crete were planted out and this population is still thriving.

PYRAMIDAL ORCHID

Anacamptis pyramidalis

This widespread and very colourful orchid of open grassland is commonest on chalk and limestone but could be found almost anywhere that has a hint of lime in the soil. When they first appear, the flower spikes form a pyramid or cone, hence the name, but as more flowers open the shape of the spike changes to more of a globe or cylinder. Pyramidal Orchid is the county flower of the Isle of Wight.

Identification

The dense, conical spikes of unmarked bright cerise pink flowers are distinctive. On close examination the flowers have a deeply three-lobed lip and a very long, thin, down-curved spur.

Similar species

The fragrant orchids flower a little earlier in the season (apart from Marsh Fragrant Orchid) and have a looser, taller, thinner and more tapering flower spike. Their flowers are slightly more purplish-pink and their lip is not so deeply cut, with the three lobes shorter, broader and more uneven in size and shape. If there is any doubt, Pyramidal Orchid can always be identified by the two prominent raised ridges or 'guide-plates' at the base of the lip, unique to the species.

Habitat

Pyramidal Orchid grows on dry, well-drained grassland on chalk, limestone or other calcium-rich soils, such as boulder clay. It is found on both close-cropped turf and in taller, ranker swards. Suitable habitats also include the grykes of limestone pavements, cliff tops, among Marram and Lyme-grass on sand dunes and, very locally, the coastal machair of the Hebrides. The species is sometimes still found in old meadows, although this habitat has almost vanished in most areas. It also grows among scrub; rarely in open woodland with a broken canopy. Pyramidal Orchid takes readily to man-made habitats, such as road verges and roundabouts, churchyards, old quarries, disused

◄ *28 June, Cambridgeshire. An opportunist, it can do well on the verges of main roads or even on roundabouts,* railway lines and abandoned industrial sites, and is one of the first orchids to move into such newly available habitats. Recorded up to 350m above sea level (Brough, Cumbria).

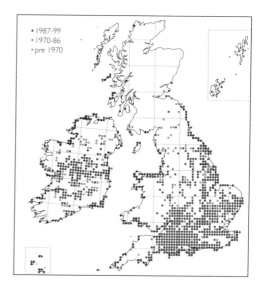

Flowering period

Early June to mid-August, very exceptionally from May, but mostly mid-June and early to mid-July.

Range

Mostly found south and east of a line from south Devon to North Yorkshire and in southern and especially central Ireland. The species clearly enjoys a mild maritime climate and ranges further north and west into coastal districts of north Cornwall, south and north Wales, northern Ireland and northeast England (north to Lindisfarne). It is also found on the Isle of Man, Isles of Scilly and Channel Islands. In Scotland it is rare and confined to a few sites in the Borders, Lothian, Fife, Angus, Sutherland, Kintyre and Dumfries and Galloway, as well as the Inner Hebrides on

Arran, Islay, Colonsay, Tiree, Gunna and Coll and on the Outer Hebrides on South Uist, Funday and Barra. **World range:** Essentially Europe but extends into North Africa and the Middle East. Occurs north to Denmark, southern Sweden and the Baltic States, east

▲ 5 July, Northamptonshire. Troops of Pyramidal Orchids add a splash of colour to high summer.

◄ 22 June, Norfolk. The spike is conical to pyramid-shaped when the flowers begin to open.

to Poland and the Ukraine and south to the Mediterranean, Crimea and Caucasus. Also found on the Mediterranean islands, in North Africa in Morocco, Algeria and Tunisia, and in the Middle East in Israel, Turkey, northern Iraq and northwest Iran.

How to find it

Generally common in suitable habitats, indeed often abundant.

DESCRIPTION

Height: 10-75cm but usually 20-60cm.
Stem: Green, slightly angled towards the tip and often rather slender and flexuous (bendy); the stems frequently have a distinct kink somewhere along their length. There are two or three brown sheaths at the extreme base.
Leaves: Green, tinged grey, keeled and strap-shaped with a pointed tip. The three or four sheathing leaves grade into five or six non-sheathing leaves that decrease in size up the stem and become bract-like towards the spike. The lower leaves may arch gracefully outwards. The sheathing leaves emerge in the autumn and are wintergreen, but they have often withered by flowering time. The spike and non-sheathing leaves do not appear until the spring.
Spike: Very dense, the 30-100 flowers are packed so closely that they often conceal the stem. When the first flowers break bud the spike is distinctly conical but as more flowers open it elongates to become domed or oval in shape and sometimes eventually cylindrical.
Bract: Green, sometimes flushed purple, narrow, a little longer than the ovary and tapering to a fine point.

Ovary: Cylindrical, twisted and green, often washed reddish-purple.

Flower: Usually vivid pink, sometimes paler pink or reddish-pink, and fading a little as the flower ages. The sepals are oval-lanceolate with a variably pointed tip and dished sides, and the petals are a little shorter and blunter. The lateral sepals are held horizontally or slightly drooping, to about 15° below the horizontal, and the upper sepal and petals form a hood over the column. The lip is white towards the base, wedge-shaped and held projecting forwards and downwards. It is deeply divided into three virtually equal strap-shaped lobes. The outer lobes broaden slightly towards their blunt, shovel-like tips, and the central lobe is more parallel-sided with the extreme tip pinched in and upwards. On either side of the base of the lip there are two prominent narrow raised ridges or 'guide-plates' that are extensions of the column. The ridges, although roughly parallel, converge towards the mouth of the spur. The spur is slender, 12-14mm long (often longer than the ovary) and down-curved. The column is white, variably washed pink. The rostellum partially blocks the entrance to the spur, and the two stigmas lie low down on either side of the column and both pollinia are joined to the same strap-shaped viscidium. The flowers are scented, the perfume most obvious in the evening and variously described as sweet or as slightly unpleasant and 'foxy'.

Subspecies

None.

Variation and varieties

Var. *albiflora* has pure white flowers but is rare (very pale pink flowers are rather commoner).
Var. *sanguinea* has blood-red flowers. It is scarce and known only from the Hebrides and northwest Ireland.
Var. *emarginata* has an unlobed lip that resembles a scallop shell. It is very rare.
Var. *angustiloba* has a very deeply lobed lip.
Var. *fundayensis* has a taller and more cylindrical flower spike. It was described from Funday in the Hebrides but is probably extinct, if it ever existed at all.

▲ 22 June, Norfolk. On a close inspection, the raised 'guide-plates' at the base of the lip are characteristic.

BIOLOGY

Pollination and reproduction

Pyramidal Orchid is pollinated by moths, both day- and night-flying, and by butterflies. Day-flying moths and butterflies are attracted by the flower's vivid coloration, and the various burnet moths may additionally be attracted by its similarity to the bright red spots on their wings. At night the flower's scent would assist its detection. The pollination mechanism is highly evolved. The walls of the spur contain a sugary sap but only an insect with a suitably long proboscis can reach this. The ridges or guide plates on either side of the mouth of the spur act as a guide correctly to position the insect's proboscis, not only to access the spur and the sap within but also to trigger the mechanism. The rostellum hangs over the entrance to the spur and when it is touched by an insect the protective, flap-like bursicle is pushed aside and the strap-shaped viscidium, complete with the two pollinia, sticks to the insect's proboscis.

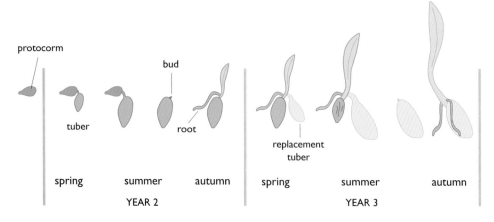

protocorm

bud

tuber

root

replacement
tuber

spring   summer   autumn   spring   summer   autumn

YEAR 2   YEAR 3

▲ *Development from seed in Pyramidal Orchid (after Rasmussen 1995).*

As soon as the viscidium is exposed to the air it contracts like a watch-spring and coils itself around the proboscis. This not only helps to attach it more firmly but also moves the pollinia apart so that they become separated by 90°. Then, a few seconds later in a second contraction, the pollinia swing forward so as to be in a perfect position to strike the sticky surfaces of the two stigmas on the next flower visited and deposit packets of pollen. The mechanism is efficient, with 65-95% of flowers setting seed.

Vegetative propagation is also possible via the production of additional tubers, which often develop at the end of short rhizomes.

Development and growth

The aerial stem grows from a pair of rounded or roughly elongated tubers and there are a few slender fleshy roots growing almost horizontally near the surface of the soil; it is the roots that are 'infected' with fungi. The basal leaves appear in autumn and die down in summer and after flowering the orchid spends the late summer and autumn 'resting' as a tuber. The Pyramidal Orchid is clearly adapted to a Mediterranean climate of mild, wet winters and hot dry summers and its overwintering leaves are probably vulnerable to hard frosts. The generally southerly distribution in Britain, with colonies further north concentrated near the coast, emphasises its preference for a mild winter climate.

It is not known when germination occurs but initially a protocorm is developed. Early researchers suggested that the seedling remained at this stage for three years but it may well be just a few months before the first tuber develops. Following this the protocorm dies off in the late summer to leave just the small tuber in a 'resting' state. In the autumn a bud on the tuber produces a short rhizome and from this one or two roots develop and sometimes also the first leafy shoot. The new rhizome and roots have to be reinfected with fungi from the soil as the tuber itself did not carry any 'infection'. This plant, including the leafy shoot, overwinters, and in the following spring a new tuber starts to develop from a bud on the rhizome and the old one starts to shrivel away. Eventually the shoot and rhizome also wither, and the plant will again spend the late summer 'resting' as a tuber. In this way the annual cycle of growth is established. Again, it has been estimated that several years elapse between the first appearance above ground and the first flowers, but this is probably far too long and the period between germination and flowering could be as little as three years.

Intergeneric hybrids

x *Gymnanacamptis anacamptis*, the hybrid with fragrant orchid (presumably Common Fragrant Orchid), has been recorded very rarely from Hampshire, Gloucestershire and Co. Durham.

Name and classification

The specific name *pyramidalis* means simply 'pyramidal' or 'conical'. Until recently the Pyramidal Orchid was the only member of the genus *Anacamptis*, but it has now been joined by Green-winged and Loose-flowered Orchids.

HISTORY AND CONSERVATION

The first British record dates from 1660 when John Ray recorded it in his *Catalogus Plantarum circa Cantabrigiam nascentium* ('A catalogue of plants found around Cambridge'): 'In many places, as in a chalkie close at Hinton near where they burn lime.'

Past and present occurrence of Pyramidal Orchid in Britain and Ireland (based on presence or absence in 10km squares of the National Grid; data from the New Atlas).

	Britain	Ireland
total historical range, 1500-1999	849	350
current range	681 (24%*)	241 (24%*)
% lost, 1500-1969	13.5%	25%
% lost, 1970-1986	6.5%	6%
% lost, total	20%	31%

* current range as a % of the total number of 10km squares

The boundaries of the range are stable but inevitably there have been declines, and Pyramidal Orchid has been lost from 20% of the historical range in Britain and 31% in Ireland. Some of the declines are due to the loss of old meadows and pastures and although it is tolerant of grazing, overgrazing may also be a threat, perhaps especially at the few sites on the machair of the Hebrides and western Scotland. Another problem comes from the development of old industrial sites and the use of old pits and quarries for 'landfill' as the species is a pioneer colonist of these habitats.

▶ *21 June, Suffolk. Once all the flowers have opened the spike is cylindrical, sometimes markedly so.*

GREEN-WINGED ORCHID
Anacamptis morio

Formerly: *Orchis morio*; Other names: Green-veined Orchid
This beautiful orchid once graced pastures and other areas of undisturbed grassland throughout much of England, Wales and Ireland, and the sight of a field splashed with the purples and yellows of thousands of Green-winged Orchids and Cowslips was commonplace. Tragically, agricultural changes have led to a dramatic decline in most areas, and the species has become rather local, although it can still be found in very large numbers at some favoured sites. It now largely depends on the sympathetic management of the few remaining old pastures as well those churchyards blessed by its presence. Green-winged Orchid is the county flower of Ayrshire.

▲ 10 May, Norfolk. Sadly, although relatively common not so long ago, Green-winged Orchid has been banished from around half its range.

Identification
A dainty and usually petite orchid with unspotted leaves. It has a few relatively large and very attractive flowers that are extremely variable in colour, from deep violet-purple to rose-pink or whitish, although most are a shade of purple. Whatever the colour, the flowers are distinctive. The sepals and petals form a hood marked with the green or bronze veins that give the species its name. The sides of the lip turn downwards to form a broad and often colourful skirt, and the long straight spur projects conspicuously back from the flower.

Similar species
Early Purple Orchid is superficially similar but usually has spotted leaves and also tends to have a longer flower spike and more flowers that are a paler purple. On close examination only the upper sepal and petals form the 'hood' because the two lateral sepals are held upright as 'wings'. Early Purple Orchid also lacks green or purple veins on the sepals and finally, although both species are found in grassland, only Early Purple Orchid is found in woodland.

Habitat
Green-winged Orchid favours unimproved grassland on neutral or calcareous soils where grazing, mowing or other factors keep the grass relatively short and the sward open. It is very strongly associated with old species-rich grassland and is slow to colonise new sites.

The optimum habitats are damp pastures on clay soils, but it is also found on dry chalk or limestone grassland and sometimes on sands and gravels, including pockets of neutral grassland on otherwise acidic heathland. The species can tolerate both mowing for hay and grazing. Because unimproved damp meadows and pastures are now rare Green-winged Orchid is almost as likely to be found on more marginal sites such as stabilised dunes, lime-rich eskers, old railway cuttings and banks, village greens (especially those which are 'commons'), churchyards and golf courses. Occasionally it is found on lawns or on old industrial sites, for example, alkaline waste produced in the manufacture of washing soda. It is intolerant of shade, and although it can be found among scrub it is seldom if ever found in woodland. Recorded up to 305m above sea level (Co. Roscommon).

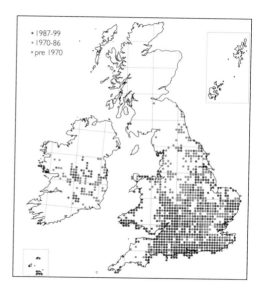

- 1987-99
- 1970-86
- pre 1970

Flowering period

Mid-April to mid-June but mostly in May. It is earliest in the west and exceptionally has been recorded flowering in mid-March.

Range

Widespread in England, formerly north to a line from Morecambe Bay to Holy Island in Northumberland, although absent from much of Devon and Cornwall and the Pennines. Now it is greatly reduced and absent from much of northern England, the Midlands, East Anglia and the Home Counties. In Wales it is largely confined to coastal regions, and in Ireland to the central limestone belt, from Co. Dublin west to Co. Galway and from southern Co. Tipperary north to Co. Longford, with

▲ 10 May, Norfolk. Green-winged Orchid can occur in large numbers, especially on clay soils, on old commons and greens, and on unimproved pastures and meadows

▲ 12 May, Norfolk. The bold, parallel, green veins on the sepals are diagnostic.

to flowering as the leaves are wintergreen. Nowadays most colonies are on protected sites, such as reserves and SSSIs or on private land with a sympathetic landowner.

DESCRIPTION

Height: 5-50cm but usually 7.5-15cm and rather compact, and seldom more than 30cm.
Stem: Yellowish-green, washed purple towards the tip and slightly angled, with two or three thin whitish sheaths at the extreme base.
Leaves: There are up to seven bluish-green basal leaves, varying from roughly elliptical to lanceolate, keeled and held semi-erect, and two or three leaves higher on the stem that are more pointed and become bract-like below the spike. The leaves are wintergreen, emerging in September-October and dying down by mid-June.
Spike: Rather open and loose with four to 14 well-spaced flowers.
Bract: Green, typically washed purple, and lanceolate in shape, two-thirds to twice the

a few sites in Co. Cork and just one site in Northern Ireland, on the coast of Co. Down. It is very rare in Scotland, where it is found on the coast of Ayrshire with an old record from near Tomintoul in the Grampians. **World range:** Predominantly European, extending marginally into North Africa and the Middle East. It ranges north to southern Norway, southern Sweden (Gotland) and Estonia, east to westernmost Russia and eastern Ukraine and south to the Mediterranean, including many of the Mediterranean islands, the Crimea and Caucasus. Also Lebanon, Israel, Turkey, northwest Iran and Morocco.

How to find it

In favoured localities Green-winged Orchid can still be found in thousands or even tens of thousands; a site in Sussex, for example, holds up to 50,000 flower spikes. Odd plants can, however, be inconspicuous and are easily missed, especially if they are very short. The number of plants producing flowers varies greatly from year to year, with a wet winter and spring probably being most conducive

▲ 10 May, Norfolk. All the sepals and petals are arranged together to form a tight hood over the base of the lip.

length of the ovary, which they curl around and sheathe.

Ovary: Green, variably tinged purple, cylindrical, strongly curved (through around 90°), ribbed and twisted.

Flower: Mostly various shades of purple but a few are rose-pink or whitish. The sepals are oblong-oval, the upper a little narrower than the lateral sepals. They are generally whitish with a variable violet-purple wash, deepest on the upper sepal and the upper margins of the lateral sepals, which have three to seven bold, green or bronze parallel veins that are visible on both their upper and underside. The petals are coloured as the upper sepal but are shorter, narrower and more strap-shaped. The petals and sepals form a 'hood' that encloses the column. The lip is rather broader than long and divided into three lobes. The side-lobes are rather larger than the central lobe, rounded, often with crinkled (crenate) edges and folded downwards. The central lobe is roughly equal in length to the side-lobes. The lip is typically violet-purple, whiter in the centre and at the mouth of the spur, and there are usually some violet-purple blotches and spots in this paler central area. The column is whitish, washed purple around the pollinia. The spur is coloured as the lip, around half the length of the ovary, narrow but flattened towards the tip, where it is often notched and slightly curved upwards. At least some flowers have a vanilla-like scent, and the white-flowered forms may, on average, have a stronger perfume although some people cannot smell it at all.

Subspecies
None.

Variation and varieties
Var. *alba* has white flowers, sometimes very faintly tinged pink, but still with green veins. It is usually scarce (0.1-1% of plants) but sometimes makes up as much as 15% of a population.

Var. *bartlettii* is small with very small flowers and **var. *churchillii*** is tall; neither seems well defined.

▲ 24 May, Norfolk. Var. alba. A variable but usually very small proportion of plants are white; the stripes on the sepals are retained.

BIOLOGY

Pollination and reproduction
Bees, especially bumblebees, pollinate this species. It produces no nectar and so is thought to rely upon deceit to attract insects, although as with Early Purple and Pyramidal Orchids it has also been suggested that potential pollinators can access sugary sap within the walls of the spur. When the queen bees first emerge from hibernation in the spring they are 'naive'. They have yet to learn which flowers offer a genuine reward of nectar and are easily attracted by the brightly coloured orchids. The bees usually visit

▲ 16 May, Norfolk. Some are very petite, with a few, relatively large flowers.

a single flower on each of several plants before they realise there is no reward on offer and move on to more profitable species. On each orchid visited, they start with the lower flowers of the spike and therefore these are the ones that tend to set seed. A cold spell in May, which disrupts the bees' routine, benefits the orchid because the bees have to relearn their foraging routes once the weather warms up again. Pollination is variably efficient; in a study in Sweden only 5-30% of flowers set seed but in Britain almost all the flowers may be pollinated, with each capsule producing 4,000 individual seeds. The species may also reproduce vegetatively via the formation of additional tubers.

Development and growth
It is sometimes stated that Green-winged Orchid is monocarpic and therefore usually dies after it has flowered once. However, in one population in Cambridgeshire some individual plants flowered for 17 out of 18 years and almost all flowered several times, interspersed with seasons in which they merely produced a rosette of leaves or more rarely were 'dormant' underground. At Iron Latch Meadow in Essex, Green-winged Orchids reappeared and flowered after an absence of about 30 years when closed-canopy hawthorn scrub was removed, showing just how long-lived this species can be.

Seeds are thought to germinate in the late summer or autumn, and the protocorm probably produces the first roots and even the first small leafy shoot during its first winter or spring. The plant goes on to develop its first tuber at the base of the leafy shoot, and it is this tuber alone that will persist through the late summer 'resting period', establishing the annual cycle. It is thought that plants can flower within three years of germination, and in cultivation they have flowered after just two.

Hybrids
A. x alata, the hybrid with Loose-flowered Orchid, has been recorded occasionally on Jersey and once on Guernsey.

Intergeneric hybrids
'*Orchis x morioides*', the hybrid with Early Purple Orchid, has been recorded rarely and sporadically in England and Wales. As these two species are now in different genera a new name will be needed for this hybrid.

Name and classification
The specific name *morio* means 'dull' or 'stupid'. The species was once known as 'fool stones'.

Until very recently this species was considered to be a member of the genus *Orchis*. Its overall similarity to some of the members of that genus, such as Early Purple Orchid, certainly seemed to support this. Appearances can be deceptive, however, and recent genetic studies have shown that the Green-winged

Orchid, together with Loose-flowered Orchid of the Channel Islands, should join the Pyramidal Orchid in the genus *Anacamptis*.

HISTORY AND CONSERVATION

The first British record dates from 1634 when Thomas Johnson published his *Mercurius Botanicus* ('Botanical Mercury') with the first localised record being published in 1660 when John Ray noted the 'female Fool-stones' from Cambridgeshire in his *Catalogus Plantarum circa Cantabrigiam nascentium* ('A catalogue of plants found around Cambridge').

The species is specially protected in Northern Ireland under Schedule 8 of the 1985 Wildlife Order (NI) and in Eire under the Flora (Protection) Order. Green-winged Orchid has declined dramatically in the last 50 years. Once common and widespread it has been lost from many sites and has now gone from 49% of the historical range in Britain and 60% in Ireland.

Past and present occurrence of Green-winged Orchid in Britain and Ireland (based on presence or absence in 10km squares of the National Grid; data from the New Atlas).

	Britain	Ireland
total historical range, 1500-1999	939	124
current range	479 (17%*)	50 (5%*)
% lost, 1500-1969	38%	55%
% lost, 1970-1986	11%	5%
% lost, total	49%	60%

* current range as a % of the total number of 10km squares

The decline is almost entirely due to agricultural changes. In the 19th century its favoured damp meadows and pastures were ploughed and converted to arable. In the 20th century, especially since 1945, tractors have replaced horses, and permanent pastures have become less and less a feature of most farms. Those that have survived have been drained, ploughed and reseeded. Research has shown that Green-winged Orchid will decline significantly if fertilisers are applied to grassland, probably due to competition with the increasingly vigorous grass and herbs, and the phosphorus in fertilisers may actually be toxic to the orchids. If anything, habitat losses have accelerated in the last 20 years as the last few pristine pastures have been 'improved'; overall the decline in the amount of suitable habitat must approach 99%. A typical example is Cambridgeshire, where prior to 1900 at least 36 sites held Green-winged Orchids. In the period 1901-85 this figure fell to 13 and between 1986 and 1990 the population collapsed to just five sites.

▲ *10 May, Norfolk. This delicate rose-pink is rather unusual.*

GENUS *SERAPIAS*
TONGUE ORCHIDS

This genus has only a toehold in Britain and Ireland, with two species recorded in recent years from the coast of southwest England. We consider that a natural origin, via wind-blown seed, is the most likely explanation for their occurrence, although they have also been treated, albeit without any evidence, as deliberate introductions.

Distribution

Serapias is basically a Mediterranean genus, distributed from the Caucasus Mountains through the Mediterranean basin west to the Canary Islands and Azores and extending north to Brittany. All the species are closely related and thus there is considerable disagreement as to the exact number. Between seven and 27 species are recognised in recent literature and consequently there are considerable problems in reaching a correct identification.

Classification

Genetic evidence shows that the closest relations of the tongue orchids are the bee and spider orchids *Ophrys*, the Pyramidal Orchid group *Anacamptis* and the lizard orchids *Himantoglossum*.

The genus *Serapias* is often divided into three groups: the self-pollinating Small-flowered Tongue Orchid *S. parviflora* and allies; the *vomeracea* group (the largest) and the *lingua* group, which includes Greater Tongue Orchid, and is distinguished by having a single dark boss at the base of the lip (the other groups having two bosses).

Floral structures

The column is slender, directed forwards and tapers to a long, thin point. There are two pollinia, each narrowing down into a caudicle (stalk). Both pollinia are attached to the single viscidium, which in turn is housed in a bursicle. There is no spur.

Pollination

The *vomeracea* and *lingua* groups are cross-pollinated. The flowers have no nectar and are thought to lure insects, especially bees and beetles, by providing them with shelter, both overnight and during bad weather. The dark

colour of the flower may help it to absorb heat, and its internal temperature may be 1-3°C higher than that of its surroundings. It seems likely, however, that there is more involved in the pollination process than merely the offer of shelter.

The tongue orchids are closely related and genetically very similar. The various species need to be isolated reproductively from one another to have evolved in the first place and to continue to maintain their separate identities. A mechanism that involved their pollinators would be one way for this to happen but if they merely offer 'shelter' there would be no mechanism, apart from the size of the flower, to stop insects from carrying pollen from the flowers of one species to another. Indeed, this might be why there are so many hybrids that involve the various tongue orchids. But, so far Greater Tongue Orchid *S. lingua* is the only species where additional isolating mechanisms have been observed. Small bees, apparently attracted to the flower by pheromones, attempt pseudocopulation with the flower (see also the notes on the genus *Ophrys*, p.388). In these cross-pollinated species pollination is apparently inefficient and although their flowers are self-compatible, self-pollination does not occur.

The *parviflora* group, which includes Small-flowered Tongue Orchid, is self-pollinated.

Growth pattern

At flowering time there are two to five more-or-less spherical tubers at the base of the aerial stem, the one to three youngest at the end of long, slender rhizomes.

Development from seed

Following germination, the protocorm produces its first root in the autumn and the first leaf appears shortly afterwards. The following spring the first tuber starts to grow from a bud

◀ *27 April, Extremadura, Spain. Greater Tongue Orchid.*

at the base of the leafy shoot, and during the summer 'resting period' the leaf and root die off, leaving just the tuber. From now onwards the usual sequence of annual tuber replacement takes over. In cultivation plants may flower three years after seed is sown, occasionally after just two.

Vegetative reproduction

Additional 'daughter' tubers are formed at the base of the aerial stem, usually at the end of slender rhizomes. These will go on to form separate plants as the connecting rhizome dies off in the summer.

Name

The name of the genus, *Serapias*, is derived from *Serapis* (or *Osirapis*). This is a composite Graeco-Egyptian god combining the attributes of *Apis* (the scared bull) and *Osiris* (ruler of the underworld). *Serapis* attracted an orgiastic cult and in about AD 64 the Greek scholar Dioscorides, considered one of the 'fathers' of botany, gave the name *Serapias* to an orchid that was reputed to be an aphrodisiac. The orchid in question was probably actually a member of the genus *Orchis*.

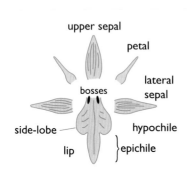

▲ *Small-flowered Tongue Orchid (After Delforge 2005).*

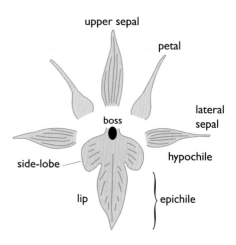

▲ *Greater Tongue Orchid.*

SMALL-FLOWERED TONGUE ORCHID
Serapias parviflora

This species is one of the most recent additions to the British flora, having been found for the first time in 1989. It is confined to just one site in Cornwall, where a handful of plants flower most years, but it could turn up almost anywhere on the south coast.

Identification
The *Serapias* or tongue orchids are very distinctive, with the sepals, petals and base of the lip forming a tight tube from which the outer part of the lip, usually coloured a rusty-brown, sticks out like a pointed little tongue. In Small-flowered Tongue Orchid the flowers are relatively small (indeed, they are the smallest of the *Serapias*), with a small lip, the projecting tip of which is 6-11mm long x 3.5-5mm wide. There are two small dark parallel raised bosses at the base of the lip, and the flowers are self-pollinated in bud, so that when they open the pollinia have already disintegrated onto the stigma.

Similar species
Greater Tongue Orchid has larger flowers with a single dark boss on the lip.

Habitat
In Cornwall it is found in short, rabbit-grazed grassland among scattered gorse on a south-facing slope near the sea. In Europe it is found in dry and wet grassland, dune slacks, open pine woods, scrub and olive groves, on calcareous to mildly acidic soils.

Flowering period
Early May to early June.

Range
Known from a single site near Rame Head in southeast Cornwall. **World range:** The Mediterranean basin from Cyprus and the Aegean Islands west through Greece, Italy, France, Spain and Portugal to the Canary Islands, and including Crete, Sicily, Corsica, Sardinia and the Balearic Islands, and also Morocco, Algeria and Tunisia in North Africa. In France it occurs on the Mediterranean littoral with a separate centre of distribution on the Atlantic coast north to Brittany.

How to find it
The British population comprises just a few plants that are very vulnerable to disturbance and damage; indeed, flowers have already been unwittingly broken off by admirers. This is one orchid that is best left alone, at least until a more substantial population exists.

▶ *7 May, Cornwall (Mike Frost). Although currently re-stricted to one site in Britain, this species can be expected to appear elsewhere.*

DESCRIPTION
(based on European populations)

Height: 10-30cm, occasionally to 40cm.

Stem: Green, blotched or streaked with red.

Leaves: At the base of the stem there is a cluster of four to seven erect, long, narrow, strap-shaped leaves with a distinct keel. Higher on the stem there are one to three smaller bract-like leaves. In Europe the leaves appear in autumn, overwinter and die down after flowering.

Spike: Three to eight flowers (rarely as many as 12) form a narrow spike with an indistinct spiral arrangement, with each flower held horizontally or angled upwards to 45°.

Bract: Pinkish-brown washed grey and with distinct dark veins; the bracts are lanceolate and held erect, clasping the ovary. They are as long as the ovary and hood put together or just a little shorter, although the lower bracts are sometimes much longer than the flower.

Ovary: Green, long, narrow, and held upright.

Flower: The sepals are lanceolate and a pale dusty-pink washed grey with distinct dark veins. The petals are a little shorter, tapering abruptly to a long narrow point, and purplish-brown at the base. The sepals and petals form a tight hood over the base of the lip and the column. The lip is 14-19mm long (extremes 13-22mm) and reddish-brown. The inner half (the hypochile) is heart-shaped with two small, raised, parallel, dark purple bosses at the base. The sides, which are almost black, curl up and round to form a 'gutter' that is totally enclosed by the hood. The floor of the lip has short, sparse, whitish hairs or is sometimes almost hairless. The outer half of the lip (the epichile) is lanceolate, much narrower than the base and bent down and under the remainder of the flower.

Subspecies
None.

Variation and varieties
None.

BIOLOGY

Pollination and reproduction
The flowers are cleistogamous, that is self-pollinated in bud. The yellow pollinia have already disintegrated onto the stigma by the time the flowers open.

Development and growth
No specific information. Stems usually arise singly, and vegetative reproduction may be relatively unimportant.

Hybrids
None.

Name and classification
The specific name *parviflora* means simply 'small flower'.

HISTORY AND CONSERVATION

First recorded in May 1989 near Rame Head in Cornwall, when two spikes were found. Three spikes appeared in 1990, with five each in 1991 and 1992, although photographers squashed two spikes in the latter year. There was then a gap of at least four years during which no plants were found, but subsequently two or three spikes have appeared most years up to and including 2004. Seedlings germinated at the Royal Botanic Gardens, Kew, from Cornish seed were planted at two nearby sites in 1993 but did not survive.

It has been suggested that the plants in Cornwall were 'deliberately introduced', but there is no evidence for this whatsoever. The plants were found hidden among gorse scrub, well away from any footpaths and in a locality highly unlikely to be chosen for an 'introduction'. It seems much more likely that the plants arose naturally from wind-blown seed. Whether this tiny population persists or the species appears elsewhere, only time will tell.

▶ *1 June, Cornwall* (Robin Chittenden www.harlequinpictures.co.uk)

GREATER TONGUE ORCHID
Serapias lingua

This species has only the most tenuous claim to be British, having been found on Guernsey in 1992 and in south Devon in 1998. These may be the vanguard of further discoveries, however, if the climate becomes more 'Mediterranean' due to global warming.

Identification
The tongue orchids are distinctive, with the sepals, petals and base of the lip forming a tight tube from which the tip of the reddish lip sticks out like a tongue. The identification of the various species is often rather difficult as they are very similar, and there are also many hybrid populations. It often requires the dissection of a flower, but the conspicuous single dark purple boss at the base of the lip, resembling a coffee bean, easily identifies the Greater Tongue Orchid and its allies. All the other *Serapias* have two bosses. Within the *lingua* group, identification depends on observation of the precise shape of the boss, the width of the lip and the overall colour of the flower.

Similar species
Small-flowered Tongue Orchid has a smaller flower with two bosses at the base of the lip and is self-pollinated.

Habitat
On Guernsey it was found on dry natural grassland on the edge of a golf course. In south Devon it was found in a meadow that had been sown with a grass mixture in the 1970s and was normally cut for hay in May or June. In 1998, when the Greater Tongue Orchid was found, it was not mown. In Europe it is found in poor grassland, wet meadows, dune slacks, scrub, olive groves and open woodland.

Flowering period
May to June.

Range
Found at single sites on Guernsey and in Devon.
World range: The Mediterranean basin, from Greece and the former Yugoslavia west to Portugal, also the Aegean Islands, Crete, Sicily, Malta, Corsica, Sardinia and the Balearics. In North Africa recorded from Morocco, Algeria and Tunisia. In France it occurs north to a line between Nantes and Lyon.

How to find it
Like the Small-flowered Tongue Orchid this species is confined to just one site in Britain, with just a few plants that are vulnerable to disturbance and damage. It is best left alone.

DESCRIPTION
(from European plants)
Height: 10-30cm, occasionally to 50cm.
Stem: Green, blotched or streaked with red.
Leaves: At the base of the stem there is a cluster of four to eight erect, long, narrow, strap-shaped leaves that have a distinct keel. Higher on the stem there are one to three smaller bract-like leaves. In Europe the leaves appear in autumn, overwinter and die down after flowering.
Spike: The two to six flowers, rarely as many as eight, are arranged around the stem in a compact spike.
Bract: Lanceolate, held erect and clasping the ovary, they are shorter than the ovary and hood, put together. The bracts are reddish or, more rarely, green tinged red towards the tip, with distinct purple veins.
Ovary: Green, long, narrow and held upright.
Flower: The sepals are lanceolate and pale lilac-grey with distinct purple veins. The petals are a little shorter, tapering abruptly to a long narrow point, and are more purplish-brown at the base. The sepals and petals form a tight horizontal hood over the base of the lip and the column. The lip is 22-29mm long (sometimes only

▶ *27 April, Extremadura, Spain. The origin of the English name 'tongue orchid' for the members of the genus* Serapias *is obvious.*

16mm), variable in colour from yellowish to fleshy-pink or reddish and only sparsely hairy. The basal portion (hypochile) is kidney-shaped with the side-lobes dark purple, rather angular and curling up and around to form a 'gutter' that is totally enclosed by the hood. There is a single shining, dark purplish-brown raised boss at the base of the hypochile, often crescent-shaped with the two horns of the crescent pointing backwards and elongated into two fine ridges. It is ungrooved or, at most, only slightly grooved. The outer half of the lip (epichile) is broadly lanceolate and slightly longer and narrower than the hypochile. It is usually 13-18mm long x 7-12mm wide but can be as small as 8mm x 4mm. It is held pointing downwards and is variably bent backwards below the rest of the flower. The pollinia are greenish-yellow and the flowers are strongly scented.

Subspecies
Disputed. More conservative taxonomic treatments consider that Greater Tongue Orchid has several subspecies, including *S. l. durieui*. More radical treatments, including Delforge (2001), treat *durieui* as a synonym of a different species, *S. strictiflora*, that is found from eastern Algeria to Morocco and in southern Portugal and southwest Spain. This is of some relevance because the plants in south Devon were identified as subspecies *durieui* on the basis of a narrow lip and longer and more elegant sepals and petals. If this identification was correct and if the more radical classification is accepted, *Serapias strictiflora* would be on the British list rather than *S. lingua*.

Variation and varieties
None in Britain.

BIOLOGY
Pollination and reproduction
It is thought that most *Serapias* are pollinated by small bees and other insects which use the flowers for shelter. However, the Greater Tongue Orchid may take this strategy one stage further. The flower mimics a nest hole and lures small male bees, which emerge before the females, with its powerful scent. In addition, the large shiny boss at the base of the lip also stimulates 'pseudocopulation', during which the pollinia are attached to the head of the bee as it attempts to copulate with the flower. This two-pronged strategy enables the orchid to attract bees both at night and on sunny days.

Vegetative reproduction may be an important means of reproduction and clusters of flower spikes are frequent.

Development and growth
No specific information.

Hybrids
None in Britain.

Name and classification
The specific name *lingua* means 'tongue'.

HISTORY AND CONSERVATION
A single plant was found on the western side of Guernsey in May 1992 but it has not reappeared at this site. In June 1998 three flower spikes were found near the coast in the vicinity of Kingsbridge in south Devon. They were identified as the subspecies *durieui* and it is speculated that the seed could have arrived with 'Saharan sand' from North Africa.

As with all the *Serapias* orchids that have been found in Britain, some botanists are sceptical as to its origins. They presumably believe that the plants originated from seed that came from an artificial source, such as a nearby plant collection or agricultural seed mix, or that deliberate fraud could be involved, with seed being sown or even mature specimens planted out. An artificial source of seed is certainly possible (see Heart-flowered Tongue Orchid, p.416) but in both Greater and Small-flowered Tongue Orchids this seems highly unlikely, while there is no evidence of fraud. Given the occurrence of Greater Tongue Orchid in much of southern France, including the Atlantic coast south of Vendée, a natural arrival in the Channel Islands or southern England seems eminently likely. Whether the species becomes established is, however, a different matter.

GENUS *OPHRYS*
BEE AND SPIDER ORCHIDS

This genus includes the most exotic and intriguing of British and Irish orchids, Bee and Fly Orchids and Early and Late Spider Orchids. Their flowers have evolved to mimic insects, predominantly bees (but definitely not spiders). In addition to their overall appearance, the pheromones produced by the flowers and the distribution of hairs on the lip are critically important in perpetuating the deception. Male bees are attracted to the orchids and attempt to mate with the flowers in a process known as 'pseudocopulation'. In doing so they carry pollinia from one flower to the other and become unwitting pollinators.

Distribution

Containing more than 250 species, this is undoubtedly the largest genus of European orchids. Its distribution is centred on the Mediterranean basin, but *Ophrys* can be found from the Canary Islands in the west to the Caspian Sea in the east, Fly Orchid ranges north to Scandinavia and other species extend into North Africa. However, just four species occur in Britain and Ireland.

The number of species recognised in this genus has risen sharply; only around 60 were listed in the 1980s. This reflects the increasing appreciation of the importance of the highly specialised pollination mechanism in the evolution of the various species.

Classification

DNA evidence suggests that the closest relatives of the genus are the tongue orchids *Serapias*, the lizard orchids *Himantoglossum* and the Pyramidal Orchid group *Anacamptis*.

Floral structures

The stiff and often elaborately designed lip renders the members of this genus distinctive. It is usually prominently hairy in places and velvety in others with a smooth, hairless central patch, the speculum. This is sometimes shiny, reflecting the light and probably therefore simulating an insect's wings. As in most orchids the lowermost flowers open first but the spike continues to elongate, sometimes substantially so, as more flowers open.

The column is long and erect. There are two pollinia, each attached by a caudicle (stalk) to a separate sticky viscidium. These are concealed and protected within separate bursicles.

Pollination

All species in this genus are cross-pollinated with the exception of one, the Bee Orchid, which is routinely self-pollinated. The Bee Orchid had clearly evolved to use the same mechanism as the other species, with an elaborate pattern and texture to its lip, but has largely abandoned cross-pollination, presumably relatively recently.

In the genus *Ophrys* the flowers have no nectar and offer their visitors no reward. Instead, the orchid exploits the sex-drive of insects with a combination of visual, olfactory and tactile deceits. The pollinators are usually bees and they are initially attracted to the flowers by chemical signals released by the lip of the orchid that mimic the pheromones produced by virgin female bees. These pheromones are complex cocktails of volatile compounds that stimulate mating behaviour in the male bees. Not only are the flower's version of the bee's pheromones an exact copy of the appropriate compounds but also the orchid produces such large quantities that the male bee may even prefer the flower's deceit to the real thing.

Male bees emerge from hibernation earlier in the spring than females, and it is thought that the orchid exploits this gap. In the absence of females the orchid is able to lure the males to

▶ *1. O.* levantina; *2. O.* umbilicata; *3. O.* flavomarginata; *4. O. (f.)* iricolor; *5. O.* lutea galilaea; *6. O.* omegaifera israelitica; *7. O.* aesculapiiformis; *8. O. (f.)* fusca; *9. O.* mammosa; *10. O.* argolia elegans; *11. O.* bormuelleri; *12. O.* kotschyi. *All Cyprus, March. The intimate relationship with a specific insect pollinator has powered the evolution of numerous species.*

◀ *14 June, Kent. Late Spider Orchid*

its flowers but once the females have emerged the orchids are ignored in preference to the real thing. In at least some species, however, this is not the case and the flowers continue to receive visits from the males even after the female bees have emerged.

The male bees home in on the orchid's pheromones, and as they get closer they catch sight of the flower and land on the lip. All three deceits now come into play. The male bee is still stimulated by the scent of the flower and the patterning on the lip but now also by the texture of the various hairy, velvety and smooth portions of the lip. This stimulates the bee to orientate himself into the 'correct' position, extend his genital apparatus and attempt copulation. Of course, the 'correct' position is the one in which he will pick up pollinia in the first flower visited and deposit the pollinia on the stigma of the second flower and so on. Eventually this process of 'pseudocopulation' is interrupted and the bee leaves. The male bees may show signs of exhaustion but ejaculation of sperm has not been observed, although it has been recorded in a similar process involving an ichneumon wasp and the Australian orchid, *Cryptostylis leptochila*.

The orchid is totally dependent on the bee. If there is no pollination, there will be no seed and therefore no more orchids; a powerful engine to drive the evolution of the orchid. Against a 'noisy' background of multitudes of chemical signals, each species of bee must be able to produce a unique pheromone in order to attract potential mates and reproduce successfully. It may do this by having a unique combination of relatively common chemicals in its sex pheromones or by using chemicals that are in themselves unique. Bees use both systems and the various *Ophrys* orchids are able to mimic both systems, too. For the orchid, the better and more precisely it mimics its pollinator the better its chance of successful pollination. Each species of orchid therefore evolves to mimic the pheromones of a particular species of bee in order to maximize its chances of attracting pollinators. In this way the genus

Ophrys has evolved many species, reflecting the many species of potential pollinator. Each one is precisely matched.

As a further complication, differences in the patterning and shape of the lip and the distribution of hairs allow two distinct species of *Ophrys* to share the same species of pollinating insect. The position and direction of the hairs on the flowers are critical in the positioning of the insect during 'pseudocopulation'. One species of orchid may stimulate the bee to have its head uppermost, facing the column and so picking up the pollinia on its head. A second species of orchid stimulates the bee to have its abdomen uppermost, and the pollinia are attached to the tip of its abdomen. In the respective flowers, the pollinia and stigma are positioned according to the orientation of the bee.

The orchid-pollinator match in *Ophrys* is very close but not always perfect. All the members of the genus are interfertile, and there are a large variety of hybrids. It is a reflection of how good the system is, however, that these hybrids tend to occur rarely and in very small numbers.

Growth pattern

At flowering time all *Ophrys* species have two more-or-less spherical tubers side by side at the base of the aerial stem together with some short, thick roots. The roots appear in the autumn, simultaneously with the leaves, and are 'infected' with fungi. The pattern of growth and the annual replacement of tubers are very similar to that of the genus *Orchis* (see p.200).

Fungal partners

In common with the other tuberous orchids, fungal activity takes place in the roots and rhizome but not in the tuber (indeed, the tuber contains the orchid's food reserve and may even be protected from fungal infection by 'fungicide', see p.9). As the orchid passes the summer 'resting period' as a tuber this presents a problem. How can the fungal 'infection' be carried from one year to the next? In damper climates there is a good chance that the fungi can persist in the soil but in the hot, dry, Mediterranean summers adult fungi cannot live in the parched soils and must survive as spores. To guarantee continuity the members of the genus *Ophrys* probably carried their fungal 'infection' from one year to the next in the surface layers of their tuber. Observations of Late Spider Orchid show that the terminal bud on the tuber starts to grow at the same time as the onset of wet weather in the autumn. Simultaneously the fungal mycelium starts to grow outwards from certain points on the tuber's surface. The orchid's new roots grow outwards through this fungal mycelium and the fungus probably enters the roots through the root hairs. As the next season's tuber starts to develop it too is 'infected' (and will carry the fungus through the next resting period) via the soil, through minute, hair-like projections on its surface.

Development from seed

Seed probably germinates in the spring to produce a rounded protocorm. In Late Spider Orchid and probably other species the protocorm produces a root in the first autumn and then a small tuber the following spring. In the summer 'resting period' the protocorm and root die off, leaving just the tuber. In the autumn the bud on the top of the tuber produces a short rhizome and roots. The first leafy shoot appears in the second spring. In cultivation flowering plants can sometimes be produced within three years of germination.

Vegetative reproduction

Additional tubers can be formed at the base of the aerial stem, perhaps often at the end of slender rhizomes, and these will go on to form separate plants as the connecting stem dies off in the autumn. It seems, however, that vegetative reproduction is either rare (Late Spider Orchid) or uncommon (Early Spider Orchid) among the British species.

Name

The origin of the generic name *Ophrys* is contentious. It may derive from 'ophrus', the Greek for 'eyebrow', perhaps an allusion to the hairy lip (or the hairy fringe to the petals). Alternatively, *Ophrys* was the name given in Ancient Greece by Pliny the Elder to a small, two-leaved plant used to dye eyebrows and hair. The plant in question was probably Common Twayblade, and Pliny's name *Ophrys* may have derived from a Greek word for snake due to the similarity of the flowers of Common Twayblade to the head and tongue of a snake.

▲ Unlike all the other members of the genus **Ophrys**, Bee Orchid is self-pollinated. Being independent of insect pollinators, it has done well in Britain, and is one of the most widespread and successful species.

FLY ORCHID
Ophrys insectifera

Formerly: *Ophrys muscifera*

Fly Orchid shows the most wonderful example of insect mimicry among British orchids, but rather than flies it has evolved to lure male digger wasps to act as inadvertent pollinators as they attempt to copulate with its flowers. For human observers the small flowers are often hard to spot but once seen have a magnetic attraction, drawing the eye back again and again. Fly Orchid is relatively common but inconspicuous in woodland and scrub on chalk in southern England and occurs at scattered localities in a variety of lime-rich habitats elsewhere in Britain north to Cumbria and Anglesey. It is also found in central and western Ireland.

Identification

Very distinctive, the individual flowers are indeed like little flies. The purplish-brown lip forms the 'body' and the lustrous slate-blue speculum shines like folded 'wings'. The two glistening depressions at the base of the lip are the 'eyes' and above these the dark, wire-like petals look just like little 'antennae'.

Similar species

None.

Habitat

Very varied, although it usually grows on calcareous soils over chalk and limestone. It is found in open deciduous woodland and in southern England is particularly associated with beechwoods. It favours the better-lit areas in glades, rides and along the edge of woodland, as well as shaded road banks and open scrub, but sometimes grows in deeper shade such as overgrown hazel coppice. In southern England Fly Orchid is infrequently found on open grassland in old pits, quarries and on spoil heaps, but when it does grow in such habitats it may occur in large numbers; it has been recorded rarely from slumped coastal cliffs. In northern England and Ireland it is probably more frequent in open areas and in addition to wooded sites is found on limestone pavements and rocky hillsides. It grows in alkaline fens and

◀ 23 May, Co. Clare. In the west of Britain and Ireland Fly Orchid will grow in the open, on limestone pavements and in fens.

on the margins of turloughs in western Ireland
and also in fens on Anglesey, often among
tussocks of Black Bog-rush. Recorded up to
390m above sea level (Helbeck Wood, Brough,
Cumbria).

Flowering period

Late April to early July but mostly in late May
and early June.

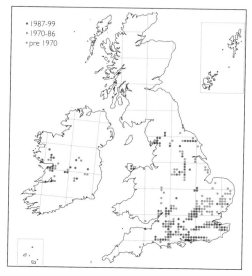

Range

It is widespread but very local. In southern
England Fly Orchid is more-or-less confined to
the North and South Downs in Kent, Sussex
and Surrey, the chalk of Hampshire, Dorset,
Wiltshire and the Chilterns, and also the
Cotswolds. There are scattered records away
from these areas in Somerset, Warwickshire,
Northamptonshire, Suffolk, Nottinghamshire,
Derbyshire and more widely in Yorkshire and
the Morecambe Bay area of north Lancashire
and Cumbria. The northernmost sites are in
the upper Eden Valley of the north Pennines
in Cumbria. In Wales it is now confined to
Anglesey and in Ireland to a central belt from
southern Co. Mayo, Co. Galway and Co.
Clare, through north Tipperary, Co. Offaly
and Westmeath to Laois and Co. Kildare.

▶ *27 May, Hampshire. Fly Orchid can grow in heavy
shade but visits by suitable pollinators are probably more
likely where it catches the sun for part of the day.*

World range: Confined to Europe, where it has the most northerly distribution in the genus *Ophrys*, ranging north to *c.* 67° in Norway and to central Sweden, southern Finland and the Baltic States. Occurs south to Spain, the Balearic Islands, Italy, northern Greece and Romania and east to the Moscow region.

How to find it

The tall slender spikes of Fly Orchid, with their small, well-spaced flowers, can be very hard to see among other vegetation and even on a bare woodland floor they can vanish with ease. But, if you can get your 'eye-in' where one Fly Orchid is found, there may be plenty more. Within the range in southeast England it can be found at many woodland and scrubby sites on chalk or limestone. In northern England sites include Whitbarrow Scar (Cumbria) and Castle Eden Dene (Co. Durham) and in Ireland it is locally common in The Burren (Co. Clare).

DESCRIPTION

Height: 15-60cm.

Stem: Pale green and slender, with one or two basal sheaths. Groups of up to ten plants may grow together.

Leaves: There are two to five shiny, dark green or bluish-green leaves. The lower are narrow and strap-shaped, flaccid but keeled and usually pointed at the tip, and the upper one or two are narrower, more pointed and loosely sheathe the stem. The leaves emerge in autumn and are wintergreen.

Spike: Although initially bunched, the one to ten flowers (exceptionally as many as 20) are well-spaced along the stem by the time the uppermost has opened.

Bract: Dark green or bluish-green and lanceolate, often with the edges rolled inwards; the lower bracts are rather longer than the ovary but towards the tip of the spike they are a little shorter.

Ovary: Pale green, slender, cylindrical, six-ribbed and held upright but curving at the tip to hold the flower facing outwards.

Flower: The sepals are yellowish-green and are

▲ *23 May, Co. Clare. The flower has evolved to mimic digger wasps. The petals form the antennae and the bluish 'speculum' on the lip resembles the glint of the wasp's folded wings.*

◄ *21 May, Hampshire.*

oval-oblong with a blunt tip but look narrower because their edges are rolled back and the inner face is concave. The lateral sepals are held horizontally and the upper sepal is vertical but arches forward over the column to a variable extent. The petals are dark purplish-brown with short, fine, downy hairs and are much smaller than the sepals (less than half as long); their edges are rolled back to give them a fine, filiform appearance and they point forward. The lip is longer than wide and hangs down almost vertically. It is divided into three lobes, with two relatively short, narrow side-lobes spreading outwards at the base and a broad terminal lobe that is in turn notched or forked at the tip. The lip is velvety in texture (the side-lobes are hairier), rich dark reddish-brown

▶ *10 May, Kent. The male digger wasp, excited by the pheromones produced by the flower, as well as by its appearance and texture, attempts 'pseudocopulation' with the orchid and in the process acts as pollinator.*

or purplish-brown, becoming a little paler towards the tip and duller with age. A more-or-less square, shining, pale slate-blue band across the centre forms the speculum, and at the base of the lip there are two shining 'pseudoeyes'. The column is short and reddish-brown with a small, circular stigmatic cavity at its base and a short, blunt 'beak'. The two yellow pollinia have their viscidia enclosed in two off-white bursicles.

Subspecies

None.

Variation and varieties

There is considerable variation in the colour and markings of the lip.

Var. *ochroleuca* has a lip that is pale yellowish-green with a white speculum. It has been recorded from Kent, Hampshire, Wiltshire and Hertfordshire.

Var. *subbombifera* has a very broad, rounded central lobe, notched as usual at the tip. It is probably uncommon.

Var. *parviflora* has flowers that are around half the normal size. It is very rare.

An un-named variety with a broad yellow

border to the central lobe of the lip, yellow tips to the side-lobes and greenish or yellow-tipped petals has been recorded rarely in Surrey, Hampshire and Anglesey.

BIOLOGY

Pollination and reproduction

Pollination is by male digger wasps *Argogorytes mystaceus* and also *A. fargeii*, a species that is rarer and emerges a little later in the season. The wasps are attracted by pheromones emitted by the orchid and by the shape and texture of the flower. They attempt to copulate with it and during this 'pseudocopulation' the pollinia are attached to their heads. Pollination rates are low, with less than 20% of flowers setting seed (Summerhayes, 1968 quotes rates of 2.1% and 7.5% for two samples of approximately 1,000 plants).

Development and growth

The aerial stem grows from a pair of tubers, the younger of which is often stalked. The first leaf appears in the winter after germination and the first tuber is formed in the second year.

Hybrids

x **Bee Orchid** has been recorded at one site in the Avon Gorge in Somerset and in West Sussex, but it is very rare. It is sometimes called *O.* x *pietzschii* but this is an invalid name. *O.* x *hybrida*, the hybrid with Early Spider Orchid, has occurred occasionally in Kent.

Name and classification

The specific name *insectifera* derives from the Latin *insecta* meaning 'insect' and *fero* meaning 'bearing', hence 'insect-bearing'.

HISTORY AND CONSERVATION

The first British record dates from 1597, when John Gerard published *The Herball, or General Historie of Plantes* in which he noted: 'The Bee, the Fly and the Butterfly Satyrions grow upon barren chalky hill…adjoining to a village in Kent named Greenhithe, upon Longfield

downs by Southfleet'….' likewise in a field… half a mile from S. Albons.'

There have been considerable losses since 1597 with the species now occupying only 42% of its historical range in Britain. Much of the decline took place long ago, especially in East Anglia. However, in Ireland, where Fly Orchid is now found in just over 50% of its historical range, rather more of the losses have been recent. Causes include woodland clearances and 'coniferisation' but perhaps equally important has been the maturation of woodland and scrub due to changes in forest management or its abandonment altogether. In such cases increasing shade probably means that the flowers are seldom pollinated and the population declines and eventually disappears. Fly Orchid is either extinct or has not been reported recently from Devon, the Isle of Wight, Middlesex, Essex, Norfolk, Cambridgeshire, Huntingdonshire, Worcestershire, Herefordshire, Shropshire, Staffordshire, Leicestershire, Lincolnshire and Co. Durham. Similarly in Wales there have been no recent reports from Monmouthshire, Glamorganshire and Denbighshire. There is an old, unconfirmed record from near Killiecrankie in Perthshire in Scotland.

Past and present occurrence of Fly Orchid in Britain and Ireland (based on presence or absence in 10km squares of the National Grid; data from the New Atlas).

	Britain	Ireland
total historical range, 1500-1999	264	31
current range	110 (3.9%*)	16 (1.6%*)
% lost, 1500-1969	47.5%	26%
% lost, 1970-1986	10.5%	22.5%
% lost, total	58%	48.5%

* current range as a % of the total number of 10km squares

BEE ORCHID
Ophrys apifera

Looking, even feeling exotic and very special, the Bee Orchid is a standard bearer for orchids and orchid conservation. Even for those with just a passing interest in wildlife, the discovery of a Bee Orchid can be a special event, and people take great pride in 'their' local Bee Orchids. An opportunistic and adaptable species, it often turns up in unexpected places; indeed, it has even taken to garden lawns in recent years. Well named, the flowers look very much like a bee and have evolved to attract male bees as pollinators. The mechanism has, however, been abandoned, and almost all plants are now self-pollinated, a process that produces copious seed, no doubt part of the secret of its success. It is widespread in England and parts of Wales and Ireland, occurring in a wide variety of open grassland sites. Bee Orchid is the county flower of Bedfordshire.

Identification

Unmistakably a 'bee' orchid, the flower looks like a bumblebee. It has large pink sepals and slender, parallel-sided, greenish or pinkish-brown petals that form the bee's 'antennae'. The lip is a 'velvety' maroon-brown with a pattern of creamy markings and noticeably hairy rounded side-lobes.

Similar species

In most of Britain and Ireland it is the only 'bee' orchid and therefore distinctive, but in southern England care should always be taken to distinguish it from Early and Late Spider Orchids.

Late Spider Orchid is superficially very similar but usually has a broader, more rectangular lip with a distinctive forward or downward pointing yellowish nib at its tip. In the Bee Orchid the tip of the lip is almost always tucked under and out of sight. In addition, the petals of Late Spider Orchid are always pinkish, short and very distinctly triangular or conical in shape. Late Spider Orchid is not usually self-pollinating and its pollinia never dangle loose.

Early Spider Orchid has yellowish sepals and petals and a shiny slate-blue speculum on its lip. It lacks any creamy or yellow markings.

◀ *24 June, Norfolk. As successive flowers open, the spike lengthens. The pointed tip of the lip is normally tucked under and out of sight.*

Habitat

Very varied and defying any easy generalisations, although Bee Orchid is essentially a species of open grassland. Most sites are on light, well-drained soils that are low in nutrients, but it also grows on heavy clays, in areas that may have standing water in the winter, or on flushed, slumped clay cliffs. It can occur on closely cropped swards, in areas with much bare ground or in ranker grassland among scrub. It is usually supposed to favour calcium-rich soils overlying chalk and limestone as well as chalky boulder clay, but it is much more widespread and any poor, free-draining soil may be suitable, although there may well be some factor that makes the soil locally more alkaline. Many habitats are obviously man-made, such as road verges, railway embankments and cuttings, old quarries, pits, spoil-heaps, gravel pits, brownfield industrial sites and garden lawns. Bee Orchids are also found in more natural areas such as sand dunes, dune slacks, limestone pavement, eskers (ridges of glacial debris) and, especially in Ireland, fens. The species is tolerant of heavy grazing and trampling. Although it is usually found in open sunny places it has been recorded growing in shady woodland with little other vegetation. In woods, it flowers a month later than nearby plants in the open (Summerhayes, 1968).

Bee Orchids often behave like 'weeds', colonising areas of bare or disturbed ground. They increase rapidly in numbers until a closed sward develops and then, being 'poor competitors', they disappear. On the other hand, they can thrive in permanent grassland and such colonies may last for many years. It occurs from sea level up to 335m (Parsley Hay, Derbyshire).

Flowering period

Early June to late July, sometimes from late May, but at least in southern England most plants will have finished flowering by the end of June.

Range

It is widespread in England north to Cumbria and Co. Durham, although sparse or absent in

▲ 16 June, Norfolk. Despite an aura of 'rarity', Bee Orchid is an adaptable and successful species and can be found in large numbers, often at 'new' sites.

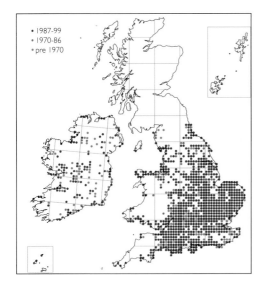

• 1987-99
• 1970-86
• pre 1970

flowering plants, but the total population, including vegetative plants and those 'dormant' underground, is much more stable.

DESCRIPTION

Height: 10-45cm, sometimes to 65cm.
Stem: Pale green with two scale leaves at the base.
Leaves: There are up to six pale green basal leaves that are clearly veined, keeled and strap-shaped but become narrower, more pointed and loosely clasping higher on the stem. There are also one or two bract-like non-sheathing leaves towards the flower spike. The leaves appear in September-November and are often scorched or otherwise damaged by the summer.
Spike: Loose, with two to seven flowers, sometimes as many as 12.
Bract: Pale green, lanceolate, pointed at the tip and much longer than the ovary.
Ovary: Green, boldly ribbed but not twisted, held upright but slightly curved; the tip bends further over to hold the flower facing outward.
Flower: The sepals are oval, tapering slightly towards the tip, concave and often hooded. They are various shades of pink, from pale rose to a deep pink tinged lilac, and have three to five variably obvious green veins. Occasionally the sepals are white. The lateral sepals are held horizontally or a little below the horizontal and are swept backwards, whereas the upper sepal is held upright but very frequently bends backwards to lie almost horizontally behind the flower. The petals are much shorter and are strap-shaped with their margins rolled back to make them appear even narrower; they are greenish through pinkish-brown to pink with fine white hairs. The lip is tongue-shaped with the sides and front strongly moulded downwards and two relatively small conical sides lobes at the base that are conspicuously hairy on the outer side. The tip of the lip has two lobes with a pointed nib in the shallow notch between them but appears rounded because the entire tip is curled up underneath. At the base of the lip there is an elongated,

north Devon and Cornwall, and the number and density of colonies declines steadily north and west of a line from Bristol to Hull. In Wales it is largely confined to areas on or near the north and south coasts. It is also found on the Channel Islands and the Isle of Man, and occurs throughout Ireland but is very local and absent from large areas. Very rare in Scotland, with a 1908 record from Kircudbrightshire, but found on an old industrial site in east Ayrshire in 2003.
World range: Europe, the Middle East and North Africa. Found north to Holland, northwest Germany, the Czech Republic and the Ukraine and south to the Mediterranean Islands, Crimea, Caucasus, Turkey, Lebanon and Israel. In North Africa occurs in Morocco, Tunisia and Algeria.

How to find it

Throughout its range Bee Orchid is rather local and as likely to be found on man-made sites as in old, species-rich grassland or scrub. It is worth looking for in any area that has been heavily disturbed to produce lots of bare ground, especially if it is on poor, chalky or sandy soils, which are slow to be recolonised by vegetation. In established colonies there are huge variations in the number of

◀ *18 June, Norfolk.*

semi-circular, hairless, dull orange area that is bordered by narrow maroon-brown and pale yellow bands. The speculum radiates from these and is a broader band of dull purple that is in turn bounded with a pale yellow band. The markings form a U or H-shape below the basal area, sometimes irregular and asymmetrical. The side-lobes are also bounded by dull purple and pale yellow bands. The remainder of the lip is velvety maroon-brown. The column is greenish and held more-or-less at 90° to the lip. In profile it is said to resemble the head of a duck with the anther at the tip forming an elongated 'beak'. The pollinia are yellow and their caudicles (stalks) lie in parallel grooves

▲ 26 June, Norfolk. The column is said to resemble the head and beak of a duck. In these flowers the pollinia have already become stuck to the stigmas.

until they are released, with the viscidia at their bases enclosed in pale yellowish-green bursicles. At the base of the column the circular stigmatic cavity is yellowish with a horizontal band of orange-brown.

Subspecies
None.

Variation and varieties

As with the other species in the genus *Ophrys*, the flowers are rather variable in structure, colour and pattern.

Var. *trollii* 'Wasp Orchid' has a long narrow central lobe to the lip that tapers to a point. The side-lobes are often longer and narrower than normal, being held away from the central lobe. The lip is marbled asymmetrically with yellow and rusty-brown and the speculum is either distorted or absent. It occurs regularly at a few sites in the West Country but is otherwise rare. The tip of the lip in 'normal' plants sometimes fails to fold under and they then have an elongated, pointed lip but retain the normal markings. For a time, 'Wasp Orchid' was considered to be a distinct species.

Var. *belgarum* has an oval lip, lacking well-defined side-lobes but with hairy 'shoulders'. It has symmetrical markings with a horizontal yellow band across the middle and smaller vertical yellow bands; there is no speculum. First described in 1998 it has been identified widely in southern England.

Var. *bicolor* has the outer half of the lip dark brown, grading to pale, unmarked greenish or pale brown at the base. There is no speculum. It is very rare but has been recorded from Dorset, Essex/Suffolk and Anglesey.

Var. *chlorantha* lacks anthocyanin pigments and has whitish sepals, yellow petals and a bright greenish-yellow lip with a 'ghost' pattern. It is rare but occurs widely, especially in the south and east. Var 'flavescens' has also been described. This is a less extreme version of var. *chlorantha* with a pale brown lip that has a normal but faded pattern. It is apparently very rare and easily confused with the old, faded flowers on normal plants.

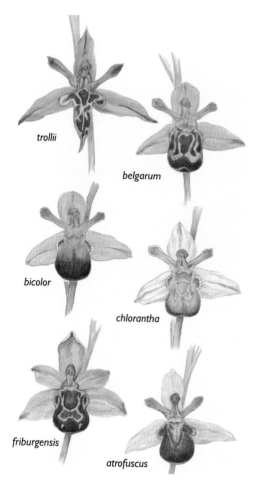

trollii

belgarum

bicolor

chlorantha

friburgensis

atrofuscus

of a few hours the pollinia drop downwards on their stalks and dangle in front of the stigma. In this position the slightest breeze will waft them on to its sticky surface and pollination will take place. This mechanism is efficient and a large proportion of flowers are pollinated. Each pod is estimated to contain 6,000-10,000 seeds. Rarely, the flowers may be cross-pollinated. 'Pseudo-copulation' involving bees has been recorded and Bee Orchid has hybridised with several other *Ophrys*; hybridisation is only possible if it is cross-pollinated at least occasionally.

Vegetative propagation may occur and in cultivation several small 'daughter' tubers were noted growing at the end of long, slender rhizomes.

Var. *friburgensis* has oval petals similar in shape to the sepals but not quite as large. They are pink or very rarely greenish. It is very rare but has occurred widely; Bee Orchids with slightly enlarged petals occur more commonly. Var. *atrofuscus* has an unmarked, dark, chocolate-coloured lip. It was found in Sussex in 2001.

BIOLOGY

Pollination and reproduction

Bee Orchid is usually self-pollinated. Soon after the flower opens the anther releases the pollinia, which have unusually long, thread-like flexible stalks. At their base these stalks are each in turn attached to a viscidium, and these remain in their bursicles (protective pouches), effectively anchoring the pollinia. In the space

▲ 26 June, Norfolk. Soon after the flower opens the pollinia are released and dangle like little balls on the end of their flexible stalks, waiting for a breeze to blow them onto the stigma.

Development and growth

The aerial stem grows from a pair of tubers. It used to be thought that Bee Orchid was monocarpic and therefore flowered just once before dying. This was given as the explanation for the large fluctuations in the number of flowering plants. The opposite is the case, however, as it is relatively long-lived. In a ten-year study in Cambridgeshire the 'half-life' of successive generations in a population of Bee Orchids averaged 6.6 years and varied from 5.8-11.2 years (the 'half-life' is a measure of the life expectancy of the orchid after its first appearance above ground and marks the point at which 50% of the population that emerged in any given year have died). Some plants live for at least ten years after their first appearance and may flower for three years in a row.

Bee Orchids can spend one or two years 'dormant' underground but do not flower again when they next emerge. They seem to need at least a year's growth as a non-flowering rosette to build-up enough reserves to flower again. At any stage in their life they can only flower if they have reached a minimum leaf area, and if they do not have a big enough spread of leaves the rosette will wither early, in May. Damage to the plants by snails and slugs tends to be slight but rabbits and deer can cause severe problems.

Seed probably germinates in the spring but there is no clear picture of the period between germination and the first appearance above ground. A 19th century author noted that germinating seeds, protocorms and plantlets with small leafy shoots were found around adult plants in March. Young Bee Orchids often appear above ground in the late winter as non-flowering plants with a single leaf but these frequently wither and die off rather quickly.

Hybrids

O. x albertiana, the hybrid with Late Spider Orchid, was recorded from Kent in 1828.
x Fly Orchid is very rare but has been recorded in Somerset and West Sussex (it is sometimes called *O. x pietzschii* but this is an invalid name).

Name and classification

The specific name *apifera* derives from the Latin *apis* 'bee' and *fero* 'to bear' or 'to carry' and means 'bee-bearing'.

HISTORY AND CONSERVATION

The first British record dates from 1597, when John Gerard published *The Herball, or General Historie of Plantes* in which he noted: 'The Bee, the Fly and the Butterfly Satyrions grow upon barren chalky hill…adjoining to a village in Kent named Greenhithe, upon Longfield downs by Southfleet' … 'likewise in a field… half a mile from S. Albons.'

The Bee Orchid is specially protected in Northern Ireland under Schedule 8 of the 1985 Wildlife Order (NI)

Past and present occurrence of Bee Orchid in Britain and Ireland (based on presence or absence in 10km squares of the National Grid; data from the New Atlas).

	Britain	Ireland
total historical range, 1500-1999	940	182
current range	785 (27.5%*)	93 (9%*)
% lost, 1500-1969	10.5%	37%
% lost, 1970-1986	6%	12%
% lost, total	16.5%	49%

* current range as a % of the total number of 10km squares

There has been a modest decline in Britain, with just 16.5% of the total range lost as sites have been destroyed by ploughing, spraying or, in the case of quarries and old pits, are either filled with rubbish or become overgrown with scrub. The losses have to some extent been compensated for by the colonisation of new sites. Bee Orchid is one of the more opportunistic and adaptable British orchids. There has been a much more significant decline in Ireland, especially in the period before 1930. The explanation for this is not clear.

LATE SPIDER ORCHID
Ophrys fuciflora

A close relative of the Bee Orchid, this is one of the rarest and most localised species in Britain and is restricted to a handful of sites in east Kent. A large proportion of the population is confined to cages as protection from grazing rabbits, and a grassy slope scattered with wire-mesh boxes is a strange introduction to such a rare plant. The flower has evolved to trick one particular species of bee into acting as an inadvertent pollinator, but the appropriate bee does not occur in England. The mechanism is therefore largely defunct, few flowers are pollinated and little seed is produced. Nevertheless, this species manages to cling on, perhaps because the individual plants are relatively long-lived.

Identification

Unmistakably a 'bee' orchid, this species has pink sepals and petals and a broad, dark, velvety lip. The size and colour of the petals and the colour of the sepals are variable, however, as is the shape and pattern of markings of the lip, but it usually has furry 'shoulders' and always has a projecting nib at the tip.

Similar species

Bee Orchid is rather similar but has longer, narrower petals that are strap-shaped rather than triangular and more often greenish than pink. It has a narrower lip that is distinctly three-lobed and never square and 'shouldered' (on the other hand, the lip of Late Spider Orchid can be three-lobed). Diagnostically, the pointed tip of the lip in Bee Orchid normally curls back and under out of sight and it therefore lacks the projecting nib. The column in Bee Orchid is a little longer with a slightly more prominent projecting 'beak', and the pollinia often hang loose over the stigma, a feature never seen in Late Spider Orchid.

Early Spider Orchid always has green sepals and long, narrow, strap-shaped petals that are much less downy and also usually greenish rather than pink. The speculum on its lip is normally H-, X- or π-shaped rather than incorporating broken rings and circles. As in Bee Orchid, its lip lacks a forward-pointing nib and the flowering periods of the two spider orchids do not normally overlap.

▲ 14 June, Kent. Growing on very closely grazed turf, allowing an unusal view of the whole plant.

▲ 12 June, Kent. As the flowers open the spike elongates; these flowers have very well-defined side lobes to the lip.

Habitat

Well-drained grassland on infertile chalky soils, grazed to produce a reasonably short sward and some bare ground and also ideally facing south. Ground disturbance of some sort may be important for the establishment of new populations. Current sites are on old spoil heaps and areas which were ploughed in the past or heavily disturbed by rabbits prior to the outbreak of myxomatosis. The individual plants are relatively long-lived, and colonies can persist when conditions are no longer suitable for seedlings to become established. Notably, the existing colonies tend to be very discrete and do not expand into adjacent superficially similar grassland.

Flowering period

Late May to late July, exceptionally to August, but mostly in early to mid-June. At Wye NNR, colonies that face west to southwest flower three or four weeks later than colonies facing south.

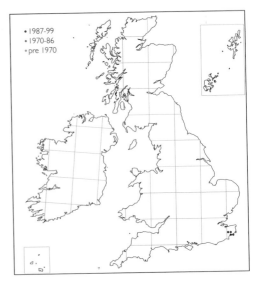

• 1987-99
• 1970-86
• pre 1970

Range

Confined to the North Downs in Kent between Folkestone and Wye. There are old records from other counties in southern England but all of these are probably errors. **World range:** Europe, from France eastwards to Romania; it extends north to southern Belgium, central Germany, Austria, Hungary and the Czech Republic and

south to Italy and the former Yugoslavia. It is
extinct in Holland. Closely related species are
found in adjacent areas.

How to find it

Around 50% of the British population is
found in six discrete colonies at Wye NNR,
many plants are caged for protection. As with
Bee Orchid, the number of flowering plants
varies widely between seasons but the overall
population is much more stable.

DESCRIPTION

Height: 5-30cm, sometimes to 37.5cm.

Stem: Grey-green.

Leaves: Grey-green and prominently veined.
The three to five lanceolate basal leaves form a
loose rosette with the lowest flat to the ground
and the remainder held up to 30° above the
horizontal. There are one to three narrower and
more pointed leaves that loosely clasp the stem.
The rosette appears above ground in October
and withers while the plant is still in flower,
usually disappearing by early July.

Spike: The two to nine flowers (rarely as many
as 14) are well-spaced along the stem.

Bract: Grey-green, lanceolate, about one to
one-and-a-half times the length of the ovary,
which they clasp at the base.

Ovary: Grey-green, slim and cylindrical, boldly
six-ribbed, slightly twisted, and also curved
through about 90° to hold the flowers facing
outwards.

Flower: The sepals are broadly oval with their
edges rolled back and under and a blunt tip.
They vary from very pale pink to a rich, dark
pink and have a prominent green midrib on
the outer surface and one to three green veins
on the inner face. The lateral sepals are held
horizontally or slightly drooping at the sides
of the flower, whereas the upper sepal may be
vertical or project out horizontally over the lip
but more often curves forwards in a graceful
arch. The petals are much shorter, triangular,
velvety-hairy and pink (often a distinctly deeper
pink, sometimes almost flame-coloured, at the
base). They may have swellings on each side

▲ 14 June, Kent. The flowers are similar to Bee Orchid
but the pointed tip of the lip is not tucked out of sight.

at the base, called 'ears' or auricles. The lip is
almost square in shape but usually broadens
towards the tip. The edges are strongly moulded
downwards apart from the tip, where there is a
prominent forward or downward projecting nib
set into a notch. This nib is usually yellowish
and sometimes three-lobed. The lip is a rich,
dark chestnut-brown or maroon-brown, usually
paler around the edges and velvety in texture.
On either side of the base of the lip there are
swellings or 'shoulders' that are variable in size;
in some plants these swellings are large, well-
defined and rounded and thus more obviously
lateral lobes. The lip is particularly hairy on the
'shoulders' and along the sides below them. At
the base of the lip below the column is a more-
or-less semicircular, smooth, orange-brown

patch that is usually bordered by a narrow, creamy 'necklace'. Radiating from this necklace the speculum is a complex and extremely variable pattern of smooth maroon or lilac-brown markings bounded by creamy-yellow lines that often forms an irregular star or other geometric shape around a central dark circle. The column is held at about 90° to the lip and is yellowish-green, becoming distinctly greener towards the tip. The stigmatic cavity is dark with a small, round, black 'pseudoeye' on either side. The projecting rostellum or 'beak' is small and the pollinia are yellow.

Subspecies
None.

Variation and varieties
There is a great deal of variation in the shape and colour of the lip and colour of the petals and sepals. One named variety is worth mentioning:

Var. *flavescens* lacks anthocyanin pigments and has whitish sepals and petals and a pale greenish lip with a very faint pattern. It is very rare.

BIOLOGY

Pollination and reproduction
This species is pollinated by insects, and in Europe bees of the genus *Eucera* are the main pollinators. The appropriate bees do not occur in England, however, and insect-pollination has not been recorded, although it must occur; pollen-beetles are possible alternative vectors. Very few ripe seedpods have been found in Kent but despite this enough viable seed is produced to maintain the populations. Self-pollination may occur occasionally, even in the bud (Summerhayes, 1968).

Vegetative reproduction is either very rare or does not occur at all. This statement is based on the observation that very few new plants appear within 10cm, or even 30cm, of existing orchids.

◀ 12 June, Kent. The column, as in Bee Orchid, resembles a duck's head but is a little shorter.

Development and growth

The aerial stem grows from a pair of tubers. It had been thought that Late Spider Orchid was monocarpic and flowered just once before dying. The opposite is the case, as it is rather long-lived. In studies in Kent the 'half-life' of a population averaged 12.5 years and varied from 7.1 to 16.8 years (the 'half-life' is a measure of the life expectancy of the orchid after its first appearance above ground and marks the point at which 50% of the population that emerged in any given year will have died). Periods of underground 'dormancy' are frequent with about 13% of plants dormant each season, and plants may spend one or two years underground before re-emerging.

There is no information on the length of the period between germination and the first appearance above ground but it is probably three or four years. Many plants flower in their first year above ground.

Hybrids

O. x *albertiana*, the hybrid with Bee Orchid, was recorded from Kent in 1828.

O. x *obscura*, the hybrid with Early Spider Orchid, has been recorded rarely in Kent. The parent species seldom occur together and the flowering periods do not normally overlap.

Name and classification

The specific name *fuciflora* derives from *fucus* 'drone' (i.e. a male bee but also meaning 'paint' or 'dye', especially red or purple colours) and *flos* 'flower' and thus presumably 'bee-flowered'.

HISTORY AND CONSERVATION

The first British record dates from 1828 when the Rev. Gerard E. Smith noted it, 'on the southern declivities of chalky downs near Folkestone' (*The English Flora*).

A *Red Data Book* species, it is classified as Vulnerable and specially protected under Schedule 8 of the Wildlife and Countryside Act 1981. Late Spider Orchid has only ever been reliably recorded from Kent, with about 20 historic localities. It is now much reduced,

with plants appearing regularly at just five sites although there are probably still sporadic appearances at several more. The low point was in the mid-1980s, and there has been a substantial recovery since then, perhaps due in part to the weather but certainly to better management. There is now a total of approximately 500 plants, almost half of which are at Wye NNR. The population there rose from about 50 in 1987 to around 220 in 1998.

Habitat has been lost because of agricultural changes but also due to changes in grazing

▲ 12 June, Kent. *The petals are always short and triangular and usually pinkish, resembling little horns.*

patterns and the reduction in rabbit numbers following myxomatosis, with grassland reverting to scrub. All the regular sites are now within SSSIs and are managed with the species in mind, but at its former localities grazing was abandoned many years ago. The Late Spider Orchid is probably best adapted to a 'dynamic' system. It needs ground disturbance and some bare ground to provide suitable conditions for seedlings to become established, as well as grazing and sometimes hand-mowing to maintain a suitable short sward for the adult plants to thrive.

The preferred pollinator is not present in Britain and few flowers produce seed. To counter this, hand-pollination has been undertaken at Wye. Fortunately, with a very low level of mortality in adult plants (less than 5% per annum), only small numbers of seedlings need to survive and flower in order to maintain the population.

Past and present occurrence of Late Spider Orchid in Britain and Ireland (based on presence or absence in 10km squares of the National Grid; data from the New Atlas).

	Britain	Ireland
total historical range, 1500-1999	6	0
current range	4 (0.14%*)	0
% lost, 1500-1969	33.3%	
% lost, 1970-1986	0%	
% lost, total	33.3%	

* current range as a % of the total number of 10km squares

◀ *14 June, Kent. The lip shape in the small English population is extraordinarily variable; in this plant the sepals are largely greenish.*

EARLY SPIDER ORCHID
Ophrys sphegodes

Just about the earliest orchid to flower in spring (vying with Early Purple Orchid for the honour), this species is almost entirely restricted to the south coast between Dorset and Kent. Although 'Nationally Scarce' it can be locally common and has appeared in vast numbers at Samphire Hoe, Dover, on spoil excavated from the Channel Tunnel. Indeed, the prospect of such a 'rare' plant dotted in hundreds or even thousands across the downland turf is almost a mockery of the term itself. The flowers may look like a spider to human eyes but have in fact evolved to trick solitary bees into acting as pollinators.

Identification
Unmistakably a 'bee' orchid, the circular deep brown lip resembles the body of a large garden spider and is marked with a lustrous bluish speculum. The sepals are green, and the petals are yellowish-green, narrow and strap-shaped with wavy edges.

Similar species
Bee and Late Spider Orchids both have similar large brownish lips but their specula are bordered by a narrow creamy line and their sepals and petals are pink.

Habitat
It is found on old species-rich grassland on chalk or limestone, growing both in short closely-cropped turf (even lawns) and in slightly ranker swards. It has some preference for previously disturbed areas, such as old quarries, spoil heaps and tracks; as with Late Spider Orchid heavy ground disturbance may aid the successful establishment of new colonies. It has been recorded rarely from shingle and almost all the current sites are near the sea.

Flowering period
Late March to early June. Tends to flower earliest in Dorset, from early or mid-April to early or mid-May and may average a few days later in Sussex and Kent. Flowering times are very variable, however, both from year to year and between colonies, even in the same area.

▶ *14 May, Kent. Many Early Spider Orchids are very small.*

For example, plants at Samphire Hoe in Kent bloom perhaps two weeks earlier than those at Lydden, just 6km away.

Range

Largely confined to the coasts of Dorset, East Sussex and Kent; in Dorset there are good populations between St Aldhelm's Head and Durlston; in East Sussex now found mostly between Beachy Head and Seaford and at Castle Hill near Brighton; in Kent there are around 30 colonies, most along the coast but including one or two inland sites such as Queendown Warren. Away from these strongholds there have been isolated recent

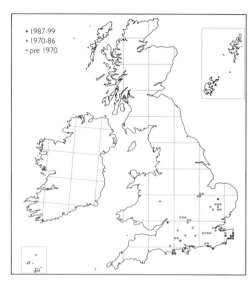

records in west Gloucestershire (from 1975), south Wiltshire (1988), Northamptonshire (2001, the first record for 230 years) and west Suffolk (where a single plant appeared from 1991 at Lakenheath, the first record since 1793). Introduced and naturalised near Bishop's Stortford in Hertfordshire. **World Range:** Mainland Europe from Spain eastwards to Greece and north to Belgium, Luxemburg, central Germany, Austria and the Czech Republic.

How to find it

One of the best and most accessible sites is Samphire Hoe below Shakespeare Cliff at Dover. This was created using five million cubic metres of marl dug from beneath the seabed during the construction of the Channel Tunnel. In 1998 there were 61 plants but by 2004 this has increased to 9,000. In East Sussex up to 50,000 plants have been recorded at Castle Hill, and it is also found at Cuckmere Haven and the Seven Sisters, and in Dorset the most accessible site is Durlston Head.

DESCRIPTION

Height: Mostly five to 15cm, sometimes to 20cm or rarely 35cm, but at Samphire Hoe plants may be as tall as 45cm.

Stem: Yellowish-green, thick and fleshy.

▲ 14 May, Kent. The greenish sepals and petals are distinctive.

Leaves: Grey-green to green and prominently veined. The three or four lower leaves are short and broadly strap-shaped with a blunt tip; the lowermost is held nearly horizontally but the remainder are more upright. The upper leaves are narrower, more pointed and loosely sheathe the stem. Some plants are wintergreen but in most the leaves appear in the early spring. All have withered by the end of June.

Spike: Most have two to seven flowers, exceptionally as many as ten, but at Samphire Hoe some tall plants may have as many as 17 blooms widely spaced along the stem.

Bract: Pale green, lanceolate, blunt-tipped and slightly longer than the ovary, which they more-or-less sheathe at their base.

Ovary: Green and boldly six-ribbed.

Flower: The sepals are oval-oblong with blunt tips and their margins rolled under. They are usually pale yellowish-green in coloration but rarely are more whitish. The petals are more strap-shaped, shorter and narrower, with a squared-off tip and edges that are frequently waved or undulate. They are often a slightly deeper yellowish-green and their margins may be more brownish with some fine hairs. Very rarely the petals are pinkish. The lateral sepals are held horizontally and the upper sepal vertically although the latter usually arches forward over the column. The lip is almost circular in shape with the edges moulded downwards to give it a convex profile. It is deep purplish-brown, usually paler and more yellowish around the lower edge and velvety in texture with a smooth, slightly lustrous, slate-grey, lead-coloured or bluish mark in the centre or towards the base (the speculum), often in the form of an H, X or the Greek letter π. On either side of the base of the lip there are two roughly conical swellings or haunches that are variable in size, and the lip is particularly hairy around these and along the edges below them. The column is greenish-white and held at about 90° to the lip with the rostellum at its tip forming a short blunt beak. At the base of the column the stigmatic cavity is circular, maroon-brown on the lower half and pale green

▲ 14 May, Kent. The 'speculum' is usually a lustrous blue or slate-grey, and the flower also has a pair of 'pseudo-eyes' on either side of the stigma.

on the upper with two 'pseudo-eyes', one on each side; it has been reported to contain 'sugar' (Summerhayes, 1968). The pollinia are yellow. The flowers fade rapidly, the lip becoming a dull pale yellowish-brown or grey-brown.

Subspecies
None.

Variation and varieties
The shape and coloration of the lip is very variable and rarely the speculum may be red rather than blue.

Var. *flavescens* lacks anthocyanin pigments and has a greenish or golden lip, sometimes brownish towards the edges, with merely a 'shadow' speculum. It is rare but can easily be confused with a normal flower that has faded with age.

BIOLOGY
Pollination and reproduction
It is cross-pollinated by bees. The specific pollinator is the male solitary bee *Andrena nigroaenea*, and the pollinia are attached to the front of its head as it attempts 'pseudo-

copulation'. The mechanism can be successful with about 25% of flowers recorded as setting seed at Samphire Hoe, but pollination rates can be very much lower with a lack of suitable pollinators being the most likely explanation for the low seed-set. It has also been suggested that British populations are probably mostly self-pollinated. Indeed, the pollinia are occasionally released to dangle in front of the stigma as in Bee Orchid, making self-pollination possible. The overall low rates of pollination suggest, however, that self-pollination is not routine.

Vegetative reproduction is thought to be uncommon or rare and as Early Spider Orchid is a short-lived orchid, dependent on seed to maintain its numbers, sufficient seed

▲ *8 May, Dorset. The lip fades rapidly to a dull brown and thus as successive flowers open only one or two at a time will be in 'good condition'.*

is presumably being produced to sustain the current colonies despite the apparently low rates of pollination.

Development and growth

The aerial stem grows from a pair of tubers, the younger of which is often stalked.

Early Spider Orchid is relatively short-lived. Few plants survive for more than three years after their first emergence above ground and the majority appear just once, flower and then die (i.e. they are monocarpic), although a tiny minority can live for at least ten years. The number of plants above ground varies widely from year to year, largely correlated with the amount of rainfall over the previous winter, and plants may spend one or two years 'dormant' underground.

Early Spider Orchid has a complex life cycle. This complicates attempts to understand its population dynamics and life history on the basis of an annual census. In a study at Castle Hill, Sussex, over a winter season, plants began to appear above ground in early September and continued to emerge through the winter, with peaks in November-December and more especially in March-May. By flowering time therefore some plants had been above ground for just two months and some for six. Those that appeared early in the winter included most of the older plants that had flowered the year before and all these early plants suffered grazing damage. Previously unrecorded plants, presumably seedlings emerging above ground for the first time, appeared throughout the season but especially from March onwards. However, around 75% of all the plants recorded up till March did not survive above ground to be counted in the annual census in May, with grazing being the likely cause of their disappearance.

There is no information on the period between germination and the first appearance above ground, but it is probably in the region of one to three years. Early Spider Orchids first appeared on spoil from the Channel Tunnel four years after it had been spread.

Hybrids

O. x *hybrida*, the hybrid with Fly Orchid, has occurred occasionally in Kent.

O. x *obscura*, the hybrid with Late Spider Orchid, has been recorded rarely in Kent. The parent species seldom occur together and the flowering periods do not normally overlap.

Name and classification

The specific names *sphegodes* derives from the Greek *sphex* 'wasp' or *sphekeion* 'small, wasp-like spider' and means 'wasp-like'.

HISTORY AND CONSERVATION

The first British record dates from 1650 when William How published his *Phytologia Britannica natales exhibens Indigenarum Stirpium sponte emergentium* ('A British botany presenting the origins of native wild plants') in which he noted it in Northamptonshire, 'upon an old Stone pit ground…hard by Walcot a mile from Barnack…Dr. Bowle'.

A *Red Data Book* species classified as Near-threatened and specially protected under Schedule 8 of the Wildlife and Countryside Act 1981. The Early Spider Orchid has vanished from at least 73% of its historical range but the majority of the losses occurred long ago, in the 19th century. This was probably largely due to the cultivation of grasslands following the Enclosures, although the retreat towards the coast of southeast England suggests that climatic factors may also have been involved. It is now extinct in the Channel Islands, west Cornwall (where recorded at Upton Towans in 1961), the Isle of Wight (a few records, the last in 1992), Hampshire (very few records, the last near Lepe in 1978), West Sussex, Surrey (last recorded from Titsey in 1942 but this record probably originated with plants transplanted from Queendown Warren in Kent), Essex, Oxfordshire (1920, with an unconfirmed record in 1975), Bedfordshire, Cambridgeshire and Denbighshire (a 19th century record).

Many sites for the Early Spider Orchid are now protected but its grassland habitat also needs careful management to maintain the populations. Grazing by sheep is beneficial, as long as they are removed during the period when the orchids flower and set seed. Any future spread may depend upon the creation of suitable bare ground and the sort of drastic disturbance that created such ideal conditions at Samphire Hoe.

Past and present occurrence of Early Spider Orchid in Britain and Ireland (based on presence or absence in 10km squares of the National Grid; data from the New Atlas).

	Britain	Ireland
total historical range, 1500-1999	63	0
current range	17 (0.6%*)	0
% lost, 1500-1969	71.5%	
% lost, 1970-1986	1.5%	
% lost, total	73%	

*current range as a % of the total number of 10km squares

▲ 14 May, Kent. Early Spider Orchids can have just one flower; this plant has especially brownish petals.

OTHER SPECIES

Several other species of orchid have been recorded from time to time in Britain and Ireland. This is a selection:

Short-spurred Fragrant Orchid
Gymnadenia odoratissima
Recorded from Black Hall Rocks in Co. Durham in 1912, but doubt has been cast on the identity of the specimen.

Frivald's Fragrant Orchid
Gymnadenia frivaldii
Found and photographed on wet heathland in Dorset in 1972 or 1973, its normal range is the Balkans and its occurrence here is a mystery (Ettlinger 1997).

False Musk Orchid (Dwarf Alpine Orchid)
Chamorchis alpina
A single plant was reported from the New Forest in Hampshire in 1976. Among the smallest of European orchids, this is a species of damp, calcareous soils in the mountains of Scandinavia and the Alps. It was probably planted.

Pale-flowered Orchid
Orchis pallens
A few specimens were recorded in the 1920s in Hampshire but there are no further details (Ettlinger 1997).

Scarce Tongue Orchid
Serapias neglecta
Found in 1918 in a cornfield on the Isle of Wight, the roots were dug up and taken into cultivation. Rather localised in coastal regions around the central Mediterranean, this species may have been introduced with imported cereal seed.

Heart-flowered Tongue Orchid
Serapias cordigera
Found in 1996 at Monkton on the Isle of Thanet in Kent, with two or three plants in 1997. They were on a south-facing bank at the bottom of a cliff in an abandoned chalk quarry. This is a common and widespread species around the Mediterranean and occurs north to Finistere. Despite apparently excellent credentials, these plants almost certainly originated from wind-blown seed coming from plants growing in pots on a patio just 300m upwind of the nature reserve.

'Bertoloni's Mirror Orchid
Ophrys bertolonii'
A single plant found in Dorset in 1976 generated much controversy as to its origins, but it eventually emerged that a holidaymaker, returning from Italy, had planted it. '*Ophrys bertolonii*' has since been divided into several species, and the precise identity of the Dorset plant cannot be confirmed.

ORCHID FAMILY TREE

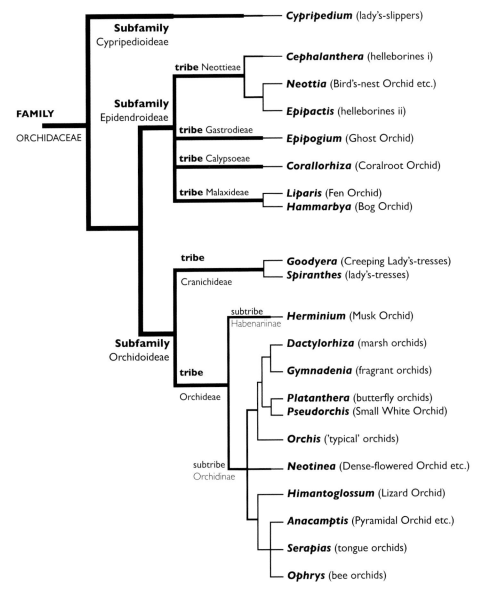

All orchids are members of the family Orchidaceae. Its most fundamental subdivisions are the subfamilies, three of which are represented in Britain and Ireland: the Cypripedioideae, with just one species – Lady's-slipper; the Epidendroideae, a heterogeneous group, many of which are woodland orchids that grow from rhizomes; and the Orchidoideae, a more homogenous group, all of which grow from a swollen underground tuber. The subfamilies are further divided into tribes, genera and, finally, individual species.

This family tree follows Bateman (2005) and has been constructed using the latest evidence from genetic research. It gives a much better idea of relationships than is possible in a simple list. For example, Bog Orchid and Creeping Lady's-tresses lie next to each other in the field guide, but it can be seen that they are members of separate subfamilies and not at all closely related.

VICE-COUNTIES

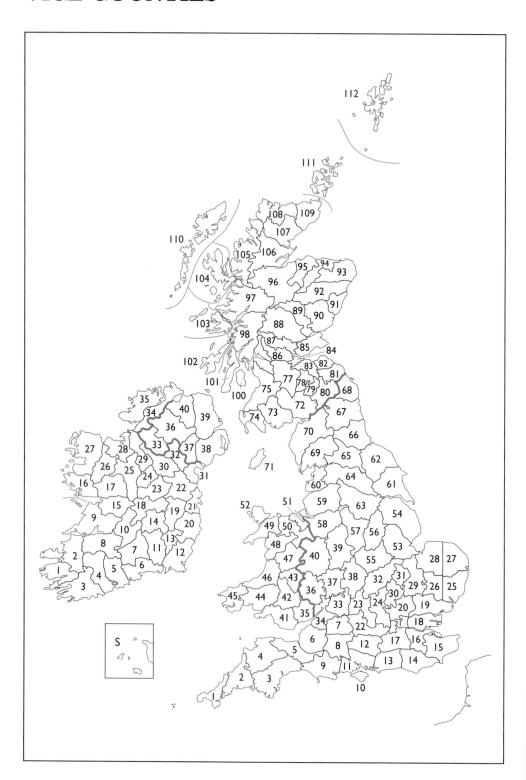

England

1	West Cornwall
2	East Cornwall
3	South Devon
4	North Devon
5	South Somerset
6	North Somerset
7	North Wiltshire
8	South Wiltshire
9	Dorset
10	Isle of Wight
11	South Hampshire
12	North Hampshire
13	West Sussex
14	East Sussex
15	East Kent
16	West Kent
17	Surrey
18	South Essex
19	North Essex
20	Hertfordshire
21	Middlesex
22	Berkshire
23	Oxfordshire
24	Buckinghamshire
25	East Suffolk
26	West Suffolk
27	East Norfolk
28	West Norfolk
29	Cambridgeshire
30	Bedfordshire
31	Huntingdonshire
32	Northamptonshire
33	East Gloucestershire
34	West Gloucestershire
36	Herefordshire
37	Worcestershire
38	Warwickshire
39	Staffordshire
40	Shropshire
53	South Lincolnshire
54	North Lincolnshire
55	Leicestershire
56	Nottinghamshire
57	Derbyshire
58	Cheshire
59	South Lancashire
60	West Lancashire
61	Southeast Yorkshire
62	Northeast Yorkshire
63	Southwest Yorkshire
64	Mid-west Yorkshire
65	Northwest Yorkshire
66	Co. Durham
67	South Northumberland
68	Cheviot (north Northumberland)
69	Westmorland
70	Cumberland

Isle of Man

71	Isle of Man

Wales

35	Monmouthshire
41	Glamorganshire
42	Breconshire
43	Radnorshire
44	Carmarthenshire
45	Pembrokeshire
46	Cardiganshire
47	Montgomeryshire
48	Merioneth
49	Caernarvonshire
50	Denbighshire
51	Flintshire
53	Anglesey

Scotland

72	Dumfries-shire
73	Kirkcudbrightshire
74	Wigtownshire
75	Ayrshire
76	Renfrewshire
77	Lanarkshire
78	Peebles-shire
79	Selkirkshire
80	Roxburghshire
81	Berwickshire
82	East Lothian
83	Midlothian
84	West Lothian
85	Fife
86	Stirlingshire
87	West Perth
88	Mid Perth
89	East Perth
90	Angus
91	Kincardineshire
92	South Aberdeen
93	North Aberdeen
94	Banffshire
95	Moray
96	Easterness (Inverness-shire)
97	Westerness (Inverness-shire)
98	Main Argyll
99	Dunbarton
100	Clyde Islands (Buteshire)
101	Kintyre
102	South Ebudes (Inner Hebrides)
103	Mid Ebudes (Inner Hebrides)
104	North Ebudes (Inner Hebrides)
105	West Ross (Ross & Cromarty)
106	East Ross (Ross & Cromarty)
107	East Sutherland
108	West Sutherland
109	Caithness
110	Outer Hebrides
111	Orkney
112	Shetland

Channel Islands

S	Channel Islands

Ireland

H1	South Kerry
H2	North Kerry
H3	West Cork
H4	Mid Cork
H5	East Cork
H6	Co. Waterford
H7	South Tipperary
H8	Co. Limerick
H9	Co. Clare
H10	North Tipperary
H11	Co. Kilkenny
H12	Co. Wexford
H13	Co. Carlow
H14	Laois
H15	Southeast Galway
H16	West Galway
H17	Northeast Galway
H18	Offaly
H19	Co. Kildare
H20	Co. Wicklow
H21	Co. Dublin
H22	Meath
H23	Westmeath
H24	Co. Longford
H25	Co. Roscommon
H26	East Mayo
H27	West Mayo
H28	Co. Sligo
H29	Co. Leitrim
H30	Co. Cavan
H31	Co. Louth
H32	Co. Monaghan
H33	Fermanagh
H34	East Donegal
H35	West Donegal
H36	Tyrone
H37	Co. Armagh
H38	Co. Down
H39	Co. Antrim
H40	Co. Londonderry

(Some alternative names are added in parentheses to allow easier reference to modern or historical counties.)

ORCHID FLOWERING PERIODS

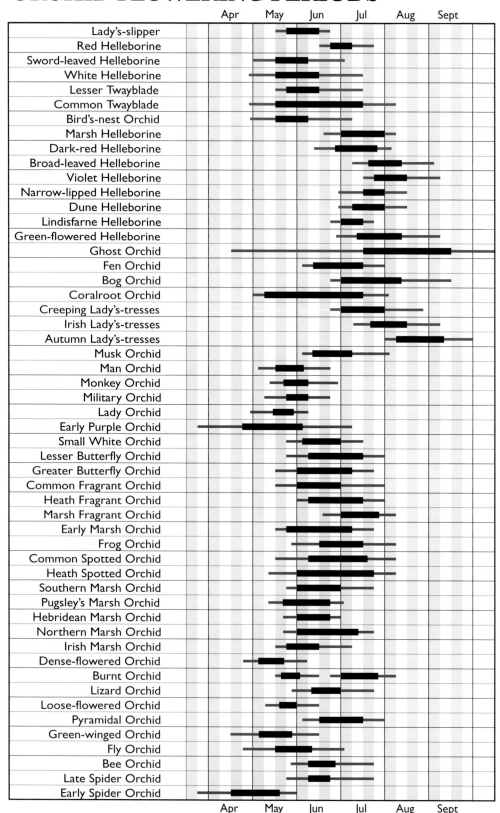

Site Guide

INTRODUCTION

The following is a selection of sites in Britain and Ireland where it is possible to find wild orchids. Of course, orchids can be found in many places, but sadly more and more of the countryside is bereft of their beauty and it is increasingly necessary to search out special places in order to experience the magic of wild orchids.

We see this selection as a starting point and would encourage everyone to explore and discover new places, to record the orchids that they find and to pass this information on to the local botanical recorder. But, in the meantime, you may be in an unfamiliar area, on holiday, or just keen to find somewhere that offers a good chance of success.

For each site we have included brief details of access (including a grid reference), habitat and the species that may be found. Many orchid sites are accessed down a maze of lanes, and it is very difficult to give concise and understandable written directions. To locate many of these sites you will need a large-scale road atlas, especially one that marks the National Grid and therefore allows you to pinpoint grid references or, even better, an OS map at 1:50,000 or 1:25,000 scale. If the site is a reserve (and most are) further information can often be found on the internet by visiting the managing organisation's website. It is also worth trawling the 'net' for information on nearby reserves or Roadside Nature Reserves which are often also good for orchids.

This selection includes sites for some of the rarer orchids but these are all accessible and welcome visitors. On many reserves, guided walks are organised from time to time by the managing body and these can be a good introduction to the site. We have not tried to include localities for every species; one or two are so rare and vulnerable that visitors are not welcome, and some species, for example Green-flowered Helleborine, occur in small, scattered, hard-to-find colonies in places that have no other orchid interest. Rather, we have tried to select areas that hold a good selection of species, or have large and spectacular displays of one or two orchids. We have also endeavoured to choose sites that are interesting and attractive, and almost all will have a great deal of other wildlife interest, be it other plants, butterflies, dragonflies or whatever. All have public access throughout the orchid season, with the exception of one or two where entry is restricted to a limited number of open days. Unfortunately, we have not been able to give details of disabled access, but it is generally rather limited.

Orchid hunting requires very little equipment. As well as a good map, a hand-lens is useful, as is a small plastic ruler and, of course, a field guide to all the other wonderful plants that will be seen.

Finally, it should be remembered that many orchids are scarce, and some are so rare that they are protected by law. All orchids are valuable, as indeed are the other plants around them. *Please look where you are going, stay on paths where possible, and leave the site as you would wish to find it.*

Inevitably there are errors in the accounts, for which we take full responsibility. We would be delighted to hear of any corrections or updates, or indeed any additional sites that could be included in future editions of the book (the authors can be contacted via their website: www.norfolknature. co.uk or via the publishers).

USEFUL ADDRESSES

An Taisce (National Trust for Ireland), Tailor's Hall, Back Lane, Dublin 8, Ireland
Tel: +353 (0)454 1786. Email: **info@antaisce.org** Website: **www.antaisce.org**

CEH Monkswood, Abbots Ripton, Huntingdon, Cambridgeshire PE28 2LS
Tel: 01487 772400. Email: **monkswood@ceh.ac.uk** Website: **www.ceh.ac.uk**

The Countryside Agency, Head Office: John Dower House, Crescent Place, Cheltenham, Gloucestershire GL50 3RA
Tel: 01242 521381. Email: **info@countryside.gov.uk** Website: **www.countryside.gov.uk**

Countryside Council for Wales, Maes-y-Ffynnon, Penrhosgarnedd, Bangor, Gwynedd LL57 2LQ
Tel: 01248 385500. Email: **enquiries@ccw.gov.uk** Website: **www.ccw.gov.uk**

English Nature, Northminster House, Peterborough PE1 1UA.
Tel: 01733 455000. Email: **enquiries@english-nature.org.uk** Website: **www.english-nature. org.uk**

Environment and Heritage Service, Commonwealth House, 35 Castle Street, Belfast BT1 1GU
Tel: 028 90 251477. Website: **www.ehsni.gov.uk**

Irish Wildlife Trust, 107 Lower Baggot Street, Dublin 2, Ireland
Tel: +353 (0)1 676 8588. Email: **enquires@iwt.ie** Website: **www.iwt.ie**

Joint Nature Conservation Committee, Monkstone House, City Road, Peterborough PE1 1JY
Tel: 01733 562626. Email: **comment@jncc.gov.uk** Website: **www.jncc.gov.uk**

National Parks and Wildlife Service, Department of the Environment, Heritage & Local Government, 7 Ely Place, Dublin 2, Ireland
Tel: +353 (0)1 888 2000. LoCall: 1890 202021 (within Republic of Ireland only).
Email: **natureconservation@environ.ie** Website: **www.environ.ie** or **www.npws.ie**

National Trust, 36 Queen Anne's Gate, London SW1H 9AS
Tel: 020 72229251. Website: **www.nationaltrust.org.uk**

National Trust (Northern Ireland), Rowallane, Saintfield, Ballynahinch, Co. Down BT24 7LH
Tel: 028 97 510721. Website: **www.ntni.org.uk**

National Trust for Scotland, Wemyss House, 28 Charlotte Square, Edinburgh EH2 4ET
Tel: 0131 2439300. Website: **www.nts.org.uk**

Royal Society for the Protection of Birds, The Lodge, Sandy, Bedfordshire SG19 2DL
Tel: 01767 680551. Website: **www.rspb.org.uk**

Scottish Natural Heritage, 12 Hope Terrace, Edinburgh EH9 2AS
Tel: 0131 447 4784. Email: **enquiries@snh.org.uk** Website: **www.snh.org.uk**

Scottish Wildlife Trust, Cramond House, Off Cramond Glebe Road, Edinburgh EH4 6NS
Tel: 0131 312 7765. Email: **enquires@swt.org.uk** Website: **www.swt.org.uk**

The Wildlife Trusts, The Kiln, Waterside, Mather Road, Newark NG24 1WT
Tel: 0870 036 7711. Email: **info@wildlife-trusts.cix.co.uk** Website: **www.wildlifetrusts.org**

BOTANICAL ORGANISATIONS

Botanical Society of the British Isles

Hon. General Secretary, c/o Department of Botany, The Natural History Museum, Cromwell Road, London SW7 5BD. Website: **www.bsbi.org.uk**

The BSBI is a learned society of professional and amateur botanists dedicated to the study of and interest in the British and Irish flora. It publishes a journal, *Watsonia*, as well as the less formal (and eminently readable) *BSBI News*. In addition, the BSBI organises the system of county plant recorders, runs field meetings and has a panel of referees to advise on plant identifications (including, of course, orchids). BSBI members provided the vast majority of the data used to produce the *New Atlas*. In short, the BSBI is *the* society for anyone with a keen interest in wild plants.

Hardy Orchid Society

Website: **www.hardyorchidsociety.org.uk**

Dedicated to the study of European orchids, including field study, photography and conservation, with an emphasis on cultivation and propagation. Publishes a quarterly *Journal* with articles on all these subjects and organises field meetings and exhibitions of cultivated orchids.

Plantlife International

14 Rollestone Street, Salisbury, Wiltshire SP1 1DX

Tel: 01722 342730. Email: **enquires@plantlife.org.uk** Website: **www.plantlife.org.uk**

The wild plant conservation charity. Plantlife International (formerly 'Plantlife') has an increasingly international focus but still does much useful work in Britain. It has a small number of reserves, runs 'back from the brink' projects for many declining species (including Sword-leaved Helleborine), organised the 'county flowers' poll and promotes various surveys to raise awareness of wild flowers, as well as gathering much useful information. Publishes a quarterly magazine, *Plantlife*, and a newsletter.

ABBREVIATIONS

BBOWT: Berkshire, Buckinghamshire and Oxfordshire Wildlife Trust
BC: Butterfly Conservation
BCNPWT: Bedfordshire, Cambridgeshire, Northamptonshire and Peterborough Wildlife Trust
BSBI: Botanical Society of the British Isles
CCW: Countryside Council for Wales
CEH: Centre for Ecology and Hydrology
EN: English Nature
FC: Forestry Commission
JNCC: Joint Nature Conservation Committee
LNR: Local Nature Reserve
LRWT: Leicestershire and Rutland Wildlife Trust
NNR: National Nature Reserve
NPWS: National Parks and Wildlife Service
NT: National Trust
RSPB: Royal Society for the Protection of Birds
SNH: Scottish Natural Heritage
SSSI: Site of Special Scientific Interest
WT: Wildlife Trust (with prefix, e.g. Sussex WT)
WT: Woodland Trust (without prefix)

Southeast England

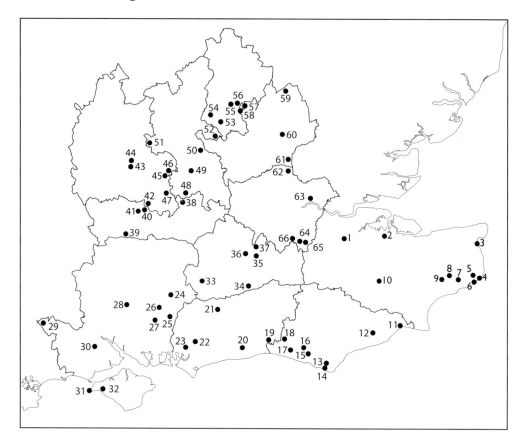

KENT

1. Trosley Country Park — TQ 642614

An area of woodland and chalk downland bordering the North Downs Way. Part of a much larger conservation area, there is an interesting chalkland flora that includes Bee, Man, Common Fragrant and Pyramidal Orchids.

The car park is off the A227 between Meopham and Wrotham, south of Gravesend. (Kent County Council)

2. Queendown Warren — TQ 827629

Excellent species-rich chalk grassland on the site of an old rabbit warren. Specialities include Early Spider Orchid and Man Orchid (although the former is declining here); other species include Common Fragrant, Common Spotted, Bee, Pyramidal, Early Purple, Fly, Lady and Green-winged Orchids and Autumn Lady's-tresses; also White and Broad-leaved Helleborines in the fringing woodland.

Near Hartlip off the A2, southeast of Gillingham. Park in Warren Lane, off Mount Lane, accessed from the Lower Hartlip Road. (Kent WT, Plantlife, Swale Borough Council)

3. Sandwich and Pegwell Bays — TR 341632

A large reserve of mixed coastal habitats including shingle, rich dune grassland, and coastal scrub. Good for Southern Marsh Orchid, Pyramidal and Bee Orchids, Marsh Helleborine and the biggest colony of Lizard Orchids in Britain (more than 4,000 were counted in 2001).

Access from Sandwich Town via the Sandwich Bay Estate, where a substantial toll operates on the private road. There are many footpaths along the beach, dunes and golf courses. Park at Pegwell Bay Country Park off the A256 or by Prince's Old Clubhouse at Sandwich Bay. (Kent WT)

4. Langdon Cliffs — TR 335422

Lying to the east of Dover, this is part of the famous white cliffs. With fantastic views, the chalk downland on top of the cliffs holds many interesting plants with Bee, Common Fragrant, Pyramidal and Common Spotted Orchids, as well as some Early Spider Orchids and Autumn Lady's-tresses.

There are footpaths to the cliffs from Dover town centre and the port. Signposted from the M20 and Dover town centre. Park past the Castle beside the Visitor Centre. (NT)

5. Lydden/Temple Ewell Down — TR 277453

One of Kent's best examples of chalk downland, which is of international importance. There is also some woodland and scrub. The speciality of the steep slopes is Early Spider Orchid, and there are also Common Fragrant, Bee and Pyramidal Orchids, Common Twayblade, Autumn Lady's-tresses, and a very few Burnt Orchids.

Close to Dover on the minor road between Lydden and Temple Ewell; access is from the south side of the railway bridge. Park behind the 'George and Dragon Centre' in Temple Ewell, from where the reserve is signposted. (NNR, Kent WT)

6. Samphire Hoe — TR 298395

Lying just west of Dover, this area of grassland bounded by a sea wall was created with waste material left over from the digging of the Channel Tunnel. The spoil was deposited at Lower Shakespeare Cliff then landscaped and sown with wildflower seeds collected locally. A wide variety of plants now grows here, including one of the largest colonies of Early Spider Orchid in Britain (9,000 spikes in 2004).

Access by car is via a tunnel through the cliffs. You can reach the tunnel from the A20; driving towards Folkestone from Dover, follow the signs for Samphire Hoe. (Samphire Hoe is owned and managed by several bodies in partnership with the White Cliffs Countryside Project.)

7. Park Gate Down — TR 168457

A chalk grassland in a dry valley fringed by woodland, this reserve has an exceptionally rich orchid flora. It is best known for its colony of Monkey Orchids (introduced here from seeds collected elsewhere in Kent). These have increased in recent years and put on a spectacular show. Other species include masses of Common Fragrant Orchids as well as Early Purple, Bee and Pyramidal Orchids, Common Spotted Orchid, Common Twayblade, Greater Butterfly Orchid, a few hard-to-find Musk Orchids and, in some seasons, a few Late Spider Orchids. Fly, Lady and Man Orchids also occur in small numbers.

Between the B2068 and the A260 on minor roads between Elham and Stelling. There is limited roadside parking. (Kent WT)

8. Yockletts Bank — TR 125477

A mixed coppiced wood on the side of a dry valley, on clay over the chalk. One of the best sites in Kent for Lady Orchid, there are also Greater Butterfly, Common Spotted, Early Purple, Bird's-nest and Fly Orchids and White and Broad-leaved Helleborines, while Common Twayblade is abundant. There are also a few Pyramidal and Common Fragrant Orchids in the small patches of grassland.

One mile west of the B2068 Stone Street (Canterbury-Hythe road), with very limited parking on the road to Waltham beside the wood. (Kent WT)

9. Wye — TR 074469

The habitats on this steep chalk downland include grassland, scrub and woodland, and an exceptional

19 species of orchid occur here. The speciality is Late Spider Orchid with around six distinct colonies, but they are hard to find and visitors should contact the warden for advice. Early Spider Orchid and Burnt Orchid also occur but are similarly elusive. Not so Common Fragrant Orchid, Common Spotted Orchid, Common Twayblade and Pyramidal, Bee and Man Orchids (the last favouring the western flank of the escarpment around Dentons Field). The woods may yield Bird's-nest, Lady, Fly and Greater Butterfly Orchids.

Northeast of Ashford on the minor road between Wye and Hastingleigh; there are several car parks and many footpaths. (NNR, EN)

10. Marden Meadows   TQ 763445

These three unimproved hay meadows have several pools and are surrounded by ancient hedgerows. Traditionally managed, there is an amazing display of Green-winged Orchids in May, when up to 500,000 have been counted.

Just west of Staplehurst off the A229. The meadows are sandwiched between the minor road to Marden and the Tonbridge-Ashford railway line. Park on the roadside. (Kent WT)

EAST SUSSEX

11. Rye Harbour   TQ 925185

A large coastal site with managed grassland, ditches, marsh, scrub and woodland. Botanical interest is focused mainly on the ditches and sandier areas, with orchids such as Common Spotted, Pyramidal and Bee. Common Twayblade, Autumn Lady's-tresses and Green-winged Orchid can also be found.

There is parking at Castle Water and a Visitor Centre southeast of Rye along Harbour Road. (East Sussex County Council)

12. Fore Wood   TQ 756126

A hornbeam and hazel coppice with some oak and alder. There are wide grassy rides and a good spring flora. Orchids include colonies of Early Purple and Common Spotted Orchids, Broad-leaved Helleborine, Common Twayblade and Bird's-nest Orchid.

Beside the village of Crowhurst, off the A2100 Battle to Hastings road. (RSPB)

13. Wild Woods at Friston Forest TV 555995

This area of forestry includes extensive Beech plantations with many wide grassy rides. A rich flora is developing, and includes a colony of several thousand White Helleborines.

Park in the Seven Sisters Country Park 'Forest' car park north of the A259 or off minor roads to the north; there is a Visitor Centre at the car park, and way-marked walks. (FC)

14. Cuckmere Haven and Seven Sisters Country Park   TV 519995

Lying just east of Seaford, the cliff-top chalk downs have Common Fragrant, Common Spotted, Early Purple, Pyramidal and Bee Orchids, Autumn Lady's-tresses and, in a few places, Early Spider, Frog and Burnt Orchids (including the late-flowering variety of Burnt).

Park in the Seven Sisters Country Park 'Riverside' car park on the south side of the A259. Paths lead east along the cliff tops all the way to Beachy Head. (Sussex Downs Conservation Board)

15. Mount Caburn   TQ 445090

Just southeast of Lewes, Mount Caburn is an important Bronze Age hill fort; its south-facing chalk slopes hold Common Fragrant and Pyramidal Orchids and a large population of Burnt Orchids (over 6,000 plants in some years; look in the dry valley to the northwest of the hill fort).

Access is from the village of Glynde, which is reached via a minor road off the A27. Follow the steep public footpath to the fort. (NNR)

16. Malling Down   TQ 423107

Old chalk pits on a steep north-facing slope, with a rich flora including a selection of orchids. Musk and Frog Orchids can be found in small numbers, with good displays of Pyramidal and Common Fragrant Orchids and stunning numbers of Common Spotted Orchids. There are also Bee Orchids and Common Twayblades.

Easily reached by walking from Lewes town centre (access in Wheatsheaf Gardens); alternatively, park in the Ringmer Road lay-by on the B2192. (Sussex WT)

17. Castle Hill   TQ 371070

East of Brighton, on the South Downs between Woodingdean and Kingston, this traditionally managed chalk grassland has Britain's largest colony of Early Spider Orchids, with up to 50,000 plants recorded.

Accessible along the track running northeast from the B2123 just north of Woodingdean (park at TQ 356063). Access without a permit is restricted to rights of way. (NNR)

18. Ditchling Beacon   TQ 330130

Lying to the north of Brighton on the South Downs Way long-distance footpath, this Iron Age hill fort has chalk grassland and scrub with Common Fragrant Orchid, Common Spotted Orchid and Common Twayblade (and also Marsh Fragrant Orchid on north-facing slopes towards Plumpton).

The site lies a little off the South Downs Way to the northwest of the National Trust car park (accessed on minor roads south from the B2116 at Ditchling). (Sussex WT)

WEST SUSSEX

19. Devil's Dyke   TQ 260110

On the South Downs to the north of Brighton, the Devil's Dyke is the largest dry chalk combe in Britain. With some woodland and scrub, the Dyke has a rich flora. The list of orchids includes Common Spotted, Bee and Frog Orchids and Common Twayblade.

Well signposted on roads north of Brighton; park in the large car park on Devil's Dyke Road. (NT)

20. Cissbury Ring   TQ 130078

A large and impressive Iron Age hill fort on the South Downs with Pyramidal, Bee and Frog Orchids among its varied chalk flora.

Three miles north of Worthing, off the A24 at Findon. Footpaths lead from Worthing and Findon. (NT).

21. Furnace Meadow and Brick Kiln Rough
SU 977277

A flower-rich meadow on clay soils, with an adjacent ancient semi-natural woodland. The varied habitats here hold a good orchid flora, with Early Purple, Common Spotted, Greater Butterfly and Bird's-nest Orchids, and Broad-leaved Helleborine among others.

Three miles from Petworth on the minor road to Ebernoe. Park beside the church. The meadow is next to the Sussex WT reserve of Ebernoe Common. (Sussex WT, Plantlife)

22. Levin Down   SU 884138

A very steep chalk downland with Juniper and patches of acidic chalk heath. Orchids include Pyramidal Orchid and Autumn Lady's-tresses.

Access on footpaths leading north from the minor road between Singleton and Charlton, which is reached via the A286. Park in the lay-by at the crossroads in Charlton. (Sussex WT)

23. Kingley Vale   SU 824088

'The finest Yew forest in the world' according to English Nature. There is much of archaeological interest too, as well as some scrub and chalk grassland. Species include Fly, Bee, Frog, Common Fragrant and Pyramidal Orchids and Autumn Lady's-tresses.

On the South Downs, 4¹/₂ miles northwest of Chichester. There is a car park and waymarked walks. (NNR)

HAMPSHIRE

24. Noar Hill   SY 740320

Medieval chalk pits that now form one of the best examples of chalk grassland and scrub in Britain. Rich in flowers and invertebrate life, 11 species of orchid can be found, including a nationally important colony of Musk Orchid. Also Early Purple, Frog, Bee, Pyramidal, Common Spotted and Common Fragrant Orchids, plus Common Twayblade and Autumn Lady's-tresses.

Leave Selborne south on the B3006 and immediately turn west towards Newton Valence. Then take the first left, signposted Noar Hill. There is limited parking by the footpath sign at SU 738323; follow this track to the reserve. (Hampshire WT)

25. Butser Hill   SU 714198

This is one of the largest areas of chalk grassland in Hampshire. It contains a variety of habitats, including Yew woodland and chalk heath. There is a good orchid flora with Early Purple, Bee and Common Spotted Orchids, and Broad-leaved Helleborine.

Part of the larger Queen Elizabeth Country Park, south of Petersfield and north of Portsmouth on the A3. There is a Visitor Centre and car parks. (Hampshire County Council, FC)

26. Chapetts Copse/Hen Wood   SU 654230

A beechwood, probably a plantation that was established on the site of an ancient woodland, with a very rich orchid flora. The star species is Sword-leaved Helleborine; the largest colony in Britain by far is found here, with more than 2,000 flowering plants. It even grows along the road bank outside the wood. Other species include White Helleborine, and Bird's-nest, Fly and Common Spotted Orchids.

Off the A32 between West Meon and East Meon; turn south at the sign for Meon Springs Fly Fishery into Coombes Lane, and park in the ride on the left after about 450 yards. (Hampshire WT)

27. Old Winchester Hill   SU 645209

A spectacular hill fort at the west end of the South Downs, comprising chalk grassland with mixed scrub, Yew and broad-leaved woodland with 14 species of orchid. On the south-facing slopes, large colonies of Greater Butterfly, Frog, Common Fragrant Orchids and Autumn Lady's-tresses can be found, with Man, Bee and Fly Orchids, and Common Twayblade in the scrub. White Helleborine, and Early Purple and Bird's-nest Orchids occur in the woodland.

From the A32 at Warnford, take the minor road southeast towards Clanfield. The car park is on the right after 2 miles. (NNR)

28. St Catherine's Hill   SU 485275

An ancient hill fort near Winchester city centre, with a rich chalk flora including Musk and Frog Orchids, and Autumn Lady's-tresses.

Access off the B3335 south of Winchester centre onto Garnier Road. There is a large car park. (Hampshire WT)

29. Martin Down   SU 061192

A vast area of chalk grassland with wonderful displays of wildflowers, as well as other habitats such as chalk heath and scrub. Various earthworks crisscross the relatively flat downland. Specialities include Burnt Orchid, which can be found around the prominent Bokerley Dyke. Other species include Common Fragrant, Pyramidal, Bee, Early Purple, Greater Butterfly and Common Spotted Orchids, hard-to-spot Frog Orchids, Southern Marsh Orchid, and a very few Man Orchids.

There is open access on foot from the village of Martin, south of Salisbury off the A354. (NNR, EN)

30. New Forest   SU 298081

The New Forest is one of the greatest biological treasures in Britain. An ancient system of grazing rights, still widely exercised, has produced a rich and varied landscape. Much of the forest is heath or woodland, with relatively few orchids, but the acid bogs and valley mires are of exceptional interest. Heath Spotted Orchid is very common, and the purple-flowered subspecies *pulchella* of Early Marsh Orchid is fairly frequent. Bog Orchid occurs in the more acidic bogs, such as Holmsley and Wilverley Bogs (on the northern side of the Avon Water around SU 230000 and SU 245005), the western fringe of Long Beech Inclosure (north off the A31 at Stoney Cross), Matley Bog (north of the B3056 2½ miles east of Lyndhurst), the area south and southwest of Hatchet Pond (on the B3054 1½ miles southwest of Beaulieu), and at Acres Down. Bog Orchid can be very hard to find, requiring patience and great care, because it is easy to tread on them; some of these sites are very wet with deep peat – beware! Another local speciality is Heath Fragrant Orchid, found in a few of the more calcareous mires, such as Stony Moors (north of Holmsley Camp Site), Dibden Bottom (west of Dibden) and Boundway Hill (near Sway). Lesser Butterfly Orchids are relatively frequent on the higher, drier ground in and around the bogs and on adjacent wet heathland. Finally, the New Forest was once home to Summer Lady's-tresses, which, although probably extinct in the wild since 1952, is reported to have been occasionally reintroduced to its old sites, secretly.

THE ISLE OF WIGHT

31. Tennyson Down   SZ 327854

On land that drops steeply to the sea to end in the famous Needles, this site is a combination of coast and downland. The chalk grassland has large colonies of Early Purple, Bee, Pyramidal and Green-winged Orchids.

Take the B3322 out of Freshwater towards the Needles, where there is car parking. (NT)

32. Compton Down   SZ 375853

The most southerly area of chalk in the country, this faces the sea. In spring there are Early Purple and Green-winged Orchids, and later Pyramidal and Bee Orchids amongst a rich chalk flora.

On the south coast of the Isle of Wight, east of Freshwater Bay and north of the A3055. (NT)

SURREY

33. Thursley Common   SU 900417

Thursley is the largest remnant of the Surrey heaths, with bog, dry and wet heath, and woodland. Southern Marsh Orchid and the purple-flowered subspecies of Early Marsh Orchid (*pulchella*) occur on the wet heath (the creamy-flowered variety *ochrantha* can also be found at Thursley—not to be confused with the very rare creamy-flowered subspecies *ochroleuca!*).

Access is from south of Godalming alongside the A3; park between Elstead and Thursley. (NNR)

34. Wallis Wood   TQ 121388

Oak-hazel coppice with a stream, ponds and pasture. There is a rich ground flora with Broad-leaved and Violet Helleborines and Common Spotted Orchid.

On the minor road north of Walliswood village, just east of the A29 south of Ockley. (Surrey WT)

35. Box Hill   TQ 180510

An outstanding area of woodland and chalk downland, Box Hill has long been famous as a destination for day-trippers from London. Surprisingly extensive, there are many walks and views towards the South Downs. On the summit there is an Information Centre and a nineteenth-century fort. There is an impressive array of orchids, with Broad-leaved and White Helleborines, Common Twayblade, Bee, Pyramidal, Common Fragrant and Common Spotted Orchids, and Autumn Lady's-tresses in reasonable numbers. Harder to find are Green-winged, Man, Musk, Early Purple, Fly, Frog and Greater Butterfly Orchids, and Violet Helleborine.

Box Hill is east of the A24 between Dorking and Leatherhead. There are several car parks around the perimeter and also along Zig Zag Road. (NT)

36. Ranmore Common, Denbies Hillside and White Downs   TQ 145510

A cluster of National Trust sites on the North Downs comprising a wooded common and chalk downland. White Helleborine, and Bird's-nest, Fly, Pyramidal and Bee Orchids occur among the scrub and trees. There are also some Man Orchids and Autumn Lady's-tresses.

The North Downs Way links Denbies Hillside and the White Downs, with car parking two miles northwest of Dorking off the A25. (NT)

37. Ashtead Common TQ 175592

A relict woodland pasture with more than 2,300 pollarded oaks. Southern Marsh and Common Spotted Orchids, Common Twayblade and Broad-leaved and Violet Helleborines can be found here.

Near Junction 9 of the M25; access is from Woodfield Road in Ashtead. Park at Ashtead Station. (NNR)

BERKSHIRE

38. Hurley Chalk Pit SU 813822

A tiny reserve in a disused chalk pit with a surprisingly rich flora amidst its grassland and beechwood. Common Spotted, Common Fragrant, Pyramidal and Bee Orchids are all abundant. There are also White Helleborines under the Beeches.

South of the B4130 Henley to Maidenhead road. Access from the bridleway south of the Black Boy Public House. (BBOWT)

39. Greenham and Crookham Commons SU 520643

Some Early Purple, Bee, Green-winged, Pyramidal, and Heath Spotted Orchids, and Autumn Lady's-tresses can be found at these sites. Also visit nearby New Greenham Park, where some very poor soils and the removal of runways from the former airfield have created good habitats for plants.

Around 3 miles southeast of Newbury; access to the commons is off the A339 through New Greenham Business Park, or from the minor road between Greenham and Thatcham.

40. Basildon Park SU 611782

Woodland with Yew and Box, and open grassland. Bee Orchid, and Narrow-lipped, Broad-leaved and Violet Helleborines are among the species to search for.

Between Pangbourne and Streatley, northwest of Reading, on the west side of the A329. (NT)

41. Lardon Chase, the Holies and Lough Down

This area of National Trust-owned downland has great views over the Thames Valley, where the river divides the Chilterns from the North Wessex Downs. The slopes form one of the largest remaining areas of chalk grassland in the county and support a wide range of invertebrates and flowers, including Bee, Common Fragrant and Pyramidal Orchids.

Just north of Streatley, west of the A417. (NT)

OXFORDSHIRE

42. Hartslock SU 616796

An area of rich chalk downland and scrub overlooking the Thames. The grassland holds Pyramidal and Man Orchids, and is the sole Oxfordshire site for Monkey Orchid. Narrow-lipped Helleborine and a handful of Lady Orchids are also present.

One mile south along the minor road from Goring Station; park by the cart track or in Goring village. (BBOWT)

43. Dry Sandford Pit SU 467997

Based around an old quarry next to Sandford Brook, with Common Spotted and Early Marsh Orchids and Marsh Helleborine.

In Cothill village, 2 miles from Abingdon, off the B4017 Wootton Road. There is a small car park and marked footpaths. (BBOWT)

44. Parsonage Moor SU 462998

Part of the Cothill Fen NNR and one of the best fenland sites in the county. Excellent woodland, fen, carr and mire communities with Southern Marsh and Pugsley's Marsh Orchids. Keep to the footpaths because the fen is deep in places.

Use the same car park as for Dry Sandford Pit (site 43). The footpath to the reserve is opposite the Merry Miller Restaurant. (BBOWT)

45. Aston Rowant SU 740968

Chalk grassland, scrub and beechwoods, now bisected by the M40, where White, Narrow-lipped and Violet Helleborines occur amongst other species.

Between Stokenchurch and Lewknor. There is a car park for the northern section of the reserve signposted off the A40, with a Forestry Commission car park at Cowleaze Wood serving the southern section. (NNR)

46. Watlington Hill SU 702935

Fine chalk grassland and scrub with some stands of Beech and Yew. There are Frog, Bee and Pyramidal Orchids at the site.

One mile southeast of Watlington, east of the B480. There is a small car park. (NT)

47. Warburg Reserve SU 720879

This incredibly rich site contains woodland, scrub and grassland in the dry valley at Bix Bottom. A network of footpaths provides access to Broad-leaved, White, Violet and Narrow-lipped Helleborines, Early Purple, Bird's-nest and Fly Orchids. Both Greater Butterfly and Lesser Butterfly Orchids are present, along with Common Twayblade, and Bee, Common Spotted and Pyramidal Orchids. BBOWT's largest reserve is a real gem.

Northwest of Henley-on-Thames. Follow signposts for Bix Bottom off the A423 at Bix. The reserve is at the end of a narrow two-mile road; there is a car park and Visitor Centre. (BBOWT)

BUCKINGHAMSHIRE

48. Homefield Wood SU 814867

Although some of the original beechwood has been cleared and planted with conifers, there is still much mixed beechwood and open chalk grassland at this site. It is traditionally managed and has a rich flora, with 11 species of orchid including Common Spotted, Fly and Bee Orchids, and it is one of only three British sites for Military Orchid.

Off the A4155 west of Marlow. Turn right before the Dog and Badger Public House. The reserve is on the left between Bockmer and Lower Woodend. (BBOWT)

49. Grangelands and Pulpit Hill SP 827049

These two sites hold a range of habitats, including chalk grassland, scrub and beechwood, with Bee, Common Fragrant, Musk, Frog, and Bird's-nest Orchids and Violet, White and Narrow-lipped Helleborines.

Northeast of Princes Risborough on the A4010, on the minor road from Askett to Great Missenden. Park in the lay-by on the left-hand side of the road. Access by the footpath going north. (Grangelands: BBOWT; Pulpit Hill: NT)

50. Dancersend and the Crong Meadow
SU 616796

Woodland and meadows in the Chiltern Hills. The chalk grassland has been cleared of scrub and has a rich flora, with Common Spotted, Bee, Common Fragrant and Pyramidal Orchids; Greater Butterfly and Fly Orchids can also be found.

Off the B4009 Wendover to Tring road. Turn towards St Leonards just before the junction with the A41; park opposite the pond. (BBOWT)

51. Bernwood Meadows SP 606111

This traditionally managed old hay meadow has a large colony of Green-winged Orchids.

Northeast of Oxford, off the minor road between Stanton St John and Oakley. Car parking is available beside the reserve on the south side of the road. (BBOWT)

52. The Ashridge Estate and Ivinghoe Beacon
SP 970131

Stretching along the northeastern edge of the Chiltern escarpment on the Hertfordshire-Buckinghamshire border from Berkhamstead to Ivinghoe Hills, this area is rich in archaeological remains. Bronze Age barrows survive around Ivinghoe Beacon and there is an impressive Bronze Age hill fort at the top. The flora is excellent. There are woodlands on the chalk scarp with Fly and Bird's-nest Orchids, and Violet and White Helleborines, wooded commons with Early Purple Orchids, Green-winged Orchids, and hard-to-find Narrow-lipped and Green-flowered Helleborines, and chalk grassland with Bee, Pyramidal, Common Fragrant, Frog and Common Spotted Orchids.

Just north of Berkhamsted, on both sides of the B4506 between the A41 and the B489. The main car park is by the Visitor Centre, just off the B4506 between Berkhamsted and Northchurch. (NT)

BEDFORDSHIRE

53. Dunstable and Whipsnade Downs
TL 000190

The extensive chalk grasslands here have fine views. The grazed slopes are plant-rich, and Bee, Pyramidal and Frog Orchids can be found.

Southwest of Dunstable, 4 miles northwest of Ashridge between the B4540 and B4541. There are car parks on the B4541. (NT)

54. Totternhoe Knolls SP 979220

Part old chalk quarry (the Little Hills), part earthworks with grass and scrub, and part beech plantation, these varied habitats hold Common Spotted and Common Fragrant Orchids, Common Twayblade and a few Musk Orchids.

Between Dunstable and Tring on the B489. Park in the picnic site car park on Castle Hill Road. (BCNPWT)

55. Sharpenhoe Clappers, Smithcombe and Sundon Hills TL 065295

Sharpenhoe Clappers is the most prominent section of chalk escarpment in Bedfordshire. This whole area is interesting; there are beechwoods on the hill tops with unimproved chalk grassland on both east- and west-facing slopes. White Helleborine and Pyramidal, Common Fragrant, Bee and Fly Orchids occur.

Reached via minor roads 1 mile southwest of Barton-le-clay. Park in the National Trust car park in Sharpenhoe village. (NT)

56. Barton Hills TL 093295

A large area of chalk grassland, scrub, beechwoods and ash-maple woodland in the Chilterns. Many species of orchid can be found including Bee, Common Spotted and Common Fragrant Orchids.

On minor roads immediately south of Barton-le-clay. Footpaths cross the area; park in Barton-le-clay. (NNR, EN)

57. Hoo Bit TL 117290

On the Icknield Way, this reserve has mixed broad-leaved woods with a good shrub layer and some chalk grassland. Adjacent to both Pegston Hills and the Herts and Middlesex WT reserve of Telegraph Hill, the whole area has a rich and interesting flora which includes Fly, Bee and Common Spotted Orchids and White Helleborine.

Between Luton and Hitchen. Park at Treasure's Grove on the minor road off the A505 between Lilley and Hexton, and walk northeast along the Icknield Way. (BCNPWT)

HERTFORDSHIRE

58. Hexton Chalk Pit   TL 107299

An old grassed-over chalk quarry with a good chalk flora, and five species of orchid. The whole area is rich in wildflowers, walks and good views.

Between Hitchen and Barton-le-Clay at Hexton. Park in Hexton off the minor road to Lilley, and walk a short distance south to the reserve. (Herts and Middlesex WT)

59. Therfield Heath and Fox Covert
TL 335400

Therfield Heath is not a heath but a fine hillside of unimproved grassland, chalk downland and hawthorn scrub. Alongside the grassland is a small, mature beechwood called Fox Covert. The flora includes Bee and Common Fragrant Orchids, with White Helleborine in the woodland.

At the roundabout on the A505 just west of Royston turn south past the 'Little Chef' and then right onto the minor road towards Therfield. Access is from the small lay-by at the top of the hill. (Herts and Middlesex WT)

60. The Meads   TQ 348141

One of the largest wetlands remaining in Hertfordshire, with flood meadows, pools and some chalk grassland where Pyramidal Orchid can be found.

Between Hertford and Ware on the A119. Park in Ware and walk west along the canal towpath to the reserve. (Herts and Middlesex WT)

61. Lee Valley Park

This is the best site in the region to see spectacular numbers of Early Marsh Orchids. They thrive on waste ash from coal-fired power stations; covering an area the size of a football pitch, they are well worth seeking out in June. There are also Southern Marsh and Common Spotted Orchids. The main areas of interest are at **Cheshunt Lock (TL 367023)** (an excellent boardwalk through a large colony of Early and Southern Marsh and Common Spotted Orchids); **Bowyers Water (TL 367020)** (near Cheshunt station) with Common Spotted, Early Marsh, Southern Marsh Orchids, and Common Twayblade; and **Fishers Green (TL 367032)** (close to Lee Valley Information Centre), where small numbers of Bee, Southern Marsh and Early Marsh Orchids surround a large artificial pond, with Pyramidal Orchids close to the nearby electricity substation.

The main access from the west is from the car park close to Cheshunt station; from the east, head to the Lee Valley Information Centre at Hooks Marsh (off the B194 at Holyfield). The Centre can provide detailed maps and directions to all these sites and information about orchid flowering times. (Lee Valley Regional Park Authority)

GREATER LONDON

62. Lee Valley Park: Rammey Marsh
TQ 370987

This area, along the outflow from King George's reservoir, has a magnificent display of Bee Orchids in most years — up to 15,000 have been counted. There are also a few Pyramidal Orchids.

Near Enfield Lock. Park by the Swan and Pike Pool and walk north towards the M25 along the canal. (Lee Valley Regional Park Authority)

63. The Ripple   TQ 467824

Once a dumping ground for pulverised fuel ash, this reclaimed industrial wasteland at Barking Reach now holds a stunning display of hundreds of Southern Marsh and Common Spotted Orchids. May and June are the best months to go.

Entrance to the site is on Thames Road/Renwick Road in Barking. (London WT)

64. West Kent Golf Course   TQ 425612

This small reserve is close to Down House, which was once the home of Charles Darwin. The chalk grassland, scrub and woodland has a wonderful flora and fauna with swathes of orchids.

Access is via a footpath from the village of Downe, along West Hill and Milking Lane. (London WT)

65. Downe Bank   TQ 438609

Lying on the North Downs, this reserve, famous for its association with Charles Darwin as his 'Orchis Bank', has mixed woodland, coppice and chalk grassland. Many species of orchid occur such as Man, Bee, Fly, Common Spotted and Pyramidal Orchids and White and Broad-leaved Helleborines.

Downe Bank is situated midway between the villages of Downe and Cudham, just south of Downe village, where it is best to park. Formerly a closed reserve, the southern half is now open for visitors. Contact the Kent WT for access to the northern half. (Kent WT)

66. Hutchinson's Bank
TQ 381616 or TQ 386607

One of the largest areas of chalk grassland remaining in the Greater London area. The grassy slopes hold Pyramidal, Common Spotted and Man Orchids. Common Twayblade and White Helleborine occur on Chapel Bank, an area of ancient woodland, scrub and grassland.

Near New Addington, Croydon. Entry is off Featherbed Lane or Farleigh Dean Crescent. (London WT)

Southwest England and Channel Islands

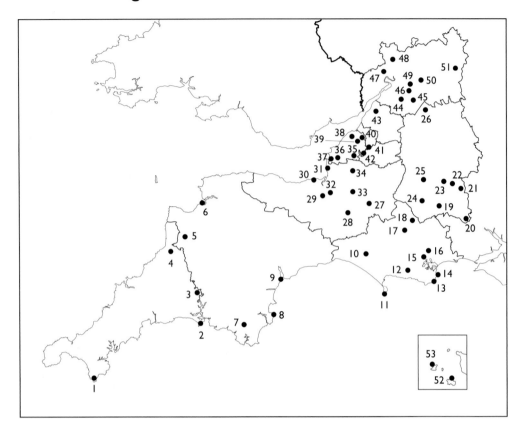

Cornwall
1   The Lizard Peninsula
2   Rame Head and Penlee Point
3   Sylvia's Meadow (St Ann's Chapel)
4   Creddacott Meadows

Devon
5   Dunsdon
6   Braunton Burrows
7   Andrew's Wood
8   Berry Head - Sharkham Point
9   Dawlish Warren

Dorset
10 Kingcombe Meadows
11 Isle of Portland
12 Tadnoll and Winfrith Heath
13 Durlston Country Park
14 Ballard Down and Nine
     Barrow Down
15 Corfe Mullen Meadow
16 Badbury Rings
17 Hambledon Hill
18 Fontmell and Melbury Downs

Wiltshire
19 West Wiltshire Downs

20 Pepperbox Hill
21 Ham Hill
22 Jones's Mill
23 Pewsey Downs
24 Parsonage Down
25 Marlborough Downs
26 Clattinger Farm Reserve

Somerset
27 Long Sutton Plantations,
28 Barrington Hill Meadows
29 West Sedgemoor
30 Porlock Bay
31 Berrow Dunes
32 Ash Priors Common
33 Great Breach Wood
34 Cheddar Gorge and Black Rock
     Nature Reserve

'Avon'
35 Blagdon Lake Pumping Station
36 Hellenge Hill
37 Walborough
38 Netcott's Meadow
39 Ashton Court Meadow
40 Avon Gorge/Leigh Woods

41 Brown's Folly
42 Folly Farm

Gloucestershire
43 Lower Woods
44 Minchinhampton and
     Rodborough Commons
45 Strawberry Banks
46 Elliot (Swift's Hill)
47 Plump Hill Dolomite Quarry
48 Betty Daw's Wood
49 Painswick Hill
50 Cotswold commons and
     beechwoods
51 Greystones Farm and
     Salmonsbury Meadows

Channel Islands
52 Le Noir Pré, Jersey
53 The 'Orchid Fields' at Les Vicheries,
     Guernsey

CORNWALL

1. The Lizard Peninsula
SW 687133 (Kynance)
SW 667163 (Predannack)

The Lizard is the most southerly point of the British Isles and has many rare native plants. Orchids, however, are of interest more from a local viewpoint than a national one. Around 10 species occur, including Green-winged and Early Marsh Orchids, which occur virtually nowhere else in Cornwall. Heath Fragrant Orchid can be locally common on the Lizard's heaths; others present include Common Twayblade and Autumn Lady's-tresses.

Many orchids can be seen from the coastal footpath between the car parks at Kynance and Predannack Wollas. (NNR, NT)

2. Rame Head and Penlee Battery   SX 436492
An area of coastal grassland with extensive gorse scrub. An interesting area, it holds Cornwall's main population of Bee Orchid and is the only known site in southeast Cornwall for Pyramidal Orchid. Early Purple and Southern Marsh Orchids can be found along the footpaths, as well as a few Autumn Lady's-tresses.

Parking is available at Penlee Battery Cornwall WT reserve and at Rame Head, from which coastal paths are easily accessed.

3. Sylvia's Meadow (St Ann's Chapel)
SX 413707

This small reserve of unimproved herb-rich grassland is one of Cornwall's best single sites for orchids, with eight species recorded. Heath Spotted, Lesser Butterfly and Early Purple Orchids can be abundant, and there may be a few spikes of Greater Butterfly Orchid. Southern Marsh Orchids and their hybrids with Heath Spotted Orchid also occur. Common Spotted Orchid is a rarity in Cornwall but a few can be found here, along with Autumn Lady's-tresses and Broad-leaved Helleborine.

South of Kit Hill and west of Gunnislake, with parking available at Honicombe. A public footpath runs south from the A390 alongside the reserve. (Cornwall WT).

4. Creddacott Meadows   SX 234963
One of the last remnants of species-rich damp culm grassland in Cornwall. Lesser Butterfly Orchid and Heath Spotted Orchid occur, among others.

Park off the B3254 Launceston to Bude road, at Week St Mary. (Cornwall WT, Plantlife)

DEVON

5. Dunsdon   SS 302080
One of the best examples of culm grassland in Devon. There are good displays of Lesser Butterfly, Heath Spotted and Southern Marsh Orchids.

Between Holsworthy and Bude, off the A3072 to Pancrasweek. The entrance to the reserve and car park is just before Gains Cross. (Devon WT)

6. Braunton Burrows   SS 464326
The largest sand dune system in the UK, with a very diverse plant community. There are vast numbers of Pyramidal Orchids, and also Southern Marsh Orchids and large colonies of Marsh Helleborines in the dune slacks. Recently named the UK's first Biosphere Reserve.

On the north bank of the Taw/Torridge estuary, west of Barnstable. There are two car parks with information.

7. Andrew's Wood   SX 707515
A fascinating reserve of ancient meadows and woods, over an old field system. The flora benefits from traditional management; there are Southern Marsh and Heath Spotted Orchids, with Broad-leaved Helleborine and Common Twayblade in the woodland.

Close to Loddiswell north of Kingsbridge, there is a track to the reserve from the car park just beyond Coldharbour Cross. (Devon WT)

8. Berry Head - Sharkham Point   SY 945567
A large coastal area comprising two headlands and a smaller promontory, Durl Head. There is an important flora on the cliff-tops, and in the grassland and scrub areas, with eight species of orchid. These include Early Purple and Green-winged Orchids, Common Twayblade, Bee, Common Spotted and Pyramidal Orchids, and Autumn Lady's-tresses.

The site lies at the southern end of Torbay past Brixham. (Berry Head Country Park, NNR)

9. Dawlish Warren   SX 983787
A range of coastal habitats around a double sand spit that extends across the mouth of the River Exe. The dune grassland is of great botanical interest and has Autumn Lady's-tresses in good numbers.

Off the A379; the car park is through the entrance tunnel under the railway in Dawlish Warren village. (Devon WT, NNR)

DORSET

10. Kingcombe Meadows   SY 555992
A large area of species-rich old grassland, hedgerows, woodland and common land – a real ancient landscape. Heath Spotted, Early Purple and Bee Orchids are abundant.

The site is at Lower Kingcombe near Toller Porcorum. There are small car parks, footpaths and a Visitor Centre at Pound Cottage, off the B356. (Dorset WT)

11. Isle of Portland   SY 685700

Famous for its limestone quarries, there is still much of interest on the cliff-tops and in the abandoned quarry workings. Two are worthy of visits to search for orchids: The Broadcroft Quarry Reserve and Tout Quarry. There is also a large car park at Portland Bill, and a variety of orchids to be found in the surrounding grasslands. Bee and Pyramidal Orchids and Autumn Lady's-tresses are particularly abundant.

Access to the Isle of Portland is on the A354 from Weymouth. Carry on to Southwell and the large car park at the lighthouse for the Bill. (BC)

12. Tadnoll and Winfrith Heath   SY 795876

A large example of Dorset heath, bogs and meadows, part of Thomas Hardy's 'Egdon Heath', with typical flora and fauna. Heath Spotted and Southern Marsh Orchids occur, along with the hard-to-find Bog Orchid, and Autumn Lady's-tresses.

From the A352, the Tadnoll entrance is along Redbridge Road, while the Winfrith Heath entrance is on Gatemore Road (with limited parking). (Dorset WT).

13. Durlston Country Park   SY 032773

Limestone grassland occurs along the south coast of Dorset and its speciality, Early Spider Orchid, can be found anywhere from Durlston Head west to Worth Matravers. Other species in the area include Green-winged, Early Purple and Bee Orchids.

Durlston Country Park lies on a minor road south from Swanage.

14. Ballard Down and Nine Barrow Down   SY 050820

On the Isle of Purbeck chalk ridge, these downs contain steep slopes and cliff-tops, with Common Fragrant and Early Purple Orchids present.

Between Ballard Head and Old Harry Rocks, the downs are easily accessible on foot from car parks at Studland (NT) *and Swanage.*

15. Corfe Mullen Meadow   SY 980967

A small but flower-rich meadow with a stunning colony of Green-winged Orchids.

Northwest of Poole on the B3074 at Corfe Mullen, with roadside parking. (Dorset WT)

16. Badbury Rings   ST 964029

An Iron Age hill fort on the Kingston Lacy Estate. A wonderful site with a rich downland flora and a great variety of orchid species. On the hill fort itself Frog Orchid is a speciality; other species include Common Fragrant and Common Spotted Orchids, Common Twayblade, Early Purple, Green-winged, Pyramidal and Bee Orchids, Greater Butterfly Orchid and Autumn Lady's-tresses, with White Helleborine and Bird's-nest Orchid under the roadside Beech trees.

Access is from the car park on the north side of the B3082 Wimborne to Blandford road. (NT)

17. Hambledon Hill   ST 845125

Dramatic chalk grassland with an impressive Iron Age earthwork. A rich chalk flora includes Early Purple and Pyramidal Orchids.

Northwest of Blandford Forum off the A350, there is limited parking off Duck Street and Shaftsbury Road near Child Okeford. Plenty of footpaths give good access to the site. (NNR)

18. Fontmell and Melbury Downs   ST 884176, ST 885187

An outstanding area of chalk downland, scrub and woodland, which includes Melbury Beacon. Autumn Lady's-tresses and Green-winged, Common Fragrant, Greater Butterfly, Frog, Pyramidal, Bee and Early Purple Orchids can all be found here.

Access is via footpaths from the National Trust viewpoint car park at the top of Spread Eagle Hill. (NT, Dorset WT)

WILTSHIRE

19. West Wiltshire Downs

A wonderful landscape of natural and archaeological features, southwest of Salisbury. There are many places to visit – here is a selection.

Coombe Bisset Down (SU 111256) Rich chalk grassland with scrub and beechwoods. There are many Bee Orchids, with the very local Burnt Orchid.

Clearbury Rings (SU 152245), with over 1,000 Burnt Orchids on the gentle, south-facing slopes of Clearbury Down.

Middleton Down (SU 043252), with Early Purple Orchids and Autumn Lady's-tresses, among others.

20. Pepperbox Hill   SU 212248

Rough chalk grassland and mixed scrub with a good selection of orchid species. Common Spotted, Frog, Common Fragrant and Pyramidal Orchids, White Helleborine, Common Twayblade and Autumn Lady's-tresses all occur.

Off the A36 southeast of Salisbury, with parking on the minor road between West Grinstead and West Dean. (NT)

21. Ham Hill   SU 334616

A small, very steep chalk downland reserve with abundant wildlife and good views. The flora includes Common Twayblade and Common Fragrant Orchid, and also a few Musk Orchids.

Off the A336 Burbage to Hungerford road, between Shalbourne and Ham on the road to Buttermere, with parking on the left-hand verge. (Wiltshire WT)

22. Jones's Mill   SU 168613

Wet woodland and fen meadows with Southern Marsh and Common Spotted Orchids.

Just north of Pewsey off the B3087 to Burbage; the reserve entrance is close to a small lay-by, just over the railway bridge. Alternatively, walk from Pewsey along the Kennet & Avon towpath. (Wiltshire WT)

23. Pewsey Downs   SU 120640

Perhaps the finest site on the Marlborough Downs, comprising Milk Hill, White Horse Hill, Walkers Hill and Knapp Hill, with some of the best habitats the region can offer. Common Spotted, Burnt, Bee, Frog, Common Fragrant, Lesser Butterfly, Green-winged and Pyramidal Orchids and Autumn Lady's-tresses all occur here.

In the Vale of Pewsey between Devizes and Pewsey, southwest of Marlborough. Access is via the unclassified road between the A361 and A345. Car parking is at Knapp Hill. (NNR)

24. Parsonage Down   SU 055415

Some wonderful downland and pastures with a history of traditional grazing management. There are many interesting species here; orchids include Green-winged, Frog and perhaps as many as 30,000 Burnt Orchids spread over 95 hectares, forming the largest colony in Northwest Europe.

The site is at Cherry Lodge Farm, Shrewton, on the south edge of Salisbury Plain, between Shrewton and Winterbourne Stoke on the B2083. (NNR)

25. Marlborough Downs

An impressive area surrounding Marlborough, mostly consisting of gently undulating chalk grassland. Traditional grazing has ensured a rich flora and fauna, with many areas now designated nature reserves. Here are two great places to visit.

Morgan's Hill (SU 025672) and Kingsplay Hill (SU 006658) On the western edge of Marlborough downs with chalk grassland and scrub; both have a good orchid flora.

Cherhill Down and Oldbury Castle (SU 046694) The chalk grassland on the southern slopes has a rich flora, including Lesser Butterfly Orchid. (NT)

26. Clattinger Farm Reserve   SU 017937

This site consists almost wholly of unimproved species-rich alluvial grasslands, with spectacular displays of hay-meadow flowers. Green-winged Orchid, Common Twayblade, Common and Heath Spotted Orchids, Early and Southern Marsh Orchids and Burnt Orchid (outside its normal downland habitat) are present.

Off the B4040 between Malmesbury and Cirencester, with parking on the roadside. (Wiltshire WT)

SOMERSET

27. Long Sutton Plantations, Burnt House and Monday's Court Lane   ST 461269

This is a wonderful mix of lanes, plantations and beech copses, with White Helleborine, Greater Butterfly Orchid and Common Twayblade in the woods and Bee and Pyramidal Orchids in the open areas.

Northwest of Yeovil, off the B3165 between Long Sutton and Mortock. Park on the road verge before the railway bridge.

28. Barrington Hill Meadows   ST 290169

Several species-rich unimproved meadows on the southern edge of the Blackdown Hills, with old hedges and ponds. There is a large colony of Green-winged Orchids.

Northwest of Ilminster on the minor road off the A358 between Bickenhall and Broadway. Park beside the road along Folly Drive. (NNR)

29. West Sedgemoor   ST 365255

Woodland and traditionally managed grazing meadows, often flooded in winter. The wet meadows contain a wide variety of flowers; one notable field, slightly higher than the rest, holds cowslips and Green-winged Orchids.

East of Taunton on the A378 Langport road. Car parking is east of Fivehead. (RSPB)

30. Porlock Bay   SS 885482

A fine area of species-rich dunes and foreshore that is particularly good for orchids, with a large colony of Autumn Lady's-tresses.

Porlock is west of Minehead on the A39. Minor roads lead to the coast and the coastal footpath.

31. Berrow Dunes   ST 299515

An area of reedbeds and dunes beside Berrow Golf Course. The dune slacks hold Southern Marsh Orchids and Marsh Helleborines in good numbers, and Heath Spotted Orchid also occurs.

Just north of Burnham-on-Sea. The golf course is on the coast road. Park beside the church. (Somerset WT)

32. Ash Priors Common   ST 151289

Scrub, grassland, woodland and heath habitats, with a good variety of orchids: Heath Spotted, Common Spotted, Southern Marsh and Early Purple Orchids, and Common Twayblade all occur.

Northwest of Taunton off the A358 at Ash Priors. Car parking is available beside the common. (Taunton and District Borough Council)

33. Great Breach Wood   ST 506325

One of Somerset's largest reserves, with mixed woodland and grassland. In some areas orchids are plentiful; there are Early Purple, Greater Butterfly and Pyramidal Orchids on the steep south- and west-facing slopes, for example. There are many rides and paths through the site.

South of Glastonbury, between Street and Somerton. Park near Butleigh Park on the minor road from the B3153. (Somerset WT)

34. Cheddar Gorge and Black Rock
ST 482545

Limestone grassland, plantation and woodland at the head of Cheddar Gorge. Part of the Cheddar complex, the area is botanically rich; orchids to be found include Broad-leaved and Narrow-lipped Helleborines.

Park at Black Rock Gate, on the B3135 just northwest of Cheddar. (Somerset WT)

AVON

35. Blagdon Lake Pumping Station   ST 503598

An excellent if unusual site for Green-winged Orchids.

Bristol Water have many open days for public access. Contact them for details of orchid flowering times. (Bristol Water. Tel: 0117 966 5881)

36. Hellenge Hill
ST 345572

Calcareous grassland and scrub on the south side of the Mendips with great views. Autumn Lady's-tresses are abundant in some areas.

At Bleadon, south of Weston-Super-Mare. (Avon WT)

37. Walborough
ST 316579

An area of limestone grassland beside the sea wall at Uphill. There are Green-winged and Early Purple Orchids and Autumn Lady's-tresses.

South of Uphill village. Park by the sluice gates near the beach and walk along the sea wall. (Avon WT)

38. Netcott's Meadow
ST 476696

An area of semi-improved neutral, damp grassland with Green-winged, Early Purple, Southern Marsh and Bee Orchids present in large numbers.

Close to Nailsea, Bristol, with parking after the railway bridge. (Avon WT)

39. Ashton Court Meadow
ST 545720

Part of the Ashton Court Estate and close to the centre of Bristol. In May the meadow is full of Green-winged Orchids.

Off the A369 Bristol to Portishead road. Park in the lay-by on Beggar Bush Lane, the B3129. (Avon WT)

40. Avon Gorge
ST 553731

A fantastic area, the Avon gorge cuts through the limestone only 2 miles from the centre of Bristol. **Clifton and Durham Downs** are large areas of limestone grassland with abundant Bee and Com-mon Spotted Orchids. There are smaller numbers of Pyramidal and Green-winged Orchids. On the west side of the gorge **Leigh Woods (ST 555730)** hold Bird's-nest and Fly Orchids, and Broad-leaved Helleborines.

The area is easily accessed from Bristol on the A4018 and the A4. Leigh Woods are on the A369 Portishead to Bristol road.

41. Brown's Folly
ST 795665

Calcareous grassland and mature secondary wood-land with some ancient semi-natural areas. Broad-leaved Helleborine together with Early Purple, Bee, Pyramidal and Common Spotted Orchids can be found on and around the grassland. Elsewhere, Bird's-nest Orchid and White Helleborine occur within the wood.

East of Bath, off the A36 at Bathampton opposite the golf course. (Avon WT)

42. Folly Farm
ST 607605

Species-rich neutral grassland and ancient semi-natural woodland. There are Common Spotted and Heath Spotted Orchids, as well as hybrids between the two. Common Twayblades are also present within the wood, with Early Purple Orchids and Vio-let Helleborines.

East of Bishop Sutton, south of Bristol; the site is sign-posted off the A368, to the east of its junction with the A37. (Avon WT)

GLOUCESTERSHIRE

43. Lower Woods
ST 743876

One of England's largest stands of ancient oak-ash woodland. It contains a diversity of habitats, includ-ing species-rich grassland, coppiced woodland and wooded common. Early Purple, Greater Butterfly and Common Spotted Orchids and Violet Hellebo-rine can all be found.

Between Hawksbury and Wickwar. Park by the Lodge on the minor road off the B4509 at Wickwar. (Gloucestershire WT)

44. Minchinhampton Common   SO 850010
and Rodborough Common   SO 850038

Some of the best areas of limestone grassland on the edge of the Cotswolds. There are great views, and Minchinhampton has much of archaeologi-cal interest. Many species of orchid have been re-corded among the varied flora. There are Common Spotted, Pyramidal, Early Purple, Green-winged, Common Fragrant, Bee, Frog and Greater Butterfly Orchids, as well as Autumn Lady's-tresses, Com-mon Twayblade and White, Broad-leaved and Nar-row-lipped Helleborines. Both commons are worth exploring.

Off the A46 between Stroud and Nailsworth. (NT)

45. Strawberry Banks   SO 910033

This limestone grassland on a west-facing slope has a rich flora. There is also some mixed scrub and a small stream. Greater Butterfly, Bee, Common Spotted, Green-winged, Early Purple and Pyramidal Orchids all occur. It is reached by walking through Three Groves Wood Nature Reserve, where Broad-leaved Helleborine can be found.

East of Chalford between France Lynch and Oakridge villages. There is a small car park. (Gloucestershire WT)

46. Elliot (Swift's Hill)   SO 877067

This area of limestone grassland and old quarry workings is carefully managed by grazing, and 11 species of orchid regularly occur. These include Pyramidal, Common Fragrant, Early Purple and Fly Orchids, and Autumn Lady's-tresses.

Just northeast of Stroud, on the minor road to Elcombe. (Gloucestershire WT)

47. Plump Hill Dolomite Quarry   SO 661171

An interesting site with steep exposed rock faces and a limestone flora on the quarry floor. There is a good colony of Autumn Lady's-tresses.

South of Mitcheldean beside the A4136. Park in the lay-by. (Gloucestershire WT)

48. Betty Daw's Wood   SO 696284

An ancient Sessile Oak woodland, part of a larger complex, with a good ground flora that includes Bird's-nest Orchid and White Helleborine.

West of Gloucester, northwest of Newent, at Four Oaks. Park and walk from the village. (Gloucestershire WT)

49. Painswick Hill   SO 869120

Excellent chalk grassland on a steep-sided hill fort, where Bee, Fly, Musk, Frog and Greater Butterfly Orchids, and Autumn Lady's-tresses can be found.

South of Gloucester on the B4073 to Painswick. There are several footpaths and two long-distance paths, the Wysis Way and the Cotswold Way, meet here.

50. Cotswold commons and beechwoods

The finest Cotswold beechwoods occur on the scarp and dip slopes between Gloucester and Stroud around Cranham, Sheepscombe and Painswick. The whole area contains important examples of ancient woods, grassland and streams and there are many designated nature reserves. **Buckholt Wood (SO 894131)** is one of the finest with an interesting shrub layer and good ground flora. Orchids typical of beech woodland occur here, such as Bird's-nest and Greater Butterfly Orchids and Broad-leaved, White, Narrow-lipped, and Green-flowered Helleborines.

Access to Buckholt Wood at various points from minor roads east off the A46, 3 miles northeast of Painswick. (NNR)

51. Greystones Farm and Salmonsbury Meadows   SP 173209

With traditional hay meadows, grazing land and streams, this is an attractive place to visit. Early Marsh and Southern Marsh Orchids are abundant in the meadows.

Close to Bourton-on-the-Water; park and follow the Oxfordshire Way, off Moor Lane. (Gloucestershire WT)

THE CHANNEL ISLANDS

52. Le Noir Pré, Jersey

Two adjoining wet meadows, the speciality here is Loose-flowered Orchid. There are also Southern Marsh, Heath Spotted and Common Spotted Orchids.

The entrance is at Le Chemin de L'Ouziere, a minor road off Le Grand Route de Mielle (Five Mile Road). There is an open day in late May, and unrestricted access for several weeks in the summer. (National Trust for Jersey)

53. The 'Orchid Fields' at Les Vicheries, Guernsey

An area of low-lying wet meadows in southwest Guernsey. The rich flora includes Loose-flowered Orchid as well as Heath Spotted, Common Spotted and Southern Marsh Orchids.

In the St Peter in the Wood region. The reserve lies close to the main coast road along the Rue du Douit du Moulin and the Rue des Vicheries, where there is a La Société Guernesiaise information board.

East Anglia

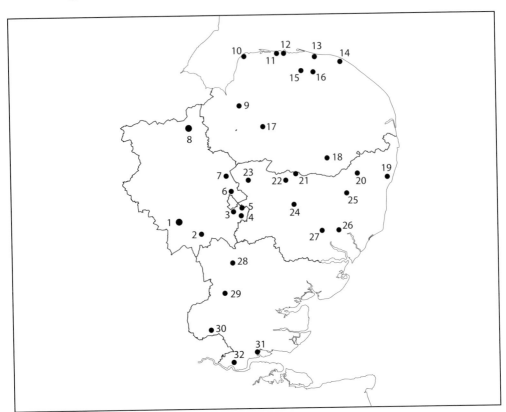

Cambridgeshire
1 Hayley Wood
2 Thriplow Meadows
3 Beechwood
4 Fulbourn Educational Reserve
5 Devil's Dyke
6 Wicken Fen
7 Soham Meadows
8 Upwood Meadows

Norfolk
9   Narborough Railway Line
10 Holme Dunes
11 Holkham
12 Wells Woods
13 Beeston Regis and Sheringham Commons
14 Overstrand
15 Foxley Wood
16 Buxton Heath
17 Thompson Common
18 New Buckenham Common

Suffolk
19 Reydon Wood
20 Wink's Meadow
21 Redgrave and Lopham Fens
22 Market Weston Fen
23 Rex Graham Reserve
24 Bradfield Woods
25 Chippenhall Green
26 Wolves Wood
27 Groton Wood

Essex
28 West Wood
29 Hatfield Forest
30 Roding Valley Meadows
31 Langdon
32 Grays Chalk Quarry

CAMBRIDGESHIRE

1. Hayley Wood — TL 294534

An ancient woodland with a long recorded history of management. There are fine displays of woodland flowers in spring, with Early Purple, Common Spotted and Bird's-nest Orchids.

On the B1046 between Cambridge and Sandy, about 3 miles from Gamlingay. Park on the road verge. (BCNPWT)

2. Thriplow Meadows — TL 445470

A small area of traditionally managed unimproved grassland. Bee Orchids are among the rich flora on the dry ground, with good populations of Early and Southern Marsh Orchids in the wetter areas.

Parking is by the Village Hall in Thriplow, south of Cambridge off the B1368. A footpath leads to the reserve from the road junction. (BCNPWT)

3. Beechwood LNR — TL 486548

A beech plantation on thin chalky soils, with a fine colony of White Helleborines (3,800 were counted in 1998) and a few Common Twayblades. Green-flowered Helleborine has been recorded here.

From the roundabout on the A1307 southeast of Cambridge turn northeast onto the minor road towards Cherry Hinton; then turn right towards Fulbourn. Park in the lay-by opposite the wood. (BCNPWT)

4. Fulbourn Educational Reserve — TL 528560

Ancient wet meadows with alder woods and scrub; Common Twayblade, Early Marsh and Southern Marsh, Common Spotted and Bee Orchids can be found in the rough pasture.

On the minor road southeast out of Fulbourn leading to Balsham. Park on the roadside. (BCNPWT).

5. Devil's Dyke — TL 616616

This massive 8-mile long earthwork, a ditch and rampart about 60 feet high, is thought to have been built in the sixth century. It bisects Newmarket's July race course and continues towards Reach. It supports important areas of chalk grassland notable for colonies of Lizard Orchids (especially to the south-east of the A45). Other species include Pyramidal and Common Spotted Orchids.

A footpath runs along the dyke from the roundabout at the junction of the A1303 and A1304, 2 miles southwest of Newmarket. The Dyke can also be accessed from the B1102 between Swaffham Prior and Burwell.

6. Wicken Fen — TL 554702

One of Britain's oldest nature reserves, Wicken Fen lies nine miles northeast of Cambridge, and contains reedbeds, sedge-fen, ditches, open water, peat diggings, and birch and sallow carr. The open fen is rich in plant life with Southern Marsh and Early Marsh Orchids (in a variety of colour forms).

Signposted from Wicken village, on the A1123 northeast of Cambridge. With nature trails and a Visitor Centre. (NNR, NT)

7. Soham Meadows — TL 608722

An area of traditionally managed unimproved grassland with Bee and Common Spotted Orchids, Common Twayblade and a small number of typically elusive Frog Orchids.

Alongside the A142 Soham bypass, with parking in the lay-by. (BCNPWT)

8. Upwood Meadows — TL 251825

A permanent pasture on calcareous boulder clay. The ridge and furrow landscape indicates an ancient arable history, but the meadows have been grassed and traditionally managed for at least 300 years. They have a rich flora with large numbers of Green-winged Orchids in May.

Two and a half miles southwest of Ramsey, which is on the B1040. Go down Meadow Road and park in Upwood. (BCNPWT)

NORFOLK

9. Narborough Railway Line — TF 750118

This sunny railway embankment was built with chalk ballast, and now supports a rich chalk flora. Common Twayblade, and Southern Marsh and Common Spotted Orchids occur along the path, with Marsh Helleborines in the pits on the sides.

Take the A47 from Narborough towards Swaffham; there is a small car park beside the railway line. (Norfolk WT)

10. Holme Dunes — TF 697438

This site includes a range of coastal habitats, with good dune and saltmarsh communities. Marsh Helleborine, Early Marsh Orchid (including the red-flowered *coccinea*), and Southern Marsh Orchid are common.

Access is from the A149 east of Hunstanton, through Holme village. There are car parks at the beach and at the reserve centre one mile further east. (NNR, Norfolk WT)

11. Holkham — TF 892441

The westward continuation of Wells Woods (site 12), but with more extensive dune slacks on the seaward side of the pines. Marsh Helleborine and Southern Marsh Orchid can be abundant, with scattered Common Spotted, Pyramidal and Bee Orchids. Creeping Lady's-tresses occurs very locally in the pinewoods.

Access is from Lady Anne's Drive (north off the A149,

opposite the entrance to Holkham Hall); the areas to the west of the car park, including the dunes past the west end of the pines, are best. (NNR)

12. Wells Woods   TF 913454

These coastal dunes are planted with Corsican Pines, but contain some relict areas of dune slacks, especially at 'The Dell', where Southern Marsh and Common Spotted Orchids and Marsh Helleborine are abundant, with a few Common Twayblades and Bee Orchids as well. Creeping Lady's-tresses occurs very locally in the pinewoods.

Access is from Wells beach car park (signposted from the town centre); The Dell lies to the north of the path 450 yards west of the kissing gate.

13. Beeston Regis and Sheringham Commons
TG 166425

A small but very diverse site with rough grassland, alkaline mires, acid heath and a little woodland. Marsh Helleborine and Common Spotted and Marsh Fragrant Orchids are abundant, as are a confusing mixture of marsh orchids (almost all intermediate between Pugsley's and Southern Marsh Orchids, with a few 'pure' plants). Common Twayblade and Bee, Pyramidal and Heath Spotted Orchids occur in small numbers; Green-winged, Early Purple and Lesser Butterfly Orchids are also present but hard to find.

Access is from the lay-by on the south side of the A149, 1 mile east of Sheringham.

14. Overstrand   TG 246411

The slumped clay cliffs at Overstrand have many flushes and seepages, and hold large numbers of the delightful red *coccinea* form of Early Marsh Orchid, as well as Southern Marsh, Common Spotted and Bee Orchids.

Access is from the cliff-top car park at Overstrand, on the coast east of Cromer. Take the path to the beach and walk north, scrambling up the slopes from time to time (it can be very slippery).

15. Foxley Wood   TF 049229

The largest area of ancient woodland in Norfolk, with wide, grassy, flower-rich rides. Early Purple, Common Spotted and a very few Greater Butterfly Orchids can be seen here.

Fifteen miles northwest of Norwich at Foxley village, off the A1067 Norwich to Fakenham Road. There is a car park at the wood. (Norfolk WT)

16. Buxton Heath   TG 172216

An area of heath and mire with a small alkaline stream. The mix of vegetation is very interesting with Marsh Helleborine, Common and Heath Spotted Orchids and Southern and Pugsley's Marsh Orchids (and some confusing intermediates).

Just east of the B1149 Norwich to Holt Road northwest of Heavingham. There is a small car park.

17. Thompson Common   TL 934967

A fascinating place to visit, with open water (Thompson Water), carr, grassland, scrub and woodland as well as a number of pingos (shallow ponds formed by glacial activity). Early Marsh (subspecies *incarnata*) and Southern Marsh Orchids can be found, and possibly Pugsley's Marsh Orchid.

Accessed from Watton on the A1075 to Thetford. Car parking is available just before Stow Bedon at the Great Eastern Pingo Trail car park. (Norfolk WT)

18. New Buckenham Common   TM 090906

This traditionally managed common has never been ploughed. The site's speciality is a large colony of Green-winged Orchids.

Four miles south of Attleborough on the B1113 at New Buckenham, with parking available beside the common. (Norfolk WT)

SUFFOLK

There are many well-managed Roadside Nature Reserves in Suffolk that hold some interesting and local orchids; look out for the wooden marker posts. In particular, the Claydon and A140 roundabouts along the A14 hold huge colonies of Pyramidal Orchids.

19. Reydon Wood   TM 480788

This small ancient wood is managed as a 'Community Wood' by local people. There is hazel coppice, ancient Ash stools, and many rides. Several orchid species occur here, including Early Purple, Common Spotted and Bird's-nest Orchids and Common Twayblade.

On the B1126 Southwold to Wangford road. Park at the end of Wood Lane. (Suffolk WT)

20. Wink's Meadow   TM 303799

This is a traditionally managed meadow with an excellent flora. Species to be found include Common Twayblade, Common Spotted, Green-winged, Early Purple, Pyramidal and Bee Orchids, and the only colony of Frog Orchids in Suffolk (they are hard to find).

Accessed via Metfield on the B1123. Take the road opposite the garage, parking on the concrete pad near the meadow entrance. (Suffolk WT, Plantlife)

21. Redgrave and Lopham Fens   TM 046797

This large reserve lies on the border between Suffolk and Norfolk in the Waveney Valley. The internationally important valley fen is flanked by woodland, open water, reed and sedge beds and wet heath. Southern and Early Marsh Orchids, Common Twayblade, and a few Marsh Fragrant Orchids are present.

Signposted between Redgrave and South Lopham on the B1113; there are car parks and a Visitor Centre. (NNR, Suffolk WT)

22. Market Weston Fen   TL 981789

A fine remnant of a valley fen dominated by Great Fen Sedge, with adjacent heath and ponds. Species include Marsh Fragrant, Common Spotted and Southern Marsh Orchids. An array of hybrids can usually be found too.

West of Diss on the B1111, off the minor road between Hopton and Coney Beeston Road. (Suffolk WT)

23. Rex Graham Reserve

This Suffolk WT reserve protects one of the few remaining British sites for Military Orchid. The Trust opens the reserve to the public on 1-2 days each year in late May or early June, to allow viewing of this very special orchid. Contact the Trust for details. (Suffolk WT)

24. Bradfield Woods   TL 935581

An ancient wood, one of the richest in the country, comprising coppice-with-standards. Parts are known to have been traditionally managed since 1252. There is a diverse ground flora, and Early Purple Orchid can be found in spring, with Green-flowered Helleborine elusive in mid-summer.

On the road between Bradfield St George and Felsham, 12 miles southeast of Bury St Edmunds. (NNR, Suffolk WT)

25. Chippenhall Green   TM 285757

A very impressive colony of Green-winged Orchids grows on this area of common land 'enclosed' by cattle grids.

Southeast of Fressingfield on the B1116. Take the minor road to Chippenhall Green at Rackham's Corner.

26. Wolves Wood   TM 054440

An ancient woodland with hazel and hawthorn coppice and scrub. The wide rides have a good ground flora with several species of orchid, including Violet Helleborine under the coppice.

On the A1071, 2 miles east of Hadleigh and 8 miles west of Ipswich. (RSPB)

27. Groton Wood   TL 976428

A stand of ancient woodland with old lime coppice, traditionally managed. The rides have an interesting flora with Early Purple Orchid and Violet Helleborine, with a particularly good colony of helleborines under the old hazel coppice on the west side of the wood.

North of the A1071; along a maze of lanes 3 miles west of Hadleigh, between Castling's Heath and Kersey Tye. (Suffolk WT)

ESSEX

28. West Wood   TL 624332

An ancient woodland on chalky boulder clay, with a rich ground flora that includes Early Purple and Greater Butterfly Orchids.

Midway between Thaxted and Great Sampford on the B1051. Park beside the road. (Essex WT)

29. Hatfield Forest   TL 547202

One of the last medieval royal forests to retain much of its original character and composition. The site contains mixed habitats of ancient woodland, pasture, glades and marshy ground, separated by ditches and banks. The ground flora includes Violet Helleborine and Bird's-nest, Bee and Pyramidal Orchids in the woods and glades, and Early Marsh and Common Spotted Orchids in the fens.

Park off the A120 at Takely near the M11 Junction 8. (NNR, NT)

30. Roding Valley Meadows   TO 430943

A traditionally managed river valley with hay meadows, scrub and woodland beside the River Roding. The wet meadows hold many Southern Marsh Orchids.

Park next to the David Lloyd Centre, Roding Lane, Chigwell. There are other footpaths on the Loughton side of the River. (Essex WT)

31. Langdon   TQ 659874

An unusual site with much social history. The abandoned 'plotlands' are patchworks of old gardens and grassland bordered by hedgerows and orchards. Green-winged Orchids can be seen in their thousands in the Lincewood area, and Common Spotted, Green-winged, Pyramidal and Bee Orchids can be found in the area of Marks Hill.

West of Basildon off the B1036. There is a car park and Visitor Centre. (Essex WT)

32. Grays Chalk Quarry   TQ 611787

A long-disused quarry now with woodland, a small area of chalk grassland and a pond. There are many orchid species present, with good numbers of Man, Pyramidal and Bee Orchids.

Park in the public car park on London Road near Grays town centre. The entrance to the site is opposite, via a short path. (Essex WT)

Central England

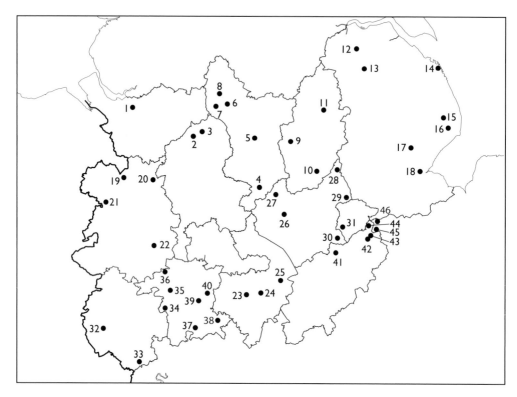

Cheshire
1 Witton Lime Beds

Staffordshire
2 Rod Wood
3 Coombes Valley

Derbyshire
4 Hilton Gravel Pits
5 Rose End Meadows
6 Derbyshire Dales
7 Deep Dale
8 Miller's Dale Quarry

Nottinghamshire
9 Bentinck Banks
10 Wilwell Farm Cutting
11 Eaton Wood

Lincolnshire
12 Messingham Sand Quarry
13 Kingerby Beck Meadows
14 Donna Nook and
Saltfleetby Dunes
15 Candlesby Hill Quarry
16 Heath's Meadows
17 Ancaster Valley
18 Moulton Marsh

Shropshire
19 Wem Moss
20 Granville Country Park
21 Llynclys Common
22 Wenlock Edge

Warwickshire
23 Snitterfield Bushes

24 Ufton Fields
25 Draycote Meadow

Leicestershire
26 Lea Meadows
27 Cloud Wood
28 Muston Meadows
29 Cribbs Meadow
30 Great Merrible Wood

Rutland
31 Prior's Coppice

Herefordshire
32 Davies Meadows
33 The Doward Reserves

Worcestershire
34 The Knapp and Papermill

35 Monkwood
36 Wyre Forest
37 Tiddesley Wood
38 Windmill Hill
39 Trench Wood
40 Eades Meadow

Northamptonshire
41 Stoke Wood End Quarter
42 Glapthom Cow Pastures
43 Short Wood
44 Collyweston Quarries
45 Bedford Purlieus
46 Barnack Hills and Holes

CHESHIRE

1. Witton Lime Beds   SJ 660746

These lime beds were produced by the chemical and salt industries near Northwich. The Aston's Flash area is notable for the magnificent show of Marsh Fragrant Orchids. More than 10,000 spikes have been recorded on the site in some years. Marsh Helleborine also occurs.

Northeast of Northwich on the far side of the Trent & Mersey Canal. Access is from the minor road west of the Flash. Park just before the village of Marston on the B5075.

STAFFORDSHIRE

2. Rod Wood   SJ 997531

With some fine meadows, woodland and marsh, the interesting flora here includes Common Twayblade and Early Purple Orchid.

Near Leek. Accessed from the A523 Leek to Ashbourne road; go past the RSPB Coombes Valley reserve (Site 3 below) to the top of the hill. Park past the cattle grid. (Staffordshire WT)

3. Coombes Valley   SK 005525

A steep valley among old woodland with the Coombes Brook running the length of the reserve. There is some good flower-rich grassland here, with Common Spotted and Greater Butterfly Orchids. *Southeast of Leek; take the A523 Leek to Ashbourne road and go along the minor road signposted to Apesford.* (RSPB, Staffordshire WT)

DERBYSHIRE

4. Hilton Gravel Pits   SK 249315

With lakes, pools, woodland and grassland, there are stunning displays of Southern Marsh Orchids here. Also many Common Twayblades. *West of Derby, off the A516 to Willowpit Lane, north of Hilton.* (Derbyshire WT)

5. Rose End Meadows   SK 140731

A series of traditionally managed meadows, wetland and woodland with a great variety of wildflowers. Species include Pyramidal, Common Fragrant and Bee Orchids, and there are many Common Spotted Orchids. *Above Cromford between the A5012 and the B5036 Cromford to Wirksworth road. Park in Cromford village.* (Derbyshire WT)

6. Derbyshire Dales

Five valleys make up the Derbyshire Dales NNR. These are two of the best for orchids. **Lathkill Dale (SK 190658)** is one of the finest, with stunning scenery and woodland, grassland and evidence of the lead-mining industry. Common Twayblade, Common Spotted Orchid and Common Fragrant Orchid can all be found among a very rich flora, with thousands of Early Purple Orchids on the grassy slopes. *Southwest of Bakewell, with numerous footpaths across the dale. There is parking at Monyash on the B5055 and at Over Haddon on minor roads from Bakewell.* **Cressbrook Dale (SK 170731)** is a beautiful place, with Early Purple, Common Spotted and Common Fragrant Orchids, and a few Dark-red Helleborines and Common Twayblades. *Northwest of Bakewell between Cressbrook and Litton. Park at Monsal Dale off the B6465 or at Tideswell Dale off the B6049.*

7. Deep Dale   SK 165698

Fantastic upland limestone grassland, with stunning displays of Early Purple Orchids in spring. Other orchids to be found include Common Twayblade.

Turn off the A6 towards Sheldon between Taddington and Ashford-in-the-water. Access is along public footpaths. (Plantlife)

8. Miller's Dale Quarry   SK 140731

One of the Wye Valley reserves, which also include Chee Dale (SK 120727), and Priestcliffe Lees (SK 147730). They have some excellent habitats, and a range of orchids can be found. These include Early Purple, Common Fragrant and Common Spotted Orchids, and Common Twayblade. *East of Buxton, with parking at Miller's Dale off the B6049 or at Monsal Dale Station.* (Derbyshire WT)

NOTTINGHAMSHIRE

9. Bentinck Banks   SK 493550

A triangle of disused railway lines; the embankments have some good limestone grassland, with Common Fragrant Orchid, Frog Orchid, Common Twayblade and Common Spotted Orchid. *Just south of Mansfield, off the B6018 between Kirkby in Ashfield and the minor road to Nuncargate. Park on the verge.* (Nottinghamshire WT)

10. Wilwell Farm Cutting   SK 568352

One of the best wildflower sites in Nottinghamshire, with grassland, acid fen and scrub on an old industrial site. There is a good display of Green-winged Orchids, as well as Bee, Common Spotted, and Southern Marsh Orchids and Common Twayblade. Vast hybrid 'swarms' of orchids also occur. *Just off the B680 between Ruddington and Wilford. Parking is available beside the reserve.* (Nottinghamshire WT)

11. Eaton Wood   SK 727772

Ancient pasture woodland with a visible ridge and furrow system that holds several species, including Greater Butterfly, Early Purple and Common Spotted Orchids, and perhaps Broad-leaved Helleborine. *Off the minor road from Upton to Eaton at East Retford, opposite Gamston Wood.* (Nottinghamshire WT)

LINCOLNSHIRE

12. Messingham Sand Quarry   SE 908032

Old flooded lagoons with fringing vegetation and remnant heath, with woodland, grassland and marsh. Several orchid species occur, including Pyramidal, Common Spotted, Early Purple and Bee Orchids. *South of Scunthorpe at Messingham, on the A159. Access is off the B1400 opposite Scallow Grove Farm. A track leads to a small car park.* (Lincolnshire WT)

13. Kingerby Beck Meadows   TF 051941

A series of herb-rich meadows with mixed boundary hedges. Orchids present include a colony of the diminutive Frog Orchid.

Northwest of Lincoln near Market Rasen. The meadows lie between Kingerby Beck and North Owersby; access from North Owersby on the minor road to Glentham. Park near the entrance. (Lincolnshire WT)

14. Donna Nook and Saltfleetby-Theddlethorpe Dunes   TF 467917

A large area of coastal saltmarsh and sand dunes, with Bee and Pyramidal Orchids and Marsh Helleborine in the dune slacks. The area of freshwater marsh can have fantastic displays of Early and Southern Marsh Orchids and their hybrids. The Saltfleetby reserve occupies the coast between Mablethorpe North End in the south and Saltfleet Haven in the north.

Access to Donna Nook is from North Somercotes, which is on the A1031 coast road; park at Stonebridge. Do not enter the danger area when the ranges are in use. Saltfleetby is easily accessed from several car parks off the A1031. (NNR, EN, Lincolnshire WT)

15. Candlesby Hill Quarry   TF 460682

An old chalk and lime pit on the eastern edge of the Lincolnshire Wolds. There is wood and scrub, and newly colonised chalk grassland with Bee and Common Spotted Orchids, among others.

Northwest of Skegness off the A1028 Skegness to Louth road, just north of Gunby Corner roundabout. Park on the verge. (Lincolnshire WT)

16. Heath's Meadows   TF 484640

Old meadows divided into small fields surrounded by large hedgerows. The meadows are traditionally managed and support a good grassland flora, including Green-winged and Common Spotted Orchids.

West of Skegness on the A158, just southwest of Burgh-le-Marsh at Bratoft Ings. Access is from Ings Lane. Park on the roadside. (Lincolnshire WT)

17. Ancaster Valley   SK 984434

A narrow, steep-sided valley with limestone grassland, scrub and woodland. Bee and Common Fragrant Orchids can be found here. Early Purple Orchid and Violet Helleborine occur in the beech woodland.

On the south side of the A153 Sleaford to Grantham road near Ancaster. Access is via the bridleway signposted east of the Ancaster crossroads. Park in the village. (Lincolnshire WT)

18. Moulton Marsh   SK 344336

The bank on the south side of the River Welland has a fantastic display of Pyramidal Orchids, with over 4,000 spikes.

Off the A17 south of Fosdyke Bank, on a minor road that leads on to the river. There is a car park. (Lincolnshire WT)

SHROPSHIRE

19. Wem Moss   SJ 472342

One of Shropshire's lowland mires, with open water, carr, woodland and a fen community that includes Early Marsh and Lesser Butterfly Orchids.

Between Wem and Ellesmere, near Northwood on the B5063. Park on the minor road to Dobson's Bridge just west of Northwood. (Shropshire WT, NNR)

20. Granville Country Park   SJ 719124

Based around reclaimed mine workings near Telford, this site contains woodland and old grassy pit mounds; the meadows have vast numbers of Southern Marsh Orchids and hybrids.

Just outside Telford, on Granville Road, Oakengates, Wellington. (Shropshire WT, Telford & The Wrekin Council)

21. Llynclys Common   SJ 273238

A mixture of habitats: woods, meadows, old quarries and scrub, where up to 12 orchid species have been recorded. These include Common Spotted, Early Purple, Pyramidal, Greater Butterfly and Bee Orchids, and Common Twayblade.

South of Oswestry on the A495. Park in the lay-by west of Llynclys crossroads opposite Dolgoch. (Shropshire WT).

22. Wenlock Edge   SO 595988

A magnificent limestone escarpment running from Much Wenlock to Craven Arms, with habitats ranging from scrub woodland and grassland to marsh. The pockets of limestone grassland have good displays of Pyramidal and Greater Butterfly Orchids, along with other limestone species.

Harton Hollow Woods (SO 481878), on minor roads off the B4368, is an excellent place to start a walk along the escarpment. The National Trust has a car park here. (NT, Shropshire WT)

WARWICKSHIRE

There are several interesting Roadside Nature Reserves in the county, notably on the A429 Ettington bypass, which has a spectacular display of Bee and Pyramidal Orchids.

23. Snitterfield Bushes   SP 200603

One of the best ancient woodlands in the county, the ash and birch woods have a good shrub layer and ground flora, with Early Purple, Greater Butterfly and Common Spotted Orchids, Common Twayblade, and Broad-leaved Helleborine.

Near Stratford-on-Avon, on the Bearley Road out of Snitterfield; the reserve is on both sides of the road, with a car park. (Warwickshire WT)

24. Ufton Fields   SP 378615

Old limestone workings with scrub, grassland and ponds and a good range of orchid species, with Common Twayblade, Greater Butterfly, Common Spotted and Bee Orchids.

Between Royal Leamington Spa and Southam, off the A425 at Ufton. There is a car park available. (Warwickshire WT)

25. Draycote Meadow — SP 448706

Warwickshire's best meadow, with thousands of Green-winged Orchids among other specialities.
Southwest from Rugby, with access off the B4453 at Draycote village. A public bridleway gives access to the meadow. (Warwickshire WT)

LEICESTERSHIRE

26. Lea Meadows — SK 506115

Unimproved meadows beside a clear stream. Signs of ridge and furrow agriculture betray medieval usage, but the fields are now traditionally managed. They contain a rich flora that includes great displays of Common Spotted and Heath Spotted Orchids.
Northwest of Leicester; take the minor road to Newton Linford from the A46. The site is on Ulverscroft Lane. (LRWT)

27. Cloud Wood — SK 899188

A traditionally coppiced ancient woodland with good rides and glades. Several orchids can be found including Bee, Bird's-nest and Greater Butterfly Orchids and Violet Helleborine.
Northeast of Ashby de la Zouch on the minor road linking Griffydam on the B5324 and Tonge on the A453. Park in the lay-by. (LRWT)

28. Muston Meadows — SK 824367

One of the best lowland meadows in England with unimproved ridge and furrow grassland. Among its rich flora is a colony of more than 10,000 Green-winged Orchids.
West of Grantham off the A52 at Muston. Park off the minor road south to Woolsthorpe. (LRWT, NNR)

29. Cribbs Meadow — SK 899188

Ancient grassland, ponds and a disused railway line. The fields lie on boulder clay and support a rich flora, including Green-winged and Common Spotted Orchids.
Between Wymondham and South Witham on the minor road between Sewstern and Thistleton. Park on the road verge. (LRWT, NNR)

30. Great Merrible Wood — SP 834962

A mixed woodland with a very ancient history. With ash, oak, and a varied shrub layer, the ground flora includes Broad-leaved and Violet Helleborines.
Southwest of Uppingham off the Horninghold to Great Easton road, southeast of the crossroads with the B664. There is roadside parking. (LRWT)

RUTLAND

31. Prior's Coppice — SK 834052

An ancient woodland on a steep slope. Under the ash-maple and ash-wych elm coppice is a rich flora, with a large colony of Early Purple Orchids and Broad-leaved and Violet Helleborines; the often-wet rides contain Common Spotted Orchids.
Southwest of Oakham, on minor roads connecting Braunston to Leighfield. Park on the road to Leighfield Lodge. (LRWT).

HEREFORDSHIRE

32. Davies Meadows — SO 375485

With three unimproved meadows, an ancient orchard, marshland and old hedgerows, this is an enchanting place to visit. The meadows contain Green-winged and Common Spotted Orchids.
On the A480 from Hereford to Lyonshall. Entrance is just past the Three Horseshoes pub at Eccles Green; park on the road verge. (Herefordshire WT, Plantlife)

33. The Doward Reserves — SO 549161

Several ancient oak and beech woodland reserves with areas of unimproved limestone grassland. They skirt the Doward, a rock outcrop in a bend of the River Wye. At **Woodside (SO 555147)**, the limestone grassland has a good flora with Early Purple and Greater Butterfly Orchids. **Leeping Stocks (SO 548162)** has White and Broad-leaved Helleborines and Greater Butterfly Orchid, while **White Rocks (SO 550158)** has Bee Orchid.
South of Ross-on-Wye on the A40 to Whitchurch, from where the reserves are signposted. (Herefordshire WT)

WORCESTERSHIRE

34. The Knapp and Papermill — SO 751522

One of the finest nature reserves in the Midlands, this is a mixture of old meadows, woods and orchards beside the Leigh Brook. Species include Green-winged, Early Purple, Greater Butterfly and Common Spotted Orchids, and Common Twayblade.
Southwest of Worcester on the A4103. Follow minor roads from Bransford along the Bransford–Smith End Green–Alfrick Pound road. The reserve entrance is on the left after about 3 miles, where the road crosses the Leigh Brook. There is limited parking near the bridge. (Worcestershire WT)

35. Monkwood — SO 804606

A coppiced woodland important for butterflies and moths, but also supporting many Early Purple Orchids, some Common Spotted and Greater Butterfly Orchids, and a few, hard-to-find Broad-leaved and Violet Helleborines.
Northwest of Worcester; near Grimley, on the minor road to Monkwood Green from the A443. (Worcestershire WT, Butterfly Conservation)

36. Wyre Forest   SO 743740

The Wyre forest covers over 6,000 acres and contains some of the best stands of ancient woodland in Britain (it is the largest continuous area of ancient woodland in England). Although predominantly Sessile Oak, just over half of the forest consists of conifer plantations. The Dowles Brook runs through one of the richest and most diverse areas of the forest, including meadows and abandoned orchards. Eleven species of orchid have been recorded, including Sword-leaved Helleborine, although there are just a few scattered populations of the latter that are hard to find. Common Spotted Orchid is abundant in some rides, and other species include Common Fragrant Orchid and Green-winged Orchid in some of the meadows (and perhaps also Heath Fragrant Orchid).

West of Bewdley on the A456 Ludlow road, with parking and a Visitor Centre at the FC's Callow Hill, which gives access to the North Worcestershire path; the New Parks Beech Wood area is a good place to start.

37. Tiddesley Wood   SO 929462

An ancient mixed woodland near Pershore with a good shrub layer. Common Spotted Orchid is widespread; there are also Early Purple and Greater Butterfly Orchids and Common Twayblade, with Bee Orchids in the open grassland; Bird's-nest Orchid and Violet Helleborine are also present but can be hard to find.

Next to the minor road signposted to Besford and Croome from Pershore on the A44. Park beside the wood. (Worcestershire WT)

38. Windmill Hill   SP 072477

Windmill Hill has a small area of limestone grassland and scrub. There is a spectacular display of Pyramidal Orchids as well as Common Spotted Orchid, Common Twayblade and small numbers of Bee and Greater Butterfly Orchids.

East of Evesham on the south side of the B4510, close to the Fish and Anchor Inn and just before the brow of the hill; park on the roadside opposite the entrance. (Worcestershire WT)

39. Trench Wood   SO 930589

An ancient woodland, with the wood managed partly as high forest and partly as scrub or coppice. Orchids present include Common Spotted, with smaller numbers of Pyramidal and Greater Butterfly Orchids.

Southeast of Droitwich on the Shernal Green to Sale Green minor road, just west of the M5. (Worcestershire WT)

40. Eades Meadow

A traditionally managed meadow on heavy clay soils, Eades Meadow has a spectacular display of Green-winged Orchids in the spring. Common Spotted Orchid, Common Twayblade, Greater Butterfly Orchid and a few Common Fragrant Orchids are also present.

Access is only possible on open days – contact the Worcestershire WT. (Worcestershire WT)

NORTHAMPTONSHIRE

41. Stoke Wood End Quarter   SP 800861

This ancient oak and ash woodland has an excellent flora on the mainly calcareous clay soils. Orchids include Early Purple Orchid, Broad-leaved Helleborine, Common Twayblade and Greater Butterfly Orchid.

North of Desborough on the B669 to Stoke Albany. Park in the lay-by. (BCNPWT, WT)

42. Glapthorn Cow Pastures   TL 005903

A scrubbed-over pasture, the resulting thickets are a haven for wildlife. The area has a rich flora, including Early Purple and Common Spotted Orchids.

Access from the minor road halfway between Glapthorn and Benefield, north of Oundle. Park on the road verge. (BCNPWT)

43. Short Wood   TL 015913

Rich deciduous woodland and coppice on boulder-clay (said to be the finest Bluebell wood in the county), with Early Purple, Bird's-nest, Greater Butterfly and Common Spotted Orchids, Common Twayblade, and Broad-leaved and Violet Helleborines.

Northwest from Oundle to Southwick on a minor road. Access is along a signposted footpath on this road. (BCNPWT)

44. Collyweston Quarries   TF 004038

A series of old grassed-over quarries, the open-cast pits and mines have created a 'hills and holes' appearance, and a rich flora has developed. Common Twayblade, Man, Bee, and Common Fragrant Orchids are present, while Pyramidal Orchid is abundant.

South of Stamford, on the A43 between Easton-on-the-hill and Collyweston. (BCNPWT)

45. Bedford Purlieus   TL 034997

A large, remarkably diverse woodland reserve, which many botanists consider to be the richest of all British woods – more than 400 species of vascular plants have been recorded on the site. Fly and Greater Butterfly Orchids can be found here, as can large numbers of Common Spotted Orchids.

North of Oundle on the A47; park on the farm track between Wansford and the King's Cliffe road. (FC, NNR)

46. Barnack Hills and Holes   TF 075045

A superb area of calcareous grassland on long-abandoned medieval limestone workings. There is an important Man Orchid colony (more than 1,000 spikes) as well as Early Purple, Pyramidal, Bee, Common Fragrant and Common Spotted Orchids.

East of Stamford; the reserve is off the B1443 on minor roads at the western end of Barnack Village, with several car parks around the perimeter. (NNR)

Northern England and Isle of Man

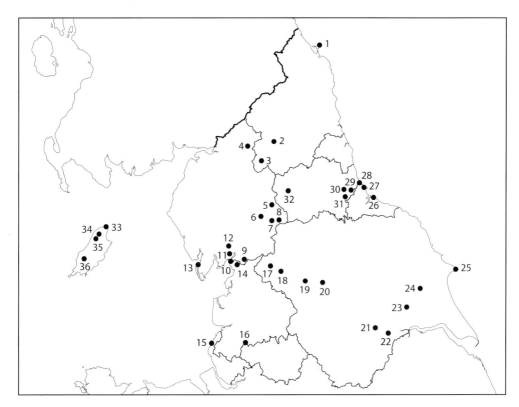

Northumberland
1 Holy Island
2 Beltingham River Gravels
3 Williamston Reserve

Cumbria
4 Geltsdale
5 Augill Pasture
6 Little Asby Inrakes and Outrakes
7 Smardale Gill
8 Waitby Greenriggs
9 Hutton Roof Crags
10 Arnside Knott
11 Latterbarrow
12 Whitbarrow
13 Sandscale Hawes

Lancashire
14 Gait Barrows
15 Ainsdale Sand Dunes
16 Nob End

Yorkshire
17 Southerscales

18 Brae Pasture
19 Malham Tarn Estate
20 Grass Wood
21 Sherburn Willows
22 Brockadale
23 Skipwith Common
24 Wharram Quarry
25 Flamborough Cliffs

County Durham
26 Coatham Marsh
27 Castle Eden Dene
28 Hawthorn Dene
29 Wingate Quarry
30 Raisby Hill Grassland
31 Bishop Middleham Quarry
32 Upper Teesdale

Isle of Man
33 Ayres Visitor Centre
34 Moaney and Crawyn's Meadows
35 Close Sartfield
36 Dalby Mountain

NORTHUMBERLAND

1. Holy Island NU 100432

The island is around three miles long, and sand dunes extend along much of the north shore. The dunes and dune slacks form an excellent orchid habitat, especially at the Snook at the western end of the island. The great speciality is Lindisfarne Helleborine, formerly treated as a subspecies of Dune Helleborine (which it greatly resembles). Following recent genetic research, the Lindisfarne Helleborine is now treated as a distinct species endemic to the island. The population is small (150-300 plants) and scattered, and it is advisable to contact the warden for advice; tel. 01289 381470. Other notable species include Coralroot Orchid in very small numbers in the dune slacks, Marsh Helleborine, Northern and Early Marsh Orchids and Common Spotted Orchid.
The road to the island is signposted off the A1 at West Mains Inn. It is impossible to cross the causeway for at least 2 hours either side of high water, and the strength of the wind and the height of the tide must also be taken into account. Tide tables are displayed on the causeway, which is a tarmac road.

2. Beltingham River Gravels NY 785640

Grassland polluted with heavy metals, woodland and scrub where 'Tyne Helleborine', the inland form of Dune Helleborine, can be found.
Off the A69 south of Bardon Mill, on the minor road from Beltingham to Willimontswick. There is roadside parking and a walk along the river to the reserve. (Northumberland WT)

3. Williamston Reserve NY 681521

This small reserve on the eastern bank of the River South Tyne comprises birch and willow woodland; this has grown on gravel and silt contaminated by 'tailings' from lead and zinc mines. The reserve is notable for its large colony of 'Tyne Helleborine', the inland form of Dune Helleborine. Common Spotted Orchid is also present.
Off the A689 Alston to Brampton road, south of Slaggyford village, signposted to Barhough Hall. Park by the road; the entrance to the reserve is via a stile immediately over the river bridge. (Northumberland WT)

CUMBRIA

4. Geltsdale NY 561557

Twelve-thousand acres of upland heather moorland, working farms, old coal and limestone workings and woodland, along the River Gelt. There are some very rich habitats where several species of orchid can be found, including Greater Butterfly Orchid and Common Fragrant Orchid.
East of Carlisle, south of the A69 off the B6413 at Castle Carrock. Park in the RSPB car park. (RSPB)

5. Augill Pasture NY 817147

Species-rich grassland and some woodland with Common Fragrant and Greater Butterfly Orchids, among others.
Just east of Brough off the A66 to Augill House Farm. Park at the end of the road. (Cumbria WT)

6. Little Asby Inrakes and Outrakes NY 699101

A small area of rough grazing notable for a colony of Small White Orchids, as well as Northern and Early Marsh Orchids, Common Spotted Orchid, Early Purple Orchid and Heath Fragrant Orchid.
West of Kirkby Stephen, which lies on the A685. The area lies north of the minor road immediately north of Little Asby.

7. Smardale Gill NY 727070

A disused railway line with a rich orchid flora; Fly and Frog Orchids can be found in small numbers, along with Greater Butterfly, Common Spotted, Northern Marsh and Common Fragrant Orchids, Common Twayblade, and Marsh Helleborine. A few Lesser Butterfly Orchids are also here but hard to find.
West of Kirkby Stephen, off the A685. Access is from the south side of the minor road running from Kirkby Stephen to Crosby Garrett. (Cumbria WT, NNR)

8. Waitby Greenriggs NY 760085

An old railway line running down a beautiful valley, with woodland and herb-rich meadows. The rich flora includes several species including all three fragrant orchids, Fly and Common Spotted Orchids, and Common Twayblade.
East of Ravenstonedale at Waitby, off the A685. Park close to the railway bridge. (Cumbria WT)

9. Hutton Roof Crags SD 543783

A large area of woodland, scrub, heath and fantastic limestone pavement, with great views. Dark-red Helleborine can be found amongst the grikes, and Fly Orchids grow in the grassland.
Off the A6070, between Burton and Hutton Roof. Park on the roadside or walk from Hutton Roof, Burton or Holme villages. (Cumbria WT)

10. Arnside Knott SD 456775

Woodland, scrub and limestone pavement sloping down to saltmarsh, with great views. Several species of orchid are present, including Early Purple, Fly and Lesser Butterfly Orchids and Broad-leaved and Dark-red Helleborines.
On the south side of the Kent estuary. Park in the National Trust car park signposted from Arnside village, which is at the end of the B5282. (NT)

11. Latterbarrow — SD 441827

Excellent limestone grassland, scrub and woodland with Early Purple and Greater Butterfly Orchids.
Near Grange-over-Sands just off the A590 at Long-howe End. Park beside the road just past the Derby Arms. (Cumbria WT)

12. Whitbarrow — SD 436859

Largely limestone, Whitbarrow Scar is just over 650 feet high. The reserve sits on top; it consists of limestone pavement, grassland, juniper scrub and woodland. It is an interesting place to visit, and Dark-red Helleborine and Fly Orchid can be found here.
Southwest of Kendal off the A5074. There is a small car park at the Kennels at Witherslack. Access is via steep and rocky paths. (Cumbria WT, FC, NNR)

13. Sandscale Hawes — SD 200756

This extensive dune system holds 10 species of orchid, with specialities including the largest population of Coralroot Orchid in England (3,000 were counted across five slacks in 1991), Dune and Green-flowered Helleborines (often more than 1,000 spikes of each), as well as Marsh Helleborine, Northern Marsh Orchid and Bee and Pyramidal Orchids.
North off the A590 to the northwest of Dalton-in-Furness, on the minor road to Roanhead. Park at the beach car park and walk west along the beach and then into the dunes (the first 'blow-out' after 550 yards holds a few Coralroot Orchids, but the farther slacks are better). (NT, NNR)

LANCASHIRE

14. Gait Barrows — SD 483775

Some of the finest limestone pavement and Yew woodland in the country. Dark-red and Broad-leaved Helleborines, and Common Fragrant, Common Spotted and Northern Marsh Orchids are important parts of a fascinating flora.
Gait Barrows is just in Lancashire, east of Silverdale and close to Arnside Knott. Off the minor road linking Carnforth to Arnside, with roadside parking. (NNR)

15. Ainsdale Sand Dunes — SD 397129

Part of the huge Sefton Coast wildlife area, the speciality here is Dune Helleborine, which is common, as well as Green-flowered Helleborine (both these helleborines can also be found in the pine plantations to the rear of the dunes). Other orchids include Marsh Helleborine, Bee and Pyramidal Orchids and Early Marsh Orchid (both pink-flowered plants and the red-flowered subspecies *coccinea*). Northern and Southern Marsh Orchids also occur here.
There is open access to the dunes, which stretch from Southport to Formby, with plenty of car parks. Ainsdale beach car park is a useful start. (NNR)

16. Nob End — SD 743070

An unusual site made up entirely of alkaline industrial waste, generated through soda crystal manufacture in the 19th century. Its weathered surface now has a unique flora, with eight species of orchids. Common Spotted Orchid and Early Marsh Orchid (subspecies *coccinea*) are common. Northern and Southern Marsh Orchids occur, and Common Fragrant Orchid and Common Twayblade are also common. Harder to find are Marsh Helleborine and Bee Orchid. The marsh orchid hybridisation at this site is stunning.
Just off the A6053 west of Little Lever, near Bolton. Access is on foot, with parking near Rock Hall Visitor Centre in Moses Gate Country Park.

YORKSHIRE

17. Southerscales — SD 742769

Part of the much larger Ingleborough NNR, this reserve has good limestone pavement with its clints and grikes, and acidic and limestone grassland. Early Purple Orchid, Dark-red Helleborine and Common Twayblade are present.
Off the B6255 Ingleton to Hawes road in North Yorkshire. Park at the Old Hill Inn or on the roadside at Chapel-le-Dale. (Yorkshire WT, NNR)

18. Brae Pasture — SD 790741

A small area of limestone pasture and damaged limestone pavement that has a very rich flora; Early Purple and Frog Orchids can be found here.
On the B6479 between Horton-in-Ribblesdale and Selside. Park on this road. A Public Footpath sign points to the reserve.

19. Malham Tarn Estate — SD 890660

Upland hay meadows and limestone grassland, limestone pavements and the NNR at Malham Tarn make up this wonderful landscape. The variety of habitats have Dark-red Helleborine and, in the wetter areas, Early, Northern and Pugsley's Marsh Orchids.
Northwest of Skipton on minor roads from the A65; the estate is north from Malham village, where there is a Visitor Centre, parking and footpaths. (NT, NNR)

20. Grass Wood — SD 983652

A wooded limestone hillside that slopes down to the River Wharfe. The wood has formed on a series of limestone terraces, and has rocky outcrops and open areas. Early Purple and Bird's-nest Orchids can be found, among others.
In Wharfedale, north of Grassington alongside the Grassington to Coniston minor road. There is a small car park. (Yorkshire WT)

21. Sherburn Willows   SE 487326

An interesting mix of habitats, with magnesian limestone grassland, scrub, and fen to the side of a small stream. Common Spotted and Bee Orchids and Common Twayblade can be seen.

West of Selby; access along Mill Dyke, off the B1222 between Sherburn-in-Elmet and South Milford. Park on New Lane or walk from South Milford Station. (Yorkshire WT)

22. Brockadale and Thompson Meadow
                                  SE 513174

Brockadale is a wooded valley with some old quarry workings and traditionally managed meadows. One of these, Thompson Meadow, is on a sloping hillside beside the River Went. The rich limestone flora includes Common Spotted, Common Fragrant and Early Purple Orchids.

Between Wentbridge and Kirk Smeaton, off the B6474 south of Pontefract, just east of the A1. The reserve car park is on an unmarked track out of Little Smeaton. (Yorkshire WT, Plantlife)

23. Skipwith Common   SE 669378

A large area of heath, marsh and woodland with Common Twayblade, Common Spotted Orchid and Broad-leaved Helleborine.

Northeast of Selby, Skipwith is north off the A163 on minor roads after North Duffield. Park and walk from the village.

24. Wharram Quarry   SE 858653

A disused chalk quarry, with steep chalk slopes and grassland. A typical chalk flora has developed, and Pyramidal Orchid, Common Spotted Orchid and abundant Bee Orchids can be seen.

Southeast of Malton close to Wharram-le-Street, on the B1248 Malton to Wetwang road. Park on the roadside close to the old railway line. (Yorkshire WT)

25. Flamborough Cliffs   TA 240722

The spectacular chalk cliffs attract thousands of seabirds but also support a varied flora on the cliff-tops. Pyramidal and Common Spotted Orchids occur here and Northern Marsh Orchids can be found in wet flushes.

East of Bridlington on the B1255 to Flamborough. There is a car park at North Landing and access to the clifftop footpaths. (Yorkshire WT)

COUNTY DURHAM

26. Coatham Marsh   NZ 586248

A wetland reserve of lakes, marsh and wet meadows. The wide variety of wildflowers include Common Fragrant Orchid, and good displays of Northern Marsh and Bee Orchids.

Off the A1085 Redcar to Middlesbrough road. Park off Tod Point Road or on the sea front on Manjuba Road. (Tees Valley WT)

27. Castle Eden Dene   NZ 435397

This spectacular wooded gorge is on magnesian limestone and boulder clay. Fly and Bird's-nest Orchids can be found in the woods, and Common Spotted and Common Fragrant Orchids occur in the open grassland.

On the south side of Peterlee, east of the A19. Castle Eden Dene is signposted from the A19 and from Peterlee town centre. Car parking is at the main entrance, and a small car park is available at Oakerside Dene Lodge. (NNR)

28. Hawthorn Dene and Meadow NZ 433457
and Beacon Hill   NZ 440455

A coastal site with extensive, steep-sided mixed woodland on limestone and some excellent grasslands with a great flora. Early Purple, Lesser Butterfly and Bird's-nest Orchids can be found among the ground flora in the woods, with Bee, Common Fragrant, Common Spotted and Northern Marsh Orchids in the pastures.

At Hawthorn off the B1432, between Easington and Seaham on the Durham coast. The site is at the end of a minor road signposted 'Quarry Traffic'. Park in the lay-by opposite the cottage. Access to Beacon Hill is along the Coastal Footpath or through the southern end of Hawthorn Dene. (Durham WT, NT).

29. Wingate Quarry   NZ 373375

An important example of magnesian limestone grassland – one of Britain's rarest habitats. There are large numbers of Common Fragrant Orchids here.

Northwest of Hartlepool, off the A181 west of Wingate. There is a car park. (Durham WT)

30. Raisby Hill Grassland   NZ 337375

Magnesian limestone grassland with fen and pools. There is a small disused quarry which has an important population of Dark-red Helleborines.

Off the A177 from Middlesbrough at Coxhoe Quarry. (Durham WT)

31. Bishop Middleham Quarry   NZ 330324

This large disused quarry on the Durham limestone is superb. It holds the largest colony of Dark-red Helleborines in Britain, with around 2,000 spikes (perhaps more than all the other populations put together). Other species include Pyramidal and Bee Orchids, Common Spotted Orchid, Marsh Fragrant Orchid and Common Twayblade.

Northwest of Middlesbrough, off the A177 west through Bishop Middleham. The reserve is on a minor road north of the village. Park in the lay-by opposite the entrance. (Durham WT)

32. Upper Teesdale NY 907282

Upper Teesdale is a botanist's paradise, with the famous reserves of Cronkley and Widdybank Fell above Cow Green Reservoir on the 'sugar' limestone. At lower altitudes, wonderful flower meadows still exist along the River Tees from Langdon Beck to Middleton-in-Teesdale. There are many orchids in the meadows and around the paths. Heath Spotted, Common Spotted and Early Purple Orchids and Common Twayblade can be found. As well as Early Marsh, Northern Marsh and Lesser and Greater Butterfly Orchids, there can be spectacular displays of hybrids.

North of Middleton-in-Teesdale on the B6277 there is an excellent Durham WT Visitor Centre at Bowlees. Information on good walks in the area is available from there. (NNR)

ISLE OF MAN

33. Ayres Visitor Centre NX 435038

The shingle near the northern tip of the island supports an unusual lichen-heath community. Dense-flowered Orchid grew here from 1966-1986 at its only British site. The lichen heath lies behind the dunes, and Pyramidal Orchid can be found here. In the dune slacks there are Early Marsh and Northern Marsh Orchids.

On the A10 Ballaghennie Road, west of Bride. There is a Visitor Centre and car park. (Manx WT)

34. Moaney and Crawyn's Meadows
SC 375957

Traditional hay meadows with a rich flora. The meadows are on the edge of the Ballaugh Curragh wetland. Heath Spotted Orchids occur in abundance.

Off the A14 from Sulby to Ballaugh Curragh. Park in the lay-by. (Manx WT, Plantlife)

35. Close Sartfield SC 358956

Part of the Ballaugh Curragh, this is the largest and most important wetland on the Isle of Man. It is a mixed area with bog, willow and birch woodland, and rich hay meadows. There is an amazing display of many thousands of orchids flowering from late May, including Heath Spotted, Common Spotted, Early Marsh and Northern Marsh Orchids, and Common Twayblade.

On minor roads off the B9 between Ballaugh village and Sulby Glen. The entrance and car park are located about 25 yards along a track. (Manx WT).

36. Dalby Mountain SC 233769

A traditional moorland with good displays of Heath Spotted Orchids.

The A27 Dalby to Round Table road passes through the reserve; there is parking on this road close to the track to Eary Cushlin. (Manx WT)

Wales

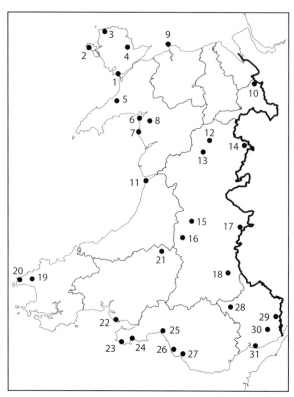

Anglesey
1 Newborough
   Warren
2 South Stack Cliffs
3 Cemlyn
4 Cors Goch

Gwynedd
5 Caeau Tan y Bwlch
6 Morfa Harlech
7 Morfa Dyffryn
8 Roman Steps

Conwy
9 Great Orme

Wrexham
10 Marford Quarry

Cardiganshire
11 Ynyslas

Powys
12 Lake Vyrnwy
13 Dyfnant Meadows
14 Llanymynech
   Rocks
15 Elan Estate
16 Nant Irfon
17 Burfa Bog
18 Pwll y Wrach

Pembrokeshire
19 Dowrog Common
20 St David's Head

Carmarthenshire
21 Allt Rhyd y Groes
22 Pembrey Burrows

Glamorganshire
23 South Gower Cliffs
24 Oxwich Bay
25 Crymlyn Bog
26 Kenfig
27 Merthyr Mawr

Monmouthshire
28 Cwm Clydach
29 Pentwyn Farm
30 Springdale Farm
31 Newport Wetlands

ANGLESEY

1. Newborough Warren   SH 415635

Lying at the southern tip of Anglesey, this is one of the largest sand dune systems in Britain, covering more than 3,000 acres. Although two-thirds of this area has been planted with Corsican Pine, there are still some fantastic dunes and dune slacks in the treeless south-eastern section of the Warren. Dune Helleborine (once again a British endemic) is a speciality, as are Northern and Early Marsh Orchids, Common Twayblade and Marsh Helleborine.

Access is from the Menai Bridge along the A4080 to Aberffraw. There are several car parks along this road around Newborough, and footpaths crossing the dunes to the foreshore. (NNR, CCW)

2. South Stack Cliffs   SH 207823, SH 218805

Situated three miles west of Holyhead on Holy Island at the western extremity of Anglesey, this area has some of the finest coastal cliff scenery in Wales. Inland, there are areas of maritime heathland rising to 853 feet at Holyhead Mountain, with a separate area of heath to the south at Penrhos

Feilw Common. Heath Spotted Orchid is common on Holyhead Mountain and four species of orchid, including Northern Marsh, can be found at Penrhos Feilw Common.

West of Holyhead on minor roads via Llaingoch and Twr to South Stack. For Penrhos Feilw Common (The Range) follow minor roads south from South Stack, or the B4545 from Dyffryn to Trearddur, and then take the minor coast road through Penrhosfeilw, parking at Gors-goch. (RSPB)

3. Cemlyn   SH 331932

On the north coast of Anglesey, a shingle storm beach has sealed off the entrance to Cemlyn Bay to form a saline lagoon. There are Autumn Lady's-tresses on the more stable parts of the beach.

Off the A5025 between Dyffryn and Cemaes, on the minor road from Tregele. There are car parks at both the eastern (Traeth Cemlyn) and western (near Bryn Aber) ends of the shingle ridge. (NT, North Wales WT)

4. Cors Goch   SH 504817

A large and diverse reserve with areas of fen, heath and grassland. The orchids here include Early Purple,

Green-winged, Early Marsh and Northern Marsh Orchids, Common Fragrant and Lesser Butterfly Orchids, and Marsh Helleborine. There are several splendid fens on Anglesey, but this is the only one with open access and with footpaths and a boardwalk. For information and permits for the others contact the CCW.

Cors Goch is off the A5025 turning to Llanbedrgoch. Parking is available in the lay-by. (North Wales WT, CCW)

GWYNEDD

5. Caeau Tan y Bwlch   SH 431488

A sloping calcareous grassland site with wet flushes; more than 2,000 Greater Butterfly Orchids can be seen in some years. Heath Spotted and Common Spotted Orchids also occur.

Off the A499 Caernarfon to Pwllheli road, near Clynnog-fawr on the Lleyn Peninsula. (North Wales WT, Plantlife)

6. Morfa Harlech   SH 555350

One of two major sand dune systems near Harlech, Morfa Harlech has a rich flora. There are various orchids present, including Early Marsh Orchid of the red-flowered subspecies *coccinea*, and also Marsh Helleborine.

Morfa Harlech can be reached by turning off the A496 to the public car park at Harlech and walking along the beach. (NNR, CCW)

7. Morfa Dyffryn   SH 560250

The second of the dune systems between Harlech and Barmouth, Morfa Dyffryn has extensive areas of dune slack with Early Marsh Orchid of the subspecies *coccinea*, Marsh Helleborine and Green-flowered Helleborine.

Morfa Dyffyn can be reached from public car parks at each end of the reserve, south of Llanbedr on the A496. (NNR, CCW)

8. Roman Steps   SH 500775

This area of hill pasture and moorland is well known for its population of Lesser Twayblades. Look for these orchids in places where the footpath passes through stands of heather.

From the B4573 at Harlech follow the minor roads to Cwm Bychan (SH 647314). Then follow the Roman Steps footpath for around 1 mile.

CONWY

9. Great Orme   SH 780832

Lying immediately north of Llandudno, this massive limestone headland covers around two square miles and rises to 675 feet, forming the eastern boundary of Conwy Bay. Dark-red Helleborine grows on the limestone pavement, with Autumn Lady's-tresses on the short turf capping.

From Llandudno, Marine Drive encircles the head and a minor road bisects the plateau, while a tramway also climbs to the top. The whole area is a Country Park.

WREXHAM

10. Marford Quarry   SJ 357560

An old sand and gravel quarry, now grassed over and developing an interesting flora, which includes Common Spotted, Pyramidal and Bee Orchids.

North of Wrexham on the B5445, between Rossett and Gresford west of the village of Marford. The reserve is on Springfield Lane; park beside the railway bridge. (North Wales WT)

CARDIGANSHIRE

11. Ynyslas   SN 610941

Lying on the southern side of the Dyfi estuary, the dunes here are excellent, with Marsh Helleborine, Early Marsh Orchid (including the red-flowered subspecies *coccinea*), Northern Marsh, Southern Marsh, Pyramidal and Bee Orchids.

Leave the A487 from Machynlleth onto the B4353, and turn north at Ynyslas onto the minor road to the dunes. There is a car park on the sand beside the Information Centre. (NNR, CCW)

POWYS

12. Lake Vyrnwy   SJ 015191

The largest artificial lake in Wales, fringed by scrub woodland and meadows with heather and grass moorland on the slopes. There are large areas of conifer plantation and deciduous woodland too. Heath Spotted Orchid is locally common and Lesser Twayblade occurs, although it is hard to find; look on damp north-facing slopes under heather.

Northwest of Welshpool, off the B4393 from Llanfyllin to Llanwddyn, from where the road continues on to circumnavigate the lake. The Information Centre is on the minor road 100 yards south of the west end of the dam. (RSPB)

13. Dyfnant Meadows   SH 998155

A typical traditionally managed upland pasture, comprising eight fields, with acidic bogs and flushes containing large numbers of Heath Spotted Orchids.

Near Dyfnant (in Dyfnant Forest), off the B4395 at Hendre, then on minor roads and forest tracks. Park by the reserve gates. (Montgomeryshire WT)

14. Llanymynech Rocks   SJ 267218

An outcrop of limestone, part of an old quarry with some woodland and a rich grassland flora; several orchids occur including Greater Butterfly, Early Purple, Bee and Pyramidal Orchids.

Near Llanymynech, between Oswestry and Welshpool, off the A483, with a footpath from the small village of Pant. Park at the end of the cul-de-sac called Pant Underhill Lane. The reserve is on the border between England and Wales. (Shropshire WT)

15. Elan Estate   SN 930652

A vast mosaic of moorland, blanket bog, Sessile Oak woodland, conifer plantations, rivers and reservoirs around the Rivers Elan and Claerwen. In the river valleys the meadows have Common Fragrant, Heath Spotted and Greater Butterfly Orchids; very much harder to locate is Bog Orchid in the upland plateau bogs.

West of Rhayader on the B4518; the reservoirs are well signposted. There is a Visitor Centre with full details of the 80 miles of leafleted walks and nature trails, and a Countryside Ranger service.

16. Nant Irfon   SN 840550

A mixture of upland habitats in a spectacular rocky valley with some beautiful Sessile Oak woodland. There are also extensive areas of pasture, meadows, flushes and upland streams with Early Purple and Common Fragrant Orchids, among others.

On the minor road from Abergwesyn to Terrain. Nant Irfon is part of a large protected area, which includes the National Trust reserve of Abergwesyn Common and another NNR at Claerwen. There is general access along paths from either end of the valley. (NNR)

17. Burfa Bog   SO 275613

The wet woodland, grasslands and mire have large colonies of Heath Spotted Orchids that produce a marvellous display in summer.

Off the B4362 Walton to Ditchyeld Bridge road, near Presteigne. Park on the road verge. (Radnorshire WT)

18. Pwll y Wrach   SO 165326

Deciduous woodland beside the River Enig with Early Purple and Bird's-nest Orchids among the interesting flora.

Pwll y Wrach is in the Brecon Beacons National Park off the A479 Talgarth to Abergavenny road, southeast of Talgarth. Park at the reserve. (Brecknock WT)

PEMBROKESHIRE

19. Dowrog Common   SM 775273

Some fantastic heathland and bog, grassland, willow carr and pools. With the neighbouring commons of Tretio and Waun Fawr, this is a large and botanically rich area. There are good colonies of Lesser Butterfly and Heath Spotted Orchids, and Southern Marsh Orchids in the wetter parts.

Just outside St David's on the A487 to Fishguard, with footpaths leading from the road. There is a small car park on the western boundary at SM 772275. (NT)

20. St David's Head   SM 734272

The walks along the Pembrokeshire Coast Path close to St David's encompass cliff grassland and coastal heathland, with good displays of Common Spotted, Heath Spotted and Pyramidal Orchids. Common Twayblade and Lesser Butterfly Orchid can also be found here.

Access is from St David's on the B4583 to Whitesand Bay.

CARMARTHENSHIRE

21. Allt Rhyd y Groes   SN 760480

Ancient woodland on the slopes of a rocky river valley; Greater Butterfly Orchids can be found in the adjacent meadows.

The site is in the Cambrian Mountains west of Llanwrtyd Wells, on minor roads from Rhandirmwyn (off the A483) to the A482 Lampeter road. There are various paths from the minor roads. (NNR, CCW)

22. Pembrey Burrows   SS 415007

Dunes and a forest of Corsican Pines on former dunes; the wide, grassy and sheltered rides are an excellent habitat for Bee Orchid and Marsh Helleborine.

Northwest of Swansea, off the B4311 at Burry Port. Car parking is at Pembrey Country Park.

GLAMORGANSHIRE

23. South Gower Cliffs   SS 470844

Large areas of the Gower Peninsula are protected as nature reserves or are in National Trust ownership. There are a wide variety of habitats; the South Gower Cliffs Reserve contains interesting cliff-top and old dune grassland, with Green-winged and Early Purple Orchids.

Access to the Gower is via Swansea or via Junction 47 of the M4. There is car parking at the beach car park at Port Eynon. (WT)

24. Oxwich Bay   SS 506870

Oxwich Bay, on the south shore of the Gower Peninsula, contains large areas of dunes and dune slacks, woodland on limestone and freshwater marsh. There are a good number of orchid species with Pyramidal and Southern Marsh Orchids, the *coccinea* subspecies of Early Marsh Orchid, Marsh Helleborine and, more rarely, Bee Orchid and Green-flowered Helleborine in the dune slacks, and Broad-leaved Helleborine in Nicholaston and Oxwich Woods.

Oxwich village is on a minor road south off the A4118,

with open access to the dunes and beach and marked paths in Nicholaston and Oxwich Woods. (NNR, CCW)

25. Crymlyn Bog   SS 694947

Just north of Swansea docks, this is the largest area of lowland fen in Wales and is of international importance for its valley mire communities. The vegetation includes rich fen, reedbed and old pasture. There are Southern Marsh, Common Spotted and Heath Spotted Orchids and hybrids.

Access is via minor roads leading off the A4217 and A483 around Kelvey Hill. There is a Visitor Centre on the west side. (NNR, CCW)

26. Kenfig   SS 780820

North of Porthcawl, this extensive area of calcareous dunes in various stages of development is one of the richest orchid sites in Wales. The speciality is Fen Orchid (of the broad-leaved variety ovata). This grows in the younger dune slacks and has been in decline in recent years due to a lack of suitable new slacks. It is hard to find; the best way is to contact the Information Centre in advance to check flowering dates, which can vary a lot (any time from early June onwards), and to make sure someone will be on hand to give precise directions. Other notable species include a few Green-flowered Helleborines, and also Broad-leaved Helleborines of the unusual subspecies neerlandica (known as 'Dutch Helleborine'), although this is erratic in its appearances and hard to find. Other orchids include Marsh Helleborine, Early Marsh Orchid (including the subspecies coccinea), Southern Marsh, Pyramidal and Green-winged Orchids, and Common Twayblade.

Kenfig can be reached from Junction 37 of the M4 and is signposted from North Cornelly, Pyle and Porthcawl. (Bridgend County Borough Council, Tel: 01656 743386; NNR)

27. Merthyr Mawr   SS 870771

The newest NNR in Wales is adjacent to Kenfig. It has sand, perched sand dunes on top of limestone, and limestone outcrops, pools and scrub – a vast and interesting area. The dune slacks hold the usual complement of orchids, including large numbers of Marsh Helleborines, and Autumn Lady's-tresses.

The reserve has open access, with parking at Candleston Castle at the end of a minor road through Merthyr Mawr village, located off the B4265 southeast of Bridgend. It can also be accessed from the beach car park at Newton, Porthcawl.

MONMOUTHSHIRE

28. Cwm Clydach Woodlands   SO 207123

Important beechwoods (close to their northern

limit) on a steep slope beside a river gorge. Little grows on the ground, but Bird's-nest Orchid can be found in some numbers.

West of Abergavenny on the A465, accessed via footpaths from minor roads which run from Clydach to Llanelly Hill. (NNR, CCW)

29. Pentwyn Farm   ST 523095

A small hill farm reserve of unimproved hay meadows with great views towards the Forest of Dean. Several orchid species can be found, including Common Twayblade, Early Purple, Greater Butterfly, Green-winged and Common Spotted Orchids among the meadows and lanes.

Located at Penallt near Monmouth, the reserve is adjacent to the Bush Inn with parking. (Gwent WT)

30. Springdale Farm   ST 401992

Woodland and grassland on limestone. The woods contain Early Purple Orchid, Common Twayblade and Broad-leaved Helleborine, and there are also many Common Spotted Orchids.

Park beside the almshouse on the minor road south between Usk and Llantrisant. (Gwent WT)

31. Newport Wetlands   ST 334834

A new reserve on the edge of Newport with reedbeds and wet grassland. Heath Spotted and Southern Marsh Orchids can be seen from the many paths.

The car park is on West Nash Road between Nash village and Uskmouth Power Station. (NNR, CCW)

Scotland

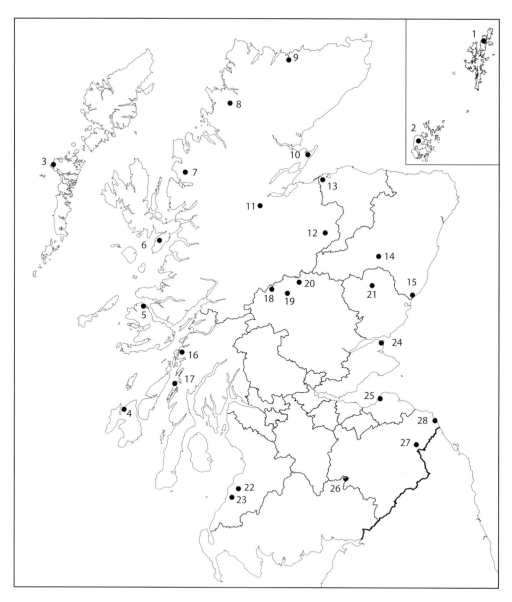

Shetland
1 Lumbister

Orkney
2 Birsay Moors and
  Cottascarth

Outer Hebrides
3 Balranald

Inner Hebrides
4 Killinallan Dunes, Islay
5 Mull
6 Tokavaig Wood, Skye

Highland
7 Beinn Eighe and Torridon
8 Inchnadamph
9 Invernaver
10 Talich
11 Glen Affric
12 Abernethy Forest and
   Loch Garten

Moray
13 Culbin Forest

Aberdeenshire
14 Glen Tanar Estate

15 St Cyrus

Argyll and Bute
16 Ballachuan Hazelwood
17 Knapdale

Perth and Kinross
18 Black Wood of Rannoch
19 Keltneyburn
20 Killiecrankie

Angus
21 Glen Cova

Ayrshire
22 Auchalton Meadow

23 Feoch Meadows

Fife
24 Tentsmuir Point

East Lothian
25 Aberlady Bay

Dumfries and Galloway
26 Grey Mare's Tail

Borders
27 Gordon Moss
28 St Abb's Head

SHETLAND ISLES

I. Lumbister   HU 485967

A series of lochs among heather moorland and sea cliffs. This reserve covers over 4,000 acres; Heath Spotted Orchids are easy to spot, but Lesser Twayblade is very inconspicuous here.

Located west of the A968 and northeast of Whale Firth; access to the site is from the lay-by just northwest of Mid Yell on the Island of Yell, north of Mainland. The Daal of Lumbister, a steep narrow gorge, makes a good walk. (RSPB)

ORKNEY ISLES

2. Birsay Moors and Cottascarth   HY 368197

Heather moorland with dry and wet heath. This large area includes the raised mire of Glim's Moss and a calcareous valley mire known as the Dee of Durkadale. Orchids found here include Lesser Twayblade, and Heath Spotted, Northern Marsh and Early Marsh Orchids.

On Mainland, on both sides of the B9057. The entrance to Cottascarth is north of Finstown off the A966, signposted 'RSPB'. Park in the farmyard. (RSPB)

OUTER HEBRIDES

The well-protected machair of the north coast of North Uist is home to the endemic Hebridean Marsh Orchid. Other species typical of the machair include 'Hebridean' Spotted Orchid (Common Spotted Orchid of the hebridensis *subspecies), Northern Marsh Orchid, Early Marsh Orchid of both the pink-flowered* incarnata *and red-flowered* coccinea *subspecies, Lesser Butterfly Orchid, Frog Orchid and Common Twayblade.*

3. Balranald   NF 714699

An area of machair and dunes interspersed with lochs and marshes, on the west coast of North Uist. Predominantly grazing land, the large stretches of machair are herb-rich, with Frog Orchid; the marshes have Northern Marsh and Early Marsh Orchids.

West of the A865 between Tigharry and Paiblesgarry, northwest of Bayhead; follow signposts for Hougharry. The cottage at Goular has information and maps. (RSPB)

INNER HEBRIDES

4. Killinallan Dunes, Islay   NR 3071

These low dunes, which stretch for a few hundred yards behind the beach, are good for Pyramidal and Frog Orchids, with small numbers of Early Purple, Early Marsh and Northern Marsh Orchids, Common Spotted and Common Fragrant Orchids and Common Twayblade. The heaths on either side of the lane contain Lesser Butterfly Orchid and Heath Spotted Orchid. A small colony of Marsh Helleborines is a speciality here.

On the northern coast of Islay beside Loch Gruinart. There is limited parking beside the kissing gate.

5. Mull

Mull is a diverse island, with mountains, sea cliffs and dune habitats – and great wildlife. Thirteen species of orchid have been recorded here. Broadleaved Helleborine and Early Purple Orchid can be found in woodland near Tobermory Lighthouse, while *pulchella* Early Marsh Orchids occur around Loch Spelve in the south. Other species to look for include Small White, Greater Butterfly, Lesser Butterfly, Common Fragrant, Common Spotted and Northern Marsh Orchids.

Mull can be accessed by ferry from the mainland at Oban.

6. Tokavaig Wood, Skye   NG 620120

This wood is on the southern shore of Loch Eishort on a wide variety of rock types and support a varied flora. Lesser Twayblade grows in the sandstone and quartzite areas; limestone areas hold Frog Orchid, Dark-red Helleborine and Common Twayblade.

The Isle of Skye can be reached from the A87, crossing at the Kyle of Lochalsh. The woods are off the A851 towards Ord and Tokavaig. (NNR)

HIGHLAND

7. Beinn Eighe and Torridon   NG 950621

Some of the finest mountain scenery in Scotland, with mountain habitats, grassland, moorland, cliffs and woodland. There is a rich flora in places with Creeping Lady's-tresses in the Caledonian pinewoods.

Between Loch Torridon and Loch Maree; enclosed by the A896 and A832, northwest of Kinlochewe. There is a Visitor Centre with information on walks. (NNR)

8. Inchnadamph   NC 250220

This is Scotland's largest area of limestone, with limestone pavements and outcrops at the head of Loch Assynt. Species of interest include Dark-red Helleborine, Common Fragrant, Frog and Small White Orchids.

To the east of the A837 at the eastern end of Loch Assynt, east of Lochinver and north of Ullapool. (NNR)

9. Invernaver NC 681612

Seashore, dunes, machair and moorland by the mouth of the River Naver, this area has some of the most interesting plant communities in the whole of Scotland. Small White, fragrant (probably Common Fragrant) and Greater Butterfly Orchids and Dark-red Helleborine can be found.

On the north coast of Sutherland around the village of Bettyhill. Access from Invernaver village, off the A836. Slightly to the west at Durness, the limestone cliffs have several orchid species too.

10. Talich NH 850786

An area of woodland, meadow and marsh on the bed of a former loch. The wet pastures contain Heath Fragrant, Heath Spotted, Early Purple and Lesser Butterfly Orchids.

North of Invergordon on the A9, at Rhynie off the B9165. (Scottish WT)

11. Glen Affric NH 235240

One of the most attractive valleys in Scotland, there are remnants of Caledonian pine forest, grassland and lochs, with Northern Marsh and Lesser Butterfly Orchids.

Southwest of Inverness, on a minor road into the Glen from Cannich on the A831. There are several car parks and footpath information. (NNR).

12. Abernethy Forest and Loch Garten NH 980188

Pine forest, lochs and wet moors – part of a remnant of Caledonian pine forest. A large area with an interesting flora, there are several orchid species, including Creeping Lady's-tresses and Lesser Twayblade.

Off a minor road between Boat of Garten and Nethybridge. Park at the RSPB centre. (RSPB)

MORAY

13. Culbin Forest NH 997614

This vast area stretches from Nairn in the west to Findhorn in the east. There are sand dunes which have been extensively planted with Corsican and Scots Pines, which hold Creeping Lady's-tresses, Lesser Twayblade and Coralroot Orchid.

Off minor roads north of the A96. There are several car parks in the area.

ABERDEENSHIRE

14. Glen Tanar Estate NO 480964

The Dee's wooded valley has areas of relict Scots Pine and birch woodland. The surrounding slopes contain bog and moorland, and extend to the peak of Beinn a'Bhuird. In the valley bottom are Lochs

Davan and Kinord. Among several species of orchid are Lesser Twayblade, Creeping Lady's-tresses and Heath Fragrant Orchid.

Off the B976 just south of Aboyne. There is a Visitor Centre across the Water of Tanar from Braeloine. (NNR)

15. St Cyrus NO 743635

A wonderful part of Montrose Bay, there are dunes and slacks, and coastal grasslands and cliffs with a rich flora, including Northern Marsh, Heath Fragrant, Heath Spotted and Lesser Butterfly Orchids.

North of Montrose off the A92. There is a car park and Visitor Centre just south of St Cyrus. (NNR)

ARGYLL AND BUTE

16. Ballachuan Hazelwood NM 763146

An abandoned hazel coppice with a good ground flora. Heath Fragrant and Northern Marsh Orchids, and Sword-leaved Helleborine can be found.

At the southern tip of Seil Island, west of the A816. Access from Ballachuan Farm on the B8003 near Cuan. (Scottish WT)

17. Knapdale NR 720835

An area of ancient Atlantic oak woodland and coniferous plantation beside Loch Sween, Knapdale is a good site for Sword-leaved Helleborine.

At the head of Loch Sween, at the north end of the Kintyre Peninsula. Off the B8025 to Tayvallich. (Scottish WT)

PERTH AND KINROSS

18. Black Wood of Rannoch NN 570536

The most extensive patch of original Caledonian pine forest in Perthshire, with Lesser Twayblade and Coralroot Orchid present.

West of Pitlochry on the B8019 and B846, to the south side of Loch Rannoch; there are two car parks with information boards.

19. Keltneyburn NN 767508

Keltneyburn is a steep wooded gorge with an adjacent herb-rich meadow, Balchroich Meadow. There are eight species to see here, including Greater Butterfly, Heath Fragrant and Small White Orchids.

On the B846 at Keltneyburn near Aberfeldy. (Scottish WT)

20. Killiecrankie NN 910620

This site includes oak woodland, farmland, birch-clad crags and moorland with wet lime-rich areas. The boggy areas have Northern Marsh Orchid, and Lesser Twayblade can be found amongst the heather. Bird's-nest Orchid occurs in the woodland.

Overlooking the famous Pass of Killiecrankie, west of the A9 to the north of Pitlochry. The reserve is signposted from the centre of Killiecrankie village. (RSPB)

ANGUS

21. Glen Clova   NO 330730

One of the five Glens of Angus, Glen Clova is popular with walkers. Within it grow Heath Fragrant, Small White, Frog and Common Spotted Orchids.

Access from the B955, to the north of the village of Kirriemuir. Parking is available at Clova.

AYRSHIRE

22. Auchalton Meadow   NS 335036

These meadows on the site of old limestone workings contain a good orchid flora, with Frog and Northern Marsh Orchids, Lesser and Greater Butterfly Orchids, and Common Twayblade.

Park off the B741 near Broomland Cottage, between Girvan and Maybole. (Scottish WT)

23. Feoch Meadows   NX 263822

Traditionally managed herb-rich meadows which have retained a good flora, including Greater and Lesser Butterfly, Heath Fragrant, Frog and Small White Orchids.

Off the A714 Newton Stewart to Barrhill Road at Killantringan. (Scottish WT)

FIFE

24. Tentsmuir Point   NO 500270

Tentsmuir Forest lies on the southern bank of the Tay Estuary across the river from Dundee. There is an extensive dune system, one of the fastest growing in Britain, with a rich flora that includes Coralroot Orchid in the dune slacks.

Access from Tayport near to the B945. Walk from here along the beach, or park at the Forestry Commission car park at Kinshaldy Beach. (FC, NNR)

EAST LOTHIAN

25. Aberlady Bay   NT 465801

The heathland and sand dunes around Aberlady Bay hold a rich flora with several orchid species, including Pyramidal, Common Spotted, Frog and Heath Spotted Orchids, and Common Twayblade. A large bay to explore, with many footpaths.

Northeast of Edinburgh. Access via the A198 with a car park just outside the village of Aberlady. (NTS)

DUMFRIES AND GALLOWAY

26. Grey Mare's Tail Nature Reserve
                                      NT 185145

Famous for its waterfall, the botanical richness of this mountainous landscape should be explored. There are upland heaths, blanket bog, rocky slopes, a loch and wonderful scenery. It is a good place to search for Lesser Twayblade under the heather.

In the Moffat Valley, northeast of Moffat on the A708 Moffat to Selkirk road. There is a Visitor Centre and car park. (NTS)

BORDERS

27. Gordon Moss   NT 635425

The largest area of semi-natural woodland in the Borders, this site consists of dense birchwoods on peat moss. Rich in plants, there are Coralroot Orchids, Lesser Butterfly Orchids and several other species to be found.

Just outside Gordon, south of the A6105 Gordon to Earlston road. Park at the reserve entrance on this road. (Scottish WT)

28. St Abb's Head   NT 914692

As well as great coastal scenery and seabird colonies, the grasslands along the top of the cliffs have many Early Purple Orchids.

From the A1107 take the B6438. This leads to the car park at Northfield Farm. (Scottish WT, NTS, NNR)

Ireland (Republic of Ireland and Northern Ireland)

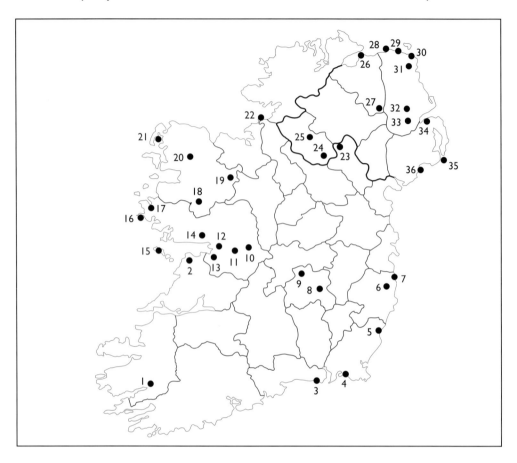

Co. Kerry
1   Killarney National Park

Co. Clare
2   The Burren National Park

Co. Waterford
3   Tramore Dunes

Co. Wexford
4   Bannow Bay
5   Cahore Polders and Dunes

Co. Wicklow
6   Wicklow Mountains National
    Park
7   Bray Head

Co. Laois
8   Ballyprior Grassland
9   Clonaslee Eskers and Derry Bog

Co. Galway
10 River Shannon Callows
11 Glenloughaun Esker
12 Rahasane Turlough

13 Coole/Kilcolgan/Ardrahan
14 Lough Corrib
15 Inishmore Island
16 Slyne Head Peninsula and
    Aillebrack
17 Connemara National Park

Co. Mayo
18 Lough Carra
19 Urlaur Lakes
20 Lough Conn and Lough Cullin
21 Blacksod Bay

Co. Sligo
22 Mullaghmore

Co. Monaghan
23 Kilroosky Lough Cluster

Co. Fermanagh
24 Crom Estate
25 Castle Coole

Co. Londonderry
26 Umbra

27 Lough Beg

Co. Antrim
28 The Giant's Causeway
29 Carrick-a-rede and Whitepark Bay
30 Fairhead and Murlough Bay
31 Slieveanorra
32 Shane's Castle
33 Lough Neagh

Co. Down
34 Belfast Harbour Reserve
35 Killard Point
36 Murlough NR

CO. KERRY

1. Killarney National Park   R 970860

The mountainous park to the south and west of Killarney around Lough Leane has good bog and moorland vegetation, and there are extensive woodlands around the famous Lakes of Killarney. There are many interesting orchids and Irish Lady's-tresses has been recorded here.

The National Park Visitor Centre is at Muckross House, at Muckross on the N71, where information on various walks is available.

CO. CLARE

2. The Burren   R 324954

One of Europe's finest areas of limestone pavement, and of outstanding botanical interest. There are turloughs (seasonal loughs), fens and some small stands of woodland, with dunes covering a large area on the west coast of Co. Clare around Lisdoonvarna and Kilfenora. The Burren is bisected by the N67, and many other minor roads allow easy exploration. Of the 30 species of orchid found in Ireland, 23 have been recorded in The Burren. Dense-flowered Orchid is the real speciality. This favours short, closely grazed turf; it is widespread but hard to spot. Another speciality is Early Marsh Orchid of the spotted-leaved subspecies *cruenta* ('Flecked Marsh Orchid'), which is found around some of the loughs in the east of the region. Early Purple Orchids are abundant and spectacular, and Heath and Common Spotted Orchids are widespread (with white-flowered Common Spotted Orchids of the variety *okellyi* common here). Irish Marsh Orchid is scattered and sometimes found in dry as well as wet grassland habitats. Fly Orchids occur in open habitats, on rocky hillsides and in fens around the turloughs; Common Twayblade and, later in the season, Dark-red Helleborine and Marsh Fragrant Orchid can also be found.

The Burren National Park covers a fairly small area in the east; the green road at R 304945 gives good access. Other productive areas include Loch Gealain, with numerous 'Flecked Marsh Orchids', Lough Bunny, and the pastures near the coast at Poullsallagh, which have some Dense-flowered Orchid colonies. Keelhilla at Slieve Carron on the northeastern edge of The Burren is also a good area; Fly and Dense-flowered Orchids occur there (roadside parking for a few cars). The grid reference above is for Mullaghmore (National Trust for Ireland) in the centre of the region, but the whole of the Burren is worth exploring.

CO. WATERFORD

3. Tramore Dunes   S 580005

A series of fixed dunes and dune slacks with Bee Orchids present.

South of Waterford on the R675. Park in the town of Tramore.

CO. WEXFORD

4. Bannow Bay   S 804064

A mosaic of sand dune habitats on both sides of the estuary leading into Bannow Bay. There are damp slacks where both Bee and Pyramidal Orchids grow.

On the south coast between Wexford and Waterford; the R734 leads to Fethard on the west side, and the R736 leads to Newtown on the east side.

5. Cahore Polders and Dunes   T 220462

An important wildlife site on the southeast coast. A 2/₂ mile-long sand dune system extends south from Cahore Point; behind the dunes there are areas of grassland, wetland and drainage channels. Pyramidal Orchid occurs on the fixed dunes at the northern end. The newer dunes to the south also have a rich flora, and Marsh Helleborine has been recorded.

Between Wexford and Arklow, south of Courtown. Take minor roads off the R742 to reach the site.

CO. WICKLOW

6. Wicklow Mountains National Park
                              T 099980

This National Park covers much of upland Wicklow, extending to Blessington Reservoir in the west, Vartry Reservoir in the east, Cruagh in the north and Lybagh in the south; the Park also includes Glendalough Wood Nature Reserve. There is heathland, blanket bog and upland grassland, small rivers and scattered lakes, with a rich flora; the Liffey Head blanket bog is one of the best of its kind in eastern Ireland. Small White Orchid and Bog Orchid occur here but are difficult to find.

The Visitor Centre is in Glendalough Valley off the R756 Green Road close to the Upper Lough (where there is a car park). It is popular walking country with many footpaths taking in the major habitat types.

7. Bray Head   O 284174

This coastal site is a plateau of high ground with rocky knolls and sea cliffs. Heath is the principal habitat but in some areas there is calcareous grassland with several species of orchids, including Bee, Fragrant, Pyramidal and Common Spotted Orchids and Common Twayblade.

Off the R761 out of Bray; walk from Bray or Greystones. The site is signposted from the road.

CO. LAOIS

8. Ballyprior Grassland   S 572924

Located at the north end of the Castlecomer Plateau and largely underlain by limestone, this site contains much orchid-rich calcareous grassland, with Early Purple, Fragrant and Common Spotted Orchids. Green-winged Orchid has also been recorded here. *The site is 2 1/2 miles south of the village of Stradbally, which is on the N80 between Portlaoise and Carlow.*

9. Clonaslee Eskers and Derry Bog   S 265110

A series of glacial moraines and eskers, including Derry Bog. The wide ranging habitats support an interesting flora including Fragrant and Fly Orchids. *Three miles west of Clonaslee, northwest of Portlaoise on the R422.*

CO. GALWAY

10. River Shannon Callows   N 014304

Callows are seasonally flooded wet grasslands. These form the largest area of lowland semi-natural grassland in Ireland. They have a good range of characteristic species, varying according to their tolerance to flooding. There are some areas of limestone pavement and calcareous grassland where Green-winged Orchid occurs, among other species. *Along the River Shannon between the towns of Athlone and Portumna; The National Trust for Ireland has a reserve at Mongan Bog (N 032318) and an information point with parking at Clonmacnoise National Monument.*

11. Glenloughaun Esker   M 8226

A fine example of dry, mostly unimproved, orchid-rich grassland on an esker. The flora includes large populations of Green-winged and Early Purple Orchids. *Three miles southwest of Ballinasloe, off the N6, along the minor roads to Kilnahown.*

12. Rahasane Turlough   M 472238

On the course of the River Dunkellin, this turlough is surrounded by damp grassland, limestone outcrops and scrubby woodland. A flora similar to that of The Burren occurs here. *Just west of Craughwell, southeast of Galway City on the N6. Access from the N6, north on a minor road towards Athenry.*

13. Coole Lough   M 430040

An area of low-lying limestone karst with deciduous woodland, pasture and limestone heath. Especially interesting are the turloughs, with limestone pavement extending to their edges in some places.

Pyramidal, Heath Spotted, Common Spotted, Greater Butterfly, Fragrant and Fly Orchids occur here. Similar habitats occur just slightly north around Caranavoodaun turlough south-east of Kilcolgan. The dry, calcareous grassland among the limestone pavement here holds Early Marsh, Lesser Butterfly, Fragrant and Dense-flowered Orchids, Broad-leaved Helleborine and Autumn Lady's-tresses. On the Ardrahan limestones, the Ballinderreen turlough has similar species with the addition of Fly Orchid. *Coole Lough (and Visitor Centre) is off the N18, north-west of Gort. (M 430040). Caranavoodaun turlough is off the N18 SE of Kilcolgan (M 4317). Ballinderreen turlough is S of Ballinderreen on the N67 (M 3914).*

14. Lough Corrib   M 121429

The second largest lake in Ireland, this is surrounded by some excellent habitats, including spring-fed fen, raised bog, limestone pavement, woodland and orchid-rich grassland. Pyramidal, Common Spotted, Early Purple, Frog, Fragrant and Greater Butterfly Orchids and Marsh Helleborine can all be found. There are good populations of Irish Lady's-tresses around the lough and on the Doorus Peninsula. *To the north of Galway City, with information points at Oughterard on the N59 and Cong on the R345; there are various picnic spots around the Lough.*

15. Inishmore Island   L 830090

The largest of the three Aran Islands, Inishmore is geologically an extension of The Burren in Co. Clare. There are some fantastic cliffs, sand dunes, machair, orchid-rich grassland and limestone pavement, as well as ancient meadows surrounded by stone walls. The rich flora includes Common Twayblade, Early Purple, Common Spotted and Heath Spotted Orchids. Dense-flowered Orchid is a speciality, and Bee Orchid occurs in the coastal machair. *The Aran Islands can be reached by ferry from Rossaveal or Doolin in Co. Clare and explored by foot.*

16. Slyne Head Peninsula and Aillebrack
L 620445

In the far west of Galway, this low-lying peninsula has some extensive areas of machair (particularly good at Mannin Bay and Aillebrack) and sand dunes backed by a mosaic of tiny fields, grassland, heath, lakes, marshes and fens. The specialities are Dense-flowered Orchid and, very locally in spring-fed fens, Pugsley's Marsh Orchid. The dry grassland supports Early Purple and Green-winged Orchids, and both Greater and Lesser Butterfly Orchids. *The area lies west of Ballyconneely on minor roads off the R341.*

17. Connemara National Park   L 670520

Connemara has mountains, bogs, heaths, grasslands and woodlands. The predominant habitats are

blanket bog and heathland. Lesser Twayblade is present but, as usual, is hard to find.
Entrance to the park is on the Clifden side of Letter-frack village on the N59. There is a car park and Visitor Centre, numerous trails and helpful staff. (NPWS)

CO. MAYO

18. Lough Carra   M 190740
A large, shallow, marl lake surrounded by limestone, with fens, woodland, grassland and limestone pavement. Early Purple and Dense-flowered Orchid occur. Nearby Lough Mask has Irish Lady's-tresses along its eastern shore.
Alongside the N84, between Castlebar and Ballinrobe. Access from minor roads around the lough, and park on the east side south of Carrownacon. There are many picnic areas on the east side of Lough Mask on the 'scenic road'.

19. Urlaur Lakes   M 520899
Three small calcareous lakes, Lough Nanoge, Lough Roe and Urlaur Lough, lie in the upper catchment of the River Lung, a major tributary of the Boyle. Swamps and reedbeds fringe the lakes, and in some areas there is flushed, species-rich heath with Lesser Butterfly, Pyramidal and Heath Spotted Orchids. Common Twayblade can also be found.
North of Ballyhaunis, on either side of the N83 near Urlaur. Access via minor roads.

20. Lough Conn and Lough Cullin   G 216048
There are fine oak woodlands around the southern shores of both these lakes, each with a mixed shrub layer and good ground flora. Sword-leaved Helleborine has been recorded here. Lesser Twayblade occurs further up the slopes on the blanket bog, while there are important populations of Irish Lady's-tresses around the lake margins.
There is information at the nearby town of Ballina. Picnic sites are on Lough Conn at Crossmolina on the N59, and on Lough Cullin beside the R318.

21. Blacksod Bay   F 700330
The Mullet Peninsula and Blacksod Bay form an important wildlife habitat. There are fixed dunes, machair and dune heath, as well as alkaline fens and coastal habitats. The dunes and machair can be found in the north of the peninsula to the west of Termoncarragh Lough, Tonamace and Cross Lough; such habitat also occurs on the eastern shore of the bay, around Doolough, Srah and Dooyork. Orchids to be found include Lesser Butterfly, Pyramidal, Common Spotted and Early Marsh, and Pugsley's Marsh Orchid has also been recorded here.
Situated in northwest Mayo, Belmullet is on the R313, from where the peninsula can be explored.

CO. SLIGO

22. Mullaghmore   G 710580
This tiny site measures just 100 x 200 yards, but it is extraordinarily orchid-rich; Pyramidal, Fragrant, Frog, Lesser Butterfly and Northern Marsh Orchids all occur, as do Common Twayblade and Marsh Helleborine. Common Spotted Orchid, the red-flowered *coccinea* subspecies of Early Marsh Orchid, and Heath Spotted Orchid are found in their hundreds.
On a headland off the N15 between Sligo and Bundoran, on the R279 to Mullaghmore.

CO. MONAGHAN

23. Kilroosky Lough Cluster   H 490276
Lough Kilroosky, Lough Burdautien, Lough Summerhill and Dummy's Lough are a series of marl lakes, low in nutrients and surrounded by fen and species-rich freshwater marsh. Nearby lakes are surrounded by reed swamp and wet woodland. Many species of orchid can be found here, including Marsh Helleborine.
Northwest of Clones, straddling the border with Northern Ireland.

CO. FERMANAGH

24. Crom Estate   H 455655 - 361245
On the shores of Upper Lough Erne, this is one of Ireland's most important conservation areas. Orchids include Common and Heath Spotted, Early Purple, Fragrant, Bird's-nest, and Greater and Lesser Butterfly Orchids, plus Broad-leaved Helleborine and Common Twayblade.
The Visitor Centre and car park lie west of Newtown-butler on the minor road to Crom, with walks through the wetlands and woodlands. (NT)

25. Castle Coole   H 378788
The landscaped grounds of Castle Coole have walks in woodland to Lough Coole, where Common Twayblade, Bird's-nest Orchid and Broad-leaved Helleborine can be found.
Just east of Enniskillen on the A4. (NT)

CO. LONDONDERRY

26. Umbra   C 726358
A dune system on the north coast, with woodland and scrub behind the beach of Magilligan Strand. The rich flora in the dune slacks includes Early Purple, Common Spotted, Northern Marsh, Early Marsh (two subspecies, *incarnata* and *coccinea*), Pyramidal and Bee Orchids, Common Twayblade and Marsh Helleborine.

Access from the A2 Coleraine to Limavady road; the site is adjacent to the Umbra level crossing on the A2, and has roadside parking. The whole Magilligan dune system is worthy of exploration. (Ulster WT)

27 Lough Beg   H 9895
Just north of Lough Neagh, this area holds Irish Lady's-tresses which can be found along the Londonderry shore. Early Marsh Orchid (subspecies *pulchella*) also occurs.

A good area to look is between the Ballydermott Road and Church Island (H 966953).

CO. ANTRIM

28. The Giant's Causeway   C 954453
These famous polygonal columns of layered basalt are a World Heritage Site. Several species of orchid can be found along and near to the North Antrim Coastal Path and beside paths to the Causeway, including Frog, Common Spotted, Heath Spotted, Northern Marsh and Early Purple Orchids, and Irish Lady's-tresses has recently been found here.

On the B146 2 miles from Bushmills. There are car parks and a Visitor Centre. (NT)

29. Carrick-a-rede and Whitepark Bay
                                                   D 062450
On the North Antrim Coast east of the Giant's Causeway, this rocky outcrop is accessible only via a rope bridge. The grasslands in this area have Common Twayblade, Early Purple, Greater Butterfly, Fragrant, Common Spotted, Northern Marsh and Pyramidal Orchids. At nearby Whitepark Bay, the dunes, grassland and scrub, with limestone cliffs to the east, support similar species.

On the North Antrim coast road; there are picnic areas, footpaths and a nature trail to Whitepark Bay. (NT)

30. Fairhead and Murlough Bay   D185430
On the north coast 4 miles east of Ballycastle, this area of rugged cliffs has limestone outcrops alongside a wooded area behind Murlough Bay. Common Twayblade, Bird's-nest, Bee, Pyramidal, Northern Marsh and Common and Heath Spotted Orchids all occur.

Access from the A2, parking at Murlough Bay. There are several paths and viewpoints. (NT)

31. Slieveanorra Forest   D 132265
Mixed woodland and moorland; there are forest tracks to the summit of Slieveanorra where there are interesting plots of peat bog at various stages of formation. The bogs contain a range of species, including Lesser Twayblade and Heath Spotted Orchid.

Slieveanorra is on the Altarichard road off the Ballymoney to Cushendun Scenic Route.

32. Shane's Castle   J 111881
Lying on the north shore of Lough Neagh, this area includes woods, parkland and farmland. Castle Meadow holds carpets of Common Spotted Orchids; there are Broad-leaved Helleborines in the woods, and Irish Lady's-tresses have been recorded along the shores of the lough.

Enter via the park gate 1 mile west of Antrim on the A6 Randalstown road. (RSPB)

33. Lough Neagh   J 050620
Ireland's largest freshwater lough, bounded by meadows, reedbeds and woodland. There are many nature reserves including the Montiaghs NNR and Lough Neagh NNR. Irish Lady's-tresses, Lesser Butterfly Orchid and Early Marsh Orchid (subspecies *pulchella*) can be found.

Situated to the west of Belfast, many minor roads lead to the shore with picnic areas. The grid reference is for the Discovery Centre on Oxford Island where information can be obtained regarding access and flowering times from the staff and the Environment & Heritage Service wardens. (Craigavon Borough Council)

CO. DOWN

34. Belfast Harbour Reserve   J 398795
The reserve and surrounding area hold Bee Orchid, Common Spotted and Northern Marsh Orchids and good displays of *Dactylorhiza* hybrids. Pyramidal Orchid and Common Twayblade may also be found.

3 miles north of Belfast city centre, off the A2 on the south side of Belfast Lough. Speak to the warden for access arrangements. (RSPB)

35. Killard Point   J 610433
Killard Point marks the southern limit of Strangford Lough, and has dunes, lime-rich boulder clay grassland, scrub, heath and low cliffs. One of the best orchid sites in Northern Ireland: Common Twayblade, and Common Spotted, Heath Spotted, Early Marsh, Early Purple and Green-winged Orchids occur in good numbers and there are also Bee, Frog, Pyramidal and Northern Marsh Orchids in smaller numbers.

Approximately 7 miles east of Downpatrick. Take the minor road between Kilclief and Ballyhornan from the A2. Park in one of the lay-bys. (NNR)

36. Murlough Nature Reserve   J 414351
This large area of dunes forms a peninsula that projects into Dundrum Bay. The rich flora includes Common Spotted, Heath Spotted, Pyramidal, Bee and Northern Marsh Orchids, and Common Twayblade.

On the coast, about 3 miles north of Newcastle. Access from the A2; park at Dundrum and walk over Downshire Bridge to the reserve. (NT, NNR)

Glossary

achlorophyllose lacking the green pigment chlorophyll and therefore unable to photosynthsise.

actinomorphic radially symmetrical; with more than one plane of symmetry.

adventitious buds and roots that appear in abnormal places on the stem.

ancient woodland woodland that has maintained a more or less continuous cover of trees, probably for thousands of years.

annular ring-shaped.

anther the pollen-bearing, male reproductive organ. In most orchids, the pollen is grouped into two pollinia.

anther cap in some orchids, such as the helleborines *Epipactis*, the anther lies on top of the column and is hinged or stalked. It may be contrastingly coloured.

anthocyanins group of pigments that produce purple or reddish colours.

apomixis reproduction by seed, originating from unfertilised egg cells.

asymbiotic when a symbiotic fungus is absent.

auricles ear-like structures.

autogamy self-pollination with pollen from the same flower (see **self-pollinate**).

back-cross cross between a hybrid and one of its parent species.

base-rich soil with a high concentration of calcium or magnesium and a pH above 7.0.

bog plant community on wet, acidic peat.

bosses irregular swellings.

bract structure at the base of a flower stalk, varying in size and shape, but often leaf-like.

bulbils tiny, round growths, e.g. along the rim of the leaf of Bog Orchid, which can separate and are capable of developing into a new plant.

bursicle the pouch-like structure on the column of some orchids that contains and protects the viscidium (q.v.).

calcareous rich in calcium carbonate, e.g. chalk, limestone or sea shells.

Caledonian woodland ancient pine woodland, a relict of the 'Forest of Caledon' that supposedly once covered Scotland.

capsule the dry seed pod of an orchid.

carapace hardened shell.

caudicle the stalk present in some orchids that attaches the pollinium to the viscidium (qq.v.).

cilia minute, thickened or fleshy hair-like structures.

ciliate with cilia projecting from the margin.

chlorophyll a green pigment, important in photosynthesis, found in discrete organelles (chloroplasts) in the cells of plants, usually in the leaves.

cleistogamy self-pollination in bud; after which the bud may remain closed or may open.

clinandrium depression on the top of the column, below the anther and behind the stigmatic zone, in which the pollinia lie.

clone individual of identical genetic make-up to its 'parent' that results from asexual, vegetative reproduction.

column specialist structure characteristic of orchid flowers in which the stamens and stigmas are fused together.

crenate with scalloped margins.

cross-pollinate pollination in which pollen from one flower fertilises another; usually taken to mean a flower on a different plant.

decurved curved downwards.

deflexed bent sharply downwards.

deltoid shaped like the Greek letter 'delta', i.e. triangular.

diploid having two matching sets of chromosomes. This is the normal state for plant cells.

ectomycorrhiza association of a fungus with the roots of a plant where the fungus forms a layer on the outside of the roots.

endomycorrhizal association of a fungus with the roots of a plant in which the fungus penetrates the tissue of the root.

epichile outer portion of the lip, often heart-shaped, in those orchid genera where the lip is divided into two (e.g. *Epipactis, Cephalanthera, Serapias*).

epidermis 'skin' or surface layers.

epiphyte plant growing on the surface of another plant without receiving nutrition from it.

esker glacial debris, often sands and gravels.

fen plant community on alkaline, neutral or very slightly acidic soil.

filiform thread-like.

flexuous wavy.

eutrophication enriched with plant nutrients, often leading to a luxuriant and eventually stifling growth of vegetation.

geitonogamy fertilised by pollen from another flower on the same plant.

glandular hair short hair tipped with a small spherical gland containing oil or resin.

hanger a wood on a steep hillside.

herbarium (plural: **herbaria**) a collection of dried and pressed plant material.

hooded formed into a concave shape resembling a monk's cowl.

hybrid plant originating from the fertilisation of one species by another.

hybrid swarm population in which the barriers between two species have largely or completely broken down. Hybridisation is commonplace and at random, producing a population that forms a continuous range of intermediates between the two parent species.

hybrid vigour when the first generation of hybrids between two species are exceptionally large and robust.

hyperchromic intensely coloured, with an excessive amount of pigmentation.

hyperresupinate when the ovary and/or pedicel twist through 360° to position the lip at the top of the flower, e.g. Bog Orchid.

hypha (plural: **hyphae**) fine, thread-like structures that make up the body of a fungus.

hypochile inner portion of the lip, often cup-shaped, in those orchid genera where the lip is divided into two (e.g. *Epipactis, Cephalanthera, Serapias*).

intergeneric hybrid a hybrid whose parents are in two different genera.

internode section of stem between two nodes.

lanceolate narrowly oval, tapering to a more or less pointed tip.

lax loose, not dense.

lignify become hardened and woody.

Leblanc chemical process used to produce washing soda.

lip highly modified third petal of an orchid; also known as the labellum.

lough Irish term for loch.

machair sandy, lime-rich soil with a species-rich sward of short grasses and herbs. The machair is confined to the coasts of western Ireland and western Scotland.

meadow grassy field from which stock are excluded for at least part of the year so that it can be cut for hay.

monocarpic flowering once and then dying.

mutualism an intimate relationship between two or more organisms from which all derive benefits.

mycorhizome early stages in the development of the underground rhizome in which the seedling is nourished entirely by fungi.

mycorrhiza association of a fungus with the roots of a plant in which the fungus may form a layer on the outside of the roots (ectomycorrhizal, q.v.) or penetrate the tissue of the root (endomycorrhizal, q.v.).

mucro very short, bristle-like tip.

mycelium the mass of branching filaments that make up the body of a fungus.

mycotrophic acquiring nutrition from fungi.

native growing in an area where it was not introduced, either accidentally or deliberately, by humans.

node point on a stem from which leaves, flowers or lateral stems grow.

non-sheathing leaf a leaf with its base clasping the stem but not completely encircling it.

ovary female reproductive organ that contains the ovules.

ovule organ inside the ovary that contains the embryo sac, which in turn contains the egg.

pH measure of acidity.

parasitic organism that lives on or at the expense of other organisms.

pasture grassland that is grazed for some or all of the year but not cut.

petals inner row of 'perianth segments', one of which is modified to form the lip.

patent projecting more or less at right-angles.

papilla (plural: **papillae**) small, nipple-like projection.

pedicel stalk of the flower; very short in many orchids, with the cylindrical and sometimes slender ovary forming the apparent 'stalk'.

pendant hanging downwards.

peloton a coil-like structure formed by fungi inside the cells of an orchid.

pheromone chemical secreted by an animal, especially an insect, that influences the behaviour or development of others of the same species.

photosynthesis production of food by green plants. In the presence of chlorophyll and light energy from the sun, carbon dioxide and water are converted into carbohydrates and oxygen.

phototrophic acquiring nutrition through the process of photosynthesis.

pollen single-celled spores containing the male gametes.

pollinium (plural: **pollinia**) regularly-shaped mass of individual pollen grains which is transported as a single unit during pollination; the pollinia are often divided into two.

propagules various vegetative portions of a plant such as a bud or other offshoots that aid in dispersal and from which a new individual may develop.

protocorm initial stage of development for every orchid formed by a cluster of cells.

pseudobulb swollen or thickened portion of stem, covered in the leaf bases. It fulfils the same storage function as a bulb or tuber; found in Fen and Bog Orchids and common in tropical species.

pseudocopulation attempts by an insect to copulate with an insect-mimicking flower.

pseudopollen structures in a flower that imitate pollen in order to attract insects, e.g. in the *Cephalanhera* helleborines.

reflexed bent back or down.

resupinate when the ovary and/or pedicel twist through 180° to position the lip at the bottom of the flower.

reticulation marked with a network of veins.

rhizoid hair-like structure on the surface of a protocorm or mycorhizome that facilitates the entrance of fungi (i.e. a root hair).

rhizome underground stem that lasts for more than one year from which roots and growth buds emerge; also a horizontal stem, either growing along the surface or underground.

rostellum a projection from the column that often functions to separate the pollinia from the stigma and thus prevents self-pollination (the rostellum is actually a modified sterile third stigma). The rostellum may exude a viscidium (q.v.).

runner horizontal stem that grows along or just below the surface of the soil.

saprophytic plants, fungi, etc. that feed on dead organic matter.

scale leaf a leaf that is reduced to a small scale.

secondary woodland woodland in which the continuity of tree cover has been broken for a substantial period of time.

secund all facing in the same direction.

self-pollinate pollination of a flower by pollen taken from the same plant; usually used in the context of autogamy, where pollination is by pollen from the same flower, but sometimes also geitonogamy, where the pollen comes from another flower on the same plant.

sepal outer row of 'perianth segments' that form the protective covering of the bud. In orchids they are either green or brightly coloured and form a conspicuous part of the flower.

sessile stalkless.

symbiosis an intimate relationship between two or more organisms; formerly used for a relationship where all participants derive benefits (q.v. mutualism) but now used in a broader sense to include parasitism

sheathing leaf main leaf on an orchid with a base that completely encircles the stem.

sinus indentation between two lobes on the lip, used especially when describing the flowers of marsh orchids and spotted orchids in the genus *Dactylorhiza*.

speculum pattern on the lip, often with a metallic lustre or shine, in the bee and spider orchids, genus *Ophrys*.

spur sack-like extension of the base of the lip which contains nectar in some species of orchid.

stamens male reproductive organs of a flowering plant.

staminode sterile stamen that forms a prominent shield-shaped structure within the flower of Lady's-slipper.

stigma receptive surface of the female reproductive organs to which the pollen grains adhere.

subsecund almost second, i.e. almost all facing to one side.

sympodial pattern of growth in which the tip of the stem or rhizome either terminates in a flower spike or dies each year. Growth continues from buds formed at the base of the old stem.

synonym former scientific name.

synsepal structure formed when the two lateral sepals are joined for almost their entire length, found in Lady's-slipper.

tetrads group of four pollen grains originating from a single 'mother' cell.

tetraploid having four sets of chromosomes.

tubers swollen underground roots or stems, functioning as storage organs.

turbary an area where peat or turf is cut for fuel.

turlough Irish term, used for a seasonal lake on limestone in which the water level may fall dramatically in summer.

viscidium (plural **viscidia**) detachable sticky exudation from the rostellum that attaches the pollinia (sometimes via a short stalk, the caudicle) to a visiting insect (qq.v.).

zygomorphic having only one plane of symmetry.

Sources of Information and Bibliography

In researching this book we have consulted many books and articles, and a complete list of consulted works appears below. We would, however, like to acknowledge several works in particular that have been especially valuable. A great debt is owed to the *Wild Orchids of Britain* (Summerhayes 1968), which beautifully summarises knowledge on the orchid flora up to that point. More recent advances, and especially the matter of subspecies, varieties and hybrids, were expertly presented by D.M. Turner Ettlinger in *Notes on British and Irish Orchids* (1997) and *Illustrations of British and Irish Orchids* (1998). Several regional orchid floras have also been a goldmine of information, for Box Hill (Sankey 2000), Dorset (Jenkinson 1991), Hampshire and the Isle of Wight (Jenkinson 1995), Scotland (Allan & Woods 1993), Suffolk (Sanford 1991) and Sussex (Lang 2001). Two other works are worthy of particular mention. Rasmussen (1995) is a comprehensive summary of development from seed and later growth, while Van Der Cingel (1995) summarises information on pollination. Note that, in the following, 'BSBI' = Botanical Society of the British Isles.

Ackerman, J.D. & Mesler, M.R. 1979. Pollination biology of *Listera cordata* (Orchidaceae). *American J. Bot.* 66: 820-824.

Adcock, E.M., Gorton, E. & Morries, G.P. 1983. A study of some *Dactylorhiza* populations in Greater Manchester. *Watsonia* 14: 377-389.

Allan, B. & Woods, P. 1993 *Wild Orchids of Scotland*. Edinburgh: HMSO.

Akeroyd, J. 1993 Wildlife reports. Flowering plants. *Brit. Wildlife* 4: 191-192.

Alexander, C. & Alexander, I.J. 1985. Seasonal changes in populations of the orchid *Goodyera repens* Br. and its mycorrhizal development. *Trans. Bot. Soc. Edin.* 44: 219-227.

Allen, D.E. 1968. *Neotinea intacta* (Link) Reichb. in the Isle of Man. *Proc. Bot. Soc. Brit. Is.* 7: 165-168.

Allen, D.E. 1971 *Dactylorhiza fuchsii* subsp. *okellyi* (Druce) Soó. - Behaviour and characters in the Isle of Man. *Watsonia* 8: 401-402.

Anon. 1956. The Military Orchid in Suffolk. *Proc. Bot. Soc. Brit. Is.* 2: 4-5.

Anon. 1958 *Spiranthes romanzoffiana* in South Devon. *Proc. Bot. Soc. Brit. Is.* 3: 37-38.

Arditti, J. & Ghani, A.K. 2000. Tansley Review No. 110 Numerical and physical properties of orchid seeds and their biological implications. *New Phytol.* 145: 367-421.

Ayasse, M., Schiestl, F.P., Paulus, H.F., Ibarra, F. & Francke, W. 2002. Pollinator attraction in a sexually deceptive orchid by means of unconventional chemicals. *Proc. R. Soc. Lond. B* 270: 517-522.

Bateman, R.M. 1985. Peloria and pseudopeloria in British orchids. *Watsonia* 15: 357-359.

Bateman, R.M. 2001. Evolution and classification of European orchids: insights from molecular and morphological characters. *J. Eur. Orch.* 33: 33-119.

Bateman, R.M. 2004. Burnt Tips and Bumbling Bees: How many orchid species currently occur in the British Isles? *J. Hardy Orch. Soc.* 1: 10-18.

Bateman, R.M. 2005. How many orchid species are currently native to the British Isles? *In* J. Bailey (ed.) *Studies on the British Flora*. In press.

Bateman, R.M. & Denholm, I. 1983a A reappraisal of the British and Irish dactylorchids, 1. The tetraploid marsh-orchids. *Watsonia* 14: 347-376.

Bateman, R.M. & Denholm, I. 1983b. *Dactylorhiza incarnata* (L.) Soo subsp. *ochroleuca* (Boll): F. Hunt & Summerhayes. *Watsonia* 14: 410-411.

Bateman, R.M. & Denholm, I. 1983c. Diploid Marsh Orchids in the British Isles. *Watsonia* 14: 448.

Bateman, R.M. & Denholm, I. 1985. A reappraisal of the British and Irish dactylorchids, 2. The diploid marsh-orchids. *Watsonia* 15: 321-355.

Bateman, R.M. & Denholm, I. 1989. A reappraisal of the British and Irish dactylorchids, 3. The Spotted-orchids. *Watsonia* 17: 319-349.

Bateman, R.M. & Denholm, I. 1989. On measuring Marsh-orchids. Morphometric procedure, taxonomic objectivity and Marsh-orchid systematics. *Watsonia* 17: 449-462.

Bateman, R.M. & Denholm, I. 1995. The 'Hebridean Marsh-Orchid': nomenclatural and conceptual clarification of a biological enigma. *Edinburgh J. Bot.* 52: 55-63.

Bateman, R.M. & Farrington, O.S. 1987. A morphometric study of x *Orchiaceras bergonii* (Nanteuil) Camus and its parents (*Aceras anthropophorum* (L.) Aiton f. and *Orchis simia* Lamarck) in Kent. *Watsonia* 16: 397-407.

Bateman, R.M. & Farrington, O.S. 1989. Morphometric comparison of populations of *Orchis simia* Lam. (Orchidaceae) from Oxfordshire and Kent. *Bot. J. Linn. Soc.* 100: 205-218.

Bateman, R.M. & Farrington, O.S. 1999. A new infrageneric orchid hybrid for Britain. *BSBI News* 80: 19.

Bateman, R.M., Hollingsworth, M., Preston, J., Yi-Bo, L., Pridgeon, A.M. & Chase, M.W. 2003. Molecular phylogenetics and evolution of Orchidinae and selected Habenariinae (Orchidaceae) *Bot. J. Linn. Soc.* 142: 1–40.

Bateman, R.M., Pridgeon, A.M. & Chase, M.W. 1997. Phylogenetics of subtribe Orchidinae (Orchidoideae, Orchidaceae) based on nuclear ITS sequences. 2 Infrageneric relationships and reclassification to achieve monophyly of *Orchis* sensu stricto. *Lindleyana* 12: 131-141.

Bidartondo, M.I., Burghardt, B., Gebauer, G., Bruns, T.D. & Read, D.J. 2004. Changing partners in the dark: isotopic and molecular evidence of ectomycorrhizal liaisons between forest orchids and trees. *Proc. Royal. Soc. Lond. B* 271: 1799-1806.

Blackmore, S. 1985. *Bee Orchids.* Princes Risborough: Shire Publications.

Bowler, J. 2003. Irish Lady's-tresses (*Spiranthes romanzoffiana*) discovered on the Isle of Tiree, Argyll. *BSBI News* 92: 25-26.

Brewis, A., Bowman, P. & Rose, F. 1996. *The Flora of Hampshire.* Colchester: Harley.

Briggs, M. 1995. Orchid seed dispersal. *BSBI News* 70: 19.

Brown, P.M. 2003. *The Wild Orchids of North America North of Mexico.* Gainesville: University Press of Florida.

Burgess, J. 1991. The scent of *Orchis morio*, 2. *BSBI News* 58: 27.

Buttler, K.P. 1991. *Field Guide to the Orchids of Britan and Europe.* Swindon: Crowood Press.

Byfield, A. 1993. *The Status and Ecology of Cephalanthera longifolia in Britain with Conservation Recommendations.* Plantlife/Hampshire Wildlife Trust.

Carey, D. 1998. Modelling the spread of *Himantoglossum hircinum* (L.) Spreng. at a site in the south of England. *Bot. J. Linn. Soc.* 126: 159-172.

Carey, D. 1999. Changes in the distribution and abundance of *Himantoglossum hircinum* (L.) Sprengel (Orchidaceae) over the last 100 years. *Watsonia* 22: 353-364.

Carey, D. & Farrell, L. 2002. Biological Flora of the British Isles No. 221. *Himantoglossum hircinum* (L.) Sprengel. *J. Ecol.* 90: 206-218.

Catling, M. 1980. Rain-assisted autogamy in *Liparis loeselii* (L.) L. C. Rich. (Orchidaceae). *Bull. Torrey Bot. Club* 107: 525-529.

Clarke, D. & Iveson, D. 2003. A new Cumbrian site for the 'Dune Helleborine' *Epipactis dunensis* (T. & T. A. Stephensos) Godfery. *BSBI News* 93: 17-18.

Clarke, W.A. 1900. *First Records of British Flowering Plants.* London: West, Newman & Co.

Cobbing, P. 1989. *Serapias parviflora* Parl. *BSBI News* 52: 11-12.

Coleman, R. A. 1995. *The Wild Orchids of California*. Ithaca: Comstock.

Coleman, R. A. 2002. *The Wild Orchids of Arizona and New Mexico*. Ithaca: Comstock.

Cowie, N.R. & Sydes, C. 1995. Status, distribution, ecology and management of Lapland marsh orchid *Dactylorhiza lapponica*. *Scottish Natural Heritage Review no. 42*. Edinburgh: Scottish Natural Heritage.

Curtis, T.G.F. & McGough, H.N. 1988. *The Irish Red Data Book. 1. Vascular Plants*. Dublin: Stationary Office.

Dafni, A. & Woodell, S.R.J. 1986. Stigmatic exudate and the pollination of *Dactylorhiza fuchsii* (Duce) Soo., *Flora, Morphol., Geobot., Oekophysiol.* 178: 343-350

Darwin, C. 1892. *The Various Contrivances by which British and Foreign Orchids are Fertilised by Insects, and on the Good Effects of Intercrossing*. London: John Murray.

Davies, P., Davies, J. & Huxley, A. 1983. *Wild Orchids of Britain and Europe*. London: Hogarth Press.

Davies, P.H. 1989. Identification. British Bee Orchids. *Brit. Wild.* 1: 37-40.

Davies, P.H. 1990. Identification. *Epipactis* Helleborines. *Brit. Wild.* 2: 106-110.

Davies, K. L. 1996. Welsh notes: the rediscovery of *Epipactis leptochila* (Godfery) Godfery var. *leptochila* in south Wales. *Orch. Rev.* 104: 299-300.

D'Ayala, R. & Snell, N. 2002. *Listera cordata* (Lesser Twayblade) in Bucks (V.C. 24). *BSBI News* 91: 33.

Delforge, P. 1995. *Orchids of Britain & Europe*. London: HarperCollins.

Delforge, P. 1995. *Epipactis dunensis* (T. & T.A. Stephenson) Godfery et *Epipactis muelleri* Godfery dans les îles Britanniques. *Natural. Belges (Orchid. 8)* 76: 103-123.

Delforge, P. 2001. *Guides des Orchidées d'Europe*. Lausanne: Delachaux et Niestlé.

Delforge, P. & Gévaudan, A. 2002. Contribution taxonomique et nomenclaturale au groupe d'*Epipactis leptochila*. *Natural.Belges* 83: 19–35.

Edmondson, T. 1979. *Ophrys apifera* Huds. in artificial habitats. *Watsonia* 12: 337-338.

Ehlers, B.K., Olesen, J.M. 1997. The fruit-wasp route to toxic nectar in *Epipactis* orchids? *Flora, Morphol., Geobot., Oekophysiol.* 192: 223-229.

Ettlinger, D.M.T. 1976. *British & Irish orchids*. London: Macmillan.

Ettlinger, D.M.T. 1979. x *Pseudorhiza bruniana* (Brügger): F. Hunt in Orkney. *Watsonia* 12: 259.

Ettlinger, D.M.T. 1991. Two new varieties of British *Dactylorhiza*. Watsonia 18: 307-309.

Ettlinger, D.M.T. 1990. The 1976 *Ophrys bertolonii* in Dorset flora. BSBI News 54: 15-16.

Ettlinger, D.M.T. 1997. *Notes on British and Irish Orchids*. Dorking: Privately published.

Ettlinger, D.M.T. 1998. *Illustrations of British and Irish Orchids*. Dorking: Privately published.

Ettlinger, D.M.T. 1998. A new variety of *Ophrys apifera* Hudson (Orchidaceae). *Watsonia* 22: 105-107.

Ettlinger, D.T. 1992. More on white orchids. *BSBI News* 60: 7-8.

Ettlinger, D.T. 1997. Yellow-edged fly orchid flowers - finale. *BSBI News* 77: 33.

Evans, P.A., Evans, I.M. & Rothero, G.P. 2002. *Flora of Assynt*. Privately published.

Ewen, A.H. & Prime, C.T. (trans. & eds) 1975. *Ray's Flora of Cambridgeshire* (Catalogus Plantarum circa Cantabrigiam Nascentium). Hitchin: Wheldon & Wesley.

Farrell, L. 1985. Biological Flora of the British Isles. No. 160. *Orchis militaris* L. (*O. galatea* Poir, *O. rivini* Gouan, *O. tephrosanthes* Willd. & Sw.). *J. Ecol.* 73: 1041-1053.

Farrell, L. 1991. Population changes and management of *Orchis militaris* at two sites in England. *In* T.C.E Wells & J.H. Willems (eds), *Population Ecology of Terrestrial Orchids*. The Hague: SPB Academic Publishing.

Fisher, J. 1991. *A Colour Guide to Rare Wild Flowers*. London: Constable.

Fitter, R. 1994. The second Oxfordshire *Orchis simia* site. *BSBI News* 66: 17.

Fitter, R.S.R. 1957. *Cephalanthera rubra* (L.) Richard in Buckinghamshire. *Proc. BSBI* 2: 234-35.

Foley, M.J.Y. 1987. The current distribution and abundance of *Orchis ustulata* L. in northern England. *Watsonia* 16: 409-415.

Foley, M.J.Y. 1989. *Dactylorhiza traunsteineri* (Sauter) Soo: variants in north-east Yorkshire. *Watsonia* 17: 355-356.

Foley, M.J.Y. 1990. The current distribution and abundance of *Orchis ustulata* L. in southern England. *Watsonia* 18: 37-48.

Foley, M.J.Y. 1992. The current distribution and abundance of *Orchis ustulata* L. (Orchidaceae) in the British Isles – an updated summary. *Watsonia* 19: 121-126.

Foley, M.J.Y. 2000. *Dactylorhiza incarnata* (L.) Soo subsp. *ochroleuca* (Wüstnei ex Boll): F. Hunt and Summerh. (Orchidaceae): A comparison of British and European plants. *Watsonia* 23: 299-303.

Foley, M.J.Y. 2004. A summary of the past and present status of *Spiranthes aestivalis* (Poir.) Rich. (Orchidaceae) (Summer Lady's-Tresses) in north-west Europe. *Watsonia* 25: 193-201.

Forrest, A.D., Hollingsworth, M.L., Hollingsworth, P.M., Sydes, C. & Bateman, R.M. 2004. Population genetic structure in European populations of *Spiranthes romanzoffiana* set in the context of other genetic studies on orchids. *Heredity.* 92: 218-27.

French, C.N., Murphy, R.J. & Atkinson, M.G.C. 1999. *Flora of Cornwall.* Camborne: Wheal Seaton Press.

Garrard, I. & Streeter, D. 1983. *The Wild Flowers of the British Isles.* London: Midsummer Books.

Gebauer, G. & Meyer, M. 2003. 15N and 13C natural abundance of autotrophic and myco-heterotrophic orchids provides insight into nitrogen and carbon gain from fungal association. *New Phytol.* 160: 209-223.

Gay, P. & Philip, E. 1999. Early Spider Orchids at Samphire Hoe, Dover. *Brit. Wildlife* 10: 165.

Gerard, J. 1633. *The Herbal or Generall Historie of Plantes.* Facsimile edition (1975) revised by T. Johnson. New York: Dover.

Gledhill, D. 2002. *The Names of Plants.* Cambridge: Cambridge University Press.

Goodfellow, G. 1991. The scent of *Orchis morio. BSBI News* 58: 27.

Graham, R.A. 1953. *Epipogium aphyllum* Sw. in Buckinghamshire. *Watsonia* 3: 33.

Green, P.R., Green, I.P. & Crouch, G.A. 1997. *The Atlas Flora of Somerset.* Somerset: Privately published.

Greenwood, E.F. & Gemmell, R.P. 1978. Derelict industrial land as a habitat for rare plants in S. Lancs. (v.c. 59) and W. Lancs. (v.c. 60). *Watsonia* 12: 33-40.

Gulliver, R.L. 1996. The status of *Spiranthes romanzoffiana* Cham. (Orchidaceae) Irish Lady's-tresses, on Colonsay, (v.c. 102) in 1995, with special reference to associated plant communities. *Watsonia* 21: 202-204.

Gulliver, R.L. 1997. Irish Lady's-tresses (*Spiranthes romanzoffiana*) on Colonsay (v.c. 102). *Glasgow Natur.* 23: 55-56.

Gulliver, R., Kiernen, M. Gulliver, M. & Sydes, C. 2000. Observations on Irish Lady's-tresses orchid (*Spiranthes romanzoffiana*) on Colonsay (VC 102). *Glasgow Natur.* 23: 9-12.

Hagger, J. 2003. The Early Marsh Orchid (*Dactylorhiza incarnata*) in Northern Europe. I – Introduction. *J. Hardy Orch. Soc.* 27: 4-9.

Hagger, J. 2003. The Early Marsh Orchid (*Dactylorhiza incarnata*) in Northern Europe. II – The purple-flowered early marsh orchids. *J. Hardy Orch. Soc.* 29: 45-51.

Hagger, J. 2004. The Early Marsh Orchid in Northern Europe. III – The British and Irish fen, marsh and bog forms. *J. Hardy Orch. Soc.* 31: 18-23.

Hagger, J. 2004. The Early Marsh Orchid (Dactylorhiza Incarnata) in Northern Europe. IV – Northern forms, blotched leaves and polymorphism. *J. Hardy Orch. Soc.* 32: 45-51.

Hall, P.C. 1980. *Sussex Plant Atlas.* Brighton: Booth Museum of Natural History.

Halliday, G. 1997. *A Flora of Cumbria.* Lancaster: University of Lancaster.

Harding, K. & Perring, F. 1959. *Spiranthes romanzoffiana* Cham. *Proc. BSBI* 3: 288-289.

Harris, S.A. & Abbott, R.J. 1997. Isozyme analysis of the origin of a new endemic orchid species, *Epipactis youngiana*, in the British Isles. *Heredity* 79: 402-407.

Hazeldon, E., Naisbitt, T. & Richards, A.J. 1991. Differential pollination efficiency within a hybrid swarm between *Dactylorhiza purpurella* (T. & T.A. Stephenson) Soo and *D. fuchsii* (Druce) Soo. *Watsonia* 18: 391-393.

Hedley, R. No date. The flowering and fruiting performance of *Cephalanthera longifolia* and the implications for conservation management. Hampshire Wildlife Trust (unpublished).

Hedley, R. 2003. Biodiversity Action Plan for *Cephalanthera longifolia* (the Sword-leaved Helleborine). Hampshire Wildlife Trust.

Henderson, S.A. 2001. The vegetation associated with *Spiranthes romanzoffiana* Cham. (Orchidaceae), Irish Lady's-tresses, on the Isle of Coll, Inner Hebrides. *Watsonia* 23: 493-503.

Heslop-Harrison, J. 1950. *Orchis cruenta* Müll. in the British Islands. *Watsonia* 1: 366-375.

Heslop-Harrison, J. 1953. Studies in *Orchis* L. II. *Orchis traunsteineri* Saut. in the British Isles. *Watsonia* 2: 371-391.

Hoare, A.G. 1997. An aberrant form of fly orchid in Surrey. *BSBI News* 75: 26-27.

Hollingsworth, M. 2003. Taxonomic complexity, population genetics and plant conservation in Scotland. *Bot. J. Scot.* 55: 55-63.

Horn, C. 1991. Variation in the scent of *Orchis morio*. BSBI *News* 57: 42-43.

Horn, C. 1995. Some colour variants of *Orchis morio* in Bedfordshire. *BSBI News* 70: 11-12.

Horsman, F. 1989. The history of the recording of *Spiranthes romanzoffiana* in Britain. *BSBI News* 53: 18-20.

Horsman, F. 1990a. Peloria in *Dactylorhiza*. *BSBI News* 55: 16-18.

Horsman, F. 1990b. *Spiranthes romanzoffiana* and John Raven. *BSBI News* 56: 5-7.

Horsman, F. 1990c. On some curious dactylorchids. *BSBI News* 58: 29-31.

Horsman, F. 1999. The Irish Lady's Tresses Orchid. *Coll Magazine* 17: 9-11.

Hoy, J. 2002. New England Plant Conservation Program. *Listera cordata* (L.) R. Br. Heart-leaved Twayblade. Conservation and Research Plan for U.S. Forest Service Region 9.

Hultén, E. & Fries, M. 1986. *Atlas of North European vascular plants north of the Tropic of Cancer*. Konigstein: Koeltz Scientific Books.

Hutchings, M.J. 1987a. The population ecology of the Early Spider Orchid *Ophrys sphegodes* Mill. 1. A demographic study for 1975 to 1984. *J. Ecol.* 75: 711-727.

Hutchings, M.J. 1987b. The population biology of the Early Spider Orchid, *Ophrys sphegodes* Mill. II. Temporal patterns in behaviour. *J. Ecol.* 75: 729-742.

Hutchings, M. J., Mendoza, A. & Havers, W. 1998. Demographic properties of an outlier population of *Orchis militaris* L. Orchidaceae in England. *Bot. J. Linn. Soc.* 126: 95-107.

Jenkinson, M.N. 1991. *Wild Orchids of Dorset*. Gillingham (Dorset): Orchid Sundries.

Jenkinson, M.N. 1995a. *Wild Orchids of Hampshire and the Isle of Wight*. Gillingham (Dorset): Orchid Sundries.

Jenkinson, M.N. 1995b. A new variety of Narrow-leaved Marsh-orchid in South Hampshire (v.c. 11). *Watsonia* 20: 263-273.

Jenkinson, M.N. 1996. A new variety of Narrow-leaved Marsh-Orchid in S. Hampshire (v.c.11). *BSBI News* 72: 64.

Jenkinson, M.N. 1997. Marsh-orchid controversy – a small or large argument. *BSBI News* 77: 29-31.

Jenkinson, M.N. & Hobson, A.G. 1989. *Epipactis purpurata* Sm. reappears in Dorset. *Watsonia* 17: 441-442.

Jermyn, S.T. 1974. *Flora of Essex*. Colchester: Essex Naturalists' Trust.

Jones, S. 1998. Aspects of the population biology of *Liparis loeselii* (L.) Rich. var. *ovata* Ridd. Ex Godfrey (Orchidaceae) in the dune slacks of South Wales, UK. *Bot. J. Linn. Soc.* 126: 123-139.

Julou, T., Burghardt, B., Gebauer, G., Berveiller, D., Damesin, C. & Selosse, M-A. 2005. A case for mixotrophy in orchids: insights from a comparative study of green and achlorophyllous *Caphalanthera damasonium*. In press.

Kemp, R.J. 1987. Reappearance of *Orchis purpurea* Hudson in Oxfordshire. *Watsonia* 16: 435-36.

Kendrick, F.M. 1983. Botany. *Trans. Woolhope Naturalists' Field Club* 44: 124-125.

Kenneth, A.G. & Tennant, D.J. 1984. *Dactylorhiza incarnata* (L.) Soo subsp. *cruenta* (O. F. Mueller): D. Sell in Scotland. *Watsonia* 15: 11-14.

Kenneth, A.G. & Tennant, D.J. 1987. Further notes on *Dactylorhiza incarnata* subsp. *cruenta* in Scotland. *Watsonia* 16: 332-334.

Kenneth, A.G., Lowe, M.R. & Tennant, D.J. 1988. *Dactylorhiza lapponica* (Laest. ex Hartman) Soo in Scotland. *Watsonia* 17: 37-41.

Kent, D.H. 1954. Plant notes. 675/1 *Cypripedium calceolus* L. *Proc. BSBI* 1: 39-40.

Killick, J., Perry, R. & Woodell, S. 1998. *The Flora of Oxfordshire.* Newbury: Pisces.

Kull, T. 1999. Biological Flora of the British Isles. No. 208. *Cypripedium calceolus* L. *J. Ecol.* 87: 913-924.

Kull, T. & Kull, K. 1991. Preliminary results from a study of populations of *Cypripedium calceolus* in Estonia. *In* T.C.E. Wells & J.H. Willems (eds), *Population Ecology of Terrestrial Orchids.* The Hague: SPB Academic Publishing.

Lacey, W.S. 1955. *Orchis traunsteineri* Saut. in Wales. *Proc. BSBI* 1: 297-300.

Land, R. No date. Management guidelines for Fen Orchid. Norfolk Wildlife Trust (unpublished).

Laney, B. & Stanley, P. 2004. *Ophrys apifera* (Bee Orchid) in Ayrshire (VC75). *J. Hardy Orch. Soc.* 32: 43.

Lang, D. 1980. *Orchids of Britain.* Oxford: Oxford University Press.

Lang, D.C. 1991. A new variant of *Ophrys apifera* Hudson in Britain. *Watsonia* 18: 408-410.

Lang, D.C. 2001. *Wild Orchids of Sussex.* Lewes: Pomegranate Press.

Lang, D.C. 2004. *Britain's Orchids.* Old Basing (Hampshire): WildGuides.

Laurence, R.J. 1986. *Ophrys apifera* Hudson subsp. *jurana* Ruppert found in Britain. *Watsonia* 16: 177-178.

Laurence, R. & Chalk, M. 2004. Hyperchromic form of *Dactylorhiza maculata* found in the New Forest. *BSBI News* 96: 28-29.

Lewis, L. & Spencer, E.J. 2005. *Epipactis phyllanthes* var. *cambrensis* (C.A. Thomas) P.D. Sell and other unusual *Epipactis* at Kenfig National Nature Reserve. *Watsonia* 25: 290-295.

Light, M.H.S. & MacConaill, M. 1991. Patterns of appearance in *Epipactis helleborine* (L.) Crantz. *In* T.C.E. Wells & J.H. Willems (eds), *Population Ecology of Terrestrial Orchids.* The Hague: SPB Academic Publishing.

Lindop, M. 1992. *Cypripedium* conservation – 1991 report. *BSBI News* 60: 45.

Lindop, M. 1994. *Cypripedium* conservation report 1993. *BSBI News* 66: 30.

Lindop, M. 1996. *Cypripedium* conservation report 1995. *BSBI News* 72: 45.

Lindop, M. 1997. *Cypripedium* conservation report 1996. *BSBI News* 75: 35.

Lord, R.M., Richards, A.J. 1977. A hybrid swarm between the diploid *Dactylorhiza fuchsii* (Druce) Soo and the tetraploid *D. purpurella* (T. & T.A. Steph.) Soo in Durham. *Watsonia* 11: 205-210.

Lousley, J.E. 1969. *Wild Flowers of Chalk and Limestone.* London: Collins.

Lousley, J.E. 1976. *Flora of Surrey.* Newton Abbot: David & Charles.

Lowe, M.R., Tennant, D.J. & Kenneth, A.G. 1986. The status of *Orchis Francis-Drucei* Wilmott. *Watsonia* 16: 178-180.

Mabey, R. 1996. *Flora Britannica.* London: Sinclair-Stevenson.

McClintock, D. 1975. *The Wildflowers of Guernsey.* London: Collins.

McKean, D.R. 1996. A chlorotic *Epipactis helleborine* in an Edinburgh housing estate. *BSBI News* 72: 35.

McKendrick, S.L., Leake, J.R. & Read, D.J. 2000. Symbiotic germination and development of myco-heterotrophic plants in nature: Transfer of carbon from ectomycorrhizal *Salix repens* and *Betula pendula* to the orchid *Corallorhiza trifida* through shared hyphal connections. *New Phytol.* 145: 539-548.

McKendrick, S.L., Leake, J.R., Taylor, D.L. & Read, D.J. 2000. Symbiotic germination and development of myco-heterotrophic plants in nature: Ontogeny of *Corallorhiza trifida* and characterization of its mycorrhizal fungi. *New Phytol.* 145: 523-537.

McKendrick, S.L., Leake, J.R., Taylor, D.L. & Read, D.J. 2002. Symbiotic germination and development of the myco-heterotrophic orchid *Neottia nidus-avis* in nature and its requirement for locally distributed *Sebacina* spp. *New Phytol.* 154: 233-247.

Madge, S. 1994. The status of *Serapias parviflora* Parl. in Britain. *Botanical Cornwall*, 6: 51-52.

Madge, S. 1995. A new orchid for Britain. *Carradon Wildlife* 11: 10.

Margetts, L.J. & David, R.W. 1981. *A Review of the Cornish Flora 1980*. Redruth: Institute of Cornish Studies.

Margetts, L.J. & Spurgin, K.L. 1991. *The Cornish Flora Supplement 1981-1990*. Zennor, St Ives: Trendine Press.

Marren, 1999. *Britain's Rare Flowers*. London: T & AD Poyser.

Merryweather, J. 2001. Comment. Meet the Glomales - the ecology of mycorrhiza. *Brit. Wild.* 13: 86-93.

Moore, S. 1997. Fly orchid aberration? Another record. *BSBI News* 76: 21-22.

Mrkvicka, A.C. 1992. Keimung, Entwicklung und Wachstumezyklen von *Liparis loeselii* (L.) L.C. Rich. am natürlichen Wuchsort. *Orchidee (Hamburg)* 43: 35-36.

Murphy, R.J. 1994. Progress report. *Botanical Cornwall*, 6: 1-7.

Murphy, R.J. 1995. *Hammarbya paludosa* (Bog Orchid) refound in Cornwall. *BSBI News* 69: 74-75.

Neiland, M.R.M. 1994. *Reproductive ecology of* Dactylorhiza lapponica *in Scotland*. Edinburgh: Scottish Natural Heritage.

Neiland, M.R.M. and Wilcock, C.C. 1994. *Survey of* Dactylorhiza lapponica. Edinburgh: Scottish Natural Heritage.

Neiland, M.R.M. & Wilcock, C.C. 1995. *Reproductive Biology and Morphological Variability of Two Rare Scottish Orchids,* Dactylorhiza lapponica *and* Dactylorhiza traunsteineri. Edinburgh: Scottish Natural Heritage.

Pankhurst, R.J. & Mullin, J.M. 1991. *Flora of the Outer Hebrides*. London: Natural History Museum.

Paul, V.N. 1964. *Epipogium aphyllum. Reading Naturalist* 16: 29-30.

Payne, R. 1991. *Orchis morio* in old Cambridgeshire. *Nat. Camb.* 33: 23-25.

Pearman, D.A. & Preston, C.D. 2000. *A Flora of Tiree, Gunna and Coll*. Dorchester: Privately published.

Perring, F.H. 1956. *Spiranthes spiralis* (L.) Chevall. in Britain, 1955. *Proc. BSBI* 2: 6-9.

Philip, E.G. 1982. *Atlas of the Kent Flora*. Kent: Kent Field Club.

Preston, C.D. 2000. Engulfed by suburbia or destroyed by the plough; the ecology of extinction in Middlesex and Cambridgeshire. *Watsonia* 23: 59-81.

Preston, C.D., Pearman, D.A. & Dines, T.D. 2002. *New Atlas of the British and Irish Flora*. Oxford: Oxford University Press.

Pridgeon, A.M., Bateman, R.M., Cox, A.V., Hapeman, J.R. & Chase, M.W. 1997. Phylogenetics of subtribe Orchidinae (Orchidoideae, Orchidaceae) based on nuclear ITS sequences. 1. Intergeneric relationships and polyphyly of *Orchis* sensu lato. *Lindleyana* 12: 89-109.

Qamaruz-Zaman, F., Fay, M.F., Parker, J.S. & Chase, M.W. 1998. The use of AFLP fingerprinting in conservation genetics: a case study of *Orchis simia* (Orchidaceae). *Lindleyana* 13: 125-133.

Ramsay, M.M. and Stewart, J. 1998. Re-establishment of the Lady's Slipper Orchid (*Cypripedium calceolus* L.) in Britain. *Bot. J. Linn. Soc.* 126: 173-181.

Rasmussen H.N. 1995. *Terrestrial Orchids from Seed to Mycotrophic plant*. Cambridge: Cambridge University Press.

Reinhammar, L.G. 1998. Systematics of *Pseudorchis albida* sl (Orchidaceae) in Europe and North America. *Bot. J. Linn. Soc.* 126: 363-382.

Rich, T. 1994. Narrow-leaved Helleborine (*Cephalanthera longifolia*) in Surrey. *PlantLife* 'Back from the Brink' *Project Report*, 38.

Rich, T.C.G. & Jermy, A.C. 1998. *Plant Crib 1998*. London: BSBI.

Richards, A.J. 1986. Cross-pollination by wasps in *Epipactis leptochila* (Godf.) Godf. S.L. *Watsonia* 16: 180-182.

Richards, A.J. 1989. Some problematic *Epipactis* in northern Britain. *BSBI News* 51: 51.

Richards, A.J. & Porter, A.F. 1982. On the identity of a Northumberland *Epipactis*. *Watsonia* 14: 121-128.

Richards, A.J. & Swan, G.A. 1976. *Epipactis leptochila* (Godfery) Godfery and *E. phyllanthus* G.E. Sm occurring in South Northumberland on lead and zinc soils. *Watsonia* 11: 1-5.

Riddelsdell, H.J., Hedley, G.W. & Price, W.R. 1948. *The Flora of Gloucestershire*. Bristol: Chatford House.

Roberts, R.H. 1959. Notes on the fen habitat of *Ophrys insectifera* in Anglesey. *Proc. BSBI* 3: 274-278.

Roberts, R.H. 1961. Studies on Welsh orchids. I. The variation of *Dactylorchis purpurella* (T. & T. A. Steph.) Vermeul. in North Wales. *Watsonia* 5: 23-36.

Roberts, R.H. 1961. Studies on Welsh orchids. II. The occurence of *Dactylorchis majalis* (Reichb.) Vermeul. in Wales. *Watsonia* 5: 37-42.

Roberts, R.H. 1966. Studies on Welsh orchids. III. The coexistence of some of the tetraploid species of marsh orchid. *Watsonia* 6: 260-267.

Roberts, R.H. 1988. The occurrence of *Dactylorhiza traunsteineri* (Sauter) Soo in Britain and Ireland. *Watsonia* 17: 43-47.

Roberts, R.H. 1989. Errors and misconceptions in the study of Marsh-orchids. *Watsonia* 17: 455-462.

Roberts, R.H. 1997. A new variety of Fly Orchid in Angelsey. *BSBI News* 74: 24.

Roberts, R.H. & Foley, M.J.Y. 1997. The taxonomic status of *Dactylorhiza majalis* (Rchb. fil.): F. Hunt & Summerh. subsp. *traunsteineri* (Saut. & Rchb. fil.) H. Sund. var. *bowmanii* M.N. Jenk. *Watsonia* 21: 374-376.

Roberts, R.H. & Gilbert, O.L. 1963. The status of *Orchis latifolia* var. *eborensis* Godfery in Yorkshire. *Watsonia* 5: 287-293.

Rose, F. 1949. *Orchis purpurea*. *J. Ecol.* 36: 366-77.

Rose, F. 1960. The rediscovery of *Orchis simia* Lam. in Kent, 1. Foreword. *Trans. Kent Field Club* 1: 50.

Rose, F. 1981. *The Wild Flower Key*. London: Frederick Warne.

Rose, F. 1991. A new subspecies of *Gymnadenia conopsea* (L.) R. Br. *Watsonia* 18: 319-320.

Rose, F. 1998a. *Gymnadenia conopsea* (L.) R. Br. *In* T.C.G Rich & A.C. Jermy (eds), *Plant Crib 1998*. London: BSBI.

Rose, F. 1998b. A new orchid hybrid for Britain – x *Orchiaceras melsheimeri* (*Aceras anthropophora* x *Orchis purpurea*). *BSBI News* 79: 19.

Rose, F. & Brewis, A. 1988. *Cephalanthera rubra* (L.) Rich. in Hampshire. *Watsonia* 17: 176-177.

Rose, F. & Davey, S.R. 1996. The three forms of Fragrant Orchid. *BSBI News* 72: 71.

Sanford, M. 1991. *The Orchids of Suffolk*. Ipswich: Suffolk Naturalists' Society.

Sanger, N. & Waite, S. 1998. The phenology of *Ophrys sphegodes* (the early spider orchid): what annual censuses can miss. *Bot. J. Linn. Soc.* 126: 75-81.

Sankey, A. 2000. *The Box Hill Book of Orchids*. Dorking: Friends of Box Hill.

Scott, W., Harvey, P., Riddington, R. & Fisher, M. 2002. *Rare Plants of Shetland*. Lerwick: Shetland Amenity Trust.

Scott, W. & Palmer, R. 1987. *The Flowering Plants and Ferns of the Shetland Islands*. Lerwick: Shetland Times.

Sell, D. & Murrell, G. 1996. *Flora of Great Britain, Ireland, Isle of Man and the Channel Islands*. Vol. 5: Butomaceae – Orchidaceae. Cambridge: Cambridge University Press.

Selosse, M-A., Faccio, A., Scappaticci, G. & Bonfante, P. 2004. Chlorophyllous and achlorophyllous specimens of *Epipactis microphylla* (Neottieae, Orchidaceae) are associated with ectomycorrhizal septomycetes, including truffles. *Microb. Ecol.* 47: 416-426.

Selosse M-A., Weiss, M., Jany, J-L. & Tillier A. 2002. Communities and populations of sebacinoid basidiomycetes associated with the achlorophyllous orchid *Neottia nidus-avis* (L.) L.C.M. Rich. and neighbouring tree ectomycorrhizae. *Mol. Ecol.* 11: 1831-1844.

Sex, S. & Sayers, B. 2004. *Ireland's Wild Orchids.* Portmarnock: Susan Sex Wild Orchids.

Silvertown, J., Wells, D.A., Gillman, M., Dodd, M.E., Robertson, H., Kakhani, K.H. 1994. Short-term effects and long-term effects of fertilizer application on a flowering population of Green-Winged Orchid, *Orchis morio. Biol. Cons.* 69: 191-197.

Sinker, C.A., Packham, J.R., Trueman, I.C., Oswald, P.H., Perring, F.H. & Prestwood, W.V. 1991. *Ecological Flora of the Shropshire Region.* Shrewsbury: Shropshire Wildlife Trust.

Société Française d'Orchidophilie 1998. *Les Orchidées de France, Belgique et Luxembourg.* Paris: Collection Parthénope.

Squirrell, J., Hollingsworth, M., Bateman, R.M., Tebbitt, M.C. and Hollingsworth, M.L. 2002. Taxonomic complexity and breeding system transitions: conservation genetics of the *Epipactis leptochila* complex (Orchidaceae). *Mol. Ecol.* 11: 1957-1964.

Stace, C.A. 1991. *New Flora of the British Isles.* Cambridge: Cambridge University Press.

Stace, C.A. 2004. *Interactive Flora of the British Isles* (CD-ROM). Amsterdam: ETI Bioinformatics.

Stace, C.A., Ellis, R.G., Kent, D.H. & McCosh, D.J. 2003. *Vice-county Census Catalogue of the Vascular Plants of Great Britain.* London: BSBI.

Steel, D.T. & Creed, C. 1982. *Wild Orchids of Berkshire, Buckinghamshire and Oxfordshire.* Oxford: Pisces.

Stewart, A., Pearman, D.A. & Preston, C.D. 1994. *Scarce Plants in Britain.* Peterborough: Joint Nature Conservation Commitee.

Stone, D.A. & Russell, R.V. 2000. Population biology of late spider orchid *Ophrys fucifera* – A study at Wye National Nature Reserve 1987-1998. *English Nature Research Report* 389.

Summerhayes, V.S. 1968. *Wild Orchids of Britain.* London: Collins.

Sumpter, J.P., D'Ayala, R., Parfitt, A.J., Pratt, P. & Raper, C. 2004. The current status of Military (*Orchis militaris*) and Monkey (*Orchis simia*) Orchids in the Chilterns. *Watsonia* 25: 175-183.

Synge, H. (ed.) 1981. *The Biological Aspects of Rare Plants Conservation.* London: John Wiley.

Tali, K., Foley, M.J.Y. & Kull, T. 2004. Biological Flora of the British Isles. 232. *Orchis ustulata* L. *J. Ecol.* 92: 174-184.

Tam, C.O. 1991. Behaviour of some orchid populations in a changing environment: Observations on permanent plots, 1943-1990. *In* T.C.E. Wells & J.H. Willems (eds), *Population Ecology of Terrestrial Orchids.* The Hague: SPB Academic Publishing.

Taylor, D.L. & Bruns, T. 1997. Independent, speciliazed invasions of ectomycorrhizal mutualism by two nonphotosynthetic orchids. *Proc. Natl. Acad. Sci.* 94: 4510-4515.

Tennant, D.J. & Kenneth, A.G. 1983. The Scottish records of *Dactylorhiza traunsteineri* (Sauter) Soo. *Watsonia* 14: 415-417.

Thomas, C. 1950. The Kenfig *Epipactis. Watsonia* 1: 283-288.

Thomas, S. 1997. Orchids from the 18th-century herbarium of Joseph Andrews (1688-1764). *BSBI News* 76: 17-21.

UK Biodiversity Group 1999. *Tranche 2 Action Plans, Vol. III: Plants and Fungi.* Peterborough: English Nature.

Van Der Cingel, N.A. 1995. *An Atlas of Orchid Pollination: European Orchids.* Rotterdam: Balkema.

Vanhecke, L.E.M. 1991. Population dynamics of *Dactylorhiza praetermissa* in relation to topography and inundation. *In* T.C.E. Wells & J.H. Willems (eds), *Population Ecology of Terrestrial Orchids.* The Hague: SPB Academic Publishing.

Waite, S. and Farrell, L. 1998. Population biology of the rare military orchid (*Orchis militaris* L.) at an established site in Suffolk. *Bot. J. Linn. Soc.* 126: 109-121.

Waite, S. & Hutchings, M.J. 1991. The effects of different management regimes on the population dynamics of *Ophrys sphegodes*. Analysis and description using matrix models. *In* T.C.E. Wells & J.H. Willems (eds), *Population Ecology of Terrestrial Orchids*. The Hague: SPB Academic Publishing.

Wells, T.C.E. 1967. Changes in a population of *Spiranthes spiralis* (L.) Chevall. at Knocking Hoe National Nature Reserve, Bedfordshire, 1962-65. *J. Ecol.* 55: 83-99.

Wells, T.C.E. 1981. Population ecology of terrestrial orchids. *In* Synge, H. (ed.) *Biological Aspects of Rare Plant Conservation*. London: John Wiley.

Wells, T.C.E & Cox, R. 1991. Demographic and biological studies on *Ophrys apifera*: some results from a ten year study. *In* T.C.E. Wells & J.H. Willems (eds), *Population Ecology of Terrestrial Orchids*. The Hague: SPB Academic Publishing.

Wells, T.C.E. & Kretz, R. 1986. *Spiranthes spiralis* (L.) Cheval. – from seed to flowering plant in five years. *Watsonia* 16: 235.

Wells, T.C.E., Rothery, P., Cox, R. & Bamford, S. 1998. Flowering dynamics of *Orchis morio* L. and *Herminium monorchis* (L.) R. Br. at two sites in Eastern England. *Bot. J. Linn. Soc.* 126: 39-48.

Wells, T.C.E. & Willems, J.H. (eds) 1991. *Population Ecology of Terrestrial Orchids*. The Hague: SPB Academic Publishing.

Weston, R.P. 1983. A Lincolnshire *Epipactis*. *Watsonia* 14: 457-458.

Wheeler, B. 1998. *Cephalanthera longifolia* in England, 1997. *Plantlife Report* 89.

Wheeler, B.D., Lambley, W. & Geeson, J. 1998. *Liparis loeselii* (L.) Rich. in eastern England: Constraints on distribution and population development. *Bot. J. Linn. Soc.* 126: 141-158.

Wigginton, M.J. (ed.) 1999. *British Red Data Books 1: Vascular Plants*. Peterborough: Joint Nature Conservation Committee.

Wilks, H.M. 1960. The rediscovery of *Orchis simia* Lam. in Kent 2: *Orchis simia* in East Kent. *Trans. Kent Field Club* 1: 50-55.

Willems, J.H. & Bik, L. 1991. Long-term dynamics in a population of *Orchis simia* in the Netherlands. *In* T.C.E. Wells & J.H. Willems (eds), *Population Ecology of Terrestrial Orchids*. The Hague: SPB Academic Publishing.

Willems, J.H., Melser, C. 1998. Population dynamics and life-history of *Coeloglossum viride* (L.) Hartm.: an endangered orchid species in The Netherlands. *Bot. J. Linn. Soc.* 126: 83-93.

Williams, J.G., Williams, A.E. & Arlott, N. 1978. *A Field Guide to the Orchids of Britain and Europe with North Africa and the Middle East*. London: Collins.

Willis, A.J. 1967. A new locality for *Liparis loeselii*. *Proc. BSBI* 6: 352-353.

Willis, A.J. 1980. *Ophrys apifera* Huds. x *O. insectifera* L., a natural hybrid in Britain. *Watsonia* 13: 97-102.

Willis, A.J., Martin, M.H. & Taylor, K.B. 1991. *Orchis purpurea* Hudson in the Avon Gorge, Bristol. *Watsonia* 18: 387-390.

Wilson, D.E. & Ingram, G.L. 1994. Distribution of Lady Orchid (*Orchis purpurea* Hudson) in an East Kent wood. *Watsonia* 20: 154-156.

Wood, J. & Ramsey, M. 2004. *Anacamptis laxiflora* Orchidaceae. *Curtis's Bot. Mag.* 21: 26-33.

Young, D.P. 1949a. Studies in the British *Epipactis*. I. *Epipactis dunensis* and *E. pendula*. *Watsonia* 1: 102-108.

Young, D.P. 1949b. Studies in the British *Epipactis*. II. The differentiation of *E. pendula* from *E. vectensis*. *Watsonia* 1: 108-113.

Young, D.P. 1952a. Studies in the British *Epipactis*. III. *Epipactis phyllanthes* G. E. Sm., an overlooked species. *Watsonia* 2: 253-259.

Young, D.P. 1952b. Studies in the British *Epipactis*. IV. A revision of the *phyllanthes-vectensispendula* group. *Watsonia* 2: 259-276.

Young, D.P. 1962a. Studies in the British *Epipactis*. V. *Epipactis leptochila*; with some notes on *E. dunensis* and *E. mulleri*. Watsonia 5: 127-135.

Young, D.P. 1962b. Studies in the British *Epipactis*. VI. Some further notes on *E. phyllanthes*. *Watsonia* 5: 136-139.

Index of Species